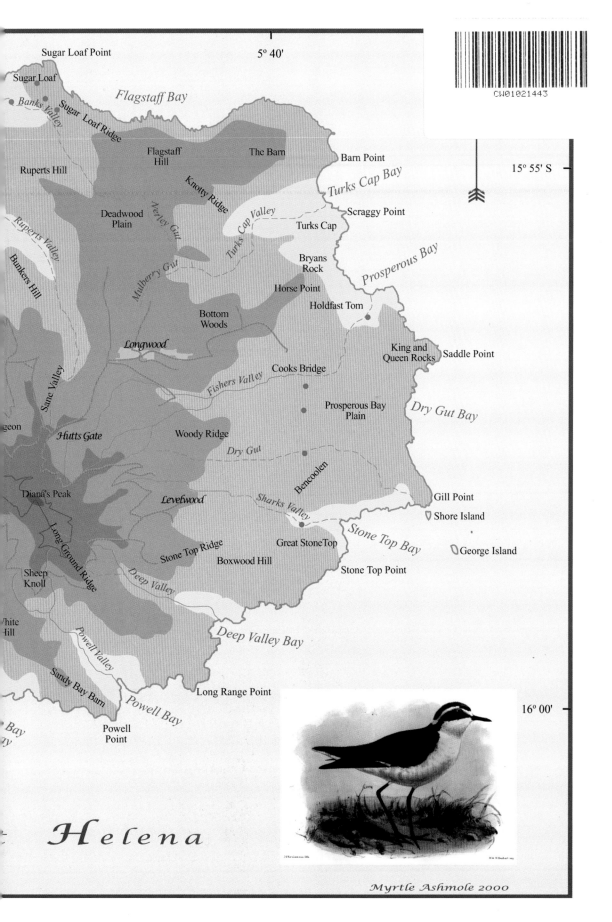

Sugar Loaf Point

Sugar Loaf

Flagstaff Bay

Banks Valley

Sugar Loaf Ridge

Ruperts Hill

Flagstaff
Hill

The Barn

Barn Point

Turks Cap Bay

Scraggy Point

Ruperts Valley

Deadwood
Plain

Knotty Ridge

Nerley Gut

Turks Cap Valley

Turks Cap

Prosperous Bay

Bunkers Hill

Mulberry Gut

Bryans
Rock

Horse Point

Holdfast Tom

Bottom
Woods

Longwood

Sane Valley

...geon

Hutts Gate

Fishers Valley

Cooks Bridge

King and
Queen Rocks

Saddle Point

Prosperous Bay
Plain

Dry Gut Bay

Woody Ridge

Dry Gut

Bencoolen

Diana's Peak

Levelwood

Sharks Valley

Gill Point

Shore Island

Long Ground Ridge

Stone Top Bay

George Island

Stone Top Ridge

Great StoneTop

Boxwood Hill

Sheep
Knoll

Deep Valley

Stone Top Point

White
Hill

Powell Valley

Deep Valley Bay

Sandy Bay Barn

Powell Bay

Long Range Point

...Bay
...y

Powell
Point

Helena

15° 55' S

16° 00'

5° 40'

CW01021443

Myrtle Ashmole 2000

St Helena and Ascension Island: a natural history

Birth of an oceanic island.

St Helena and Ascension Island: a natural history

Philip and Myrtle Ashmole

Photographs by Philip Ashmole

Maps and figures by Myrtle Ashmole

Anthony Nelson

Publication supported by:
The Foreign & Commonwealth Office

**THE ZOOLOGICAL
SOCIETY OF LONDON**

RSPB, the BirdLife International Partner in the UK

Designed by Harold Bartram
Typeset by Quetzal Communications
Printed by Redwood Books, Trowbridge, Wiltshire

Jacket pictures: Main picture front: Island of St Helena
Boxes: top left – Ebony *Trochetiopsis ebenus,*
top right – Bush cricket *Phaneracra bartletti,*
bottom left – Wirebird *Charadrius sanctaehelenae,*
bottom right – Tree Fern *Dicksonia arborescens.*
Main picture back: Ascension Island
Boxes: top left – Ascension Frigatebirds *Fregata aquila,*
top right – Hatchling Green Turtles *Chelonia mydas,*
bottom left – Ascension Spurge *Euphorbia origanoides,*
bottom right – Landcrab *Gecarcinus lagostoma.*

Contents

List of figures

List of colour plates

Dedication

We dedicate this book to the memory of Peter Mundy, inquisitive travelling naturalist of the 17th century, who left invaluable records of his visits to Ascension and St Helena. In puzzling over the origin of the flightless rail of Ascension Island, Mundy modestly proposed the idea of evolutionary change, two centuries before Charles Darwin and Alfred Russel Wallace grasped the mechanism of natural selection and transformed our view of the living world.

Acknowledgements

In writing this book we have been fortunate in having the help and encouragement of many people, both on the islands and far away; it seems impracticable to thank them all, but we must mention a few. Our guides to remote parts of St Helena included William Beard and Arthur Loveridge (in 1959), George Benjamin, Quentin Cronk, Nick Thorpe, Stedson Stroud, Raymond Leo, Muriel and Mackie Williams, Vanessa Thomas and John and Evie Bailey; all of these people, together with Basil and Barbara George, Pat Musk, Chris Lomas, Graham Sim and many others, patiently answered our questions about the island and its wildlife. On Ascension we have had help from many people, but must thank especially Philip's colleagues on the British Ornithologists' Union Centenary Expedition in 1957-59 and the Cable & Wireless staff of that time, and in relation to our visits in the 1990s, Graham Avis, Ken Simmons, John Nash, John Hughes, and Brian and Paul Bell. We also wish to thank Bill Bourne and Beau Rowlands for helping in many different ways, and Paul Pearce-Kelly, Dorothy Evans and other members of the South Atlantic Working Group of the UK Overseas Territories Conservation Forum for their patient support for the project. We would also like to express our thanks to Pedro Oromí and our other colleagues in the Canary Islands for introducing us to the study of underground fauna of oceanic islands.

During the writing itself, our debts have been especially to Trevor Hearl and John Packer, who have generously shared their deep knowledge of St Helena and Ascension, and to Rebecca Cairns-Wicks, who has tried to keep us up to date with conservation matters on St Helena. We owe a particular debt to Quentin Cronk, who has checked the identity of an assortment of plant specimens and photographs and patiently answered our questions about the ecology and evolution of St Helena plants. Brian O'Shea kindly rewrote the section on bryophytes, and Trevor Hearl kindly wrote a biographical note on J.C. Melliss. Constructive comments on draft sections of the book have also been made by Brendan Godley and Annette Broderick, Alan Gray, Roger Huxley, Timm Karisch, Paul Pearce-Kelly, Alexander Schulenberg, Nick Thorpe and Barry Weaver; we are deeply grateful for their comments, which have notably reduced the incidence of errors.

The systematic treatment of the invertebrates of St Helena is based on the comprehensive collections made 35 years ago by P. Basilewsky and his colleagues from the Musée Royal de l'Afrique Centrale, in Tervuren, Belgium, and on the work of the international team who helped to study the specimens; their efforts will remain unrivalled. The authorities of the Tervuren museum have kindly allowed us to reproduce drawings from some of the resulting publications (P. Basilewsky ed. 1970, 1972, 1976, 1977); each of these drawings is marked MRAC. We thank Tim Atkinson for allowing us to use on the Ascension map his photograph of an Ascension Frigatebird chasing a Red-footed Booby, Vanessa Thomas for her photograph of the last wild Boxwood, and Muriel Williams, Richard Gillett and Hazel Bowers for their drawings of endemic plants and ferns; the drawings of plants in Plate 5 are by Mrs J.C. Melliss. The following publishers kindly gave permission for reproduction of small images of animals in Chapter 15: Bulletin of Entomological Research, Cassell, HarperCollins Publishers, Journal of Natural History, Kluwer Academic Books, Pergamon Press, Struik Publishers and University Tutorial Press.

We are much indebted to the seventy or so taxonomists around the world who have identified specimens for us or advised on matters of classification; most of them were individually acknowledged in N.P. Ashmole & M.J. Ashmole (1997), but we would like to thank them collectively here. We especially thank John Murphy, who identified a large number of spiders from both islands, Keith Bland, who patiently traced a series of old names of Lepidoptera, Geoff Swinney and Nick Arnold, who helped with a puzzling fossil bone, and Ronald Viane, who gave invaluable help with the ferns. Finally, we should record our debt to John Charles Melliss, Arthur Loveridge, and the other pioneer naturalists whom we list in the bibliography.

Publication of this book, with its colour illustrations, would not have been possible without generous financial help from the Foreign & Commonwealth Office, the Royal Society for the Protection of Birds, the Zoological Society of London and Trevor Hearl: we thank them all, and hope that they will be pleased with the outcome.

Preface

St Helena and Ascension are two islands so remote and small that few people would have heard of the former if Napoleon had not been sent there, and hardly anyone could have placed the latter on a world map before its airstrip was used as a staging point during the Falklands War. It is, however, the isolation and small size of these islands, together with their endemic plants and animals, that make them so exceptionally interesting to naturalists.

Questions shout to be answered. How old are the islands and how did they change over the millennia? How and when did the forerunners of the native plants and animals arrive? Having reached the islands, what evolutionary changes did they undergo? What are their relationships with species in other parts of the world? What were the islands like before human activities changed them? In this book we have tried to address these questions and many more.

The native plants of St Helena are famous among botanists worldwide, cherished by the islanders and admired by visitors. The animals are no less remarkable, but like both the flora and fauna of Ascension, they are less well known. We have drawn on the writings of many travellers and scientists who have visited or lived on the islands since their discovery five centuries ago, and have tried to explain the notable contributions to scientific knowledge that these people made. In some cases we include biographical details; science is done by individuals, whose character determines the thrust of their research.

Both Ascension and St Helena have played important parts in our lives. Philip first went to Ascension as a post-graduate student in 1957 and stayed there for 18 months; at the end, he and a colleague made a three week visit to St Helena, where they collected fossil bird bones. Philip was a member of the British Ornithologists' Union Centenary Expedition to Ascension Island, and his study of the breeding cycles of some of the seabirds earned him his doctorate. In 1990 we returned to Ascension together, again primarily for ornithological reasons. The International Council for Bird Preservation (now BirdLife International) was organising a workshop on Seabirds on Islands at their conference in New Zealand in 1990, and Philip was asked to assess the status of the Ascension seabirds 30 years after the BOU studies. However, we had in the meantime – through an initiative of Myrtle's – spent some years studying the specialised insects and other small invertebrates that live on barren lava flows and in caves on remote volcanic islands; the opportunity to see what Ascension had to offer was too good to miss. We were there for only a month, and spent all the spare time from the ornithological work underground and on the most barren parts of the clinker. We found many surprising things, and to some extent felt we had compensated for the lack of interest that Philip had shown – three decades earlier – in the non-feathered animals of the island.

Late in 1994, fulfilling a longstanding pledge to ourselves, we went to live for six months on St Helena. Our main project was a systematic search for underground invertebrates. In particular, we wanted to compare the subterranean fauna of the mature island of St Helena with that of the youthful Ascension Island. On our way back to Britain we spent another month on Ascension. This time Philip was acting as a consultant – along with a wildlife management team from New Zealand – on the feasibility of a scheme for eradication of feral cats and rats from Ascension Island. We took this opportunity to do more work on the animals of the lava and caves that we had found during the 1990 visit, and to exploit the new ways of sampling the underground fauna that we had developed for the research on St Helena.

It may seem presumptuous, to people living on the islands, for us to write a book after such relatively short visits. However, for much of the past 15 years we have been studying the biology of other oceanic islands, including the Hawaiian Islands, Canaries, Azores and Galápagos. Knowledge of the origin, evolution and general natural history of these islands allows us to view St Helena and Ascension in terms of oceanic islands in general.

Although our personal experience and the observations of many other naturalists form the basis of this book, it should be mentioned that a remarkable first-hand record of the day to day management of a remote island colony is provided by the St Helena records of the East India Company, dating back to the late 17th century. In the unfamiliar guise of historian, Myrtle spent many hours examining more than 100 volumes of hand written records in the archives of the St Helena Government, extracting references to plants and animals. These have provided fascinating insight into the impact of human activities on the island, and form the foundation for our chapter on the ecological history of St Helena.

We have tried to write the book that we felt we needed on our visits, and it naturally reflects our own interests. We hope that it will help the people of St Helena and Ascension to understand more about their islands, and that it will also be of interest to visitors and those in the worldwide scientific community whose disciplines impinge on these remote places. This is a broad audience and we hope that non-scientific readers will be patient with the use of Latin names, and that scientists will be tolerant of our inevitable naivety with respect to many of the topics we cover. In the first half of the book we give general accounts of the islands and some of the research carried out there. In the second half we have tried to put into manageable form a summary of the available information on the plants and animals.[1] This was a formidable task and we are less than satisfied with the result, but hope that the attempt was worthwhile.

Completing this book in the first days of a new millennium, we look back at our personal time as naturalists, spanning the second half of the twentieth century, a period in which both biology and the earth sciences have played a major role in changing human perceptions of the planet we inhabit.

In biology, of course, the seminal advances were made a century earlier, with realisation of the inevitable role of natural selection in directing the growing branches of the evolutionary tree, together with dawning understanding of the genetic mechanisms that mediated the process. It was the twentieth century, however, that saw evolutionary reasoning permeating all discussion of the living world, while the accelerating discoveries of molecular biology rivetted our attention, and television screens brought home to millions of people, images of extraordinary living organisms and insights into their intriguing adaptations. At the start of the new millennium, few would argue with the classic comment, that nothing in biology makes sense, except in the light of evolution.

---

[1] We stop at the sea shore, partly because of our ignorance of marine biology and partly because Alasdair Edwards has produced a superb book on the Fishes of St Helena, which also includes many of the Ascension species.

In geology, the cataclysmic events took place a century later than in biology, the theory of plate tectonics belatedly opening the door into a new realm of understanding. The origin of oceans and mountain ranges, and the patterns of earthquakes and volcanoes – frustrating puzzles for so long – were soon elegantly solved, and earth scientists gained a secure base from which to pursue their increasingly sophisticated investigations of planet earth.

We find it hard to believe that there will ever again be a time in which natural history is so rewarding, still offering the simple excitement of discovery of new species and new phenomena, bringing echoes from the time of the great explorer-naturalists, but also the unravelling of the genetic code and the extraordinary thrill when the new geology broke the mould.

Oceanic islands, tiny spots peppered around the oceans of the world, have provided a lens to enhance our human view of the evolutionary play. The relative simplicity of their biological communities has enabled dedicated scientists to understand some of the ways that new species form, and to observe and measure evolutionary change as it continues, episodically, over the years.

These islands, however, have another claim on our attention. As discrete entities with comprehensible scale, they demonstrate only too clearly the power of people, by inadvertence or intention, to bring environmental catastrophe to pristine pieces of our world. The pace at which the natural biological communities of islands can be despoiled should alert us to the more insidious degradation of the continents and seas.

Having suffered so much, islands also offer a ray of hope, since they provide unique opportunities for initiatives in ecological restoration. We cannot bring back those plants and animals that we have driven to extinction, but we have a chance to nurture those that have survived, restoring their populations sufficiently for these islands once more to become healthy ecosystems, demonstrating that at least on a small scale and over human lifetimes, environmental change can sometimes be for the better.

Philip and Myrtle Ashmole
Peebles, Scotland, January 2000

Part I

Volcanoes in the sea

Chapter 1

The islands come to life

From the depths of the ocean

Why did St Helena and Ascension – two minute specks of land in the immensity of the South Atlantic Ocean – appear when and where they did? To begin to understand this we need to think of the structure of the earth as dynamic rather than static, and to take our minds back into the distant past.

The upper surface of the earth is made up of rigid, brittle plates of rock that move over the slightly fluid underlying mantle. Seven major plates and six smaller ones fit together like a jigsaw to form a shell around the whole of our planet. All but one of the major plates include continents (composed of lighter rock) and these are carried with the plates as they move imperceptibly in their stately dance across the surface of the globe. As they collide, pull apart or slide past each other, mountains are built, oceans formed, and earthquakes and volcanic eruptions occur.

St Helena and Ascension are in the South Atlantic Ocean, which started to form more than 100 million years ago. A split appeared in a plate and the continent that it carried, and ever since then the two new continents of Africa and South America have been drifting apart on separate plates. They are still diverging at a rate of about four centimetres per year, in a process known as seafloor spreading. Along the centre of the widening ocean is a zone where new rock is being added to the edges of both plates – in a roughly symmetrical manner – by submarine volcanic activity. This new rock is initially hot, but it cools very slowly and increases in density as it gradually moves sideways – to both east and west – with the addition of yet younger material in between. Because the newer hotter rock is lighter, it floats higher on the underlying mantle, and so builds up a broad ridge along the middle of the ocean floor – the Mid-Atlantic Ridge – which runs roughly from north to south (see Figures 1 and 2).

The energy for plate movements comes ultimately from radioactive decay within the earth and the transfer of heat from the hot, deep interior to the cooler surface. Some of this transfer takes place by means of convection currents within the mantle, and where these rise (for instance at mid-ocean ridges) and bring hot material to the surface, plates tend to diverge.

In many cases, however, as a plate moves away from a ridge (cooling and becoming denser on the way) its leading edge is in contact with the adjacent plate at a convergent boundary, and here 'subduction' occurs: the denser plate slides under the edge of the other and sinks back into the mantle, eventually melting. It has recently been shown that once a system of this kind is in motion, most of the energy driving it comes from the pull of the leading edge as it sinks. The floating plate is analogous to a tablecloth which is stable so long as the edges overhang to a similar extent on the two sides, but which is liable to slide off if it becomes asymmetrical, because of the tug of the heavier overhanging edge.

An obvious question is how such a system starts, and what determines where a split in a plate occurs, creating a new spreading axis: a rift valley or mid-ocean ridge. Some geophysicists suspect that a key role is played by 'hotspots' where especially intense convective plumes of mantle material rise from great depths. Hotspots remain almost

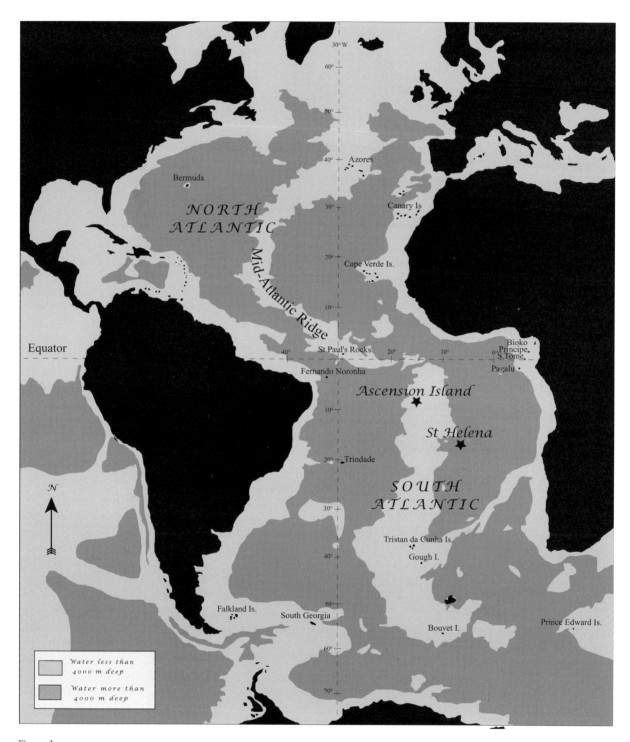

Figure 1

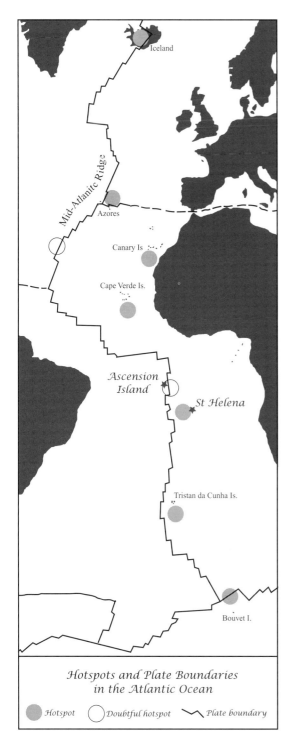

Hotspots and Plate Boundaries
in the Atlantic Ocean

● Hotspot   ○ Doubtful hotspot   ⋏ Plate boundary

Figure 2

stationary in the mantle, and although their plumes are only about 100 km across, the mantle material that impinges on the underside of the plates forms spreading mushroom heads perhaps ten times as broad, weakening the plate above. The formation of the South Atlantic Ocean may have resulted from the collective effect of the Cape Verde, Ascension, St Helena and Tristan da Cunha hotspots.[1] More locally, the convection currents associated with hotspots may sometimes melt a series of holes in the plates moving over them, leading to seafloor volcanism, and in extreme cases – such as Hawai'i – to the formation of a trail of islands across an oceanic plate, with the oldest ones furthest from the hotspot.

About 240 km to the west of St Helena is the hotspot that is implicated in its origin (Figure 2). However, another 500 km to the west is the Mid-Atlantic Ridge, where new ocean floor is being created, leading to gradual movement of the African plate to the east and the South American plate to the west. The African plate on which St Helena rides is moving eastwards at about 18 millimetres per year. One can therefore estimate that St Helena would have been over the hotspot a little over 13 million years ago. This is a reasonable match to St Helena's estimated age of 14 million years, although it might have taken another million years or so for the volcano to build up to the surface from the ocean floor more than 4000 metres below. Intriguingly, 130 km to the west of St Helena is another enormous volcano, the Bonaparte Seamount, which rises to within 105 metres of the surface. It was doubtless produced by the St Helena hotspot after an interval of reduced activity during which the plate had carried St Helena some distance to the east. Since global sea level during the last ice age fell to about 130 metres lower than it is now, Bonaparte was probably an island less than 20,000 years ago.

Ascension lies just under 100 km west of the Mid-Atlantic Ridge (Figure 2). It is thus on the South American plate, and while St Helena is moving east, Ascension is travelling westwards at about the same rate; it stands on oceanic crust formed 5-6 million years ago, but probably started forming only about two million years ago, at a location some 35 km closer to the ridge. Like St Helena, Ascension is associated with a hotspot (although this is a somewhat atypical one) which is now centred about 260 km southeast of the island, on the other side of the Mid-Atlantic Ridge. This position places it a quarter of the way to St Helena and roughly underneath the Grattan Seamount, which is now only 72 metres below the surface. This seamount has probably

[1] T. Tanimoto & Y-S. Zhang (1992). Relationships of the ridge, St Helena and Ascension and their associated hotspots are well shown by J.M. Brozena & R. S. White (1990).

been an island in the past, and may emerge again if there is either renewed volcanism or a new ice age.

The water depth around Ascension is a little less than near St Helena, but the total height of the Ascension volcano is more than four kilometres. Both islands are the tips of enormous cones built up by a succession of massive emissions of lava. Initially, the undersea eruptions were of very hot and liquid material, which was discharged rapidly and spread out into enormous sheets. These eventually formed rugged and irregular platforms on the sea floor, around 100 km across and 1 km thick. As the new rock accumulated, however, fresh emissions occurred more slowly and at a lower temperature, so that the lava was less liquid and travelled only short distances before solidifying in lobes – rather like toffee poured out of a pan onto a cold surface. This process gave rise to pillow lavas, which accumulated in precipitous piles close to the eruptive vents and often subsequently collapsed.[2] The result was a steep-sided volcanic cone, resting on the wider plinth formed in the earlier phase and gradually building upwards.

About 14 million years ago, the tip of one of these submarine volcanoes finally reached the surface of the South Atlantic Ocean. Nobody was there to see the birth of St Helena – and indeed in Africa, the evolutionary lineage that was to give rise to humans had reached no further than primitive apes – but the spectacle would have been worth watching. We can paint a rough picture of it, since new volcanic islands still emerge once in a while and there are eye-witness accounts of the origin of several of these (see Frontispiece).

Years before the emergence of St Helena, the blue waters of the Atlantic were sporadically thrown into turmoil by undersea eruptions, or discoloured by ash or mottled by rafts of floating pumice. The birth itself was foreshadowed by a series of small earthquakes. Then, as submarine eruptions brought the summit closer and closer to the surface, spouts of steam and great bubbles of gas escaped and the water around boiled. Finally, as the vents came clear of the sea, pointed jets of blackish ash shot up, towering more than a kilometre into the sky and accompanied by white clouds of steam that rose to much greater heights. From time to time violent explosions occurred as seawater broke into the volcano and met the red-hot magma.

Within a few weeks an island had been formed by the accumulating mass of steaming cinders and rocks thrown out by the volcano. A cratered cone developed, lop-sided because of the wind, with its walls built up by the fall of ash but occasionally collapsing dramatically as the waves plucked at the unstable pile, so that the size of the island was in a continual state of flux. The eruptions often gave rise to torrential rains and brought down a sludge of fine ash on to both land and sea, producing a great plume of brownish water extending many miles to the west, as the finer particles were carried away by the current.

During the following years, as the island grew, emissions of ash were interspersed by eruptions of lava. A split suddenly formed on the side of the cone, and a red glow – reflected

---

[2] This process has become clearer as a result of direct observations of submarine volcanoes (seamounts) from submersibles. A few years ago, geologists investigating a seamount at a depth of 1600 m in the Pacific, found that near the summit there were many 'pillow-cones' about 50 m across and 25 m high (P. Lonsdale & R. Batiza 1980). These proved to consist of clusters of steeply sloping lava tubes radiating from old vents; below them on the sides of the volcano (which here sloped at 20-30°) were 'stone streams' 100 m or so long, made up of rocks about 15 cm across and consisting of 'hyaloclastite' (literally, glassy broken piece). This granulated glassy debris is formed when basaltic lava is suddenly quenched by cold seawater, as when it emerges in a relatively thin stream from a tubular pillow. The geologists were startled – when they tried to collect rocks from the stone stream using a hydraulic arm – to find that the fragments were cemented together by a crust of manganese and iron oxides, derived from the volcano but deposited gradually from seawater after the eruption. Unlike loose scree slopes on land, these stone streams become static and are eventually enveloped by the next eruption.

in the clouds at night – was followed by the appearance of a series of fountains of incandescent lava, rising tens of metres into the air. Spilling out of the newly formed vents, the lava formed glowing streams down the sides of the cone and hissed into the sea.[3]

The active volcanic phase in the development of St Helena continued for about seven million years, to be followed by a similar period of quiescence. But even during the active phase eruptions were far from continuous.[4] There were doubtless long quiet intervals, during which plant and animal communities developed. These were interrupted by periods of intense activity, lasting decades or a few centuries, when parts of the island were smothered by thick layers of ash, or repeatedly inundated by flows of basalt lava such as those that built the cliffs around Jamestown almost ten million years ago. Even at these times, however, other parts of the island were probably quiet, so that vegetation and some animal populations had a chance of survival.

The birth of Ascension Island doubtless followed a similar course, but the island is much younger than St Helena. It has probably been above the surface for only about one million years and is still an active volcano: the last eruption on land may have been within the last thousand years and more are to be expected in the future.

The great difference in age is largely responsible for the contrast between the two islands noted by Charles Darwin:-

> "At Ascension, the surfaces of the lava-streams are glossy, as if just poured forth, their boundaries are well defined, and they can often be traced to perfect craters, whence they were erupted; ... and the coast round nearly the entire circumference is low, and has been eaten back (though too much stress must not be laid on this fact, as the island may have been subsiding) into a little wall only from ten to thirty feet high ... On the other hand, at St. Helena, the course of no one stream of lava can be traced ... and ... the entire circuit of the island has been deeply worn back into the grandest precipices."

Early arrivals

As soon as St Helena and Ascension Island emerged from the sea as chaotic piles of rock and ash, colonisation by microbes, plants and animals was initiated. There were, however, repeated setbacks as a result of the massive volcanic activity that continued sporadically on both islands.[5]

---

[3] A witness to an eruption in February 1825 on another young island described the events in graphic terms:-
  "The heavens appeared to be one blaze of fire, intermingled with millions of falling stars and meteors; while the flames shot upward ... to the height of at least two thousand feet in the air ... A river of melted lava was now seen rushing down the side of the mountain, pursuing a serpentine course to the sea ... presenting the appearance of a tremendous torrent of melted iron running from the furnace ... The demon of fire seemed rushing to the embraces of Neptune; and dreadful indeed was the uproar occasioned by their meeting. The ocean boiled and roared and bellowed ..." The writer was captain of a ship desperately creeping out under sail from a sheltered bay at Fernandina Island in the Galapagos, but he was also coolly making scientific observations:- "...the Tartar slid along through the almost boiling ocean at the rate of about seven miles an hour ... At the time the mercury in the thermometer was at 147 degrees but on immersing in water it instantly rose to 150 degrees. Had the wind deserted us here, the consequences must have been horrible." (B. Morrell 1832).
  We were ourselves only too aware of this account when the same volcano suddenly erupted in 1991, half an hour after we had landed on the uninhabited island from a fishing boat. Fortunately, that eruption proved less formidable, though our photographs of the main explosion could easily be mistaken for that of a nuclear bomb.

[4] On Tenerife, a volcanic island that is still active, there have been only five eruptive episodes during the last 500 years, each of them lasting only a few months: the volcano is quiet for more than 90% of the time.

[5] We can make reasonable guesses about the early stages in colonisation because the process has been studied on a few recently formed volcanic islands such as Surtsey (formed in 1963 off the coast of Iceland) and an islet in the crater of Krakatau in Indonesia, as well as on fresh lava flows in Hawai'i and the Canary Islands (see discussion in C.H. Lindroth et al. 1973, I.W.B. Thornton et al. 1988 and N.P. Ashmole et al. 1992).

Marine mammals and seabirds would have visited the islands immediately: we have been told of terns settling on Capelinhos volcano in the Azores in the 1950's while the newly formed rocks were still warm. However, the first living organisms to establish permanent populations on the islands may have been bacteria capable of using hydrogen sulphide as a source of energy; they would have colonised the moist borders of the volcanic craters, as they do on Surtsey. Other pioneers included free-living cyanobacteria (blue-green algae), primitive organisms that may have reached the islands on the feet of visiting seabirds. They can survive on volcanic deposits or lava flows even when no other living things are present, since they have the ability to use solar energy and nitrogen from the air; sometimes they form gelatinous masses in damp places, especially close to windward shores.

Lichens – which are formed by an association between green algae and fungi – were undoubtedly also early colonists, since they too can live independently on otherwise sterile rock. Many kinds of lichens have reproductive stages that can be transported long distances by the wind, and are doubtless also dispersed by birds. Mosses, liverworts and fungi have similar dispersal mechanisms, and it is likely that all these groups became established relatively quickly. Ferns also produce great quantities of spores, most of which are minute and may be transported long distances in air currents; some species will have established themselves as soon as soil began to form, but as with other plants and animals, they will not be a random assortment of ferns in the nearest continents, but will be ones with characteristics that fit them for long distance dispersal and for establishment on arrival.[6]

Colonisation by flowering plants

Considering the extreme isolation of St Helena and Ascension from continental land, it may seem hard to believe that flowering plants could have reached them naturally. Few flowering plants can equal the dispersal ability of the ferns, and the arrival and establishment of a species on the islands was doubtless extremely rare.

On St Helena the endemic flowering plants (i.e. those found nowhere else) are probably derived from about 25 colonising stocks (see Chapter 4). There are also a few non-endemic species that seem to be indigenous (native) to St Helena but which also occur elsewhere. The flora in 1502 (when the island was discovered) was thus the result of only about 40 colonisations. On this basis, the establishment of one species of flowering plant about every 300,000 years would have been sufficient to generate the diversity of the native plants of St Helena. However, the real rate of colonisation must have been somewhat higher than this, since a few more plants (including two kinds of palm trees) are known to have once been on the island: their fossil pollen has been identified from ancient deposits. These species are now extinct, probably along with a number of others of which we have no record.

Ascension Island, in contrast, was apparently colonised by only about eight species of flowering plants before humans arrived. The pristine vegetation there – especially high up – consisted largely of ferns, mosses, liverworts and lichens. On this island an average rate of one colonisation about every 100,000 years would be enough to account for the native flowering plants. In practice, a few kinds of plants that are particularly good dispersers doubtless reached the islands quickly, with other species

---

[6] R. Tryon (1970).

arriving subsequently as a result of a rare combination of circumstances; such arrivals will continue indefinitely.

The contrast in overall richness of the flora between St Helena and Ascension reflects mainly the difference in the time available for colonisation of the two islands: 14 million years for St Helena and one million years for Ascension. In spite of the roughness of the estimates, the figures show that colonisation of each of the islands happened as a result of a series of extraordinarily rare events. Transport across such large expanses of ocean is very improbable, but given a long enough timespan, it sometimes occurs.

How do the plants cross the ocean? Those colonising St Helena and Ascension must have either drifted by air or by sea, or have been carried by birds. Although the spores of lower plants can be transported long distances by air, transoceanic aerial dispersal of seeds of higher plants seems to be rare. An important group of endemic plants on St Helena belong to the family Compositae, which includes many species particularly well adapted for aerial seed dispersal, since the seed is attached to a plumose (feather-like) appendage that functions as a parachute. Even in this group, however, seeds are unlikely to have remained airborne long enough to make the crossing from Africa, and it is more probable that the seeds were carried to the island after the feathery part became tangled in the plumage of seabirds.[7]

Arrivals by sea were doubtless mainly of sea shore plants, adapted to salty conditions. A good example is the Camels-foot Creeper *Ipomoea pes-caprae*, which seems to be native on Ascension and was recorded from St Helena in the past. It occurs on an enormous number of tropical islands and its seeds are evidently readily dispersed by sea; however, the possibility of bird dispersal of this species also exists, since seeds have been found in the stomach of a dead White Tern. Another relevant plant is the purslane *Portulaca oleracea*, which has small seeds that are not buoyant but are capable of resisting immersion in sea water; this species probably colonised both islands by means of seeds lodged in crevices in logs drifted from Africa (see Figure 3).

Oceanic drift may also have led to colonisation by plants not typical of the strand line, including the ancestor of three of the original endemic trees on St Helena – Ebony, Dwarf Ebony and Redwood. Fossil pollen shows that the stock from which these closely related species are derived was already present on St Helena half way through its geological history (see Chapter 4). Unopened seed capsules of this group float, and might drift long distances in ocean currents and then open to release the seeds while drying out on a beach. It seems a chancy way of travelling, but given several million years of opportunity, the odds improve.[8]

---

[7] Studies on other islands support the role of birds as the transporting agent for most species of plants. For instance, an analysis of the plants of the Hawaiian archipelago concluded that seeds of an overwhelming proportion of the native plants must have been transported by birds, either in their guts, in caked mud on their feet, or attached to the plumage by sticky secretions or by minute hooks (S. Carlquist 1974). An example of a species with the latter dispersal mechanism is Hogweed *Commicarpus helenae*, a rambling plant well adapted to harsh desert conditions and occurring on both St Helena and Ascension, which it could well have reached as a result of seeds becoming attached to seabirds.

[8] Assuming that the ancestors of these St Helena trees did indeed arrive by sea, there is an intriguing question as to where they came from. One possibility is that they drifted round South Africa from islands in the Indian Ocean, where allied species are still present. Even today, in the southern hemisphere summer, eddies of warm Indian Ocean water travel west past the Cape of Good Hope in the Agulhas Current and are then carried northwards in the Atlantic by the Benguela Current; similar situations may well have arisen in the distant past. However, it is perhaps more likely that the St Helena stock is derived from ancestors in southern Africa that subsequently became extinct there; in this case the voyage would have been less formidable.

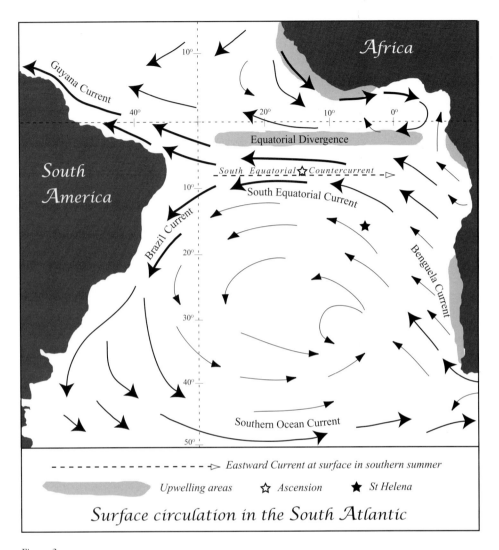

Figure 3

Colonisation by animals

Animals, of course, also soon started to colonise the islands. Sea turtles and perhaps seals doubtless arrived quickly, as did the truly oceanic birds such as Sooty Terns, tropicbirds and petrels. Landbirds, however, only occasionally reach islands as isolated as these, and most of those that do so either die or leave again. Migrants arriving from the northern hemisphere are genetically programmed to fly back to the north before breeding, and are thus unlikely to become established; furthermore, even if a vagrant or lost bird stays on the island for a while, it is unlikely to find suitable habitat or a mate.

Nonetheless, occasional observations show the potential for colonisation. For instance, when Philip was living on Ascension in June 1958, he was breakfasting at camp in the cinder desert near Mars Bay when a young Moorhen walked in, totally exhausted (Plate 21). It allowed itself to be picked up, drank a mixture of Guinness and milk, and ate Rice Krispies from his hands. The bird had clearly just arrived on the island, presumably from Africa. There is no habitat suitable for Moorhens on

Ascension, and although this individual walked out of camp a few days later it was probably doomed. The incident, however, helps one to understand the origin of the extinct Ascension Rail – a Moorhen relative – whose ancestors became established on the island in the distant past (Chapter 5).

For St Helena there is an earlier relevant observation. The Records of the East India Company for October 1727 include the entry:-

> *"there being several birds of a different species from those that frequent the island, lately come hither, the bodies of which are as large as a pheasant, their legs long and black but their claws open and not webbed like sea-fowl, with long bills resembling those of a snipe but thicker and longer in proportion to the bulk of their bodies which probably may breed here if not destroyed or disturbed"* ... *"All persons be publickly forbid by advertisment either to kill or disturb any of the said birds or destroy any of their egge".*

This description suggests the Glossy Ibis *Plegadis falcinellus*, a waterbird which is widespread in the tropics and forms flocks on migration. In spite of the attempt to give the vagrant group protection, they apparently did not remain on the island, which would not have offered them suitable habitat.[9]

It is harder to understand how less mobile animals could reach such remote islands. Many, of course, do not. There are no no native freshwater fish, amphibians, land reptiles or land mammals on either island, and many other less obvious groups are poorly represented. It is now known, however, that many insects, spiders and other tiny animals often drift in the air, and can be transported great distances under special meteorological conditions.[10]

Some large and conspicuous insects take part in visible migratory movements under their own power, but are also helped by the wind. Many species of moths and butterflies, for instance, are known to migrate long distances overland and are often recorded at sea or noticed as vagrants on islands. The Painted Lady, one of the butterflies known on both islands, is famous in this respect, and in 1939 a swarm – probably from Africa – was seen in mid Atlantic 1600 km to the west of (i.e. beyond) St Helena. The few species of butterflies native to the two islands doubtless arrived in this way.

Many moths may also have reached the islands by air, and thus are natural colonists. It is difficult to be sure of this, since several of the species have larvae that are agricultural pests, and some of them could have been imported recently with produce from Africa or elsewhere. We became more convinced that many of them are natural colonists when our analysis of the list of moths found on Ascension Island showed that a strikingly high proportion of the species are well known as migrants, and are thus especially likely to have drifted naturally to the islands during exceptional weather disturbances. These species include some migratory members of the family Noctuidae whose larvae are known as armyworms, which are notorious migrant pests in Africa and do much damage on both Ascension and St Helena.

---

[9] Further insight into bird colonisation of St Helena is provided by the records of the Cattle Egret in recent years. This white heron has recently expanded its world range in a dramatic way, spreading from Asia into Australasia and crossing the Atlantic from Africa to South America about a century ago; it went on to colonise much of the New World. Cattle Egrets have not yet bred on St Helena, and may be unable to establish themselves in the absence of nest sites protected from predatory mammals. However, the fact that they now occur almost regularly on the island demonstrates that if an abundant and strong flying African bird has a sufficient tendency to wander, individuals are likely to reach St Helena from time to time, and are thus potential colonists. Cattle Egrets are now also seen routinely on Ascension, but this island is even less suitable for colonisation.

[10] These movements have been demonstrated by using insect nets mounted on ships and aircraft in the Pacific and by other studies elsewhere; references can be found in N.P. Ashmole & M.J. Ashmole (1988 and 1997).

Also relevant is the presence on St Helena – at least in the past – of an endemic dragonfly, *Sympetrum dilatatum*. Many species of dragonflies are migratory and there is evidence that they sometimes make transoceanic movements which must occasionally result in establishment on islands.[11] Locusts are also well known as wanderers and it seems clear that wandering swarms of both Desert Locusts and Migratory Locusts occasionally reach Ascension from Africa.[12] However it is not certain that they would have maintained permanent populations in the past: conditions for these species on the island may well have improved with the arrival of grasses brought by humans. St Helena seems not to have permanent locust populations, although the Desert Locust has been recorded there at least once. Another large insect which occurs on both St Helena and Ascension is the widespread cricket *Gryllus bimaculatus* (Plate 23); these populations are probably derived from similar wandering swarms.

Spiders are well represented on both islands, and the well known tendency of many different kinds of spiders to migrate by drifting in air currents on silk threads gives credence to the idea that many could reach the island by air. On Ascension many of the spiders present are widespread species, so it is hard to be sure whether they are native or introduced. On St Helena, however, the high proportion of endemic species in each of several different families shows that the ancestors must have colonised the island naturally; some of these ancestors arrived so long ago that they have had time to evolve into a number of distinct species on the island (Table 5A).

Few, if any of the natural colonists will have reached the islands entirely under their own power: assistance from the wind is probably always needed by insects as well as spiders. In some tropical oceans, hurricanes are important in drifting animals out to sea and transporting them long distances, but hurricanes do not now occur in the South Atlantic and may never have done so. Furthermore, the South-East Trade Winds that prevail over the ocean between Africa and the islands might not bring many insects from the continent fast enough for them to avoid exhaustion and death.

There are, however, special weather systems which may play a part. A recent analysis showed that some heavy rainfall events on Ascension were associated with westward moving disturbances originating in central equatorial Africa.[13] These are termed easterly waves and can involve easterly winds of at least 50 km/hour at heights of 3-5 km. Such disturbances could transport insects from Africa to Ascension in much less than two days. Significantly, one of the few recorded sightings of a dragonfly on Ascension Island was early in a period of highly abnormal weather in March 1963, which culminated in a fall of nearly 11 inches of rain at the end of the month. Similar disturbances may transport insects and some other animals to St Helena.

Transport of animals to islands by sea probably occurs mainly in species adapted to salty, coastal conditions. One of the invertebrates that we found on Ascension in 1990 was a species of beach-dwelling woodlouse that is widespread in the tropics including the coast of West Africa: it probably reached Ascension on driftwood. In the same part

---

[11] For example, two yachtsmen whom Myrtle met on St Helena explained that on 1st November 1994, they were about 200 miles south of Madagascar sailing east against the wind, and saw a series of swarms of 3-inch long dragonflies, with greenish metallic coloration. There would be 50 or so around the boat, then none, and then another swarm. They were seen over a period of about three days, and were reported by a couple of other yachts, one of them 150 miles further to the northeast.

[12] Most locust movements are within the continents, but they are often seen far out to sea, and in October 1988 a swarm of desert locusts crossed the North Atlantic from east to west, covering a distance of some 5000 kilometres and making a landfall in the West Indies (M. Ritchie & D. Pedgley 1989).

[13] B.A. Hall (1989).

of Ascension, in a muddy deposit under rocks behind Shelly Beach (which accumulates many objects that drift with the current from the east) we found a new species of soil centipede.[14] It belongs to a group that is tolerant of salty conditions and it probably also arrived with driftwood. On the same beach – and also in Wideawake fairs (breeding colonies) – we found a tenebrionid beetle *Clitobius ovatus* that is typical of sandy shores and also occurs in the Canary and Cape Verde archipelagos. In 1994 we also found it on a beach in Namibia, and realised that an individual boarding a log there might end up on Ascension some three months later.

Only a handful of other beetles seem to be native to Ascension, which is not surprising since long distance aerial migration is found in only a few beetle groups. The puzzle is that many families of beetles have endemic representatives on St Helena and a few (especially weevils) have a large number of species. The groups concerned are mainly flightless and it seems likely that their ancestors reached the island by sea. Conceivably, a natural raft might reach the island from Africa every million years or so;[15] such rafts have been seen well offshore elsewhere, occasionally with standing trees, but as far as we are aware, no-one has yet been able to search a large one for animals.

Birds provide potential means of transport for other animals, as they do for plants; for really small animals, hitchhiking is also conceivable on other flying animals such as moths. Seabirds must always have offered the most potential as a means of assisted transport between continental regions and islands, since many of them are wide ranging and some are known to come ashore in places where they do not breed. The most likely hitchhikers are species that live in seabird colonies. External parasites such as ticks, feather lice and hippoboscid flies will certainly have arrived in the plumage of their avian hosts, for instance frigatebirds, boobies and terns.

More intriguing in this respect are the pseudoscorpions, tiny spider relatives with large pincers, looking like scorpions without the stinging tail. They are known to attach themselves to birds (and sometimes to insects) and can potentially be transported to islands in this way. On Ascension this group is remarkable in having four species, all of which are apparently endemic to the island; two of them have only been recorded from the seabird colony on Boatswainbird Island. Presumably their ancestors arrived long ago with birds, and have subsequently evolved their distinctive characteristics (Figure 29 and Plate 22).

Landbirds may also have been significant transporters of invertebrate animals to the islands. The ibises and egrets already mentioned, for instance, are both typical of waterside habitats and would be potential transporters of small individuals or eggs of molluscs, worms, crustaceans or aquatic insects, all of them groups that would have little chance of reaching the islands unaided.

From our analysis of the Ascension fauna we concluded that of the about 320 species of land animals that have become established, about 90 probably arrived naturally or are descended from ancestors that did so; about 80 are of doubtful origin; and about 150 have probably been introduced by humans[16]. An analysis of this type has not yet

---

[14] References are given in N.P. Ashmole & M.J. Ashmole (1997). Reference to a new species implies that it is new to science, not simply previously unknown on the island.

[15] We use the term 'natural raft' to refer to a tree trunk or mass of floating vegetation which could carry animals. Such pieces of flotsam picked up close to coasts often have live invertebrate land animals on board, but in the open ocean survivors are rare (H. Heatwole & R. Levins 1972).

[16] Table 12. Many of the introduced species travel with edible cargoes in ships, or are accidently included in packages (A.D. Aitken 1975, 1984).

been done for St Helena, which has a much richer fauna. It is obvious, however, that multiplication of species on St Helena has been of greater importance than on Ascension: many species not only established themselves but diverged evolutionarily to produce clusters of closely related species, which came to occupy distinct ecological niches (see Chapter 5). This process is only in its earliest stages on Ascension.

Getting established

Recent experience on Ascension and elsewhere has provided a new perspective on establishment of invertebrate animals on newly created volcanic islands[17]. This research suggests that certain members of many animal groups (for instance pseudoscorpions, spiders, mites, woodlice, springtails, crickets, earwigs, psocids and even a few beetles and moths) may be able to colonise barren lava habitats before an extensive plant community has developed. These animals can shelter in cracks in the lava or among the cinders by day, emerging to forage at night. They include scavengers, normally living on insects and scraps of dead plants drifted by the wind, and hunters that prey on the scavengers. On young, barren and isolated islands, however, where there is little organic input from richer ecosystems elsewhere, these pioneering animals may live mainly by exploiting material derived from the marine environment. Organic matter from sea foam, guano and scraps of food from seabirds and marine mammals, carrion, driftwood and the resources of the intertidal zone will all supplement the small primary production by colonies of cyanobacteria, lichens, mosses and scattered strand plants that may support some minute herbivorous animals.

Recently created volcanic islands may therefore tend to have a fringe of populated land around the coast, with a community of inconspicuous and mainly nocturnal invertebrate animals gradually spreading inland and changing in composition as more conventional ecosystems develop in higher parts of the island. This view of establishment helps to explain why so many of the endemic animals on Ascension Island are associated with subterranean habitats. In daytime on a barren tropical island, small animals are in constant danger of dehydration, but they can find humid and equable conditions in the network of cracks and interconnecting spaces below the surface. Since the food arrives on the surface, they will generally forage there by night. However, the scene is also then set for separate groups of individuals to exploit distinct ecological niches, and eventually to form separate species and so follow independent evolutionary pathways. Some may remain linked to the surface, with its relatively abundant food and attendant dangers, while others may gradually evolve adaptations to the subterranean environment, with its damp warm darkness and scanty supplies of food.

Intriguingly, simple invertebrate communities of barren lava coasts may also provide some insight into the first colonisation of dry land habitats by animals, hundreds of millions of years ago, when conditions on the fringes of the land masses were analogous to those found today on coasts of young volcanic islands.

Seabirds are another group of animals that would have had little difficulty in becoming established on the islands, since they need land only for breeding and roosting, the rest of their lives being spent at sea. In contrast, most animals and plants adapted to life in continental regions, would have faced great difficulty. Even if a founding unit managed to breed, the offspring would have been genetically adapted to other conditions, and there would have been many failures for each success. The

---

[17] I.W.B. Thornton et al. 1988, N.P. Ashmole & M.J. Ashmole (2000) and included references.

species most likely to establish themselves would have been those that were widely distributed in the areas from which they came, and thus were capable of living in a variety of environments.

Having initially colonised the islands, populations of animals and plants faced several threats to their permanent establishment. Most of these problems of extinction are specific to island populations. On continents, many species have large populations, often spread over a variety of areas and habitats, so that threats to one group often leave others untouched.

One obvious risk was that the volcanoes continued to erupt periodically, potentially exposing whole populations to asphyxiating gases, molten lava or enveloping ash. Sometimes, parts of the island would have escaped the worst effects and recolonisation of the devastated areas could subsequently take place, but species with restricted distribution must have been extremely vulnerable. The absence from St Helena in 1502 of several plants represented by pollen in the fossil deposits laid down in an interval between major eruptive episodes, suggest that extinctions are sometimes caused in this way.

Another threat came from climate change. Although small islands far out in the ocean are buffered to some extent against such changes – since the sea tends to keep humidity relatively high and temperatures moderate – reduced rainfall in certain periods could well have endangered some species on both St Helena and Ascension. Sometimes temperature changes can be sufficiently drastic to have gross effects on populations within a few decades, giving little opportunity for evolutionary change that might enable species to adapt to the new conditions. On continents, climatic changes typically lead to alterations in the ranges of plants and animals: warming conditions generally allow species to move their ranges uphill, as well as northwards and southwards in their respective hemispheres; cooling conditions lead to the reverse effects. Populations on islands, however, cannot move far in response to climatic change, and on small ones have only limited scope even for changes in altitudinal range.

Climatic change would also have brought about alterations in the distribution of water masses around the islands and hence the food supplies available to seabirds. If this led to longer commuting distances to feeding grounds it would inevitably have significant effects on breeding success and could thus lead to extinction of the population. There is evidence from the fossil record on St Helena that the relative abundance of the different seabirds varied enormously over time, and at least one species (a shearwater) apparently became extinct long ago (see Chapter 5); these changes in the seabird communities probably reflect environmental fluctuations.

A third hazard to the establishment of permanent colonies on the islands could have been simply bad luck of the kind that operates in very small populations[18]. If, for instance, exceptional weather resulted in complete breeding failure in a given season, extinction could happen very rapidly. Events of this type seem to be the main reason for the typical absence from small islands of predatory birds and other species (especially large ones) whose population densities are inevitably low. Similar effects may also occur in somewhat larger populations, especially of species with short lifespan and ecological characteristics routinely leading to wide fluctuations in numbers.

A final type of problem faced by colonists during establishment relates to their reproductive systems and genetics. In species that can reproduce without sex

[18] T.W. Schoener & D.A. Spiller (1987).

involving two individuals – either by self-fertilization, by a female producing young from unfertilized eggs, or simply by vegetative propagation – a single individual has the potential to found a new population. Since getting to remote islands is so chancy, species with this capacity must be at an initial advantage, and it can be no accident that islands often have asexual species (mainly plants, but also some snails and other invertebrates). Such species, however, may have problems with inbreeding after establishment (if they self-fertilize), and may also be vulnerable to changing conditions due to a lack of genetic diversity in the population. They will also tend to have little evolutionary potential, being unlikely to evolve into groups of new species on a single island.

The St Helena Dogwood seems to have evolved a solution to these problems. The source population is thought to have consisted of individuals with both male and female parts, but with mechanisms normally preventing self pollination. The island population was probably founded by a single individual that managed to produce at least a few offspring by self-pollination. If this continued, however, later generations may have suffered from bad effects of inbreeding. This will have favoured the renewal of the ability to cross-pollinate and thus produce fitter offspring. The result, according to a recent study by Diana Percy & Quentin Cronk, is the evolution in the Dogwood of effectively separate sexes: in half the individuals only the female parts of the flowers become fully functional, and in the other half only the male parts, thus preventing self-pollination. Hoverflies seem to be responsible for transporting the pollen and ensuring cross-pollination of Dogwood, and it is reasonable to assume that these were present when the plant's ancestors reached the island. It is obvious, however, that plants incapable of self-pollination and requiring specialised pollinators are unlikely to become established on islands.

Animal species that always reproduce sexually can found a new population only if individuals of both sexes arrive at the same time (unless a female arrives already pregnant). Furthermore, if only a small number of individuals arrive the subsequent inbreeding will tend to lead to deleterious effects. Experience from attempts to found laboratory populations – for instance of fruitflies – by capturing single pregnant females in the wild, suggests that inbreeding must result in extinction of many new island populations within a few generations. [19]

Having traced the birth of the islands from the depth of the ocean through to the establishment of plants and animals, we can now turn our attention to their discovery by people and the changes which those events brought about on the islands in the subsequent half millennium.

---

[19] The genetic problems of inbreeding arise mainly when individuals receive from each parent, a copy of the same defective or mildly deleterious gene. An abnormal gene may have little or no effect when it is received from only one parent, since adequate function is often assured by the presence of the normal version received from the other parent; however, the same abnormal gene may be lethal or severely handicapping when received in double dose. Since all individuals have many different abnormal genes in single dose and transmit them randomly to some of their offspring, inbreeding among related individuals leads to a risk of offspring receiving the abnormal type of the same gene from both parents. In plant or animal species in which a degree of inbreeding has been common in the past, natural selection will have filtered out many of the abnormal genes: individuals receiving copies from both parents will often have died without reproducing, removing the genes responsible and thus reducing their abundance in the population. Colonists drawn from such populations will thus have a good chance of founding an island population capable of surviving through the first few critical generations when numbers are low and inbreeding intense.

Part II

St Helena

"St Helena is an Island in the Ocean, soe called by the Portugalls, being found on St Hellens day. I conceive it to bee the farthest from any other Land then any other Island or part of the World beside ... It is verie rockey, hilly and steepie towards the waterside, for the most part makeing sundrey partitions or vallies, which have each or most of them a litle brooke or Rillett of Fresh water ... Each of them will bring you upp alofte where is a verie fine molde of Earth, although mountainous up Hill and downe Hill, yett neither steepie nor Craggy, excepting neere the Sea as aforesaid."

Peter Mundy, writing in 1634 (see R.C. Temple 1914)

Exploring St Helena in 1502

As João da Nova and the expectant crew of his tiny Portuguese vessel approached St Helena on 21st May, 1502, their first concern was to get around to leeward and to find a sheltered bay. The towering, crumbling cliffs of the Barn and the coasts of naked black lava and chaotic rubble slopes were best kept at a distance. Rounding Sugar Loaf Point, however, the calmer northwest coast offered anchorage and several possible landing places; a boat full of sailors was soon pulling in to the sandy beach in the valley where a chapel would soon be constructed.

What did the pioneers find in those first days? The accounts left by them and the other early travellers are fragmentary, but we can now – with a little licence – try to reconstruct their experience. Above all, there must have been a feeling of overwhelming strangeness, both at the rugged volcanic landscape and the unfamiliar plants – hardly any of them known to the sailors from their explorations along the west coast of Africa.

It was animals, however, that first caught the sailors' attention. They were eager for fresh meat, and the bay looked promising. On the beach they found ridiculously tame seals, several of which they quickly clubbed to death, and in the evening also turtles, which they turned on their backs and took on board the next day. The rocky slopes on either side of the valley mouth, formed from rubble and silt washed down by past torrential rains, were dazzlingly white in the sun, coated with guano deposited by swarms of seabirds. Tropicbirds – solidly built birds providing a good deal of meat – were nesting in crevices, while boobies and noddies roosted and bred on the slopes; the birds were tame and easy to catch by hand, or to kill with sticks or stones. Fishing from the rocks was also productive, so that provisions were soon replenished.

Chapel Valley had a stream, where water barrels were soon being filled. Along it there were thickets of Dwarf Ebony, with hairy leaves and beautiful white flowers reminding the sailors of miniature tulips. The rockier slopes had scattered blue-grey Samphire – one plant that they recognized – with patches of the slightly succulent Salad Plant, which was tart and refreshing to eat raw. On the few dusty level patches close to the sea were bizarre clumps of Babies' Toes, with swollen yellow green stems and surprising delicate white flowers almost concealed in the tips of the stems.

The party struggled on inland, at first forcing their way through thickets in the valley, but soon deciding to make for the rocky ridges with more open vegetation. The shrubs here included the Scrubwood, which they had seen from the sea, with straggly branches profiled against the edges of sheer cliffs; now on closer view it had showy white daisy flowers. As they pushed through the bushes they scattered clouds of tiny, harmless jumping bugs that had been feeding on the leaves, and of small brown moths that were resting on the trees and in the litter underfoot. They also found slopes covered by the Tea Plant, a wiry, spreading bush with tiny leaves and equally small white flowers, with branches swaying in the wind. In clefts in the rock were clumps of Old Father Live Forever, obviously a geranium, with swollen, shiny-barked stems hugging the rocks, hairy leaves and flowers nodding on long, slender stalks. These flowers were also white, setting a pattern that was to become more striking as they went further inland.

As they gained height and reached relatively level places, the sailors came to groves of real trees, but of quite an unfamiliar kind. Like the 'cabbage trees' that they encountered later, these Gumwoods and Bastard Gumwoods were 'composites': relatives of dandelions and thistles, but here in abnormally large versions, forming trees with arching branches and clusters of flowers on long stalks. The leaves – reminiscent of the well known herb, Sage – were crowded at the ends of the branches and formed elegant patterns against the sky. These were sticky plants, like their relatives the low-growing Scrubwoods, and the sailors' clothes and hands quickly became covered with gum. When they needed a fire, the resinous Gumwood branches proved ideal, but they were startled – while moving rocks to build the fireplace – by giant earwigs as much as three inches long and a black beetle also larger than any they had ever seen.

Climbing up through the woods, they blessed the fact that none of the plants were prickly, but were annoyed by the tough webs of an enormous, striped, black and white spider strung between the trees. They found no mammals or reptiles, but did see birds. In the open areas, and also in the drier woodlands, a boldly patterned hoopoe reminded the sailors of the one they knew at home in Portugal, though the St Helena bird was larger and was reluctant to fly. In the woods there was a small green cuckoo in the tree-tops, and they glimpsed small flightless rails – streaked brown birds with strong legs – as they scuttered away through the undergrowth; once they disturbed a larger rail – the size of a small chicken – but were unable to catch it although it too seemed unable to fly. When they reached a more level area they found plovers – later named Wirebirds – running around among the scattered bushes on the arid plains to the east, and sometimes taking off in mild alarm.

In the moister uplands the Gumwood trees became mixed with the Redwood, a real timber tree reminding them of the Dwarf Ebony which they had seen lower down, but quite different in shape and with pale green leaves and larger, drooping flowers that were white when fresh but changed to purple when dying.

Only after a serious climb did the sailors reach the most striking vegetation on the island: the cabbage tree woodland of the central highlands. Tree Ferns, growing as high as a house, spread enormous fronds in the canopy. Their shaggy trunks – thicker than a man's leg and exuding red gum – acted as seedbeds for many of the other plants of this damp forest; also on the ferns were many small yellow woodlice, recognizable as such but covered with sharp spines, reminding the sailors of hedgehogs at home in Europe. Apart from the Tree Fern, the dominant tree here was the False Gumwood, which was similar to the Gumwood that they had already seen, but there were also patches with the tall and slender She Cabbage and He Cabbage trees, with large, fleshy leaves; conspicuous on these were hoary beetles with blunt snouts and slender, elbowed antennae held out in front as they moved slowly around. Progress was made difficult by a thick undergrowth of ferns, especially the Black Scale Fern which grew more than waist high, together with two kinds of erect, woody bellflowers.

Some of the more energetic members of the group pushed on upwards and found themselves in a region where there were still Tree Ferns but also some new types of trees that thrived only in the mists shrouding the crest of the ridge. There was the Black Cabbage Tree – with a spreading crown and glossy leaves – and also the St Helena Olive, Dogwood and Whitewood, all of them totally unlike any trees that they had seen elsewhere on their travels. The understorey here included dense stands of Milkwood (later called Lobelia) with upright, fleshy green stems and small white flowers. Less common was the Stringwood, with curious pendent red flowers, and the Large Bellflower with beautiful white blossoms.

In gullies where trickles of water cut channels through the deep humus were patches of Jellico, a spectacular giant relative of celery that towered over the sailors' heads; being starved for vegetables some of them took a cautious nibble and found it succulent and refreshing. They were soon eating eagerly, though first removing the small pinkish snails that were crawling on the stems. Before moving on they made up bundles of stems to carry back to their shipmates.

Reaching the summit ridge, the sailors found themselves at the top of a sheer cliff, and were rewarded with a spectacular view to the southeast. Below them was an enormous valley (Sandy Bay), cradling a tiny beach that offered a possible landing place though no safe anchorage. To their right was a longer vista, dominated by towering grey rocks with circling clouds of seabirds. There was no time, however, to explore the valley even if they could have found a way down, and so they started the long trek back to the bay where they had landed, where fish and seabirds were roasting over fires in a makeshift camp close to the shore.

Chapter 2   # The island and its people

St Helena is an oceanic island in the tropical South Atlantic. It lies at latitude 15°58'S and longitude 5°43'W. The nearest continental land is Angola, just over 1,800 km to the east; the coast of South America is 3,260 km to the west. The closest island is Ascension at a distance of exactly 1,300 km to the northwest. The island lies directly on the shortest route between Ascension Island and Cape Town, which is just under 3,100 km southeast of St Helena.

The island is roughly rectangular, just over 17 km long, about 10 km wide and with an area of 121.7 km². The highest point is 820 m above sea level and the 300 m contour is rarely more than one kilometre inland from the coast; in several places the sea cliffs rise to more than 400 m. There are breaks in the cliffs at intervals where water courses have cut down to the sea forming steep-sided valleys, and one major valley system - Sandy Bay - occupies the whole space between the summit ridge and the central part of the south coast. The interior of the island is deeply dissected and topographically complex, with large areas of level ground only in the northeast of the island, in the Deadwood Plain and Longwood area and at Prosperous Bay Plain.

Discovery and early visitors

St Helena was discovered in May 1502 on the homeward bound leg of the 1501 Portuguese voyage to India.[1] It was apparently named in honour of St Helena, mother of the Emperor Constantine, whose anniversary was celebrated on the supposed date of discovery, 21st May. On this first visit or soon afterwards, goats and pigs were left on the island to provide fresh meat for visiting sailors, thus initiating the destruction of the natural vegetation. The first resident of the island was a mutilated Portuguese gentleman named Fernão Lopes who was banished from Portugal in 1516 and lived on St Helena with only one break until he died in 1546.[2] Lopes seems to have been routinely left provisions by visiting Portuguese ships and was doubtless responsible for the establishment of many edible plants on the island.

In about 1550 five slaves - three men and two women - escaped from a ship and eventually increased to about 20; they were apparently re-captured prior to 1589. Throughout the 16th century there were more or less annual visits, usually around May and June, by Portuguese fleets returning from the East Indies. The island was even visited by the Patriarch of Abyssinia and later by three Japanese princes accompanied by Jesuits, who were on an embassy to the Pope. Convalescent Portuguese sailors sometimes stayed for a year and even engaged in trade: an account of the animals on the island in 1578 included the passage:[3]

---

[1] Recent accounts of the discovery and early history of St Helena are provided by N.M. Wace (1999) and R. Gill & P. Teale (1999). Our account of later periods is based mainly on P. Gosse (1938, 1990) and G.C. Kitching (1937, 1995).

[2] B.W. Rowlands (1992).

[3] Translation quoted by B.W. Rowlands et al. (1998).

"All which beasts and fowls are so secure and tame, that they fear not a man, because they do not know in what danger they are to be killed; so that the inhabitants take of them daily, and powder them with salt ... and the flesh thereof, being thus preserved, they give to the sailors that arrive at the island."

The first visit of an English ship was that of the *Desire* in 1588, with Captain Thomas Cavendish in command. For more than 80 years the location of St Helena had apparently been unknown to English mariners; Cavendish was guided to the island by the pilot of a Spanish ship which he had captured in the Pacific. He stayed on St Helena for twelve days and described how, on 9th June 1588:[4]

"in the afternoon, we went on shore, where we found a marvellous fair and pleasant valley, wherin divers handsome buildings and houses were set up, and especially one which was a church ....There are two houses adjoining the church".

In the following year the Dutchman Jan Huyghen van Linschoten visited the island, piloting the annual Portuguese East India fleet. He was also much impressed, stressing the productivity of the island:[5]

"The Portingales have by little and little brought many beastes into it, and in the valleyes planted al sorts of fruites: which have growne there in so great abundance, that it is almost incredible. For it is so full of Goates, Buckes, wild Hogges, Hennes, Partridges, and Doves, by thousands, so that any man that will, may hunt and take them: & ther is alwaies [plentie and] sufficient, although there came as many shippes more into the Iland as there doe: and they may kill them with stones and staves, by reason of the gret numbers of them. Now for fruites, as Portingall Figges, Pomgranets, Oranges, Lemons, Citrons, and such like fruites, there are so many, that growe without planting or setting, that all the valleyes are full of them, which is a great pleasure to beholde, for that it seemeth to bee an earthly Paradise."

After this time the Dutch and the English began competing in the trade to India and often called at St Helena on the homeward voyage. The southeasterly tradewinds made it easy to reach the island from the south but difficult from the north. For the next several centuries, outward bound ships from Europe normally crossed the Atlantic near the equator, travelled south with the Brazil Current, then crossed back in the westerlies to pass just south of Africa. On the return trip, both St Helena and Ascension lay on the best route from the Cape of Good Hope to Europe: more reliable trade winds were encountered, and a shorter distance run, by staying in mid ocean until north of the equator than by keeping near the African shore.

Shortly before and after the end of the sixteenth century more or less hostile interactions between the Portuguese and the Dutch and English led to frequent vandalization of the chapel, houses and fruit trees.[6] The year 1625 saw the start of more serious fights over the island between Dutch and Portuguese fleets. The first fortifications were built by the crew of a Portuguese ship that sank at anchor after a fight with the Dutch; they mounted their guns on shore, built dwellings with timber

---

[4] P.L.Teale (1981).

[5] P.A. Tiele (1885).

[6] In 1614 Thomas Best, commander of the English East India Company's tenth voyage, recorded that there were no lemons in Chapel Valley; visiting Lemon Valley, however, his crew were able to harvest 12-14,000 lemons and to catch 30 hogs (Foster 1934). In 1634 Peter Mundy found only 20 lemon trees in Lemon Valley and about another 20 elsewhere on the island (R.C. Temple 1914).

from the ship and later successfully defended the landing place against the Dutch. In the following years, however, the Portuguese began to avoid St Helena in favour of safer African ports, while the island was used more regularly by the English and Dutch. In 1633 the commanders of a Dutch fleet made a formal claim to the island and stated the intention of their government to fortify and populate it; it appears, however, that no colony was actually established.[7]

The colony and its history

In 1649 the East India Company decided to make strategic use of St Helena, ordering all their ships on the way home to England to assemble there so that they could be escorted through the dangerous seas further north by a man-of-war. Less than a decade later Richard Cromwell granted a charter to the Company, authorising it to occupy territory. The first settlers arrived on St Helena from England in May 1659, after spending a few days at the Cape Verde Islands to obtain plants and seed for establishing the new plantation, and with instructions also to procure: *"five or six blacks or negroes, able men and women .... provided they may be had at or under 40 dollers per poll."* Slavery was to be basic to the economy of the island for one and a half centuries.[8]

The island was initially divided into 150 parts; 15 were allotted to the East India Company, five to the Governor and one to each planter with his wife and servant. Planters paid rent in kind to the Company and had an obligation to help defend the island. By 1666 they were producing a good range of fruit and vegetables and cattle were multiplying, but rats were a major problem. A further group of immigrants arriving in 1667 included Londoners dispossessed by the Great Fire.

The island was captured by the Dutch in 1673, but was recaptured four months later and has remained in British hands ever since. In December 1673 King Charles II granted a new charter to the East India Company, making them Lords Proprietors of St Helena with all the rights of sovereignty. A few years later the king arranged a free passage to the island for Edmund Halley, who was later astronomer royal. He came in 1676 (when he was only 20) to map the stars of the southern hemisphere, supplementing the work of John Flamsteed at the Greenwich observatory which had just been established by King Charles; the aim was to collect astronomical data that might enable navigators to fix their longitude at sea. Working in an observatory on a hill at Hutts Gate which became known as Halley's Mount, the young astronomer was much troubled by the low cloud which is common in that part of the island, but observed a transit of Mercury and fixed the positions of 341 southern stars, an achievement which earned him election to the Royal Society.[9]

---

[7] A substantial enclosure was noted by Peter Mundy in 1638 some way up Lemon Valley: "wee Found a certaine wall off stone by pilying them one on the other, enclosing a pretty peece off ground, and aboutt 22 or 23 Severall Names off Dutchmen written and graven on the stones in Anno 1637." (R.C. Temple 1919). Such an enclosure does not necessarily imply settlement; Gosse (1990) plausibly suggested that it was built by the Portuguese some years previously for the pigs they imported, and that the names were those of some Dutch ship's company visiting the island in the year before Peter Mundy.

[8] The quotation and the following notes are derived from P. Gosse (1990). Although the first slaves on the island were of West African origin, many were apparently soon brought from the East India Company's bases in the Indian subcontinent. Other slaves came from Madagascar: late in the 17th century, English ships trading there were obliged to leave a slave on St Helena on their return voyage, and the settlers even dispatched ships specially to obtain slaves from Madagascar. The Malagasy are a mix of Indonesian, East African and Arabic racial groups, and the former were apparently preferred. Slaves were also brought from elsewhere as opportunity offered, as in 1735 when a group of natives of the Maldive Islands were found drifting in a boat in the Indian Ocean and were brought to St Helena.

[9] One and a half centuries later the laborious cataloguing of southern stars was continued on St Helena by the astronomer Manuel Johnson, who used an observatory on Ladder Hill which was constructed by the East India Company in 1826-28 but abandoned when the island was transferred to the Crown in 1834.

By 1676 the population had reached 390 (blacks and whites). The staple diet at this time was evidently the St Helena Yam (Taro).[10] Life on the island was harsh, and the occasional mutinies were soon suppressed and severely punished. During a war between England and France starting in 1689 no supply ships reached the island for three years, causing considerable hardship. The explorer William Dampier, visiting St Helena around this time, commented that young women were keen to get away by marrying seamen. In 1693 a mutiny led to the death of the Governor and the escape of 27 soldiers. There were also problems with the slaves, and an incipient revolt was savagely repressed in 1694.

In 1708 the outstanding Governor John Roberts arrived and immediately set to work improving the fortifications and laying out the square in Jamestown. He also irrigated and cultivated the 'New Ground' near Plantation, partly to feed extra slaves that he evidently imported.[11] Throughout this early period most of the houses in Jamestown were owned by settlers who occupied them only when a ship called.

The 1740s were a time of particular difficulty on the island, with an epidemic in 1742 which may have been plague, and a severe drought a few years later. On five separate occasions during the period 1744-47 slaves stole boats and set off from the island, probably dying at sea. Later in the century stable government led to reasonable prosperity, although discontent among the soldiers still led to occasional desertion, and in one case a group of soldiers successfully reached the coast of Brazil in a longboat. At the end of 1782 there was a major rebellion. When it was put down 99 mutineers were sentenced to death but were eventually decimated, lots being drawn and one in ten being shot.

The situation improved greatly after the arrival of Colonel Robert Brooke, who served as Governor from 1787 until 1801. Morale in the garrison quickly became so good that over a period of years about 900 discharged soldiers on their way home from India re-engaged on St Helena and in many cases were eventually returned to India. Governor Brooke also undertook major reorganisation of the defences of the island and ensured that forces based on St Helena played an active role in episodes involving the Dutch in the early years of the Napoleonic Wars, both at sea and at the Cape of Good Hope. One of these actions was followed by the temporary presence on the island in 1795 of about three hundred prisoners taken from a captured Dutch fleet. These included some Danes, Norwegians and Swedes who changed allegiance and enlisted as soldiers in the service of the English East India Company. The majority, however, were Malays, who were also recruited as soldiers; they were kept on the island for about two years and eventually formed the basis of a Malay regiment in Ceylon.

Governor Brooke was also responsible for major changes relating to slavery. A new code of laws was introduced for the control and protection of slaves; it limited the authority of slave owners to punish slaves and gave the slaves the right to prosecute masters who exceeded their powers. Furthermore, the importation of slaves was prohibited in 1792. This led to a labour shortage in the following decades, which was eventually countered by bringing in Chinese labourers from Canton, starting in 1810,

---

[10] In 1682 a visitor commented that the islanders grew yams because they were too bitter (until boiled) to be eaten by the rats, which ate potatoes while they were still in the ground. By 1690 the inhabitants were said to be subsisting primarily upon yams and half a century later yams were still a staple, at least in the diet of slaves. In Napoleonic times St Helenians in general were sometimes referred to in England as 'yamstocks', implying a lack of sophistication.

[11] A census in 1719 showed that there were 320 whites and 411 blacks on the island, but by 1723 the population was said to be: whites - 50 men, 79 women, 251 children; officers and soldiers - 120; blacks - freemen 18, slaves 610.

with contracts for three years which were sometimes extended to five. The Chinese colony exceeded 600 at one time, and some of the labourers remained on the island permanently.

In 1807 came perhaps the greatest medical crisis in the history of St Helena. A slave ship with measles on board, which had previously been the source of an epidemic at the Cape of Good Hope, arrived at St Helena. Warning came too late and the virus got ashore, leading to an epidemic which killed one hundred and sixty people within two months and many more shortly afterwards: the final death toll was probably around five percent of the population of roughly 3,500. During the previous decades the island had been remarkably free of infectious disease and the inhabitants were extremely vulnerable. Another epidemic of measles occurred some 35 years later, but was not so catastrophic.

As a result of the measles epidemic in 1807 a programme of vaccination against smallpox was immediately undertaken, little more than a decade after the procedure was invented. The vaccine material was brought from the Cape of Good Hope by an ingenious relay: Governor Patton arranged for six drummer boys from the garrison to be sent to the Cape, where they waited until a ship was available to bring them back. Two of them were then inoculated and the infection was transmitted to the others in succession during the voyage, thus bringing the vaccine to the island.

Throughout most of the history of the colony problems have been caused by alcohol abuse. Early in the 18th century many stills were set up to produce arrack - a local distilled spirit - and the death rate on the island rose to 10% in 1719, this high rate being attributed to the enormous consumption of arrack punch. Excessive use of spirits continued through most of the 18th century, both among the settlers and in the garrison. Major-General Alexander Beatson, who was governor from 1808 to 1813, decided to tackle the problem. He prohibited the public sale of spirits and strictly controlled their import. At the time the garrison numbered 1250 men, of whom 132 were sick in hospital; four months later, there were only 48 soldiers in hospital. Beatson's drastic action, however, together with the simultaneous raising of the price of subsidised food imported by the East India Company, led at Christmas 1811 to a mutiny in the garrison which was quickly suppressed.

A small printing press had been brought to the island in 1806. It was soon taken over by the government and Beatson used it to disseminate his advice on the improvement of agriculture on the island. This was a period of prosperity for farmers on St Helena, since hundreds of ships were now calling at the island each year. Potatoes were particularly valuable for provisioning visiting ships, and introduced pests had not yet devastated the fruit and vegetable crops. Furthermore, the farmers formed a marketing ring by agreeing among themselves exorbitantly high prices for produce; a single cabbage would sell for as much as 18 pence and a turkey for two guineas. Entrepreneurs also benefitted from the high volume of shipping. Lodgings in Jamestown were expensive, and traders imported manufactured goods from Europe and sold them at inflated prices to passengers on the ships coming from India and beyond; the sale of songbirds to passengers was also flourishing.

It was at this time that St Helena first obtained a dedicated supply ship. She was the Schooner *St Helena*, nominally of 136 tons, stationed at the island and used to bring cattle, grain and stores from the Cape of Good Hope.[12] She arrived at St Helena on

---

[12] B.B. Montgomerie (1994).

12th January 1815 with a crew of fifteen, and it was immediately realized that she was on the small side for the job. During the next 16 years she made 64 voyages but had a chequered career, the mishaps including missing the island, with consequent heavy losses among the livestock on board. In 1830 she was despatched to England via Sierra Leone for repairs, but was attacked by pirates. The officers, a passenger and some crew members were murdered but a few survivors managed to sail the disabled ship to Sierra Leone; she was refitted there and eventually reached England, where she was sold. The East India Company did not replace her, preferring to let supply contracts at the Cape for stock deliverable at St Helena. The name *St Helena* was revived by a second world war American built lease-lend frigate, but the island was not again to have its own supply ship until 1979, after Union Castle ships en route to the Cape ceased to provide a service. The first modern RMS *St Helena* then provided a vital link until replaced by the present specially built 'RMS' in 1990.

The best known episode in the history of St Helena is the imprisonment of Napoleon Bonaparte on the island after the Battle of Waterloo. He arrived on 15th October 1815 on board HMS *Northumberland*, with only four days warning, causing far-reaching local changes and focusing the eyes of the world on a previously obscure island. The British authorities requested the East India Company to appoint a government nominee, Lieutenant-General Sir Hudson Lowe, as Governor; until he arrived, however, Napoleon remained in the custody of Rear-Admiral Sir George Cockburn who had brought him to the island. After staying one night in Jamestown and two months in a small pavilion at the Briars, Napoleon was installed at Longwood House; a new house was built for him nearby, but the move into it was forestalled by his death.

Elaborate precautions were taken to prevent Napoleon's escape, including the garrisoning of Ascension Island and severe restrictions on ships calling at St Helena. The population of the island was roughly doubled by the arrival of several regiments of soldiers as well as an array of people directly associated with Napoleon and his guardians, and food and other supplies tended to run short. Military camps were established at Deadwood and at Francis Plain, and the social life of the island was transformed for a period of nearly six years.

This whole structure collapsed when Napoleon died on 5th May, 1821. He left behind, however, an indelible mark: a fact about St Helena that can be recalled by people around the world, many of whom – if presented with a globe – would not be able to locate the island. Napoleon was buried at the head of Sane Valley just north of Hutts Gate. In 1840, however, his body was exhumed and taken to France, embarking from the island on the 15th October, precisely one quarter of a century after the *Northumberland* had arrived bringing the Emperor into exile; his remains were buried with great ceremony under the great dome of Les Invalides in Paris. Within a few years after Napoleon's death both Longwood House and New Longwood were put to agricultural use; they soon fell into disrepair and New Longwood was eventually demolished. In 1858, however, the tomb, together with Longwood House and the land immediately surrounding it, were formally vested in His Majesty Napoleon III and his heirs for ever; since that time, they have been cared for as a historic part of France.

The period after Napoleon's death was economically difficult and the authorities tried hard to stimulate agriculture; a regular market was established in Jamestown and an abortive silkworm farm was started at the Briars. A decade later a whale fishery was established on the island but was soon abandoned; a second attempt in

1875 led to the same outcome. Initiatives relating to education were more successful. The public library had been established in 1813 and there was now much building of schools. By 1823 four hundred children were attending schools of the Company and of the Benevolent Society. Another significant advance was the construction of the 600-step ladder flanked by inclined planes up the face of the cliff south of Jamestown. The ladder provided an important short-cut, and the planes - on which waggons travelled on tramways, powered by mules and a capstan at the top - were used for hauling all kinds of stores and materials up from Jamestown.

This period also saw the phasing out of slavery on the island. As a result of a personal initiative of Sir Hudson Lowe, from 1818 children of slaves were born free, and in 1832 the East India Company purchased the freedom of the 614 remaining slaves for the sum of £28,062 17s; however, the former slaves eventually had to reimburse the company for their emancipation.

A fundamental change in the status of St Helena was brought about by the Act of Parliament of 28th August 1833, by which the British Government took over the administration of the island from the East India Company, with effect from 22nd April 1834. The economic effects of the change were momentous. Within a few years the garrison had been much reduced and many civilian employees of the Company had lost their jobs. Pension provisions were not generous and many people were forced to leave; some still had roots in England, but many families and young people emigrated to the Cape of Good Hope.

The young naturalist Charles Darwin visited the island in 1836, just after the transition, and worried about the future for the working people. He commented that the emancipated slaves were extremely poor and that they complained of the want of work. He noted that the chief food of the working classes at this time consisted of rice with a little imported salt meat. Although it seems likely that yams were still much eaten in country districts, Darwin's comment suggests that the dependence of the islanders on imported foods, which is so noticeable today, had its origins at least a century and a half ago.

During the middle decades of the 19th century St Helena was used as a base for the Royal Navy's West African Squadron, which was engaged in suppression of the slave trade; the activity associated with this operation provided some economic support to the local population. Numerous intercepted slave ships were brought to the island and many thousands of slaves were freed. Disembarkation of living, moribund and dead slaves took place at Ruperts Bay, and the Liberated African Depot was established there to provide temporary care for the survivors. When they recovered, most of the freed slaves were given passages to the British West Indies or British Guiana, but some had the opportunity to go to Sierra Leone; others remained to work on the island and became integrated into the local population.

The latter part of the 19th century was perhaps the nadir for the inhabitants of St Helena. The West African Squadron left in 1864 and termites devastated the buildings of Jamestown (see Chapter 15). Steamships tended to bypass the island, and even if they called, took on little in the way of supplies because of advances in refrigeration technology. Furthermore, Anglo-Indian passengers on their way home often preferred to avoid the Atlantic route, instead travelling overland from the Red Sea to the Mediterranean; this reduced the flow of wealthy visitors through St Helena even before the Suez Canal was opened in 1869. The decline in shipping traffic continued subsequently: during the decade from 1873 to 1882, the number of ships calling at St

Helena fell from 717 to 497 and the tonnage was reduced by 12%. There were also persistent efforts by the British Government to reduce the cost of maintaining an island which had ceased to have an obvious function.

One effect of the declining economic situation was massive emigration. In the period prior to 1876 about 1500 of the poorest inhabitants left for Natal and the Cape of Good Hope, and emigration continued in subsequent decades. This led to consolidation of land holdings, with large acreages coming into the hands of a few wealthy families. The resulting pattern of land ownership had important effects during the development of the flax industry in the early 20th century (see Chapter 7).

St Helena received its last major influx of people from overseas in the first years of the 20th century, when some thousands of Boer prisoners of war were brought to the island and housed in camps on Deadwood Plain and at Broad Bottom near the head of Lemon Valley. The Boer War also brought with it an improvement in communications, since a telegraph line was laid from Cape Town to St Helena in 1899 and was subsequently connected to Ascension Island and Britain.

Another result of the war and the consequent establishment of crowded camps was an epidemic of typhoid, which caused the deaths of many prisoners and some guards before the end of the war in 1902. Soon after this the Boers were repatriated. While on the island most of the prisoners had been isolated from the St Helenian population, but some were employed as craftsmen on various building projects and made many contacts with local people. After the war, a few of the Boers stayed on and became residents of the island.

Apart from the recorded arrivals of different groups of people, St Helena has been a temporary home for thousands of soldiers, themselves of diverse origins, and has been visited by countless sailors. For centuries the East India Company ships routinely stopped on their way home, as did many other trading ships, while periodic naval visits have continued to the present day. Furthermore, throughout the nineteenth century the island was a key rendezvous for American whaling ships based in New England. In 1855, for instance, at least 43 whalers called at the island, and even greater numbers were mentioned by J.C. Melliss in his book published in 1875. Whaling was a major source of employment for St Helenian men up to the end of the century and Jamestown was used for rest and recreation by the crews. The St Helenian community must rival Hawai'i and other oceanic crossroads in the diversity of its genetic origins.

The 'Saints' today

At the end of the 20th century there are on the island about 5,300 'Saints' (the name by which the islanders refer to themselves); another 1100 (including dependants) work overseas, mainly in the Falkland Islands and on Ascension. In addition, many people of St Helenian origin have long been resident in Britain, South Africa and elsewhere.

Administratively, St Helena is a British Overseas Territory, one of the few remaining fragments of the British Empire and one of the more isolated inhabited places on earth. The Governor is normally from Britain and is directly responsible to the Foreign & Commonwealth Office in London. Several other senior administrators are also British expatriates. A Legislative Council (LEGCO) is made up of the Governor, the Speaker, the Chief Secretary and the Treasurer, together with 12 elected members. Five of the elected members chair the council committees and oversee government departments; they also join the Governor and the other ex-officio members of LEGCO to form an Executive Council (EXCO).

There are three main population centres: Jamestown at sea level, Half Tree Hollow high up just to the south of it and Longwood inland on the northern plateau. In addition there are several smaller settlements which are quite isolated from one another. This is a consequence of the precipitous landscape in which points appearing almost adjacent on the map may be remote by road. Although the island is little more than 10 miles long, it may take forty minutes to drive from Jamestown to one of the outlying districts. Driving requires skill and care; top gear is rarely appropriate and first is in use almost as much as third. There is no public transport, although some employees are taken to and from work by bus. Even today, pedestrians often use steep short-cuts, and in the past these paths were doubtless normal routes for people and their donkeys.[13]

Like most western societies today, St Helenians have high rates of car ownership, supermarket-style shopping, video shops and access to the internet. Medical facilities are good, there is a modern high school and education is free and compulsory for children between 5 and 15 years old. The government is the main employer, and agriculture, forestry and fishing are the main occupations. Unemployment, however, is very high. The island, lacking in natural resources, is almost entirely dependent on imports for food and other necessities. There is not even a dairy on the island and an attempt to establish a brewery eventually failed. However, a fish-processing plant is operating and a recent coffee-growing initiative has generated significant new employment.

In spite of modern developments, the isolation of the St Helena is in some ways greater than in earlier times. Traffic by sea is now only a tiny fraction of what it was 100 or 200 years ago, and the only regular transportation link with the outside world is by means of the island's ship, the RMS *St Helena*, which sails between Britain, Ascension Island, St Helena and South Africa. On the latest schedule she makes about 24 visits in the year, but on many of these she is shuttling to and from Ascension Island; there are only four departures a year from Britain. There is no airfield, although the pressure to construct one is growing. An airfield would undoubtedly result in great changes on the island, both social and ecological, and local people are divided on the question of the advantages and disadvantages. Many would like the security of an air link for medical emergencies, though they tend to be less certain that it is desirable on other grounds. Possible sites for an airfield are available on Deadwood Plain and Prosperous Bay Plain.

Opportunities for St Helenians to settle or work outside the island have become more limited over the course of centuries. The Royal Charter of 1673 conferred on the inhabitants of St Helena and their descendants born on the island, comprehensive rights identical to those enjoyed by people born in England. However, after the island came under the direct rule of the British Government in 1834 it was viewed as a colony, rather than as a detached part of the realm, which led to a subtle change of status for its inhabitants. Although this had no immediate practical effect, it was relevant a century and a half later. The UK 1981 Nationality Act was passed at a time when there was a perception in Britain of the possibility of imminent arrival of millions of Hong Kong Chinese. The act classed St Helenians as British, but as Dependent

---

[13] Over the centuries, communities have evidently been much more effectively isolated. Benjamin Grant, local printer and writer, in his guide to the island published in 1883, commented in relation to Sandy Bay that: "Upwards of 200 persons reside in the Bay and strange to say that nearly all of them are relatives - a sort of happy family." Intermarriage of close relatives in the past is probably a cause of the rather high incidence of hereditary disorders in some of the more remote parts of the island.

Territories Citizens rather than British Citizens. As such, they required visas to enter the UK and their historic rights were abrogated. It is only now, at the start of the new millennium, that this act is being rescinded and full citizenship rights restored.

Emigration from St Helena had for a long time been relatively easy. Departures continued after the mass movements of the 19th century and emigration to South Africa was still significant during a period of hardship early in the 20th century; by that time, however, it was constrained by requirements for educational qualifications which were hard to acquire on the island. Even after the second world war substantial numbers of islanders went to Britain, often to undertake agricultural or domestic work, and many of them remained indefinitely; smaller numbers settled elsewhere. However, the opportunities for emigration to South Africa were largely eliminated after 1950 and settlement in the UK became increasingly difficult after 1968.

At the start of the 21st century, with prospects of employment on Ascension in decline, St Helenians are largely confined to their tiny island. The economy of the island and its lifeline to the outside world - the RMS *St Helena* - both require massive support from the UK Government. In the wake of the Montserrat disaster of 1997 and the reversion of Hong Kong to the Chinese, more attention is being paid to St Helena and the other overseas territories. However, the future for St Helena and its people is hard to predict.

Chapter 3

The physical environment

Landforms and geology

The volcano and the island

The island of St Helena is only the remnant of the top of an enormous, conical, steep-sided composite volcano resting on the ocean floor. The volcano is about 130 km across at its base and is over 5,000 metres high, but less than one sixth (820 m) of its height and only a small fraction of its volume is exposed above the surface of the sea (see Figure 4).

After a prolonged gestation as the great heap of rubbly rock grew upwards through four kilometres of water, St Helena emerged into the air in the middle of the Miocene Epoch, about 14 million years ago. The volcano remained active – intermittently but often with overwhelming effect – for more than seven million years after the birth of the island. During this period the size of St Helena gradually increased and was probably greatest during the last intense eruptive phase, eight million years ago. At that time the island may have had an area of about 270 km², compared with 122 km² at the present day. The maximum height was probably in the range 1200-1500 metres, more than one and a half times the present height.

The modern island comprises the heavily eroded remains of two shield volcanoes that have coalesced. The term shield volcano refers to a broad but shallow volcanic

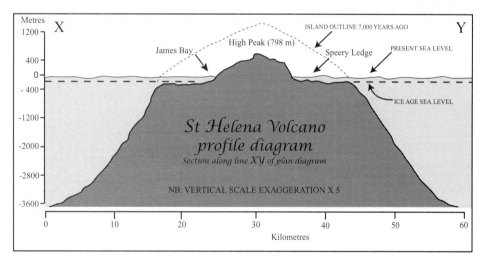

Figure 4

---

[1] Basalt is dark-coloured, and is a 'basic' rock characterized by relatively low - 45-50% - content of silica. The wide spread of the lava is possible because cooling in air is much slower than under water; it creates land with a very low profile, as seen in parts of the western coasts of Ascension Island (and even more strikingly on Santiago in the Galápagos). Because of the different behaviour of basaltic lava on land and under water, many volcanic islands - even during their active building phase - tend to be somewhat flat-topped cones, with the underwater slopes steeper than those above the sea surface. For the same reason (together with different effects of erosion and some other complications), volcanoes build upwards much more quickly during the submarine phase than during their active life above water.

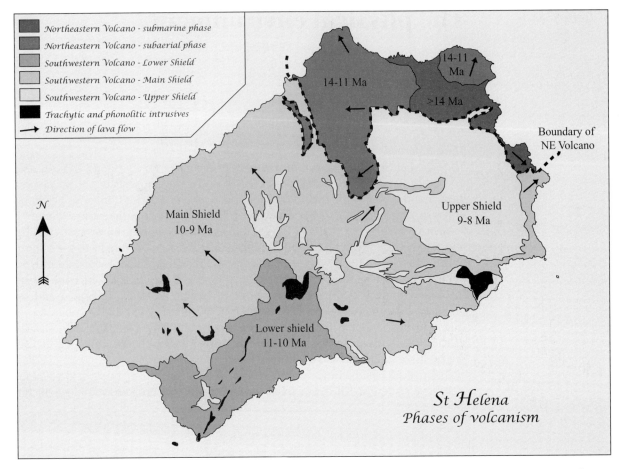

Northeastern Volcano - submarine phase
Northeastern Volcano - subaerial phase
Southwestern Volcano - Lower Shield
Southwestern Volcano - Main Shield
Southwestern Volcano - Upper Shield
Trachytic and phonolitic intrusives
Direction of lava flow

14-11 Ma

14-11 Ma

>14 Ma

Boundary of
NE Volcano

N

Main Shield
10-9 Ma

Upper Shield
9-8 Ma

Lower shield
11-10 Ma

St Helena
Phases of volcanism

Figure 5
Adapted from I. Baker
(1964)

cone built up when a long series of relatively liquid flows of basaltic lava spread out rapidly into sheets and travel several kilometres before solidifying.[1] On St Helena eruptive activity has been concentrated in two areas, often referred to as the Northeastern and Southwestern Volcanic Centres. These two volcanoes were active successively; the former had its peak near Flagstaff Hill and Knotty Ridge, the latter somewhere on the Sandy Bay side of the present central ridge (Figure 5).[2]

It was the activity of the northeastern volcano which led to the emergence of St Helena from the sea, and this centre remained active for a further three million years. It formed an island that extended around the modern Flagstaff Hill, and the rocks that it produced form the coastal cliffs from Mundens Point eastwards round to just north of King and Queen Rocks, as well as Ruperts and Banks Valleys, Sugar Loaf, Flagstaff, the Barn and Turks Cap Valley (though not the ridge). A large proportion of this original island has now disappeared as a result of erosion by the sea, rain and wind, while other parts of it have

[2] Clear modern accounts of the volcanic history of the island and of the rock strata are provided by Barry Weaver (1991, 1999). Weaver - a professional geologist with family connections on the island - based his account on personal observations and background knowledge, and on the thorough geological survey by Ian Baker in 1964-66. Baker published several scientific articles about his work and gave a manuscript copy of his complete university thesis to the public library in Jamestown. More recently, Patrick D. Nunn edited an account of the geomorphology of St. Helena which was published by University College London Press. The most important previous interpretations of the rocks of the island had been made by Robert F. Seale in 1834, Charles Darwin a little later, J.R. Oliver in 1869 and R.A. Daly in 1927

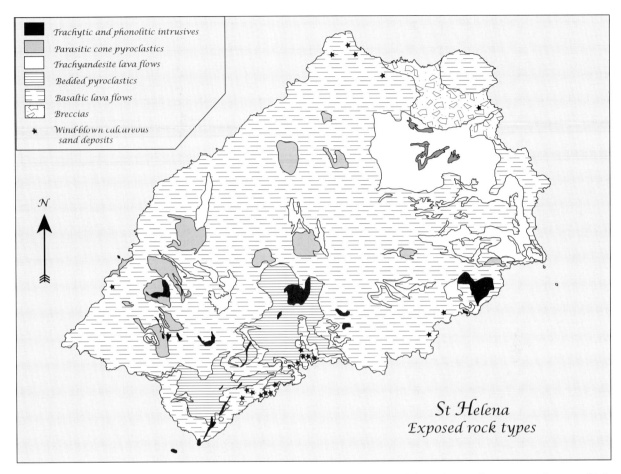

Legend:

- ■ Trachytic and phonolitic intrusives
- ▨ Parasitic cone pyroclastics
- □ Trachyandesite lava flows
- ▤ Bedded pyroclastics
- ▦ Basaltic lava flows
- ▨ Breccias
- ✶ Wind-blown calcareous sand deposits

N

St Helena
Exposed rock types

Figure 6
Adapted from I. Baker
(1964)

been covered by later lava flows. These originated from the southwestern volcano, which became active about 11 million years ago, when the northeastern one ceased its activity; and which gave rise to the shield comprising the whole of the southern and western part of St Helena. In the early stages activity was in the Sandy Bay area, but it may have shifted towards the northeast later on, becoming concentrated around the modern day Peaks.

The rocks of St Helena

The rocks of St Helena are almost entirely of volcanic origin (Figure 6). The oldest strata were formed underwater by the northeastern volcano. They are volcanic breccias, made up of fragments deposited close to their source, a submarine volcanic vent. The breccias consist of small, angular rocks set in a fine-grained yellowish or pinkish matrix (Plate 4). They are easily eroded and are exposed mainly in inaccessible places, but can be seen on the ridge from Flagstaff to the Barn and below Turks Cap. Up to 400 m thickness of breccias are now exposed above sea level, implying that the original island was uplifted after their formation under water. However, worldwide sea level at the relevant time was some 150 metres higher than it is at present, so the required subsequent uplift of the rocks relative to the ocean floor is only about 250 metres.[3]

[3] B.U. Haq et al. (1987).

Above the basal breccias there is in some places a confusing transition zone comprising various types of scoria and boulder beds which are probably of subaerial origin (i.e. deposited above sea level, as opposed to submarine). Above these is a thick mass of shield-forming basaltic lava flows, with a trend towards trachybasalts in the upper (younger) part of the sequence. Among the lava flows are some deposits of 'pyroclastics'; these are volcanic rock fragments deposited from the air, usually after explosive eruptions. The lava flows were mainly erupted from elongated fissures in the Knotty Ridge area. The total thickness of the surviving flows is at least 800 metres, and the original mass of lava was probably thicker than this in some places.

The succession is conveniently seen on the coastal path from Mundens towards the north. The flows here are between one and three metres thick; the centre of each one is solid, but at top and bottom the rock is more like clinker. Small crystals of green or bronze-coloured olivine (a silicate of magnesium and iron) can be seen in some of these lavas. Rocks formed by the northeastern volcano can also be seen in the 'erosional window' of the Jamestown Valley (see Geological maps), where the eroded west-facing slopes north of the Briars expose more than 150 m of basaltic lava flows, overlain by much later flows (from the southwestern volcano) along the ridge between Two Gun Saddle and Mundens Hill.

The rocks erupted from the southwestern volcano are thought to make up about five-sixths of the volume of the island exposed above sea level. They are grouped in three phases: the Lower Shield erupted about 11-10 million years ago, the Main Shield 10-9 million years ago and the Upper Shield 9-8 million years ago.

The Lower Shield rocks form the great eroded wastelands in the southwest of the island, from just west of Sandy Bay Barn to west of Manati Bay. Whereas the rocks derived from the northeastern volcano were very largely lavas, the first rocks laid down in the south included a high proportion of pyroclastics. They were interspersed with lava flows, but the susceptibility of the pyroclastics to weathering and breakdown has led to rapid erosion, and thus to the formation of the great amphitheatre of Sandy Bay. Some of the pyroclastic rocks (for instance those around Fairyland, which are among the youngest strata of the Lower Shield) are very rich in crystals of the black mineral pyroxene, which can be up to 5 cm long.

The rocks of the Main Shield make up almost the whole surface of the island apart from the areas previously mentioned. They form the coastal cliffs from Mundens Point south to South West Point and round to Man and Horse Cliffs, and also from King and Queen Rocks southwestwards to Powell Point. The gorge-like valleys that reach the sea on these sections of coast are cut down through the lava flows of the Main Shield, so that the sequence can be clearly seen. The total thickness of the Main Shield lavas is at least 800 metres, and a sequence of 200 metres can be seen from Jacob's Ladder in Jamestown.

The Main Shield rocks are formed predominantly of basalt and trachybasalt lava flows. Between some of these flows are soft, orange-red sedimentary deposits formed when layers of soil, or volcanic debris in drainage channels, were covered by a new lava flow and thus baked and dehydrated. They indicate substantial intervals between lava flows during which weathering, erosion and soil formation occurred and vegetation developed. The flora and fauna of St Helena, during their development, must have been subject to repetitive episodes of expansion and catastrophe.

Also dating from the period of formation of the Main Shield are a number of 'parasitic cones'; these features – which are much more obvious on Ascension than St Helena – are piles of rock fragments ejected from an eruptive vent on the lower flanks of a large volcano. On St Helena, High Knoll and the Saddle south of Horse Pasture are good examples. These vents emitted not only a large volume of pyroclastics but also lava flows, although these may date from a later period than the pyroclastics; from High Knoll came a trachybasaltic flow which forms the east-facing scarp between there and Ladder Hill, while from the Saddle a mass of trachyandesite flowed northwards and now forms the western rim of Lemon Valley. A few other thick trachyandesite flows are more definitely associated with the Main Shield; these form the western face of High Peak, a smaller area at Head O'Wain and the ridge northeast of Old Woman's Valley.

After the formation of the Main Shield there was a prolonged period of erosion, during which a broad depression (as well as several minor valleys) was carved into the flanks of the older volcano in the northeast and the younger one in the southwest. These eroded areas were then largely infilled by the flows which formed the Upper Shield, and which consisted of basalt, trachyte and trachyandesite.[4]

At this stage in the formation of St Helena activity was centred near the Peaks of the modern island, and the basaltic flows from the earlier part of the sequence formed part of the central ridge, as well as the area east of Pounceys. A series of thick basaltic flows also flowed east to form the foundations of Prosperous Bay Plain and the surroundings of Fishers Valley; several of them can be seen in section on the way down to Prosperous Bay.

More erosion ensued before the eruption of the massive trachyandesite flows which produced the modern land surface in the Deadwood, Longwood and Horse Point area. Turks Cap Ridge, Bryans Rock and the adjacent cliffs around Horse Point are formed of thick flows of trachyte and trachyandesite. These flows were much less fluid than the earlier basaltic ones and did not spread out so freely. The lava behaved rather like stiff porridge, forming individual flows up to 30 metres or more in thickness, and often with the upper surfaces almost perfectly horizontal. At Turks Cap itself three trachyandesite flows directly overlie the breccias formed underwater by the northeastern volcano some five million years earlier. Trachyandesite also flowed eastwards into the Dry Gut and Gill Point area, as well as forming Shore Island and George Island.

Almost the last lava flows erupted on the island have been referred to as the Eastern Flank Flows. Great and Little Stone Top are the eroded remnants of two trachytic domes formed by multiple flows of lava so viscous that it hardly moved away from its point of emission; they formed on top of Upper Shield lavas which themselves overlie a thick sequence of Main Shield lavas. In the same area – and perhaps even younger – are Bencoolen and Boxwood Hill, which were formed by an unusal type of trachyandesite flow.

About seven and a half million years ago there was a Late Intrusive Phase, in which trachyte magma was forced into conduits that had earlier fed the basaltic lava flows of the southwestern volcano. This magma solidified *in situ*, forming massive and weather resistant intrusions of trachyte and phonolite, some of which were then exposed by the gradual erosion of the more friable older rocks to form a series of landmarks in the southwest of the island. High Hill and Powells Valley Hill are trachytic, but a larger group are of phonolite, a similar pale grey rock that is resonant when struck. The phonolitic intrusive masses are often columnar in structure. They tend to form lines in a northeast-southwest direction, and include the Riding Stones, Lot and Lot's Wife, the Asses Ears, Castle Rock, Speery Island and Hoopers Rock.

---

[4] Trachyte has higher silica content than basalt and is also more alkaline, with sodium and potassium oxides together exceeding 5%. Both trachyte and trachyandesite are lighter in colour than basalt and often have a porous, gritty structure; the trachyandesite found on St Helena is typically of the form known as mugearite (D.J. Chaffey et al. 1989).

Lava flows younger than these intrusive rocks occur on the ridge that forms the southeast wall of the Sandy Bay amphitheatre, which includes White Hill, Sandy Bay Barn and a small hill between them. This Late Extrusive Phase probably occurred a little more than seven million years ago and marks the end of volcanic activity on the island. During the last part of the Miocene and throughout the subsequent Pliocene and Pleistocene Epochs (starting respectively about five and about two million years ago) the plants and animals lived and evolved on St Helena without volcanic interruptions.

Dykes and sills

Dykes are striking geological features formed mainly before and during certain kinds of eruptions, when magma forces its way upwards in thin sheets through pre-existing strata towards fissures that form the volcanic vents. Near the end of the eruption some of the magma cools and solidifies before reaching the surface. It then forms sheets of rock – typically a few centimetres to a few metres in thickness – which are often harder than those they penetrate. They are termed dykes if they cut across the layering of the pre-existing strata and sills if they squeeze between the layers, forming sheets between and parallel to these; dykes are commoner and are often more or less vertical. Dykes grade into larger intrusive masses which may be exposed by erosion of surrounding softer strata. The rock of a dyke or sill is typically of a different colour from the rock it penetrates, and at the boundary between the two it is often possible to see that the original rock has been altered by the heat and pressure as the magma squeezed through it.

Swarms of thin vertical dykes can be seen in many parts of St Helena. The oldest rocks of the island, the breccias of the northeastern volcano, in places give the impression of a chaos of innumerable dykes; in the Knotty Ridge area, however, where they are especially numerous, there is an evident pattern, with most of the dykes aligned north-south. Some of the clearest exposures are on wave-cut platforms at the foot of cliffs, for instance at Lot's Wife's Ponds, Manati Bay and Prosperous Bay. In such places one can often see a vertical section through a dyke in the face of the cliff, continuing as a horizontal section through the same dyke on the platform between the foot of the cliff and the edge of the sea (Plate 3).

Erosion and weathering

When any new island is formed, waves immediately start to cut away at its sides, and for the first half of St Helena's existence a see-saw battle was fought between the volcano increasing the size of the island and the waves eroding it.[5] On balance, the volcano gained, and the island must have grown especially rapidly some ten million years ago when there was a precipitous (though relatively short-lived) worldwide lowering of sea level.[6]

Since volcanic activity ceased, erosion has been the dominant force. The cutting away of the lava and ash along the coasts gradually formed cliffs that became higher and higher with time, as the sea worked its way inwards towards the central part of the original island. These cliffs, which in many places are sections through long series of roughly horizontal lava flows, are weakened by the presence of the occasional sedimentary layers, which are easily eroded and so give rise to overhangs and eventual

---

[5] The speed of this erosion can be startling if the volcanic deposits are loose pyroclastics rather than solid lava. We have watched the sea cutting into the shores of Capelinhos volcano in the Azores, where a new island (later connected as a peninsula) which formed in 1957-58 was reduced to less than 50% of its original area within the following decade.

[6] B.U. Haq et al. (1987).

52

collapse. Overlooking the Barn on any rough day one can see marine erosion of the friable rocks in progress, as the sea is discoloured by ash in a broad band around the coast. On the east and south coasts of St Helena, exposed to the prevailing winds, marine erosion is now almost continual, while on the west it is concentrated mainly in periods when there are rollers. The fact that rollers come mainly from the opposite direction from the tradewinds has contributed to the formation of high cliffs all round the island, rather than mainly on the windward side.

During the erosive process enormous quantities of ash and rock are washed out to sea. The present volume of the island above sea level is about 60 cubic kilometres, but at least another 20 cubic kilometres have been removed by erosion. The products of erosion, in the form of pulverized rock and silt, have mostly been deposited on the sides of the submarine cone. Where the scouring effect of the currents is strong, only the larger particles accumulate; finer sediments predominate around the western flanks of the island, where smaller particles have been carried by the current.

Since marine erosion is caused by waves and occurs almost entirely at sea level, the underwater part of the St Helena volcano was left intact while the waves were gnawing away at the cliffs. The effect has been to produce a broad platform around the island, just below the sea surface (see Figure 4) This gently sloping wave-cut platform was probably formed mainly between six and three million years ago, when worldwide sea level was rather higher than it is at present. The St Helena volcano became largely flat-topped, but with the modern island – the eroded remnant of the original conical summit – still surviving near the centre of the platform. St Helena stands like a mountaintop castle on a gently sloping lawn; but beyond the lawn the slopes of the mountain suddenly steepen, and in this case, plunge into the deep ocean. The implications of this profile are explored later.

Although marine erosion is the dominant force in forming the coastline of St Helena, it is rain – and to some extent wind – that have shaped the inland areas. Rainwater, funnelled by surface relief and energized by gravity, exerts a powerful scouring effect. Trickles and streams, though in many cases ephemeral, have cut steadily downwards through the strata, and simultaneously edged their way back from near the coast towards the high interior. Gradually, valleys have been deepened and lengthened, vigorous watercourses capturing weaker ones and converting them into tributaries, and transforming families of surface gullies into the major gorges that are such striking features of the landscape of St Helena, and which typically fall 700 m within a course of 3-4 km. Always, the water has sought out the soft strata and the weak places, leaving the hardest lava flows, dykes and other intrusions projecting as pinnacles, ridges, platforms and the lips of waterfalls.

The running water, as it abrades the rocks, carries away particles of all sizes. Most of the finer ones are drifted out to sea, but many are deposited where the water flow is slower, or left behind when a sudden flood subsides. There they form sedimentary layers, sometimes elegantly sorted by size, sometimes mixed together in a chaotic mass of rubble. In a number of places on St Helena these deposits contain snail shells or the bones of birds that were carried away by the power of the water.

Erosion of the surface of St Helena has not occurred primarily as a continual, gradual process, but has been concentrated in catastrophic episodes occurring irregularly at intervals of decades or centuries. Even before the removal of most of the natural vegetation following the arrival of humans, occasional severe rainstorms will have had disproportionate effects. Because of the global climatic instability of the last few million years (manifested as ice ages at high latitudes) severe storms at St Helena have undoubtedly been more frequent at some times in the past than they are now. Floods in these periods could have been mainly responsible for the transformation of the elegant cone existing at the time that volcanic activity ceased, into the deeply dissected pile of lava that constitutes the modern island of St Helena.

Weathering – the breakdown of rocks and minerals at the earth's surface by the action of physical and chemical processes – is very evident on St Helena. The rocks of this tropical island are not attacked by ice, but they are exposed to the intense sun, strong winds and heavy rainfall. Few of the minerals of which they are formed are resistant to weathering, so they become much altered, giving rise to a variety of clay minerals. Some rocks are more resistant, as testified by upstanding dykes in many parts of the island, as well as the prominent masses of intrusive phonolite such as Lot and Lot's Wife. Special effects of weathering are noticeable in some places. Spheroidal forms can be seen on exposed basalt surfaces, especially in the valleys around Deadwood Plain such as Netley Gut. Honeycomb weathering of trachyandesite has produced intriguing small-scale patterns on rock surfaces on the southwest side of Boxwood Hill, and elegant sculptures have been formed near Lot's Wife's Ponds by the action of wind on consolidated deposits of shell sand.

One of the long term effects of weathering is that fine particles produced in the surface layers are carried down with percolating water and gradually block the channels along which this water flows, reducing the permeability of the ground. A biological result of this blockage, of which we are particularly aware, is that it reduces the extent of the network of underground cracks and spaces where subterranean animals can live. At the same time, it prevents the transport of organic material from the surface to caves and other underground spaces, thus removing the food supply of these same animals. The deep weathering that has occurred on St Helena is thus one of the reasons why we found few cave-adapted invertebrates during our work in 1995, although the discovery in a lava tube of one blind insect, clearly a representative of an ancient stock, showed that such animals have evolved on the island.

Apart from ordinary weathering, the rocks were doubtless affected by hydrothermal activity in periods when igneous intrusions were occurring. Hot water associated with the intrusions must have percolated through the rocks, leading to physical and chemical changes. Small amounts of manganese-rich minerals in the Prosperous Bay Plain and Turks Cap areas may have been produced by hydrothermal alteration of basalt lava flows. Some of the brightly-coloured, clay-rich materials that are so conspicuous in many of the higher parts of the island may also have a hydrothermal origin.

Soils

More than 400 soil samples from St Helena have now been analysed, providing a clear picture of a complex situation.[7] The soils are extremely variable from place to place, both in their chemical composition and their physical structure. However, they are in general heavy clays with poor structure, and a tendency to change rapidly from a sticky, unworkable state when wet to a hard and intractable state when dry; in most areas they are acid. Nitrogen content is extremely variable, very low in the eroded areas but high in the peaty areas with indigenous vegetation on the central ridge. Phosphorus is generally high, so that phosphate fertilizer is generally not required, and both potassium and

---

[7] L.C. Brown (1981).

magnesium are readily available from breakdown of the volcanic rocks. However, there are serious salinity problems in the dry eastern parts of the island and in Sandy Bay.

High salinity in these areas is one manifestation of the patterns of soil formation on the island. Low-lying areas receive drainage water from surrounding catchments, and if these are formed of easily weathered rocks such as trachyandesite (which has a high sodium content) exchangeable bases can accumulate. The most striking example of this effect is at Prosperous Bay Plain, a poorly-draining area with almost horizontal strata which for millions of years has received groundwater from a catchment dominated by trachyandesite flows (see Figure 6). In western areas, where basalt predominates, saline conditions are largely confined to arid coastal areas.

In contrast, the high rainfall and high relief of the central ridge leads to strong leaching and so to the development of extremely acid, peaty soils, very low in exchangeable bases; however, there is much spatial diversity in soil conditions, and some of the complexities are discussed in Chapter 6. Even in many places at lower levels, the steep slopes suffer continual or episodic erosion, leading to a thin or partial soil covering. Where gradients are gentle, however, soil formation was uninterrupted until the last few centuries; since many of the underlying rocks are easily weatherable, very deep and mature soils developed in the long period following the cessation of volcanic activity. Areas with these soils can still be found around Longwood, but are much reduced in size, since the advent of man has led to vastly accelerated rates of erosion. The removal of the natural vegetation by overgrazing and exploitation has led – in many parts of the Crown Wastes – to the previously existing humic clay topsoil being washed away, leaving surfaces that are difficult for plants to colonise.

Sea level changes and the size of St Helena
The origin of St Helena as a submarine volcano and its subsequent erosion to a wave-cut platform has long been understood. Attention has only recently been drawn, however, to the striking implication of the resulting shape: St Helena's size fluctuated wildly during the latter part of its history due to the changes in sea level during the last

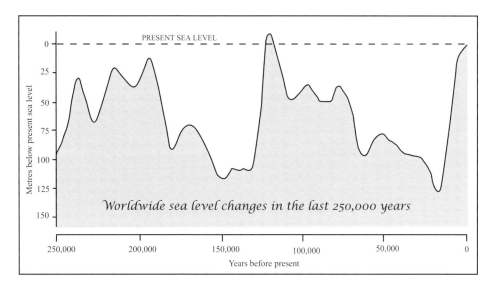

Figure 7

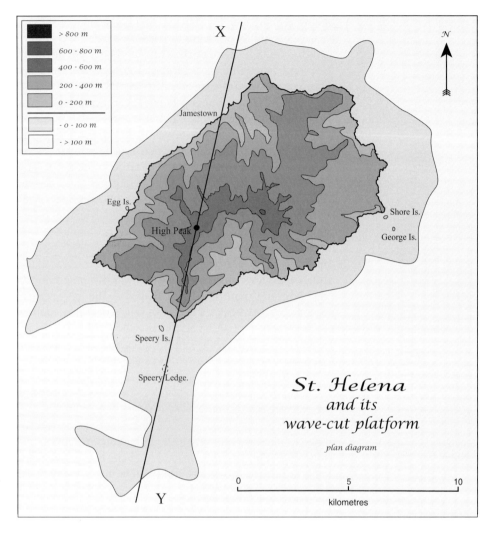

Figure 8
Note. X-Y is the line of the section in Figure 4

three million years, associated with alternating glaciations (ice ages) and interglacials.[8] These changes were far more rapid than those brought about by erosion.

During the most severe period of the last ice age, about 18,000 years ago, the contraction of seawater caused by cooling, together with the large quantity of water locked up in ice sheets on the continents, caused sea level to be lowered worldwide by about 120 m.[9] Although this was a brief episode, sea level during the last three million years has rarely been as high as it is now; the fluctuations over the last few hundred thousand years are shown in Figure 7. The rapid rise between 13,000 and 7,000 years ago (which probably gave rise to the biblical flood and analogous legends of

[8] In an article on "The Real Shape of St Helena" in "Wirebird" for Autumn 1995, David Holt pointed out a number of intriguing features of the submarine topography of the area around St Helena, as indicated on the recently revised Admiralty chart.

[9] R.G. Fairbanks (1989).

other peoples) inundated land that had been intermittently exposed in the preceding three million years. During this long period sea level was rarely stable, and the shoreline – with its pounding surf – repeatedly advanced and retreated across the broad apron surrounding the precipitous cliffs of St Helena.

Because the advances and retreats by the sea were across the gently shelving platform previously cut by the waves, a relatively small change in sea level made a large difference to the amount of land exposed. Lowering sea level by 100 m will have more than doubled the area of the island, from its present 122 km² to about 266 km² (Figure 8). When the sea was even lower than this the area would have been yet larger, though not by much, since almost the whole of the platform would already have been exposed. More important were the much longer periods when sea level was intermediate, and when a large but variable proportion of the island surface consisted of the exposed inner part of the platform that has now vanished beneath the waves (see box in Chapter 6)

Sand and 'limestone'
Conditions at present, with sea level high, do not favour the accumulation of shell sand on land, since corals and the shells of molluscs, barnacles and urchins are broken up on steep shores and the fragments are deposited in relatively deep water. Shell sand is sometimes washed in to the coast, but there are few places where it can form permanent beaches because the sea laps against cliffs almost all round the island. Nonetheless, large underwater patches of white sand can even now be seen offshore on calm days from high points on the cliffs, for instance off Potato Bay and Sandy Bay.[10]

In periods when sea level was lower and the waves broke on gently shelving shores (see above under *Erosion and weathering*), beaches were doubtless numerous and sand would often have accumulated behind them, as it does on Ascension today. It would then have tended to blow up the slopes and shallow gullies in the hinterland, and in some places it evidently reached the base of the cliffs (which were then some distance from the sea) and was funnelled up the steep valleys of the island as we know it. Deposits of more or less consolidated and almost pure shell sand are found in several parts of the island, occurring at elevations up to 275 metres above sea level (see Figure 6).[11] The main sites are on Sugar Loaf Ridge above Banks Valley, in the valley running northeast from the gardens behind Sandy Bay beach, in the two valleys running east and north from Potato Bay, and in several places near Lot's Wife's Ponds (Plate 4).

In the past the deposits were probably much more extensive. The demand for lime mortar in the decades after settlement of St Helena led to an intensive search for 'limestone'. The shell sand served the purpose well, and the first limekiln was built at Sandy Bay in about 1712. As a result, the surviving sand deposits in that area can bear little relation to those originally present. We can assume, however, that before the arrival of people, sandy deposits would have been washed out of the mouths of the larger valleys by occasional flooding caused by heavy rainfall.

[10] These were noted long ago by the American geologist Reginald Daly (1927).

[11] These sand deposits have attracted the attention of many naturalists and geologists, including Charles Darwin, who wrote an excellent discussion of them in his book on volcanic islands visited during the voyage of the Beagle (see C. Darwin 1844, 1890). Similar deposits have been found on Porto Santo in Madeira, and we have seen others on Fuerteventura in the Canary Islands. The figure of 275 m as the maximum height above sea level is from M.D. Muir & I. Baker (1968), who also provide a map of the sand deposits; in our map we have used their data supplemented by those in P.D. Nunn (1982). The deposits mentioned by D. Holt (2000) at heights of up to 823 m on Flagstaff include some earthy deposits that are probably of different origin.

The origin of the St Helena sand deposits has been disputed, partly because some of them are so far above sea level. It has been suggested that their formation involved the blowing of sand up the valleys during periods in the Pleistocene when winds may have been stronger than at present.[12] We suspect, however, that the key factor was increased sand production and accumulation when sea level was lower and more land was exposed, and that although stronger winds would have hastened the movement of sand inland, they were not prerequisite for it. On a day with ordinary trade winds, Philip was startled, while clambering up the deposit at the head of Potato Gut, to find sand dislodged by his feet blowing past him up the steep slope. The small size of the shell particles (typically 1 to 1.5 mm across) and their relatively low density, coupled with the funnelling effect of these particular valleys, enables sand to accumulate at high levels. As Darwin pointed out, this method of *"winnowing"* explains the *"equal-size and minuteness of the particles, and likewise the entire absence of whole shells or even of moderately-sized fragments"*.[13]

Once formed, the sand deposits became ecologically important, because shell sand is readily consolidated as a result of percolation by rainwater, which dissolves and redeposits calcium carbonate (which constitutes about 70% of the material of the sand) and other salts. The deposits then become suitable for use by seabirds that nest in burrows, especially shearwaters and storm-petrels; many of the fossil bird bones described in Chapter 5 were found in these deposits, and it is not uncommon to find complete eggshells. The shell sand deposits also provide an opportunity for development of populations of land snails with heavy calcareous shells; this may be partly responsible for past confusion between marine and terrestrial mollusc shells on St Helena.

Caves

Some oceanic islands have many volcanic caves, especially lava tubes. These are formed during eruptions of relatively liquid lava termed 'pahoehoe'. This type of lava is not common on St Helena, but along the shore north of Jamestown we have seen 'ropy' lava that was probably part of a pahoehoe flow.

There are remains of lava tubes in a few places on St Helena. One runs down to the Needles Eye in James Bay, another is just south of Ruperts Bay, on the track that leads round to Jamestown. Both these caves are a couple of metres in diameter and run steeply down the cliff; the one at Ruperts has been largely filled with rubble, probably as a safety precaution, but is still of great biological interest (see Chapter 6). From a boat going south from Jamestown towards Breakneck Valley one can see the mouth of what appears to be a substantial lava tube, high in the vertical cliff which forms a section through a series of thin lava flows that may have been pahoehoe. Exploration of this tube will require the use of rock-climbing techniques.

---

[12] M.D. Muir & I. Baker (1968).

[13] This comment by Darwin, which conforms with our own observations, conflicts with the article by David Holt in Wirebird for Spring 2000. Holt implies that marine shells are found in the high sand deposits, but we have not seen this. There are many deposits on the island containing shells, but as Darwin points out, many of these are earthy rather than sandy, and the shells are of land snails, which are often associated with fossil bones of seabirds. Some deposits with marine shells have been recorded, most carefully by P.D. Nunn (1982), but it is noticeable that most of the high sites he mentions are in areas in the northeast of the island where there are breccias that were deposited under water and subsequently uplifted; these deposits are distinct from the typical shell sand beds. We agree with F.D.P. Wicker (1990), who gave the arguments against the sand beds being marine deposits and pointed out that the low density shell particles could have been carried up the valleys by the wind from areas exposed by low sea level during ice ages.

Whereas volcanic caves may occur at any level on the island, sea caves are all near the base of the cliffs, having been formed recently or at times in the past when sea level was at a similarly high level. Patrick Nunn and his colleagues mapped about 40 sea caves at sea level or within 10 metres above it.[14] Many of these are noticeable when walking on the wave-cut platform or when viewing the coast from a boat; a few are now just under water.

Earthquakes

Major earthquakes are not typically associated with oceanic islands, but minor ones have been noted occasionally as affecting St Helena. Melliss stated that only four: "*so slight, that they scarcely need to be noticed as occurring at all*" had been recorded since the discovery of the island; these were in 1756, 1780, 1817 and 1864. One that he did not mention was perhaps a little more impressive, since the St Helena Records for June 3rd 1763 report that:-

> "*On the 21st last month about 5 o'clock in the morning was felt a violent shock of an earthquake. The agitation was so strong in the South part of the Island as to shake the china, etc, off the shelves in the houses, but thank God no damage ensued.*"

Climate

St Helena has a sub-tropical but oceanic climate, tempered by the South-East Trade Winds. The dominant meteorological features are the Intertropical Convergence Zone (ITCZ) to the north, where the trade-wind systems from the two hemispheres tend to converge, and a sub-tropical high pressure zone named the South Atlantic High Pressure Cell; this is centred to the southwest of St Helena and lies some 1500 km away in summer and rather less in winter.[15]

St Helena has moist and equable conditions, with relatively slight seasonal variation. Day length varies seasonally by nearly two hours. The relatively low-lying fringes of the island are much warmer and more arid than the high central ridge, which is often shrouded in mist; in the drier season, however, this regularly clears in the middle of the day. Typical temperature differences between sea level at Jamestown and high on the island at Hutts Gate are as great as they are between the warmest and coolest times of year at a single spot.

Winds

St Helena lies in the heart of the South-East Trade Wind belt and southeasterly winds are dominant at ground level throughout the year. Historically the steady trade wind was sometimes referred to as 'the Doctor' and was considered a major factor in the healthy climate of St Helena. One of the few sets of data on wind direction covers the period 1952-1975 at Hutts Gate, high up in the centre of the island; it shows the southeast 45° quadrant accounting for 48% of records, with another 27% in the south, 4% in the east and 18% calm. In an earlier series of records (1893-1903) from St Mathews Vicarage discrimination of direction was finer, with quadrants of 22.5°; 51% of records were from the southeast, 31% SSE, 9% ESE and only 3% calm. Westerly and northerly winds occur for no more than a handful of days per year.

Wind speeds on the island have been measured regularly at only a few sites and variation between them is substantial. The highest overall average speed has been recorded from Deadwood, with 28 km per hour, while Hutts Gate, Woody Ridge and Bottom Woods all

---

[14] P.D. Nunn (1984).

[15] I.K. Mathieson (1990) from which the following information is mainly derived.

show an average of 20 km per hour. Scotland, however, had an average of only 7 km per hour in the only year recorded. At all sites seasonal changes in the winds speeds are slight, ranging from 20%-50% higher in August to December than in May to June.

Temperature

The South-East Trade Winds cross cool waters between the west coast of southern Africa and the island. The winds at St Helena are thus cool for the tropics, and minimum (night-time) air temperatures at sea level are around 20°c in winter and 24° in summer. However, air temperature varies strongly with altitude; while the average annual maximum temperature at Jamestown is 26.5°c and the minimum 21.8°, at Hutts Gate (600 m) the figures are respectively 18.5° and 14.5°. This indicates a drop of about 1.3° for each 100 m increase in elevation.

The daily temperature range at a given site averages 5-6°c. Seasonal changes also have an average range of about 5°. The warmest months are February to March and the coolest August to October. Variations from the mean temperatures are never extreme; it is an unusual year when any part of the island has temperatures of less than 10° or more than 30° for longer than a day or so.

Relative humidity is almost constant throughout the year. Above 300-400 m humidities are generally in the range 80-95%. Although there are few reliable records for coastal areas, values are probably normally in the range 75-80%. However, humidity can drop to between 50 and 60% on sunny days, giving an intense drying effect that has critical implications for both plants and invertebrate animals.

Cloud and rain

A temperature inversion (a layer within which temperature increases rather than decreases with altitude) is formed between the cool trade winds and the warmer upper air moving down from the equatorial region; over St Helena this inversion is at a height of some 1800-2000 m. The relatively low inversion stabilizes the climate since it inhibits build-up of a great depth of cloud. Cumulo-nimbus storm clouds cannot easily develop and thunderstorms are extremely rare; they usually occur during the summer when the inversion is at its weakest because the South Atlantic High is further away.

When the inversion is strong a sheet of strato-cumulus cloud with a high water content is present for much of the time. This leads to an unusual degree of cloudiness for an island within the tropics. An analysis carried out in the 1950s showed that Hutts Gate (at just over 600 m) had an average of only two clear days a year and 290 cloudy (overcast) days, comparable with the dullest skies of the subantarctic ocean; even Jamestown had 128 cloudy days in an average year.[16] The local cause of much cloudiness and rainfall is condensation as the moist trade winds impinging on the island are subject to orographic lift: as the air rises over the high southeastern cliffs and slopes it expands and cools, producing condensation and saturation of the lower levels of the cloud sheet. This effect causes much of St Helena's rainfall.

However, mist that does not precipitate is blown over the central ridge and down the other side, re-evaporating and being lost as potential precipitation for the island. Thus mist interception is an ecologically important phenomenon, and since trees tend to intercept mist, it has been suggested that deforestation of the island has reduced precipitation.

---

[16] The high incidence of cloudiness is partly caused by the frequent presence of altostratus cloud associated with weak frontal activity. Remarkably, this is apparently related to cold outbreaks from the Weddell Sea and elsewhere in the Southern Ocean, many thousands of miles away, which affect St Helena some six days later (H.H. Lamb 1957).

There is no easy way of proving this, but it is clear that eroded barren ground intercepts little moisture, especially when it has been heated by the sun. Pasture is the worst type of vegetation for mist interception. The original forest canopy on the ridge is quite good, as are the introduced conifers such as Norfolk Island Pine and Cape Yew.

Some years ago Quentin Cronk carried out a simple experiment at High Peak, using fifty beer cans with the tops removed. Half were inserted in pasture, the other half in the Tree Fern thicket a few metres away, under the canopy of a large Dogwood: this tree is a good mist condenser, with erect branches and leaves tapering to 'drip-tips' where droplets tend to converge and fall off (see Plate 31). After four days of misty weather the pasture traps had caught an average of 25 mm and the thicket traps 45 mm of water. On the basis of this result, with others obtained in subsequent trials, it has been suggested that in parts of the island above 500 m mist could increase precipitation by at least 50%, given the right type of vegetation.

The distribution on the island of direct precipitation (the type of rainfall that is measured by a rain gauge away from vegetation) is closely related to altitude, with an average of 1050 mm per year at the wettest part of the central ridge but only 175 mm at Sandy Bay on the southeast coast (Jamestown has about 230 mm). Storms tend to follow the line of certain valley catchments and greatly influence the local rainfall.

Rainfall follows a strong seasonal pattern. It rises from a minimum in November to a peak in March, followed by a brief trough in April-May and a second peak in June-July, followed by a steady decline. In Jamestown the wettest month has some ten times as much rain as the driest.

Rainfall intensity is generally low, seldom exceeding 25 mm in an hour, and with falls of more than 50 mm in 24 hours rare even in the wettest areas. However, at irregular intervals the island experiences severe rainstorms, which cause considerable damage and spectacular erosion. The effect of one such storm in 1719 is described in Chapter 7; a comparable one in 1756 led to floods accompanied by heavy breakers which combined to cause major damage to military installations in Lemon Valley, Breakneck Valley, Ruperts Bay, Banks Valley and Sandy Bay, as well as causing havoc in Jamestown and washing away the crane at the landing place. A storm in March 1787 apparently left a sheet of water in Prosperous Bay Plain for five or six days afterwards, and one on 25th April 1797 was said to have occasioned the most dreadful floods ever remembered.

The historical records also refer to occasional droughts on the island, but are based on personal experience rather than rainfall data. The first drought mentioned was in 1712-13, when it was said that there had been no rain for ten months; several more droughts of equal or greater severity were noted later in the 18th century. One in 1791-2 was linked to an exceptionally strong global meteorological and oceanographic disturbance of a type now known as El Niño or an ENSO event.[17] The effects of this one were felt in many parts of the tropics. The drought of 1791-2 was quickly followed by

[17] This phenomeno was originally described from the coast of Peru, where it tended to start at about Christmastime. During El Niño in Peru the surface waters become very warm; as a result, the anchovies that normally support a major commercial fishery and enormous populations of guano-producing seabirds temporarily disappear, taking refuge in deeper, cooler water layers, and millions of the birds may die. In recent years scientists have realized that El Niño is a worldwide meteorological and oceanographic phenomenon which they call the El Niño / Southern Oscillation (ENSO). The 1982-83 event in the Pacific was considered to be the greatest in 500 years; it had devastating effects on seabirds over an enormous area, including Peru in the east and Christmas Island in the Central Pacific. In the atmosphere over the Atlantic there was an abnormal southward displacement of the Intertropical Convergence Zone - which was reflected in the 1984 rainfall on Ascension - and associated changes in the ocean. Another massive El Niño is in progress as we write in 1998. An intriguing number of the years with abnormally heavy rainfall on Ascension (1934, 1974, and 1984-85) coincide roughly with exceptionally dry periods on St Helena, in 1933, 1973 and 1984. Presumably this relationship reflects the profound abnormalities in the world weather system associated with ENSO events.

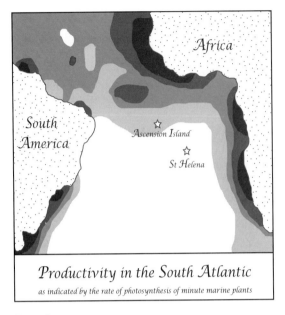

Productivity in the South Atlantic
as indicated by the rate of photosynthesis of minute marine plants

Figure 9

another, recorded in the Annual Register for 1798: *"A scarcity of rain for three successive years had caused great mischief and want at St. Helena. Several of the breadfruit plants which had been left by Captain Bligh on his return from the South Seas had fallen to decay."*

For the 19th century there are a few periods with annual rainfall records. In 1860 less rain fell in Jamestown than in any other documented year; furthermore, the figures for 1858 and 1859 are respectively third and fifth lowest ever recorded. This period thus appears to represent the most severe sea-level drought supported by rainfall data, with average rainfall in these three years less than half the average during the present century. In the 20th century, the driest years were 1933, 1958, 1973 and 1984. The last three all coincide with ENSO events in the Pacific.

Hydrology
The volcanic rocks of St Helena are in general highly permeable, so that in spite of the relatively high rainfall in the centre of the island there are few permanent streams. Impermeable layers above which one can often find lines of springs are usually formed by consolidated – and often reddish – fine material accumulated in intervals between flows of lava. On the map of St Helena in the endpaper we differentiate between permanent streams and the more abundant intermittent and ephemeral ones, which flow only in the wet season or at times of exceptional rainfall.

The largest perennial flows are in James Valley, Sharks Valley and Sandy Bay, although in the former much of the flow is diverted for use. Other permanent streams are found in Lemon Valley, Swanley Valley, at Manati Bay, in Powells Valley, Deep Valley and the upper part of Fishers Valley. In several other valleys permanent flows occur over short distances but fail to reach the ocean except in wet periods.

Many of the streams on St Helena are saline, and tend to show a progressive increase in salinity downstream; above 550 m salinity is generally low. There is a seasonal pattern in some streams, with salinity in Fishers Valley and Sandy Bay markedly higher during dry periods; in Sharks Valley, however, there is little seasonal variation.

Surrounding sea

In this book we do not attempt to discuss marine life. However, the productivity of the sea has a direct bearing on the populations and biology of seabirds and for this reason we include the following brief account.

In oceanographic terms, St Helena lies near the edge of the great South Atlantic anticyclonic gyre, which is centred to the south and west of the island (Figure 3). The circulation is in an anticlockwise direction and is convergent, tending to draw surface water in towards the centre. In such systems the water column is very stable, with almost all of the nitrates, phosphates and other nutrients necessary for the growth of plant plankton trapped in deeper water below a thermocline (a layer within which temperature declines particularly sharply as depth increases); in this area the thermocline is about two hundred metres below the surface. The warm water above the thermocline is light and does not mix with the cooler, heavier water below, and therefore cannot be enriched. Regions like this have such low biological productivity that they can be considered as vast marine deserts (see Figure 9).

Though well within the tropics, St Helena is oceanographically semi-tropical because it is influenced by the cool Benguela Current sweeping up from the south; this prevents the seas around St Helena from showing tropical characteristics throughout the year.[18] This current flows northwestwards from the coast of southwestern Africa out into the Atlantic, then turns westwards to form the South Equatorial Current.[19] In winter the sea surface temperatures are below 16°c near Africa and normally below 22° near St Helena; during the course of the summer the figures rise by 3-4° as the surface waters are heated by the stronger solar radiation.

A useful general indicator of tropical conditions is provided by the 23°c sea surface isotherm (effectively a 'contour' of temperature); waters warmer than this are associated with a characteristic pelagic tropical fauna. For instance, at least one species of flying fish changes its distribution seasonally in such a way as to remain within waters at least as warm as 23°c. In the southern winter the relevant isotherm lies between St Helena and Ascension, with cooler waters around St Helena. In summer, however, warm water extends well to the south of St Helena. The seabirds now breeding on St Helena are almost all species characteristic of tropical waters, and the sketchy information on their breeding seasons on the island suggest that they breed mainly in summer when more tropical conditions prevail.[20] Little is known about the feeding areas of these birds around St Helena, but Wideawakes and Masked Boobies normally depend on schools of tuna and other predatory fish in the open ocean to drive flying fish and other small fish and squid to the surface, where

[18] The presence of the Benguela Current is also relevant to the productivity of the sea. In zones with well developed thermoclines almost the only places where nutrients from deep water can reach the surface layers are where there is upwelling induced by the wind. An important area of upwelling occurs off the coast of southwest Africa, enriching the waters of the Benguela Current. This stimulates the growth of plant plankton in a broad band along the coast. However, as the waters drift northwestwards the plants are eaten by animal plankton and these are largely harvested by fish and other larger animals before the waters reach St Helena.

[19] Waters reaching St Helena seem generally to come almost directly from the Cape of Good Hope. Dramatic evidence in support of this came in March 1851 when a missionary, the Rev. J.H. Beck, died while a passenger on a ship en route from Cape Town to St Helena. He was buried at sea, but some days after the arrival of the ship at St Helena his coffin was washed up on the island.

[20] This is part of a worldwide pattern: for instance, Philip showed many years ago that in the Wideawake (Sooty Tern) - a characteristic tropical species - colonies in the Atlantic, Pacific and Indian Oceans are almost all on the warm side of the 23°c isotherm at the season when the birds are breeding.

they become vulnerable to the birds. Tropicbirds probably also range far from the island.

Some of the seabirds – for instance the noddies and Brown Boobies – feed relatively close inshore. They benefit from enrichment of the surface waters around St Helena caused by the turbulence and mixing as the current from the southeast impinges on the pedestal on which the island stands. The strongest effects are probably around Speery Ledge, 6 km offshore and only three metres below the surface. This area is much used by seabirds and also by local fishermen, who benefit both from the enrichment and the availability of bottom-living fish.

The tidal range at St Helena is up to about 1.2 metres at spring tides but sometimes as little as one third of a metre at neap tides. Since tropical storms do not occur in the South Atlantic severe rough seas in the area of the island are rare. However, St Helena (like Ascension) is affected by rollers, especially in the period from December to March. These are related to weather disturbances in the northwest Atlantic, which travel several thousand kilometres and approach the island from the northwest. The rollers are imperceptible in the open sea but can generate major breakers as they reach shallow water, making landing at Jamestown pier difficult and fishing from the rocks dangerous.

The most dramatic episode of rollers occurred on 18th February 1846. As Gosse recounts, for several days previously the southeast trade winds dropped and the atmosphere became extremely oppressive:

> *"Then in the night the sea suddenly rose higher than had ever been known before and huge waves or "rollers" broke upon the shore, so that at daylight next morning the sea opposite the town was one sheet of white foam and yet there was not a breath of wind. The Road was filled with shipping at the time, including eighteen slavers which were lying at anchor waiting to be broken up. At eleven o'clock the same morning, one of these, the Decobrador, was bodily lifted from her anchors and thrown broadside on top of another slaver, the Cordelia, and both were swept by the huge seas and deposited high and dry in front of the sea-guard gate. Altogether thirteen vessels were wrecked and smashed into pieces by the time the sea subsided the same evening."*

This account implies that great waves persisted for much longer than would be expected from a 'tsunami', which is caused by a submarine earthquake or volcanic explosion, or by slumping of masses of rock or sediment down submarine slopes. They are more likely to have been caused – like the more normal rollers – by a storm in the northwest Atlantic. Their exceptional severity was probably a result of the calm period that preceded their arrival, which would have reduced the extent to which their force was dissipated by the more chaotic waves of the open sea as they travelled towards the island.

Lot, an intrusion of phonolitic rock exposed by erosion, towers above Fairyland

The south coast, with Castle Rock and Speery Island

PLATE 1
ST HELENA

St Helena from the
east-north-east
PHOTO: Beau Rowlands

James Bay viewed from
RMS *St Helena*, offering safe
anchorage, fresh water
and access to the
hinterland

Passengers disembarking
from RMS *St Helena*, the
island's lifeline

Jamestown, crowded into a
narrow valley

PLATE 2
ST HELENA

Top left Fishermen starting a descent down the cliffs using formidable traditional routes in aptly named Breakneck Valley

Top right Friends showing us fossil bird bones exposed on the surface among Samphire and Tungies on Donkey Plain

Centre left Hutts Gate with donkeys used for transporting flax when the industry was at its peak; now, only a few are still in use on the island

Centre right Sandy Bay in 1959, with fortifications relatively intact

Bottom left Myrtle looking at the intricate pattern of geological dykes at Prosperous Bay

Bottom right Arthur Loveridge (right) retired to St Helena in 1957 and spent the rest of his years observing and recording the wildlife. This creeper waste was originally covered with gumwood forest

PLATE 3
ST HELENA

Top left Philip emerges from one of the few lava tubes on the island, near Ruperts Bay; this was the site of discovery of a blind cavernicolous insect

Top right Breccia at Gregory's Battery, formed underwater around the time of birth of the island

Centre left Deposit of old guano in the sides of the ravine in Banks Valley. Before the arrival of people, there were extensive colonies of seabirds on the main island

Centre right Lot's Wife, Lot's Wife's Ponds, and shell sand deposits formed from sand blown up from ancient beaches on the 'apron' around the island, now submerged   PHOTO: Beau Rowlands

Bottom left The cast of a tree trunk in lava on Mundens Hill is evidence of large trees on the island more than seven million years ago

Bottom right Colourful erosion gullies near Horse Point are the result of deforestation

PLATE 4
ST HELENA

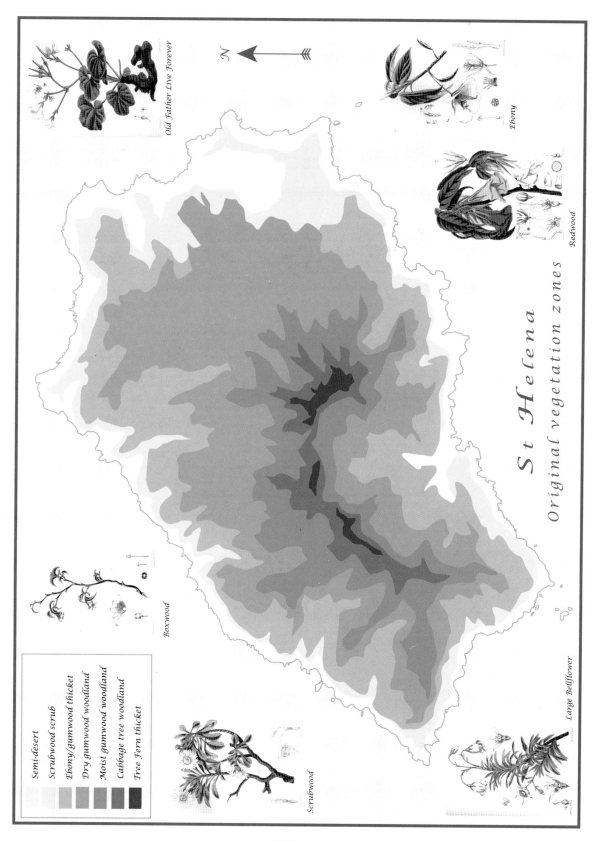

S t   H e l e n a

Original vegetation zones

Old Father Live Forever

Ebony

Redwood

Boxwood

Scrubwood

Large Bellflower

Semi-desert
Scrubwood scrub
Ebony/gumwood thicket
Dry gumwood woodland
Moist gumwood woodland
Cabbage tree woodland
Tree Fern thicket

PLATE 5
ST HELENA

Top left Lot's Wife's Ponds – a favourite but hazardous bathing place reached after a strenuous walk

Centre left George Island and Shore Island, both important breeding sites for seabirds. On the right is Gill Point, where we found wings of Bulwer's Petrel, a possible new breeding species for St Helena PHOTO: Beau Rowlands

Bottom left Great and Little Stone Tops from Gill Point, with Philip's tent. The cliffs of Great Stone Top are the site of St Helena's largest colony of Trophy Birds *Phaethon aethereus*

Top right Scrubwood at Great Stone Top; this shrub, now largely confined to cliff tops, was once dominant in Scrubwood scrub that covered large areas around the fringes of the island

Centre right The Gates of Chaos, Lot and the central ridge from near distant cottage

Bottom right Prosperous Bay Plain, home of many of St Helena's endemic dry-land invertebrates

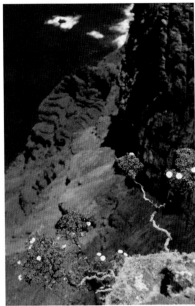

PLATE 6

ST HELENA

Top left The Asses Ears viewed through a screen of Thorn *Erythrina caffra*

Top right Gumwood *Commidendrum robustum* at Peak Dale

Far left Epiphytic New Zealand Flax *Phormium tenax* on Cape Yew *Podocarpus elongata* on the Peaks, with Tree Fern *Dicksonia arborescens* below

Left Waterside vegetation below the Gates of Chaos, with Wild Celery *Apium graveolens* and the sedge *Scirpus prolifer*

Bottom left Tree Fern thicket on Diana's Peak, with Black Cabbage *Melanodendron integrifolium* (left) and Dogwood *Nesohedyotis arborea* (right)

Bottom right The lower part of Fishers Valley and Prosperous Bay. The banks of silt on the right of the stream contain major deposits of subfossil bird bones

PLATE 7

ST HELENA

Top left The only two surviving wild Ebonies (in centre and bottom right), discovered in 1980 on cliffs north of the Asses Ears

Top centre Staff of the Environmental Conservation Section in 1995 planting Ebony and clearing invasive shrubs from below High Peak

Top right Ecological restoration at Horse Point; Myrtle learning from George Benjamin about the planting programme in 1995

Centre left The wall of the Great Wood, built in the 1720s in an attempt to preserve native forest, winds across eroded land at Bilberry Field Gut; with Flagstaff and Knotty Ridge behind

Bottom left Seabird and cat remains collected near Gill Point; a vivid reminder that seabirds cannot thrive in the presence of feral cats

Bottom right Quentin Cronk and George Benjamin resting in Tree Fern thicket on the Peaks during a field trip in 1995

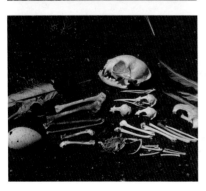

PLATE 8

ST HELENA

Chapter 4 | **The native plants and their discovery**

Discovery of the St Helena flora

At the time of the first human visit in 1502, St Helena was an extraordinary natural ecosystem, with flora and fauna derived from a tiny number of chance colonisations and matured by ecological and evolutionary processes continued over millions of years. However, goats and pigs and other animals were introduced by seamen early in the 16th century, so major changes in the vegetation took place before the island was settled by the English in 1659. Records left by travellers who visited the island in the century and a half before settlement are fragmentary but valuable.

One of the earliest accounts was that by Vice-Admiral Francois Wittert, who wrote of a visit in 1608:[1]

> "Most of the mountains are covered with verdure, and some with wild trees. Amongst others, there is one whose leaves are like those of sage, and nearly the same odour. It is that which furnishes ebony. Its flowers also furnish a gum of the colour of gum arabic, and of the odour of benzoin. There are other great trees which produce fine flowers, carnation coloured and white like tulips, and which are a very fine ornament, and a little fruit nearly like buckwheat."

The first description is likely to refer to the Gumwood, in spite of the mention of ebony wood, which must be due to confusion. The next references are probably to the St Helena Redwood and Ebony respectively. Admiral Wittert also referred to a number of herbs and fruit trees that had evidently been introduced by the Portuguese, and then went on to describe what must be the St Helena Salad Plant:

> "There grows upon the mountains a certain herb like lavender, the sourish taste of which is very agreeable, and which throws out leaves the length of a finger, which terminate in a point like the ears of a rabbit."

He continued with a description that may refer to Jellico:

> "There grows also much cress, with another herb which is like tobacco, having an odour strongly approaching that of the leaves of the walnut tree. The trunk rises a fathom and a half. We believed it had medicinal value, and without doubt in future someone will test it."

A few decades after settlement, a significant advance in botanical understanding resulted from the arrival of Stephen Poirier, a Huguenot refugee and future Governor of St Helena who came to the island with his family in 1690. Poirier had owned vineyards in France and was interested in botany; around the turn of the century he sent to London specimens of a number of endemic plants including the Dwarf Ebony and the Large Bellflower.[2]

Little further progress in knowledge of the plants of St Helena was made until late in the 18th century, when collections were made by the naturalists on Captain Cook's first two expeditions. On the last leg of the voyage of the *Endeavour* in May 1771,

---

[1] St Helena Almanack 1882, reprinted 1913, reproduced by P.L. Teale (1978, 1981).

[2] Quentin Cronk and Richard Grove have emphasized that the availability of these island plants to a group of naturalists associated with Dr Hans Sloane, then secretary to the Royal Society, marked the start of a process of realisation that some plants were confined to particular islands (endemic); this in turn led to recognition of the potential vulnerability of species to human activities.

Joseph Banks and Daniel Solander visited the island. Four years later, in May 1775, Johann Georg Forster carried out more work on the way home in the *Resolution*.[3] Banks continued to take an active interest in the natural history of St Helena; he introduced the Redwood to cultivation in England in 1772, and in the 1780s obtained help from David Corneille – another Huguenot Governor – who provided a number of specimens. Cooperation continued with Corneille's successor Robert Brooke, and in 1789 Sir Joseph Banks encouraged the establishment of a small botanic garden in Jamestown; he also actively promoted the planting of trees on the island.

More comprehensive botanical investigations were not carried out until the early years of the 19th century, when William John Burchell spent five years on the island (see box).

William John Burchell (1782-1863)

W.J. Burchell was the son of a Fulham nurseryman, who worked at Kew Gardens after leaving school. He left England after an unhappy love affair and was aged 23 when he arrived on St Helena on 13th December 1805. He had been serving as a midshipman on the East India Company's ship *Northumberland*, but when she sailed, the ship's log recorded that he had been left invalided on the island. Some premeditation is implied by the drawing up – before his departure from England – of a deed of partnership between himself and William Balcombe of The Briars to trade as merchants and agents at St Helena.

Burchell had no permission from the company to stay on the island, but got on well with Governor Patton, who arranged for him to be appointed School Master and acting Botanist. He suffered ill health at first, and did not penetrate as far as Sandy Bay ridge until 10th October 1807. On that day – as well as observing many of the endemic plants – he became the first person to record the Spiky Yellow Woodlouse. Burchell's main botanical field work was in 1808 when he collected all the plants that he found growing wild on St Helena. He prepared a comprehensive catalogue of these and also listed large numbers of garden plants, some of which later escaped into the wild.

Richard Grove has pointed out that Burchell's St Helena Journal shows his gradually increasing awareness of the high degree of endemism in the flora, and also of the concept of rarity and the closeness to extinction of some of the endemic plants; all these ideas were of relatively recent origin among European naturalists. Burchell also had well developed aesthetic appreciation of pristine landscapes, together with strong feelings about destructive exploitation of the natural environment.

Burchell's talents included great skill as an artist. While on St Helena he made many botanical sketches and watercolour drawings of landscapes, some of them including charming self-portraits; most of his St Helena drawings are now in the Library of the Royal Botanic Gardens at Kew.

Burchell's botanical work on the island had little influence in the 19th century because it remained unpublished. However, it has great value now, as the first comprehensive investigation of the plants of St Helena, providing evidence as to which of the non-endemic plants are likely to be indigenous.

[3] G. Forster (1777).

Burchell collected and catalogued about 200 plants that he found growing wild on the island; these included the first wave of introductions. His work was so thorough that plants that he did not record are likely to be later introductions; this suggests, for example that the Saltbush (*Atriplex*) is a recent arrival. A striking conclusion from Quentin Cronk's analysis of Burchell's data is that a maximum of only about 80 known species can be considered native to the island.[4] In fact the number is probably little more than 70, including about 25 ferns (Tables 4A, 4B, 4C at the end of this chapter). A few more species may have become extinct after 1502 but before they were found by botanists. The small size of the native flora reflects the extreme isolation of St Helena.

Another key visitor was Dr William Roxburgh, who had previously been Chief Botanist of the East India Company and Superintendent of the Calcutta Botanic Garden. Roxburgh was on St Helena from June 1813 to March 1814 and during this time he compiled a catalogue in which he named many of the St Helena plants that had not previously been formally described; he also made the first explicit attempt to distinguish between native and introduced species.[5] Roxburgh's work essentially completed the discovery phase of botanical work on St Helena. A detailed picture of the status of plants of the island in about 1870 was provided in the classic book by a long-term resident, John Charles Melliss.

Some 19th century visitors used the flora of St Helena as an example demonstrating wider principles of plant geography or evolution. Most notable was Joseph Hooker, who spent only a few days on the island (in 1839 and 1843) but also studied Burchell's collections and gave a seminal lecture on insular floras to the British Association for the Advancement of Science in 1866. The version published in the following year is still well worth reading. Hooker was writing less than a decade after the publication of Charles Darwin's *The Origin of Species* in 1859. Even prior to the appearance of Darwin's book, Hooker had beeen convinced that species were capable of change; he immediately became an advocate of Darwin's ideas on variation, natural selection and consequent evolution. In his lecture he carefully analysed – and in general supported – another hypothesis that had been given its first serious presentation by Darwin: that oceanic islands acquired their flora and fauna by trans-oceanic migration, and that the immigrant species then evolved to become different from their parental stocks.

Four decades after Hooker's visits W.B. Hemsley made a careful assessment of the continental affinities of the endemic plants, drawing heavily on Hooker's information and specimens. After this time very little original work on the flora of St Helena was carried out for almost a century.

Origin and evolution of the native plants

The extreme isolation of St Helena has meant that even over its life of more than 14 million years, relatively few kinds of plants have reached it naturally. These plants, however, make up in interest what they lack in numbers. The endemic species include 37 species of flowering plants, six of which are now extinct (see Table 4A). These 37 species seem to be derived from only about 25 ancestral stocks, since some groups (for instance the gumwood relatives and the ebony-redwood group) have evidently split into several species after reaching the island. In addition there are up to 18 flowering plants which may be indigenous (native), although they are not

---

[4] Q.C.B. Cronk (1988).

[5] After Roxburgh's death in 1815 his catalogue was published as an appendix to Governor Beatson's (1816) *Tracts relative to the Island of St. Helena*, and was republished in various places, including E.L. Jackson's (1903) *Saint Helena, the Historic Island*. Q.C.B. Cronk (1995b) provides a full discussion of his specimens.

endemic, being found also in Africa or elsewhere (Table 4B). There are also 13 endemic ferns, and up to 12 that seem to be indigenous (Table 4C), as well as an unknown number of lower plants (mosses, liverworts, algae and lichens). A few more plants are known to have been present on the island several million years ago but apparently became extinct through natural processes well before 1502 (see below).

It is the great age of St Helena combined with its extreme isolation that makes study of the evolution of the plants so fascinating. Alfred Russel Wallace, the great nineteenth century naturalist who independently formulated the theory of natural selection at about the same time as Charles Darwin, published his classic book *Island Life* in 1880. In the chapter devoted to St Helena, Wallace made perceptive comments on the ferns of the island which are still relevant today, but his most important botanical contribution related to the flowering plants. He clearly recognised that the very distinctive plants found on the island were relicts of groups that had been widely distributed in Africa and elsewhere in the distant past, but whose ranges had subsequently become fragmented. This idea forms the foundation for current thinking about the origin and evolution of the endemic plants. These plants can be conveniently considered in four groups, according to how long they have been evolving on the island.

Group 1. Relict endemic genera
Plant species in this group are so distinct from continental forms that they are placed in endemic genera. These unique plants are trees or – in a few cases – shrubs, and grow mainly in wet thickets in the uplands of St Helena. They now have only distant relatives outside the island, and intriguingly, in most cases the relatives that can be identified are now absent from Africa, but exist in scattered sites around the southern hemisphere. There is no suggestion, however, that the highly distinctive forms colonised St Helena from the far-flung areas where their relatives are now found. Quentin Cronk, who has done the most recent analysis of the flora, believes that their ancestors lived in southern Africa long ago, but became extinct when the wet forest in that area largely disappeared as the climate became drier, starting some ten million years ago.[6] By this time, or shortly afterwards, the ancestors of all the most distinctive of the endemic plants had already reached St Helena; they are thus ancient relicts, derived from an African flora that was largely replaced long ago.

Some botanists have suggested that the plants that colonised the island early in its history underwent fundamental evolutionary changes in adapting to their island environment, and that this is why they are so different from their closest relatives elsewhere.[7] The discussion centred around the gumwoods and cabbage trees, which are some of the few tree-sized members of the family Compositae. It was suggested that the ancestors of the gumwoods were herbaceous plants similar to fleabanes of the genus *Conyza* and *Erigeron* and that those of the He Cabbage and She Cabbage trees might have been not unlike species of *Senecio* such as Groundsel. It was supposed that these plants developed into woody trees because the scarcity of other trees on the island left an evolutionary opportunity: there was a vacant 'ecological niche'.

Cronk, in contrast, argues that the great distinctiveness of these St Helena plants can be explained simply on the basis that the ancestral African stocks are now extinct and that the St Helena plants and their surviving relatives further afield have been evolving independently

---

[6] Q.C.B. Cronk (1987, 1992).

[7] S. Carlquist (1974).

over very long periods, and thus gradually diverging. He points out that the family Compositae seems to have arisen long ago from a woody stock and that several of the St Helena genera are allied to groups with woody, tree-sized representatives. Probably, therefore, the composites that colonised St Helena long ago were already woody when they arrived.

The gumwood group and the Black Cabbage may have arisen from a single colonising group that reached St Helena millions of years ago. The Black Cabbage is the most distinctive (hence the creation of the genus *Melanodendron*) and evidently split off from the gumwoods long ago. The various other species (placed in the genus *Commidendrum*) seem to be adapted to different habitats. The Scrubwood is capable of living in exposed and arid sites with little soil, including crevices on cliffs. The Gumwood itself is also drought tolerant and replaces the Scrubwood on relatively level ground with more soil but still with low rainfall; in such places it seems to have grown in the past alongside the Bastard Gumwood. In moister areas, between 500 and 650 m on the central ridge, these two trees were largely replaced by a subspecies of the Gumwood, *Commidendrum robustum gummiferum*. Higher up again, in the cabbage tree woodland at altitudes of up to 750 m, the False Gumwood was the main representative of the group; at this level the Black Cabbage also made its appearance, though it was a dominant species only in the Tree Fern thicket at around 750 m and above.

Most of the modern members of the gumwood group can thus be placed at different places on a moisture gradient. The interesting question is, did the distinct forms separate gradually *in situ*, or did they become adapted to different conditions when they were spatially separated on different parts of the ancient island, and only subsequently spread so that they came into contact with one another? The answer is not yet known, but may become clearer when more genetic information has been gathered.

Perhaps the most distinctive of all the endemic plants is another composite, the Whitewood, which seems to be distantly related to species in French Polynesia. The wide geographical spread continues with two more endemic genera: the Dogwood has its closest relatives in Asia and Lobelia has relatives in South America and on some of the Pacific islands. The Boxwood, however, is now thought to be related to a genus occurring in Africa and the Canary Islands

Somewhat less distinctive than the plants just discussed are the ebony-redwood group and the St Helena Olive. The Ebony, Dwarf Ebony and Redwood (which probably all evolved on the island from a single colonising stock) are generally considered to comprise an endemic genus *Trochetiopsis*, but it is similar to a group of plants found in Madagascar and the Mascarene Islands (the genus *Trochetia*).[8] The ancestors of the modern St Helena species are known from fossil evidence to have been on the island as early as nine million years ago, so we include them in the group of relict endemic genera.

The St Helena Olive is now normally considered to constitute an endemic genus *Nesiota*, but it has relatives – though fairly distant ones – in the genus *Phylica*, which occurs in Africa and the Mascarene Islands. Though generally considered as an ancient relict genus, the Olive seems to fall on the boundary between this group and the next.

Group 2. Old endemic species
These are clearly defined endemic species, but are quite closely related to species in the same genus that still occur in Africa or its Indian Ocean islands. These species are thought to be derived from ancestors that reached St Helena between 10 and 3 million years ago; that is, before the onset of the drastic climatic fluctuations that gave rise to the ice ages. This group

[8] W. Marais (1981).

includes trees, shrubs and perennial herbs. Some of the species occur in the wet zone on St Helena, but most show adapations to seasonal drought, though not to severe aridity.

The species in this group probably arose from eight successful colonisations; in two cases it is likely that a single founding stock gave rise to the several endemic species by evolutionary divergence on the island. The bellflower ancestor *Wahlenbergia* produced two shrubs (both now extinct) and two straggling herbs; and the Jellico ancestor *Sium* split to give rise to a tall and a dwarf species adapted respectively to sheltered and exposed sites. The other six colonising stocks did not split into distinct species (as far as we know) but evolved into the single endemic species of Diana's Peak Grass,[9] Rosemary, Tea Plant, St Helena Plantain, and the extinct Stringwood and Shrubby Heliotrope.

Group 3. Young endemic species
This third group of flowering plants comprises herbs and sub-shrubs. They are considered sufficiently distinct to merit the status of endemic species but have close relatives in southern Africa and have probably been evolving independently for less than two and a half million years. Cronk refers to these as recent relicts, but we prefer to call them 'young endemics.' These species are typical of the arid coastal zone on St Helena, and their relatives almost all occur in dry environments in Africa. One stock of tuft-sedges in the genus *Bulbostylis* has split to form two endemic species (one extinct) and Quentin Cronk tells us that there are two endemic species of *Eragrostis*, but the others have only one species on the island: Babies' Toes, Salad Plant, Boneseed, Old Father Live Forever, Hair Grass and the St Helena Goosefoot

Group 4. Indigenous non-endemic species
Finally there is a small group of species which are considered indigenous but not endemic. They probably colonised the island naturally but have not yet evolved characters enabling them to be clearly distinguished from their relatives in Africa and elsewhere. Because it is so difficult to be sure that these species were not brought to the island by people, this group is only provisional; techniques of molecular biology may provide more definite conclusions in due course. The species concerned are listed in Table 4B.

In this section we have been discussing only the flowering plants, since their evolution is fairly well understood, but the ferns are also ecologically important. St Helena has 13 endemic ferns and perhaps another 12 indigenous ones (Table 4C). Ferns are better dispersers than flowering plants and it has been argued that certain types of ferns are typically missing from islands because suitable habitats are lacking rather than because they have inadequate powers of dispersal. Furthermore, some species that do become established may fail to evolve differences from their mainland ancestors because the island populations are frequently augmented by the arrival of additional spores; this would inhibit the slow statistical genetic changes to be expected in truly isolated populations. Even the non-endemic indigenous ferns on St Helena may therefore have been present for several million years.

A reconstruction of the pristine vegetation
It is natural to assume that the landscape one has been brought up in – or the landscape one sees as a visitor to an unfamiliar area – is the one that has been there for thousands of years. In many parts of the world, however, landscapes have been transformed within

---

[9] *Carex dianae* occurs in two distinct forms, and has sometimes been considered to comprise two species, *C. dianae* and *C. praealta*.

Flowering time, pollination and coevolution in the endemic trees of St Helena

The term 'coevolution' refers to situations in which evolutionary changes in one species affect the evolution of other species. Biologists have found that the results of coevolution are most often detectable in ecological communities that have remained stable over long periods. St Helena - before its discovery by humans - was a good example of such a community. There is a strong suspicion that the flowering times of the main trees near the central ridge may have diverged as a result of coevolutionary selective pressures generated by competition for pollinators.

Before the introduction of alien insects the primary pollinator for a whole series of white-flowered or small-flowered trees was probably the hoverfly *Loveridgeana beattiei*.

For cross-fertilization to occur, plants need to receive pollen from other individuals of their own species. If two different kinds of plants are attractive to the same species of pollinator and are flowering in the same place at the same time, fertilization will often fail because the pollen brought to a plant has come from the wrong species; furthermore, many flowers may remain unvisited if there are too many of them available, relative to the number of pollinating insects.

If there is some spread in flowering time within a species, individual plants will gain more attention from pollinators if they flower when few members of other species are flowering. They will thus be more likely to be pollinated, to receive the right kind of pollen, and so to set more seeds and to leave more descendants than individuals that flower at the same time as other species. As a result, if flowering time is partly an inherited characteristic, the average for the population will gradually shift away from the time when other species are in flower.

On St Helena it has been noted that a series of fly-pollinated generically endemic trees have largely separate flowering seasons, suggesting that natural selection has operated in this way. Black Cabbage flowers from September to December, Dogwood from December to March, Whitewood from March to June and He Cabbage (and also Gumwood) from June to August.

the last few centuries or millennia by the activities of humans and the animals associated with them. The accounts of mariners make it clear that a large part of St Helena was forested at the time of its discovery in 1502, but the immediate introduction of goats and other herbivores led to massive destruction of trees, and in some areas the characteristic vegetation was quickly destroyed.

Several attempts have been made to 'reconstruct' the vegetation of the island just before its discovery by people; the most recent is that by Quentin Cronk, who made use of historical records and herbarium specimens, together with his own knowledge of the modern distribution of the plants and of the island's habitats.[10] The box at the start of Part II provides an imaginative view of the island as seen by the Portuguese sailors in 1502, and we here summarize Cronk's conclusions more systematically. The pattern is complex, because of the high relief and consequently large range in rainfall and temperature, together with the variety of rocks and soils. Cronk divided the island into seven vegetation

---

[10] Q.C.B. Cronk (1989).

zones, largely correlated with altitude. We have calculated from his data the approximate percentage of the area of the island that would have been included in each zone, and in Plate 5 we attempt to map the vegetation zones on the island in its pristine state.

'Saline semi-desert' included the very dry and relatively level areas, from sea level up to an altitude of a little over 300 m on Prosperous Bay Plain; it may have covered at least 6% of the island. Here the commonest plants were salt-tolerant species such as Samphire and Babies' Toes, together with Salad Plant, French Grass and Boneseed; three more plants probably native to the island – Hogweed, Camel's-foot Creeper and *Tribulus cistoides* – may also have been present close to the sea. It is especially this zone that would have been greater in extent during periods of low sea level during the ice ages of the last few million years; this would have provided much more opportunity than at present for plants typical of sandy places near the sea (see box in Chapter 6).

'Scrubwood scrub' was the characteristic vegetation in more exposed and dry areas of the island, but it was fully developed only where these conditions were mitigated by onshore winds rising against cliffs and producing condensation. Such areas occurred from close to sea level up to 350 m altitude, depending on the local topography, and may have covered about 19% of the island. The dominant species were Scrubwood and Tea Plant. People who have seen the spindly surviving individuals of the Tea Plant in remote parts of the island may find difficulty in imagining this species forming a major component in the vegetation; our own view of it was drastically altered on seeing the dead remains of many large, spreading bushes below Castle Rock Plain, and looking across to a flourishing colony a little further to the west. Other species present in this community included Dwarf Ebony (in the arid north), Ebony (in the south), Samphire, Boneseed and Old Father Live Forever, and in gullies perhaps also Hogweed and the extinct Shrubby Heliotrope. The Salad Plant probably also occurred in some places, as well as the fern *Ophioglossum polyphyllum* and – in moist crevices – *Asplenium haughtoni*.

'Ebony/Gumwood thicket' occupied perhaps 24% of the island, in rocky areas between 100 and 500 m; it thus overlapped considerably in altitude with the next zone. Ebony/Gumwood thicket was a low-growing community dominated by these species but also including other plants such as Scrubwood, Old Father Live Forever and St Helena Plantain, along with Hair Grass and the endemic St Helena Tuft-sedges (*Bulbostylis* species); the fern *Asplenium haughtoni* was again present, along with *Cheilanthes multifida*. The Boxwood and Dwarf Ebony and other plants were also represented locally.

'Dry gumwood woodland' occupied more than a quarter (27%) of the island, in the altitude range of 300-500 m, which was still relatively dry. The woodland was formed of Gumwood supplemented by Bastard Gumwood and some Rosemary and Scrubwood; the canopy height was 5-6 m. There was very little undergrowth, but the St Helena Tuft-sedge and Thatching Rush were characteristic, and Hair Grass and St Helena Goosefoot were also present, along with the ferns *Cheilanthes multifida* and *Hypolepis rugosula*. A vivid impression of this type of woodland is provided by Burchell's description (quoted by Linda Brown)[11] of a fragment of it that survived at Bottom Woods in the early 19th century:

> *"just like a copse, innumerable young gum trees with here and there large old ones between. Nothing green was to be seen, not a blade of grass beneath them; and even the dry curled up leaves on the trees looked like so many pieces of whitish wollen cloth (a light pepper and salt colour). Instead of its being a green cool shady copse it was a hoary white, ovenlike, (in heat), sunny, shadeless collection of dry trees."*

---

[11] L.C. Brown (1982).

'Moist gumwood woodland' occupied a much smaller area (perhaps 11%), mainly on the slopes of the central ridge between 500 and 650 m, where conditions were more humid. In these woods the canopy was formed by Gumwood, together with Redwood and Rosemary. The undergrowth was mainly of ferns, with the St Helena Tuft-sedge and Thatching Rush in damp places, and the Small Bellflower on rocky outcrops. False Gumwood and Bastard Gumwood were also present.

'Cabbage tree woodland' is today virtually nonexistent, but in the past may have occupied about 9% of the area of the island, at altitudes between 600 and 750 m. It would thus have formed a broad crescent along the central ridge. The canopy of this woodland may have been as high as 6 m in places, and where mature was formed mainly by False Gumwood, Redwood and Whitewood, with Tree Ferns playing a major role, especially near the ridge tops. In places where landslips or the death of a major tree let in the light, two short-lived 'weedy' trees – She Cabbage and He Cabbage – quickly established themselves and grew up into the canopy. As well as the Small Bellflower, two other species of bellflower (Roxburgh's and Burchell's) may also have occurred in the undergrowth, as well as the shrub Lobelia; in areas with richer soil there were many ferns, especially the Black Scale Fern.

'Tree Fern thicket' originally occupied only about 3% of the area of the island, but ironically, it is the only past vegetation type that survives to any significant extent (although it is seriously endangered). It previously clothed the highest parts of the central ridge of the island from about 700 to 820 m. The vegetation at this level is frequently surrounded by mist, and in its pristine state the main species forming the canopy (at 3-4 m) were the Tree Fern and the most drought-intolerant endemic trees: Black Cabbage, Olive and Dogwood. The undergrowth in the Tree Fern thicket included Lobelia, Jellico, Large Bellflower and the extinct Stringwood, together with several endemic ferns and sedges. Epiphytic plants thrive under these moist conditions, and seedlings of many of the endemic flowering plants become established on the trunks of the Tree Ferns. Although some elements in the community have been lost, fragments of it are preserved in Diana's Peak National Park, and one can still get a feeling for what it was like.

Fossils from the distant past – a detective story

There is only scanty evidence about the kinds of plants that existed on St Helena during the millions of years between its origin and its discovery by humans. One type of clue is merely tantalizing, consisting of cylindrical holes in the rocks. These are left by tree trunks which were surrounded by a lava flow and resisted the incinerating effect of the lava long enough for it to cool and solidify around them.[12] Melliss described several casts in lava on Ladder Hill, and Captain J.R. Oliver, in his account of the geology of the island, also mentioned casts of tree trunks, saying that they were numerous in a district that implicitly included High Knoll and Friar's Ridge. The geologist Ian Baker commented that the lavas referred to by Melliss are around 10 million years old, but there is a late trachybasalt lava flow between High Knoll and Ladder Hill that may be only 7.5 million years old.

We have not seen these casts to the south of the Jamestown valley, but we found a striking one in lava near Saddle Battery on Mundens Hill (Plate 4) which may well belong to the same series of lavas. We also found a less certain example in a loose lava boulder in Broad Gut. The casts we saw did not show detailed surface features, but Melliss mentioned that: *"there was no difficulty in tracing, on the side of the casts, an imprint of the coarsely imbricated form of the stem, showing it to have borne the characteristics of a palm or*

---

[12] We have found such casts in the Galápagos Islands, clearly formed by trees only two or three inches in diameter.

large tree fern." Captain Oliver also said that the cavities – which were about 14 inches in diameter – in some cases were: *"marked with a perfect network, much resembling the impressions of the bark of trees found in the coal measures".*

These comments are of particular significance in the light of the evidence of ancient plants on the island obtained from a thin layer of deposits on the southern side of Turks Cap Valley. The deposit consists of detritus apparently carried down by streams during ancient erosion of the uplands. This occurred in a quiet period after the building of the whole of the south and west of the island by the massive volcanism of the Lower and Main Shield eruptions from the southwestern volcano. The deposit contains numerous fossilized pollen grains and spores, and was discovered by Ian Baker during his geological work on the island in the 1960s; we searched for it during our visit, but without success.

An exciting aspect of the find is that the deposit is sandwiched between two lava flows, for both of which an approximate age is known. The plant remains are therefore older than about 8.5 million years (the estimated age of the overlying lava flow), but younger than the roughly 9.2 million year age of the underlying flow. Preliminary identifications of the plants represented were given in an article by Muir & Baker in 1968. Ninety percent of the grains counted were spores of ferns and clubmosses, but there were some pollen grains from flowering plants, including one unidentified type, two kinds possibly representing palms and one apparently of the mallow family (Malvaceae).

The story did not end there, however, since Quentin Cronk, looking at the published illustrations, was struck by the resemblance of the last type of pollen to that of modern Redwood and Ebony trees, which belong to the family Sterculiaceae (closely related to the Malvaceae). He therefore went to the Murchison Museum of Imperial College London and eventually found Baker's original sample, now unlabelled but unmistakable from its content. A second look at the material led to a series of dramatic discoveries.[13]

First, Cronk compared the 'Malvaceae' pollen grains with pollen from surviving individuals of Redwood and Ebony and confirmed the similarity (see Figure 10). It seems, therefore, that an ancestor of these trees was already present on St Helena nearly nine million years ago. However, the fossil pollen grains are not identical to either Ebony or Redwood, the differences presumably reflecting change in the pollen of this group of trees during their evolution on the island.

One of the other types of pollen in the sample was found by Cronk to belong to the genus *Lachanodes*, which now occurs on the island in the form of the She Cabbage. Similarly, the commonest type of fern spores belonged to the tree fern genus *Dicksonia*, showing that this important component of the island's flora was also established at this early time; tree ferns could thus have produced the lava casts referred to above. Various other types of spores also proved to belong to groups still present on the island, including the fern genera *Hymenophyllum*, *Grammitis* and *Pteris* and the clubmoss genus *Lycopodium*.

Cronk has recently told us that his study of Baker's sample from the pollen deposit has produced two additional intriguing discoveries. First, Muir & Baker had suspected that two species of palms were represented in the deposit, and it turns out that one of these is reminiscent of the genus *Voamniola*, an ancient stock of palms now found only in Madagascar; the other kind of palm pollen is of a generalized type which has not been identified. Second, Cronk has identified pollen of the genus *Gunnera* (family Haloragaceae). Gunneras are indigenous on many oceanic islands, probably because

---

[13] Q.C.B. Cronk (1990, 1993).

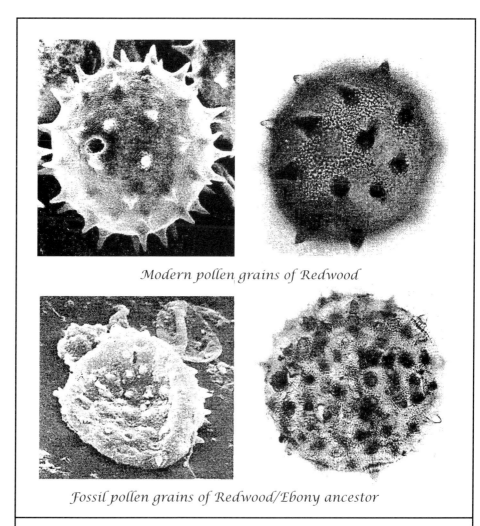

Modern pollen grains of Redwood

Fossil pollen grains of Redwood/Ebony ancestor

Modern and fossil pollen grains

Left: pictures from a scanning electron microscope
Right: pictures from a light microscope

Figure 10   From photograph in Q.C.B. Cronk (1990).

their fruits are eaten by migratory birds which disperse the seeds. They thrive on volcanic rocks in damp situations (one is an invasive weed in the Azores) and probably once dominated the flora of guts on St Helena.[14] Neither the palms nor *Gunnera* are represented in the modern flora. They survived the massive volcanism of the Lower and Main Shield eruptions in the south and west, but perhaps succumbed – just over eight million years ago – to the intense activity of the Upper Shield, which was centred near the present Peaks but had major effects on the northeast of the island.

---

[14] Gut is an old word for a narrow passage between two declivities, which is widely used on St Helena to refer to a valley, usually fairly small.

Table 4A. **Endemic flowering plants of St Helena**

Species are listed alphabetically by family, genus and species scientific name

FAMILY and local/English name	Scientific name	Status	Location of closest relatives
AIZOACEAE			
Babies' Toes	*Hydrodea cryptantha*	Young endemic species	Southern Africa
Salad Plant	*Hypertelis acida*	Young endemic species	Southern Africa
BORAGINACEAE			
Shrubby Heliotrope (extinct)	*Heliotropium pannifolium*	Old endemic species	Tropics of Africa etc
CAMPANULACEAE			
Lobelia	*Trimeris scaevolifolia*	Relict endemic genus	South America & Pacific islands
Small Bellflower	*Wahlenbergia angustifolia*	Old endemic species	South Africa or South America
Burchell's Bellflower (extinct)	*Wahlenbergia burchellii*	Old endemic species	South Africa or South America
Large Bellflower	*Wahlenbergia linifolia*	Old endemic species	South Africa or South America
Roxburgh's Bellflower (extinct)	*Wahlenbergia roxburghii*	Old endemic species	South Africa or South America
CHENOPODIACEAE			
St Helena Goosefoot	*Chenopodium helenense*	Young endemic species	Tropics of Africa etc
COMPOSITAE			
Gumwood	*Commidendrum robustum*	Relict endemic genus	Australia, South America
Bastard Gumwood	*Commidendrum rotundifolium*	Relict endemic genus	Australia, South America
Scrubwood	*Commidendrum rugosum*	Relict endemic genus	Australia, South America
False Gumwood	*Commidendrum spurium*	Relict endemic genus	Australia, South America
She Cabbage	*Lachanodes arborea*	Relict endemic genus	South America, Mascarene Islands, Australasia
Black Cabbage	*Melanodendron integrifolium*	Relict endemic genus	Australia, South America
Boneseed	*Osteospermum sanctae-helenae*	Young endemic species	Southern Africa
Whitewood	*Petrobium arboreum*	Relict endemic genus	French Polynesia
He Cabbage	*Pladaroxylon leucadendron*	Relict endemic genus	South America, Mascarene Islands, Australasia
CYPERACEAE			
St Helena Tuft-sedge	*Bulbostylis lichtensteiniana*	Young endemic species	Africa
Dwarf St Helena Tuft-sedge (probably extinct)	*Bulbostylis neglecta*	Young endemic species	Africa
Diana's Peak Grass	*Carex dianae*	Old endemic species	African mountains, Azores & Mascarenes

Table 4A. Continued

FAMILY and local/English name	Scientific name	Status	Location of closest relatives
EUPHORBIACEAE			
Stringwood (extinct)	*Acalypha rubrinervis*	Old endemic species	Mascarene Islands
French Grass	*Euphorbia heleniana*	Young endemic species	Tropics of Africa etc
FRANKENIACEAE			
Tea Plant	*Frankenia portulacifolia*	Old endemic species	Africa & South America
GERANIACEAE			
Old Father Live Forever	*Pelargonium cotyledonis*	Young endemic species	Southern Africa
GRAMINEAE			
Hair Grass	*Eragrostis saxatilis*	Young endemic species	Southern Africa
Cliff Hair Grass	*Eragrostis* new species	Endemic species	Not yet clear
PLANTAGINACEAE			
St Helena Plantain	*Plantago robusta*	Old endemic species	Pacific islands, Africa & South America
RHAMNACEAE			
Olive	*Nesiota elliptica*	Relict endemic genus	Africa & Mascarene Islands
Rosemary	*Phylica polifolia*	Old endemic species	Mascarene & Southern Ocean islands
RUBIACEAE			
Dogwood	*Nesohedyotis arborea*	Relict endemic genus	India & Malaysia
SOLANACEAE			
Boxwood	*Mellissia begoniifolia*	Relict endemic genus	Africa
STERCULIACEAE			
Ebony	*Trochetiopsis ebenus*	Relict endemic genus	Mascarene Is. & Madagascar
Redwood	*Trochetiopsis erythroxylon*	Relict endemic genus	Mascarene Is. & Madagascar
Dwarf Ebony (extinct)	*Trochetiopsis melanoxylon*	Relict endemic genus	Mascarene Is. & Madagascar
UMBELLIFERAE			
Jellico	*Sium bracteatum*	Old endemic species	Africa
Dwarf Jellico	*Sium burchellii*	Old endemic species	Africa

Table 4B. **Non-endemic flowering plants perhaps indigenous to St Helena**

FAMILY and local/English name	Scientific name	Status	Comments
AIZOACEAE New Zealand Spinach	*Tetragonia tetragonioides*	Possibly indigenous	Cultivated by settlers
CHENOPODIACEAE Samphire	*Suaeda fruticosa*	Indigenous	Host to endemic insects
CONVOLVULACEAE Camel's-foot Creeper	*Ipomoea pes-caprae*	Indigenous	Perhaps now absent; also on Ascension
CYPERACEAE Thatching Rush	*Scirpus antarcticus* *Scirpus chlorostachys* *Scirpus nodosus* *Scirpus prolifer*	Possibly indigenous Possibly indigenous Probably indigenous Possibly indigenous	
GRAMINEAE Wire Grass Tropical Finger Grass	*Agrostis bergiana* *Cynodon dactylon* *Digitaria ciliaris* *Eragrostis cilianensis* *Panicum coloratum* *Polypogon monspeliensis*	Possibly indigenous Possibly indigenous Possibly indigenous Probably indigenous Possibly indigenous Possibly indigenous	Perhaps now absent Also on Ascension Probably also on Ascension Perhaps also on Ascension
JUNCACEAE Star Grass	*Juncus bufonius*	Possibly indigenous	
NYCTAGINACEAE Hogweed	*Commicarpus helenae*	Probably indigenous	Also on Ascension
POLYGONACEAE	*Polygonum glabrum*	Possibly indigenous	
PORTULACACEAE Purslane	*Portulaca oleracea*	Probably indigenous	Also on Ascension
ZYGOPHYLLACEAE	*Tribulus cistoides*	Probably indigenous	

Table 4C. **Endemic and probably indigenous ferns of St Helena**

FAMILY and name		Comments
ASPLENIACEAE		
Asplenium aethiopicum		Indigenous species
Asplenium compressum (Plastic Fern)	Endemic species	Possibly also on Trindade
Asplenium erectum		Indigenous species; also on Ascension
Asplenium haughtoni (Barn Fern)	Endemic species	Previously considered as an endemic variety *Ceterach cordatum* var. *haughtoni*
Asplenium platybasis	Endemic species	
DENNSTAEDTIACEAE		
Hypolepis rugosula (Sticky Fern)		Indigenous species; possibly also on Ascension
DICKSONIACEAE		
Dicksonia arborescens (Tree Fern)	Endemic species	Previously in Cyatheaceae
DRYOPTERIDACEAE		
Diplazium filamentosum (Black Scale Fern)	Endemic species	Previously known as *Diplazium nigropaleaceum*
Dryopteris cognata (Kidney Fern)	Endemic species	
Dryopteris napoleonis (Lesser Kidney Fern)	Endemic species	
GRAMMITIDACEAE		
Grammitis ebenina		Indigenous species; may be distinct from its rare African relative
HYMENOPHYLLACEAE		
Hymenophyllum capillaceum (Filmy Fern)	Endemic species	
LOMARIOPSIDACEAE		
Elaphoglossum bifurcatum (Mossy Fern)	Endemic species	Previously known as *Microstaphyla furcata*
Elaphoglossum conforme (Common Tongue-fern)		Indigenous species
Elaphoglossum dimorphum (Toothed Tongue-fern)	Endemic species	
Elaphoglossum nervosum (Veined Tongue-fern)	Endemic species	
LYCOPODIACEAE		
Lycopodium axillare		Indigenous species; probably also on Ascension, at least in the past
Lycopodium cernuum (Buckshorn)		Indigenous species; also on Ascension
OPHIOGLOSSACEAE		
Ophioglossum polyphyllum		Indigenous species; previously identified as *O. opacum*
POLYPODIACEAE		
Pleopeltis macrocarpa		Indigenous species

Table 4C. Continued

FAMILY and name		Comments
PTERIDACEAE		
Cheilanthes multifida		Indigenous species
Pteris dentata subspecies *flabellata*		Indigenous species
Pteris paleacea (Lays Back Fern)	Endemic species	
THELYPTERIDACEAE		
Christella chaseana		Possibly indigenous species
Pseudophegopteris dianae (Brown Scale Fern)	Endemic species	

Chapter 5

The animals: discovery, evolution and extinction

Studies of the native fauna of St Helena are hampered by the fact that many of the species are now extinct. This applies to almost all of the landbirds, which would have been the most conspicuous element in the endemic fauna: the evidence about them and the original seabird communities comes largely from fossils. Among the invertebrate animals many are already presumed extinct and others have not been found for decades. The fossil record tells us something about the land snails, but we shall never know how many other terrestrial invertebrates became extinct before they were found by naturalists.

During the period between the discovery of St Helena in 1502 and its settlement in 1659 the native fauna remained almost unknown. The earliest visitors commented on seabirds, seals, sea lions and turtles, but during the next century and a half mariners tended to mention only the introduced birds and mammals that were potentially of use for food. Seabirds were sometimes mentioned, but most of the native landbirds may have already been extinct and invertebrates were of little concern to sailors. The 17th century traveller Peter Mundy made important observations, but it was not until the 19th century that trained naturalists started visiting the island and recording their findings systematically.

Discovery and evolution of invertebrates

Much of the zoological interest of St Helena stems from the startlingly diverse array of invertebrates (especially insects, spiders and snails) that are endemic to the island. However, the only relevant observation from the period prior to human settlement is a comment in an excellent account of the island in 1608, apparently by the Dutch Admiral Wittert: *"All that there is troublesome are large spiders and flies as big as locusts"*.[1] The spiders were probably *Argiope trifasciata* (Plate 22), a large and conspicuous species with a bold pattern of black and white bars, which hang upside down on huge orb webs that often stretch between trees and can be annoying when walking. The enormous flies, however, are a puzzle; if they really were flies they must have become extinct fairly soon; it is tempting to guess that they may have been relatives of the enormous predatory flies in the family Asilidae that are conspicuous members of the endemic fauna of the Canary Islands.

Scientific studies of the insects got off to a bad start. A group of beetles collected in 1771 by Joseph Banks during Captain Cook's first voyage of exploration on the *Endeavour*, labelled by him as coming from St Helena and described as such by the distinguished Danish entomologist J.C. Fabricius, were apparently collected in South Africa but incorrectly labelled. Soon, however, Fabricius acquired from a different source, at least one insect that really was from the island. This was the Giant Earwig, which he described in 1798 as *Forficula herculeana* (now placed in the genus *Labidura* instead of *Forficula*). This insect – the world's largest earwig – may therefore also have the distinction of being the first new animal species to be scientifically described from St Helena.

W.J. Burchell, the botanist who lived on the island from 1805 to 1810, also collected animals including the Giant Ground Beetle, *Aplothorax burchelli*, which G.R.

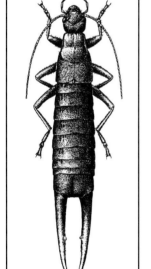

Giant Earwig
Labidura herculeana
50 mm   MRAC

Figure 11

---

[1] P.L. Teale (1978, 1981).

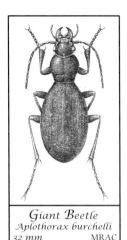

Giant Beetle
Aplothorax burchelli
32 mm   MRAC

Figure 12

Waterhouse named after him in 1842. Several other small collections of invertebrates were made during the early part of the 19th century.

Charles Darwin visited both St Helena and Ascension in 1836, and as always, wrote meticulous and perceptive accounts of his visits.[2] On St Helena he was much intrigued by the extinct land snails, and was given a large collection of the shells by the island naturalist Robert F. Seale. Darwin also made a major contribution to the geology of St Helena and collected a number of insects, of which a few were formally described and named. The most interesting was the endemic click beetle *Anchastus atlanticus*, which is found in rotten wood but now has very restricted distribution on the island.

It was during the two decades following 1860 that more detailed information about the invertebrate fauna became available, mainly through the efforts of three naturalists. The first of these was John Charles Melliss (see box), whose encyclopaedic book – published in 1875 – lived up to its comprehensive title. Melliss had been studying the animals of the island for many years, and had sent specimens to a variety of taxonomists. An important group were the spiders, which were studied by the Rev. O. Pickard Cambridge, the foremost British specialist of the time; he published two articles describing St Helena spiders, which included representatives of eight of the 12 endemic genera now known to be present on the island. Among many other species he formally described (and named in honour of Melliss) the Golden Sail Spider *Argyrodes mellissi*.

Thomas Vernon Wollaston, already well known for his work on beetles of other Atlantic islands, was so intrigued by the collections of beetles that he had been sent from St Helena (mainly by Melliss) that he decided to go there himself. He spent six months on the island with his wife Edith in 1875-76, and while he studied the beetles (and also the land snails), she worked assiduously on the moths and butterflies. He published several articles and two books: *Coleoptera Sanctae-helenae* and *Testacea Atlantica*, while she wrote a major article on the Lepidoptera that still remains the only serious account of this group on St Helena.

T.V. Wollaston's work demonstrated for the first time the extraordinary diversity of certain families of beetles on St Helena; three quarters of the more than 150 endemic species of beetles now known from the island were first described by him. Some of these species, first found by Wollaston, were also last seen by him. In the ground beetle tribe Bembidiini, for instance, five out of the twelve endemic species have not been seen for more than a century and are likely to be extinct.

T.V. Wollaston also collected other insects, and the bugs (Hemiptera) that he obtained formed the basis of a thorough study by F. Buchanan White, published in 1878. Although various small zoological collections were made on the island subsequently, almost a century was to elapse before any substantial advance was made over the knowledge obtained in the time of Melliss and the Wollastons. The pause was brought to an end by two initiatives in the second half of the 20th century. The first of these was the decision of the herpetologist Arthur Loveridge to spend his retirement on St Helena working on the animals of the island (see box).

The second initiative was by the Musée Royal de l'Afrique Centrale at Tervuren, in Belgium, which undertook a systematic investigation of the whole land and freshwater fauna of the island in the 1960s. The entomologists at the museum,

[2] C. Darwin (1844, reprinted 1890). Darwin was apparently the first person to realise that isolated islands such as St Helena and Ascension were quite distinct in geology and fauna from islands on continental shelves; he argued that oceanic islands had separate origins, had never been connected to continents and were therefore colonised only by long distance dispersal (see A.R. Wallace 1880).

J C Melliss

Figure 13
Photograph reproduced by
kind permission of Melliss
and Partners.

John Charles Melliss (1835-1910)

John Charles Melliss was only 40 when his classic study, *St. Helena: A physical, historical, and topographical description of the island, including its Geology, Fauna, Flora, and Meteorology*, was published in London by Lovell Reeve in 1875. Born on the island on 23rd January 1835, he was the fourth child and second son of Lieut. George Whalley Melliss (St. Helena Artillery) and his wife Julia (née Weston). His father, best known for building Ladder Hill Inclined Plane in 1829, was one of the few East India Company officers taken into the new colonial administration in 1836, first as Surveyor, then Civil Engineer. 'J.C.' succeeded him in 1860, having been Clerk of Works after professional training in London at King's College and the Metropolitan Board of Works.

His devotion to collecting, and to correspondence with eminent naturalists, was encouraged by his father, a keen early photographer, and later by his wife, Alice (née Stace), who sketched many of the indigenous plants for him. But in 1870 came a blow which could hardly have been foreseen when, under government retrenchment, the military took over public works making him redundant at 35 without any prospect of employment. Pensioned off at £186.6.8d p.a., he had little choice in 1871 but to leave the Island and start a new life in England. For a few years he found work managing water engineering projects in the Midlands, at Nuneaton, Coventry and Leyton, and in 1874 became an Associate (in 1891 Member) of the Institution of Civil Engineers.

Meanwhile his St. Helena studies were becoming recognised, earning him Fellowships of the Linnaean and Geological Societies by 1874. Plans for the publication of his *magnum opus* were then well advanced and it appeared in 1875 dedicated to the memory of his father who had died earlier in the year.

Melliss concentrated now on his profession. In 1878 he founded J.C.Melliss & Co., consulting engineers, with offices in the City, undertaking large scale commissions in water engineering, principally in the Thames Valley. The firm flourished, becoming J.C.Melliss & Son under his son Hugh until after the Second World War, today as Melliss & Partners of Guildford. 'J.C.' published several professional papers on "the sewage question" in the 1870s, but wrote little more on St. Helena. The strategic and economic consequences of withdrawing the garrison in 1906, however, prompted him to address the Royal Colonial Institute on Britain's responsibility towards its South Atlantic outpost, and in 1908 he helped found a St. Helena Relief Committee in London of which he became Hon. Treasurer. He died at his Hampstead home on 23rd August 1910.

(I am indebted to the family researches of Barrie and Christine Spratt for much of the biographical detail.)

Trevor W. Hearl   August 1996

Arthur Loveridge (1881-1980) - naturalist, collector, curator and taxonomist   Plate 3

Arthur Loveridge was born in Wales on 28th May 1881 and by the age of ten had decided to become a museum curator. His first work was in museums in Manchester and Cardiff, but in 1914 he started his long connection with Africa when he went to Nairobi and became Director of the British East African Museum; he stayed in Africa for ten years. During the first world war he took part in the East African campaign, but this did not interrupt his collecting: his first specimen of one rare burrowing amphibian was obtained while 'digging in' under shellfire.

In 1924 Loveridge took his African collections to the Museum of Comparative Zoology at Harvard University in the United States, and for the next 33 years worked there as curator of reptiles and amphibians. He repeatedly returned to Africa for long expeditions, making extensive zoological collections. He was totally devoted to his work and passionately neat and meticulous, traits invaluable in a curator; the Harvard herpetological collections became famous throughout the scientific world. He was kind and helpful with those who shared his high standards. It was also said that: *"he preferred clarity, was unhappy with complication, was impatient of subtlety"*. He was always a naturalist, collector and curator rather than an academic biologist. He was a prolific writer and during his career published 328 scientific papers and popular accounts of animals, including five books.

To the puzzlement of his American colleagues, he retired in 1957 to St Helena, ironically an island with no indigenous amphibians or land reptiles. The *Boston Globe* of July 21st 1957 had a headline *"Retiring Curator to Avoid Work Temptation"*, but we doubt that this was ever his intention. Philip met him on his voyage to the island in 1957, and on visiting him at Varneys in 1959 found him heavily involved in zoological research. Being driven by him around the island while searching for fossil bird bones was a hair-raising experience, and we were later told that in Cambridge, Massachusetts his survival to retirement age was surprising in view of his habit of stepping out into busy highways while looking firmly away from the oncoming traffic.

During his retirement Loveridge visited Africa and continued publishing articles on African reptiles and amphibians. However, the main achievement of the last 17 years of his life was his massive contribution to knowledge of the zoology of St Helena. Like Melliss a century earlier, he avidly collected specimens of many different groups of animals, recorded them precisely and sent them to specialists around the world. His correspondence from St Helena amounted to nearly 7,000 letters at the time of his death, and he also wrote many articles on the animals of the island.

Many of the animals that Loveridge discovered were found at Varneys and several of them bear his name; these include the endemic hoverfly genus *Loveridgeana*. He left behind him detailed manuscript notes on both invertebrates and vertebrates of the island, with many original observations on the behaviour of birds and mammals. These are kept in the St Helena Archives in the Castle in Jamestown, and have been used extensively by the Belgian entomologists and also by us.

Loveridge's wife died in 1972; his son Brian joined him on St Helena four years later and built Little Varneys. Loveridge himself died on the island on 16th February 1980, at the age of almost eighty-nine.

impressed by the isolation of St Helena and the consequent importance of understanding the origin and evolution of its plants and animals, argued that a comprehensive inventory of these was needed before the full scientific benefits could be reaped. The project was organised by P. Basilewsky, a well-known specialist on beetles, and involved the mounting of two expeditions, each comprising three experienced zoologists, who spent the periods 8th November 1965 to 23th January 1966 and 21st January to 4th June 1967 on the island. During this total of seven months the team members used a wide variety of collecting techniques and amassed collections of more than 100,000 invertebrate animals.

Perhaps even more impressive than the intensity of their field work was the way in which the Belgian workers organised the subsequent study of their collections. For each of the more than 150 taxonomic groups (families or orders) it was necessary to find a specialist with the knowledge, inclination and above all, time, to identify previously described species, ascertain which specimens represented new species, and for these, choose names and prepare full scientific descriptions. The members of the expedition studied a third of the groups themselves and recruited nearly 90 other taxonomists to work on the rest.[3]

The Belgian entomologists have not been free from criticism. Inevitably, the taxonomists whom they recruited varied in their thoroughness. Arthur Loveridge, in his unpublished notes, expressed irritation at the way in which specimens that he had previously sent to various museums were sometimes overlooked. Data were also occasionally quoted incorrectly; for instance, Loveridge had collected feather lice from a Sheathbill, an Antarctic seabird which had reached St Helena on a ship from the Falklands and whose scientific name is *Chionis alba*; these were described as having come from the locally breeding White Tern, *Gygis alba*. We sympathise with Loveridge, but having ourselves coped with diverse invertebrate collections, we are well aware of the difficulty in getting them all studied satisfactorily within a reasonable time.

More serious is the criticism of the large numbers of specimens of some rare species that the Belgians collected. Such concern is an indication of the growing understanding of the need to conserve populations of insects and other invertebrates, as well as those of larger and more conspicuous animals such as mammals and birds. But it has to be admitted that twenty five years ago, few ordinary people or professional zoologists paid much attention to the matter. For the Belgians, the priorities were to find out what animals were present and to work out where they lived on the island. It is an unfortunate fact that the identity and relationships of most invertebrates can only be established by detailed microscopic study and comparison with specimens in museum collections. Today, we can see that the Belgians were at fault in not restricting their collecting of animals that were already scarce. It was they, however, who provided a secure basic knowledge of the fauna, without which it would be hard to plan conservation work.[4]

The present authors were on the island from 15th December 1994 until 8th May 1995. We were searching for subterranean insects and other invertebrates in caves

---

[3] The extraordinary achievement of the organisers was that in December 1977 - little more than 10 years after the end of the second expedition - they were able to publish the last of four volumes of articles giving detailed accounts of almost every group of land and freshwater animals known from the island (P. Basilewsky, ed. 1970, 1972, 1976, 1977). The only major exception was the butterflies and moths, for which they were unable to find an appropriate specialist.

[4] Increasing understanding of the need for conservation of St Helena's endemic animals has come mainly from the inspiration of some more recent visitors to the island, based at the Invertebrate Conservation Unit of the Zoological Society of London; see especially P. Pearce-Kelly & Q.C.B. Cronk (1990).

and underground cavities, and also studying the fauna of the most barren surface habitats on the island. We have found that these sorts of places tend to be ignored by entomologists, but that they often provide habitats for interesting species. This proved to be the case in one of the few caves on the island, where we discovered a blind cavernicolous insect evidently representing an ancient colonising stock (see section on caves in Chapter 6). We also spent time hunting for insects on endemic trees and other plants, with the aim of increasing knowledge of the insect communities on particular plant species. Our work confirmed that several of the endemic trees of St Helena still have an array of endemic insects associated with them. Several of the species that we found are new to science, showing that knowledge of the endemic invertebrates of the island is still far from complete.

Nonetheless, enough is known to demonstrate that the native animals of St Helena are in some ways as remarkable as the plants, as well as being far more diverse. They have not, however, been the subject of a modern evolutionary analysis of the kind that Quentin Cronk has provided for the flowering plants: the Belgian entomologists published no general analysis of their results, apart from one paper on the origin of the beetle fauna.[5] All we can attempt here is a brief discussion of outstanding general features of the native fauna. In Part IV we treat the animals of the island systematically and expand on the evolutionary significance of certain groups.

The total number of animal species on St Helena, including those recently extinct and also those introduced by humans and now living wild on the island, is around 1130 (see Table 5A). About half of these have been introduced by people. Of the remainder, about 420 are endemic and have evolved their unique genetic characteristics while living on the island; the rest of the fauna – including the surviving seabirds – comprise species that are indigenous to the island but not endemic.

Many of the endemic animal species – like the plants – are so distinctive that they are considered to represent endemic genera; this usually implies that they are ancient relicts that lack close relatives in Africa or elsewhere. Current classifications list between 80 and 90 endemic genera of animals, but in a few groups the number seems inflated and is likely to be reduced after taxonomic revisions.

The distinctiveness of some of the endemic animals from their closest relatives in Africa or elsewhere results from millions of years of independent evolution after the colonising stocks reached St Helena. This is partly caused by chance evolutionary changes, which tend to occur more frequently in small populations as a result of the process known as random genetic drift, but it is also caused by pressures of natural selection resulting from differences in the ecological conditions experienced by the populations on the island and their relatives remaining on the continent.

A recent discovery relevant to the second point relates to the moth family Pyralidae, which have 'tympanal' hearing organs on the abdomen enabling them to detect the ultrasonic signals produced by bats when hunting, and thus to take evasive action. Five endemic species of pyralid moths described by Mrs Wollaston have recently been grouped in a new endemic genus, *Helenoscoparia*, implying that they have evolved from a single ancient colonisation.[6] Intriguingly, one of the characteristics that distinguishes them from their relatives on the African continent is the low degree of development of the tympanal organ. This is plausibly interpreted as relating to the

[5] P. Basilewsky (1985).

[6] E. Wollaston (1879), M. Nuss (1999).

lack of bats on St Helena: in the absence of predatory bats using ultrasound in hunting, the moths do not need a sophisticated sound detection system, and it has been gradually lost during evolution.

More obvious indications of the active evolution that has been proceeding on St Helena for many millions of years are provided by the extraordinary diversity of certain groups. The overall figure of 420 endemic animal species on St Helena compares with about 30 for Ascension Island, which is much the same size and similarly isolated, but only about one tenth as old (Table 12A).[7] It is possible to estimate the number of colonising stocks within each of the groups that include endemic species. For instance, the 46 endemic species of spiders on St Helena are spread among about 16 families and seem to have resulted from as many as 30 different colonisations; this implies that spiders are good colonists, but that having arrived, they show only moderate tendency towards diversification.

The beetles, however, present a very different picture. Most beetles cannot travel long distances by air and they do not easily colonise islands. But simple analysis of the beetles of St Helena suggests that during the history of the island some 23 colonising stocks have arrived naturally (an average of about one every half million years). The number of colonisations is less than in the case of the spiders, but the present fauna implies that in about six groups of beetles, after a colonising group (or single fertilized female) reached the island and developed into a successful population, it split into two separate species (speciated), which then split again, and so on to produce a modern group of closely related endemic species.

It is worth noting that if a particular stock of animals has characteristics that tend to increase the chance of speciation (e.g. snails or other sedentary animals living in small populations in favourable areas within a patchwork landscape) a large number of species may be generated relatively rapidly. Although the chance of speciation in any one stock may be low, the chance of it occurring in the group as a whole is greatly increased if there are already many independently evolving stocks. Each time a stock splits into two by speciation, there are two stocks within which future speciation can occur. Diversification is thus an exponential (multiplicative) process.

This may be the kind of process that has operated in the six types of beetles in which there is a cluster of closely related species on the island. They comprise three separate groups of weevils (with a total of 77 endemic species) in the family Curculionidae, 27 species of fungus weevils (Anthribidae), 12 species of ground beetles (Carabidae) some of which prey on the weevils, and five species of darkling beetles (Tenebrionidae). Since many of the weevils and the ground beetles live in rotting trunks of Tree Ferns, there is a strong suspicion that the original colonisations by both these groups may have taken place in floating trunks of the ancestral Tree Fern.

Sometimes in evolution, the splitting of lineages (speciation) is accompanied by occupation of different ecological niches, so that the resulting species live in somewhat different ways; for instance occupying different climatic zones or feeding on different kinds of plants. In this case the whole process is referred to as adaptive radiation of the group. In some of the St Helena beetle groups, however, there is no obvious pattern of this kind. For instance, the 12 species of ground beetle seem to have very similar niches, with a number of closely related species occurring together and making their living in much the same way (although it has to be admitted that

[7] N.P. & M.J. Ashmole (1997).

detailed ecological studies have not been carried out). It is not easy to understand how these species originated. It is possible that small populations were previously temporarily isolated on separate hilltops, ridges or other 'habitat islands' resulting from past climatic fluctuations. If the isolation lasted long enough, the populations would have diverged genetically and might not have interbred – and thus merged – when they eventually made contact again. This sort of non-adaptive radiation has recently been suggested for land snails on Porto Santo (Madeira),[8] and the general idea may be relevant to both ground beetles and the extinct snails of St Helena.

In some groups in which two or more related species are present, splitting of a single stock on the island may not have been involved. Instead, there may have been more than one colonisation of the island from the continent. A plausible (though unproven) example is provided by two species of crickets (Plate 23). *Gryllus bimaculatus* is a migratory African cricket which has established populations on both Ascension and St Helena. On the latter island, however, there is also a closely related flightless cricket, *Gryllus abnormis*, which presumably evolved from a group of the *G. bimaculatus* stock that colonised St Helena long ago. Probably, when more members of that stock arrived relatively recently, they did not interbreed with the now distinct *G. abnormis*. Whenever two or more species in a single genus are found on a remote island, evolutionists need to consider this kind of origin, by double (or multiple) colonisation, as a possible alternative to speciation of the stock on the island after a single colonisation. Modern techniques of molecular biology, generally involving study of the genetic material DNA, offers hope of distinguishing between these hypotheses, but no relevant work has yet been done on St Helena.

St Helena cannot compete in diversity with the richest archipelagos; the Hawaiian chain, for instance, has more than 5,500 endemic species.[9] Nonetheless, the endemic fauna of St Helena is of enormous interest. It demonstrates that given enough time, even a single island that is extremely remote from continental land can be reached by enough colonising stocks to get evolution started on the process of creating biodiversity. Illuminating comparisons can also be made with Ascension Island, since its geographical situation is analogous but its age an order of magnitude less.

On St Helena, much of the work of millions of years of evolution has been undone in the few centuries since 1502. The apparent extinction of the Giant Ground Beetle and Giant Earwig spring to mind, but many other species have also disappeared. The case of the land snails is particularly depressing. In 1502 St Helena was home to some 20 endemic species and five endemic genera of land snails; now there are either one or two endemic species. The definite survivor is the Blushing Snail *Succinea sanctaehelenae* (Plate 22), a distinct species but a member of a widespread genus. Two families have borne the brunt. In the Subulinidae, all eight species in the endemic genus *Chilonopsis* are presumed extinct. In the Charopidae, a family which is also well known for its adaptive radiation on the high islands in the Pacific, St Helena had seven species in three endemic genera; now there is one possible survivor, *Helenoconcha relicta*, which was found by the Belgians on Cabbage Tree Road.

The causes of the extinctions of invertebrates are largely a matter of guesswork. The three likely agents are: habitat change associated with the destruction of the native vegetation; the introduction of predatory animals, especially rats, mice and the large

---

[8] R.A.D. Cameron, L.M. Cook & J.D. Hallows (1996).

[9] F.G. Howarth & W.P. Mull (1992).

centipede *Scolopendra morsitans*; and the introduction of highly competitive though non-predatory species capable of replacing some endemic island forms.

Destruction of vegetation must have had devastating effects on many animals; the numerous snail species that were adapted to humid conditions would have been particularly vulnerable to desiccation. For many snails and other invertebrates, however, predation may have been crucial. The island always had predatory birds (rails, the hoopoe and the cuckoo) but these would have been mainly diurnal, so that most of the larger invertebrates doubtless sheltered in holes or under rocks by day, emerging to forage at night. The arrival of nocturnal rodents would have found many of these animals defenceless. Loveridge noted that the large introduced *Helix* snails are eaten by *Rattus rattus*, and the endemic snails were doubtless important prey when the rats were first brought to the island. Competition is notoriously hard to demonstrate, and we are not aware of any clear cases of animal extinction caused in this way on St Helena; but this is not to say that it is unimportant.

In the case of the ground beetle and the earwig, habitat loss must have had a severe effect, but mice may have delivered the *coup de grâce*: the retreats of these large insects would have been more accessible to mice than those of some of their smaller relatives which survive on the island. We do not know the diet of the large centipedes, but in dry parts of the island where they can be found under so many large rocks, it is not hard to imagine the fate of small native animals that join them there.

The St Helena Green Turtle population

It is said that João da Nova, arriving at St Helena in May 1502, found turtles in abundance; in view of the season, we are a little sceptical. If they were present, they were probably Green Turtles, although Hawksbills do occur around the coasts of the island in small numbers. None of the early naturalist travellers seem to have noticed turtles; by bad luck, all of Peter Mundy's three visits were at seasons when most Green Turtles would have been absent. The scarcity of references to turtles continues after settlement of the island.

We are convinced, however, that rather than implying that Green Turtles were absent, the negative record merely reflects the fact that they nested primarily at Sandy Bay Beach, a part of the island extremely remote from the anchorage and main population centre. In 1883 Benjamin Grant, in his detailed and fulsome account of St Helena, wrote that the turtle: *"for 3 or 4 months in every year visits our waters and is taken in such quantity and size as to afford Turtle soup to the poorest family."* Grant also commented in relation to the beach at Sandy Bay, that: *"turtles have frequently deposited their eggs, but are seldom allowed to do so undisturbed."*

In 1962 John Packer made the long trek down, and visited one of the families at Sandy Bay.[10] He was told that turtles used to lay their eggs there, and that local people used to turn the adults and also collect and eat their eggs; unsurprisingly, they were now seldom seen. However, Loveridge recorded that some eggs were dug up there in 1963. Even in 1995 a lady living near Sandy Bay Beach recalled the collecting of turtle eggs in her childhood, and another islander told us of turtle eggs being brought into the house when he was a boy, although he did not know where they came from. We found what looked like a pit made by a turtle at the western end of Sandy Bay Beach, and another at Prosperous Bay, although it was hard to be sure that people were not responsible. Some

---

[10] J.E. Packer (1968a).

dried turtle egg shells were dug up by Henry and Edward Thorpe a few years ago near the shore below Turks Cap, but their age is unknown. It is doubtful whether turtles ever breed successfully on St Helena now, but they still visit the island regularly in small numbers between about December and March;[11] these are roughly the limits of the laying season on Ascension. We saw one turtle in Ruperts Bay in early January 1995.

The settlers doubtless ate both turtles and their eggs whenever opportunity offered, although the earliest written record that we have found is a government notification of 1869 specifying a charge of five shillings each for the slaughtering and dressing of turtle in the market of Jamestown. Melliss records that in the 1870s about six or eight turtles of a very large size were brought to market each year; other information implies a similar rate of capture over a long period. Several people on the island still recall turtles for sale in the market, on occasions up to the early 1980s. We imagine that these turtles were caught at sea, and Joseph Cunningham, who went to St Helena in 1909 to investivate the fisheries resources, was told that turtles were normally captured at sea in the act of copulation. Cunningham never heard of turtles nesting on St Helena, but he may have spent most of his time in Jamestown during his five week stay, and have had little if any contact with the people of Sandy Bay.

We do not suggest that St Helena has had, during the last few thousand years, a turtle population comparable to that on Ascension; but there is every reason to suppose that there was a small rookery centred on Sandy Bay Beach in which breeding attempts continued well into the 20th century and possibly up to the present. During periods of lower sea level associated with the ice ages of the past two million years, sandy beaches would have been much more extensive on St Helena (see box in Chapter 3) and turtles would have had plenty of space for laying their eggs in sand above the tide mark. At these times, the turtle population was probably very large. Even in periods of high sea level, including the last ten thousand years or so, there may have been enough sand for nesting in several bays around the island.

After settlement by people in 1659, however, sandy beaches were progressively barred by the construction of fortifications or sea-walls, or reduced by removal of sand. There now seem to be few suitable sandy patches at Sandy Bay, and hardly any in other parts of the coast. It seems that the history of the Green Turtle on St Helena, one of only a handful of rookeries in the South Atlantic Ocean, is a small environmental tragedy that has gone almost unnoticed by naturalists and conservationists. In Chapter 8 we consider whether the population might yet be restored.

Marine mammals

When St Helena was discovered there were probably colonies of at least one type of seal, since the record of the earliest visit mentions both seals and sea lions. But these marine mammals were so vulnerable to human predation that we do not even know for certain what they were. As on several other matters, the only clear records come from Peter Mundy. In 1656 he described and made a careful sketch of a sick animal that he found and killed on the shore:[12]

> *"Being sett on shore near Chappell Vally, as I went along uppon the beach, I saw a strange creature lying along theron, as I drew near, I perceaved it was alive. It was very weake and (as afterward was found) hurtt in divers places. However, when I toutched it, raised his forepart, gaping on mee with his wide and terrible jawes. It had the coullor (yellowish) and*

[11] A. Edwards (1990) suggests perhaps as late as June.

[12] R.C. Temple & L.M. Anstey (1936).

Peter Mundy's "Strange Creature"

Figure 14

terrible countenance of a lion, with four greatt teeth, besides smalle, long, bigge smelling haires or mustaches. Afterwards itt made way towards the sea, when I tooke uppe a good bigge stone with both my hands flung it att his head, which staggred him, and then with more stones made quite an end of him: in length aboutt ten foote and five foote aboutt the middle. Some say it was a seale, others nott. I terme itt a sealionnesse, beeing a femall. There wee left itt, being near after the forme hereunder: the haire very shortt, butt the mouth exceeding wide, wider then here sett downe, according to proportion of the rest."

This description, with other records, suggests that Mundy's *"strange creature"* was a Southern Elephant Seal *Mirounga leonina*, a member of the true seal family Phocidae.[13] This species is widely distributed in the Southern Ocean and still occasionally breeds in South Africa, as well as in the Tristan group. Although this wounded individual had probably drifted to the island, the presence of a breeding colony in 1502 is not unlikely. The animals referred to by the first settlers as sea cows or manatees (as in 'Manatee Bay', which had already received its name by 1679) were probably of the same species. Captures were sufficiently frequent for the East India Company – in 1682 – to give explicit permission for any inhabitant finding: *"any of the sayd fish called Sea Cows or other of the like nature and quality"* to *"boyle the same, and convert it into oyle, and take it to his own proper use and behoofe"* provided that he delivered a proportion of the oil to the Company. Another possibility is that there was a colony of monk seals (genus *Monachus*), a group now found in the Mediterranean and Hawai'i and in the past also in the Caribbean; these warm water seals might be well suited to conditions around St Helena.

The eared seal family Otariidae, which includes both sea lions and fur seals, may also have been represented in the original fauna of the island. The mention of sea lions by the first visitors could refer to the Cape Fur Seal *Arctocephalus pusillus*, which looks much like a sea lion and still breeds on the coast of Namibia.

Native birds in historical times
The present day native bird fauna of St Helena consists of about eight species of breeding seabirds, one endemic landbird (the Wirebird) and one indigenous but non-endemic landbird (the Moorhen). In addition there are nine introduced landbirds (see Table 5B).

During the first century after the discovery of the island there is little useful information about the native birds. Only one tantalizing hint is provided in an account (reproduced by P.L. Teale) relating to a Portuguese visit in 1578. A list of mammals introduced to St Helena is followed by *"... and partridges, and wild hens, and pigeons, and other kinds of fowles, both great and small."*

Another report reproduced by Teale and dating from 1599 states: *"It seems that in past times this island did not have any animals or birds than those brought by the Portuguese."* The writer continues: *"The birds that we saw on the island were ... and pigeons. There are not many pigeons, the meat thereof is blue skinny and untastey so that I wondered where from these birds*

---

[13] A. Edwards (1990).

could grow so well as there is no fruit and 'wast'?" It seems likely that the *'pigeons'* in question were actually White Terns, which nest in trees inland and do have blue skin; there are other later records which clearly refer to White Terns as St Helena Pigeons.

This 1599 report is also noteworthy as the earliest we have seen that mentions the presence of mice, rats and cats; pigs were probably there nearly a century earlier. It seems likely that all the more vulnerable of the endemic landbirds became extinct during the 16th century under the onslaught of this diverse array of predators to which they were not adapted. The ground nesting seabirds would have been equally vulnerable, and the devastation caused by cat predation that we can currently witness on Ascension, occurred on the mainland of St Helena centuries earlier. Even now it is not hard to find cat lairs full of seabird bones on St Helena, testifying to the way in which recolonisation of the main island is prevented by the presence of feral cats. Pigs may have played a major part, being omnivores and capable of getting at seabirds in burrows as well as on the surface. Rats probably also had serious effects, especially on the petrels, which leave their young unattended while still small and defenceless.

Peter Mundy, on his second visit in October 1638, was the first person to record the Wirebird, St Helena's only surviving endemic bird. He noted: *"a smalle land Foule and butt only thatt one kind here to bee seen"*. On his third visit in May 1656, Mundy amplified, providing a description that clearly relates to the Wirebird (also known as the St Helena Plover): *"allso a smalle land foule, somwhatt like a larcke in collour, shape, flight and note. Itt would run like a lapwing."* [14]

The only surviving indigenous (but not endemic) landbird is the Moorhen, which was first recorded in 1715 by Captain Daniel Beeckman. Although Philip Gosse, from whom we take this record, commented in 1937 that the Moorhen was not present on the island, he may have overlooked it. A suggestion has been made, however, that the Moorhen may not have been able to establish itself on St Helena until after the extinction of the endemic flightless rails which are discussed below.[15] The modern population may be intermittently supplemented by vagrants arriving from the African continent.

Seabirds on the coasts and offshore islets may have suffered serious direct predation by humans in the 16th century. It is clear from van Linschoten's account that Portuguese ships were visiting the island on an annual basis by 1589, sometimes leaving behind sick sailors so that they could recuperate and be picked up in the following year.[16] The impact of this traffic on the seabirds breeding in places readily accessible from the anchorages off the east coast can be judged by Wittert's account of a Dutch visit in 1608:

> *"At the southern side of St. Helena lie certain small iles or properly rocks, where we see thousands of black gulls, and other white or speckled, some of which have the neck long and others short. They lay their eggs upon the rocks, and these eggs are very good to eat. The multitude of these birds is so great that one takes them in thousands, and they allow themselves to be killed with blows of a stick: on this account they call the seagulls "boobies" but they are very good taste."*

More evidence of exploitation comes in 1634, when Peter Mundy made his first visit to the island:[17]

---

[14] R.C. Temple (1919), R.C. Temple & L.M. Anstey (1936).

[15] S.L. Olson (1973, 1975).

[16] P.A. Tiele (1885).

[17] R.C. Temple (1914).

92

"Our Captaine etts. merchants went one day in the Shallopp to certaine little rockie Islands to the westward, where, with our sticks and hands, wee struck downe and Caught neere 100 Sea fowle, russett Coulour, almost as bigg as a pidgeon but tast very fishey. By reason there was a great su{r}ffe wee could not land att the principall place or Island where were Tropicke birds, Gunnett, Seameues, etts."

Seabirds and their eggs would have been used extensively for food by early sailors before the island was settled; after 1659 they doubtless became an important resource for the settlers. The colonies in Chapel Valley (Jamestown), Ruperts and the accessible western offshore islets such as Egg Island would have been especially vulnerable. Colonies on cliffs or the more remote offshore islets in the east and south probably suffered much less: three out of the four most important stacks – Speery, Shore and George Islands – lie in exposed positions where landing is difficult and dangerous.

The danger of over-exploitation or excessive disturbance of the birds was evidently quickly realized. The records for 1707 indicate that the *"egg islands"* were considered company property and that egg collecting in season had for some years been restricted to Tuesdays, Thursdays and Saturdays. Several other entries around this time also refer to efforts to exercise control over egg collecting; for instance, on August 17th, 1714 it was stated:

"Several persons as well for their own pleasure as to catch fish hath gone upon shore on the Egg Islands and made fires which impudence hath caused the Egg fowles to settle and lay on the main and in such places as was impossible to gather their eggs without great danger. To prevent which for the future these are strictly to forbid and enjoyn all persons on the said island not to presume to go on shore or to make firs upon the aforesaid Egg Islands upon any pretence whatsoever."

The *"egg birds"* or *"egg fowles"* mentioned in the early records were probably mainly Sooty Terns (Wideawakes), and although there is little information on the exploitation of these or other seabirds during the following centuries, the tradition of collecting Wideawake eggs persisted at least into the 1980s.

The catching of Trophy Birds (Red-billed Tropicbirds) in their nest holes may persist to this day. A member of the Agriculture & Forestry Department told us how, early in the 1990s, he was walking in a remote area with two local people; they disappeared for a moment and came back carrying a couple of dead Trophy Birds. Most such captures in recent times were probably made casually during fishing excursions, but we have heard of more systematic collections being made relatively recently on ledges on the enormous cliffs below Great Stone Top. In the past, when food shortages and even famine occurred, exploitation of seabirds was doubtless much more intense than it is today. This human predation has doubtless played a part in the elimination of Wideawakes from breeding places on the main island and in limiting successful breeding of Trophy Birds to inaccessible sites. Melliss describes how tropicbirds were persecuted in the last century for the sake of decorative plumes for ladies' hats.

Although there has doubtless always been good local knowledge of the surviving native birds on St Helena, scientific studies have been sporadic and, in general, less thorough than those on the other animals and the plants. The Belgians were primarily entomologists and did not undertake ornithological field work, and earlier naturalists had paid little attention to birds. Melliss, for instance, started his account by writing:

"The feathered portion of the St. Helenian fauna can scarcely be said to be so interesting from a scientific point of view as the rest".[18]

---

[18] His own lack of interest seems to be reflected in his account of the seabirds, which is somewhat casual; it fails - for instance - to distinguish clearly the two species of noddy, both of which are abundant on the coast south of Jamestown.

The first comprehensive ornithological survey was carried out by Major E.L. Haydock in 1952. He collected specimens of most of the birds and also of parasitic insects found on them. On 25th November 1952 he circled the island by boat, making only the second recorded ornithological landings on several islands including Speery, Shore and George islands (the first landings were in 1925 by members of the American *Blossom* expedition, who never published their records).

In 1958 and 1959 some observations on seabirds were made by members of the British Ornithologists' Union Centenary Expedition, on holiday from Ascension.[19] However it was Dr Trevor Trueman who, during his visit from late November 1987 to the end of March 1988, first brought to St Helena the approach of a dedicated modern birdwatcher. In particular, Trueman made observations from Jamestown wharf at dusk once or twice a week during his stay, greatly increasing knowledge of the non-resident seabirds.

The most recent systematic ornithological work on St Helena has been carried out by Beau Rowlands, who visited St Helena several times between late 1988 and early 1992, with the primary intention of documenting the breeding distribution of seabirds; he has landed on almost all the offshore islets. With several colleagues including Trueman, Rowlands has now published a comprehensive account of the birds of the island, including a more detailed historical treatment.[20]

The fragmentary historical record of the birds of St Helena is tantalizing in many ways. For instance, frigatebirds no longer breed on St Helena, but in his account of the island published in 1817 J. Barnes described: *"the frigate pelican, or man of war, pelicanus aquilus"* as *"a large, dark-coloured bird, in length from three to four feet, and ten to fourteen feet in width, from the extremities of the wings"*. These dimensions are somewhat exaggerated but probably refer to the Great Frigatebird, fossils of which have been found on the island (see below). This species is sometimes over three feet in length and with wingspan up to seven and a half feet. Melliss in 1875 wrote of the *"Man-of-war-bird"* and recorded that there was still: *"living evidence of its having once frequented the landing steps at Jamestown"*.

There are also hints that there have been significant changes in the status of some species in more recent decades. For instance, in 1995 Graham Sim told us that seabirds had been more abundant – at least in the Jamestown area – prior to the late 1970s. Fishermen used to have to clear their boats of roosting noddies before setting out in the morning, and the noddies often fed on bait fish in James Bay; this has not happened in recent years.

An apparent positive change in status is of the Masked Booby, a species that is represented in small numbers in the recent fossil deposits (see below) but which may have been temporarily lost from the island after 1502. The historical records are ambiguous, but no Masked Boobies were found by Major Haydock on George Island or Shore Island during his careful survey in 1952, and Douglas Dorward and Philip saw

---

[19] Bernard and Sally Stonehouse were on St Helena from 4th to 26th November 1958, and Douglas Dorward and Philip Ashmole from 14th April to 6th May 1959. Bernard Stonehouse later described both visits in his book "Wideawake Island" about the BOU expedition to Ascension Island. He also published (in 1963) an article on the breeding seasons of St Helena seabirds, as well as doing some research on the seasonality of human reproduction on the island in the 19th century.

[20] B.W. Rowlands et al. (1998).

none when looking out over these islands from Gill Point on 5th May 1959 (they did see one Brown Booby and one adult white-phase Red-footed Booby on Shore Island). However, Graham Sim told us that he landed with his children on George Island in the first half of 1968 and found Masked Boobies nesting there; he thought that breeding had started in the middle of the 1960s. The first ornithologist to record this colony was Trevor Trueman in 1987-88.

There is evidence that some other seabirds may try to breed on St Helena from time to time. We were told by several people of a bird that made a strange call at night, both in Sandy Bay and elsewhere on the island. Arthur Loveridge reported that in 1975 a bird was heard calling at night near Levelwood, and on 27th February 1976 a small shearwater flew into a lighted room, apparently in Jamestown. Bill Bourne and Loveridge concluded that this bird was a small shearwater of the *Puffinus assimilis/lherminieri* group, which is one of the commonest seabirds in the fossil beds on the island. Either there is a tiny surviving remnant of the original population, or these records are of stray birds, perhaps from the Cape Verde Islands. In 1995 we found a couple of burrows near Sandy Bay that could have been made by shearwaters, but we were unable to confirm breeding.

Other strange seabirds have also been seen within recent decades. One fisherman told us of a bird that could be attracted by a torch; it was grey all over and its flight was direct and fast rather than fluttering. We also talked to Alfred (Sammy) and Ethel Stevens, who live just below Hoopers Ridge and who in the late 1980s repeatedly saw and also handled a large petrel (wingspan about 81 cm) that frequented the area; it was eventually photographed and described in March 1988 by Trevor Trueman. Sammy was able to attract the bird by imitating its call and it sometimes settled on his water tank. It was seen to eat berries of Diddly Dight and even made a nest of twigs under an aloe.

This bird was clearly a gadfly petrel of the genus *Pterodroma*. Sadly, the shape of its head seems to exclude it from being a surviving individual of *Pterodroma rupinarum*, the extinct petrel that is so abundant in the fossil deposits (see below). The gadfly petrels vary in plumage and are taxonomically difficult, but this bird was probably a Murphy's Petrel *Pterodroma ultima* (Plate 6).[21]

Our own contribution in this field was made on 14th February 1995, when we found fresh wings of two individuals of Bulwer's Petrel (with those of one Madeiran Storm-petrel) at the top of the cliff at Gill Point, opposite Shore Island.[22] These birds were presumably killed either by a fisherman or by a feral cat. It is not clear whether the dead Bulwer's Petrels were visitors from North Atlantic breeding sites or whether there is a small breeding population on St Helena. Petrels rarely come to land except at their breeding colonies but we are inclined to think that these were merely visiting St Helena. The species has no known breeding stations in the South Atlantic but has been seen there during the northern winter; the nearest known colony is in the Cape Verde Islands.

Introduced birds

With the exception of the Moorhen and the Wirebird, all the breeding landbirds have been introduced. They fall into three groups. The first comprises the Chukar Partridge, Ring-necked Pheasant and probably the Feral Pigeon, which were brought to the island by the Portuguese shortly after its discovery in the 16th century; the motive in

[21] B.W. Rowlands & T. Trueman (2000).

[22] N.P. Ashmole, M.J. Ashmole & W.R.P. Bourne (1999).

this case was the provision of food for visiting seamen or temporary residents of the island. The second group consists of the Peaceful Dove, Madagascar Fody, Java Sparrow, Common Waxbill and Yellow Canary, all small, brightly coloured, seed-eating birds that were encountered by travellers to the East Indies. The complex evidence marshalled by Rowlands suggests that all these reached the island between 1750 and 1780. At this time the island authorities made explicit orders for the purchase of stocks of 'canaries' from Madagascar (probably implying songbirds in general, since Madagascar has no native canaries) and for a variety of mammals and birds (including 'canary') from the Cape of Good Hope. This was a period when more and more ships were calling at St Helena on their way back to Europe, many of them doubtless with songbirds on board. The importations may have been simply because island residents liked the idea of having attractive birds around, but the idea of trading in them doubtless soon occurred to local children or adults; the birds quickly became an economic resource, but also agricultural pests. A visitor in 1776 commented: *"The Java Sparrows .... were first brought from China and Batavia for their beauty, but from their wonderful increase, are become a great annoyance to the farmers."*[23] The third group comprises only the Indian Myna, brought to the island in 1885.

It would be interesting to know whether the introduced birds that still survive have undergone significant evolutionary change since they arrived. Studies of species such as Mynas introduced to other islands have given intriguing results, but interpretation is often difficult – as it would be for St Helena and Ascension – because of uncertainty as to how many individuals were brought in, and exactly when and where from.[24] All the introduced species would also repay detailed ecological study. In particular, they have had ample opportunity to occupy a wider range of habitats than would be possible in their native lands where they would be competing with a much wider range of other species.

In addition to the introduced birds now breeding on the island and listed in Table 5B, many other species of landbirds have been introduced but have eventually died out. The following species maintained populations for a decade or so: Feral Chicken *Gallus gallus*, Peafowl *Pavo cristatus*, Helmeted Guineafowl *Numida meleagris* (present for several hundred years), Blackbird *Turdus merula*, Song Thrush *Turdus philomelos*, Hill Myna *Gracula religiosa*, House Sparrow *Passer domesticus* and Red Bishop *Euplectes orix*.

Ancient bird communities

In spite of the paucity of early records, collections of fossil and sub-fossil bird bones have made it possible to build up a picture of the ancient bird communities of St Helena. Today only about eight species of seabirds breed on the cliffs and offshore islets of St Helena (most of them in small numbers) and there are only two native landbirds (one endemic). Before 1502, the numbers and diversity of native birds were very different. Colonies of at least 15 species of seabirds were present on the main island at some stage and six species of endemic landbirds are known from fossils; there may also have been small songbirds in the forests.

Deposits of bird bones occur in many places on the island. Some of these are considered subfossils, bones preserved in dry deposits for a few hundred years. Others that are older and are partly mineralized clearly rate as true fossils. Some of the richest

[23] J. Forbes (1813).

[24] A.J. Baker & A. Moeed (1987).

fossil beds are associated with the banks of consolidated shell sand in the Sandy Bay and Sugar Loaf areas. Probably the birds had made burrows in the sand and were then suffocated or drowned when exceptional rainstorms caused the burrows to collapse. Other rich accumulations occur in silt deposits washed down from higher areas by disastrous floods. The most dramatic of these are at Prosperous Bay and in Dry Gut east of Levelwood, but there are smaller ones in several other places.

Deposits of bird bones were clearly described in 1834 by Robert F. Seale in his book: *The Geognosy of the Island St. Helena*. Seale mentioned the presence of *"the phaeton ethereus and diomedea exulans"* (Red-billed Tropicbird and Wandering Albatross) commenting that the latter bird was no longer present on the island; the bones concerned probably belonged to frigatebirds. He described the Prosperous Bay location precisely, saying that:

> *"The bed, or ossuary, in which these fragments are found, extends about a mile in length from the water's edge, from one hundred to three hundred and fifty yards in an opposite direction, and is from ten to ninety feet deep."*

Today, these deposits are much more restricted and have evidently been largely eroded away in the last 150 years. Numerous bones can still be found, however, bleached white by sun and rain where they project above the surrounding reddish brown silt.

Collections of bird bones were made a few years after Seale's time by Captain Wilkes, R.N. and by J.H. Blofeld; both collections were presented to the Geological Society of London. Wilkes' bones were labelled as having been found in Turks Cap Bay, but probably actually came from the Prosperous Bay deposit. Blofeld's bones came from a site: *"about half a mile behind Longwood, at an elevation of about 1,700 ft above the level of the sea, on a hill-side which is worn into numerous clefts or ravines by the heavy rains."*[25] No one has since been able to find this deposit, *"behind Longwood"* being an unfortunately ambiguous description.

Blofeld's and Wilkes' collections were examined by the eminent Victorian palaeontologist Richard Owen, who commented that they comprised *"marine birds, with some of the Wilkes' belonging to the sub-genus* Puffinus*"* (shearwaters). The collections were subsequently mislaid, but in 1977 they were found and fully identified; they turn out to include many of the seabirds and several landbirds identified in the intervening period.[26]

In 1956 Bill Bourne published a description of a seabird skull collected on St Helena by Lieut. Turton, pointing out that it belonged to a medium-sized gadfly petrel. This was the first scientific account of one of St Helena's extinct birds, and the species was later named as *Pterodroma rupinarum*. Bourne also commented: *"It seems probable that the original sea-bird community of the island once included some or all of the tropical Boobies, Terns, Tropic-birds, and Frigate-birds still found at Ascension and South Trinidade to the north and west, and also several petrels, which may have included some of the subtropical species now found at Tristan de Cunha further south"*. He was to be proved right.

Bernard and Sally Stonehouse collected a few bones in 1958. They visited the Prosperous Bay site but also discovered a previously unrecorded deposit in Dry Gut, north of Bencoolen. Encouraged by this, Douglas Dorward and Philip began looking for bones immediately after arriving at St Helena in April 1959. It soon became

---

[25] J.H. Blofeld (1852).

[26] C.A. Walker (1977).

obvious that this was treasure trove. There were easily recognizable bones of frigatebirds, boobies, petrels and terns; but there were also bones of unfamiliar seabirds, and some that seemed to be of landbirds. These fossils clearly deserved serious study, so the holiday soon became dominated by the search for bones. Arthur Loveridge, who had recently retired to the island, helped us to locate some of the deposits, and William Beard – who knew the island like the back of his hand – took us to many other remote places; in the end, we collected mainly at Prosperous Bay, Dry Gut and Sugar Loaf.

We were unable to make precise identifications on the island, so we merely collected as many bones as we could, packed them carefully and took them back to Britain. Not long afterwards Douglas left for a job in Australia and it fell to Philip to study the bones, in the Natural History Museum in London. No-one there at that time was expert on bird bones, but there was free access to the collection in the basement. Also in the museum was a box of bones from Sugar Loaf collected by Norman R. Kerr, who had been headmaster and education officer on the island a few years previously and who kindly gave permission for his material to be studied along with the new collection.

The museum's reference collection dated largely from Victorian times, and a frustratingly large number of the boxes contained only breastbones – presumably extracted from the birds when preparing specimens for the 'skin' collection. Our collections were mainly of wing and leg bones, which are left in museum skins, where they can be measured roughly but not compared in detail with fossils.

For most of the intact bones it was easy enough to confirm the general group of birds, but identifying them to the species level took practice and a lot of measurements and comparisons. It was eventually possible to demonstrate the presence in the bone deposits of several of the seabirds that still breed on the island or adjacent islets, together with four species that no longer breed there, but do so elsewhere in the Atlantic: Audubon's Shearwater, White-faced Storm-petrel, Red-footed Booby and Lesser Frigatebird. More intriguingly, there were bones of a species similar to (but not identical with) the Wedge-tailed Shearwater, which does not now breed anywhere in the Atlantic; this was later described as an extinct endemic species, *Puffinus pacificoides*. There were also many bones of two gadfly petrels: the larger of these – which was the one originally noted by Bill Bourne – was later named *Pterodroma rupinarum* and the smaller species became *Bulweria bifax*.

The landbird bones presented more problems. The best technique was to pick up a bone and walk round the collection, comparing it with examples from all the likely groups of birds. Eventually, one found oneself 'getting warm', with an obvious resemblance. It was slow work, but more and more pieces of the jigsaw eventually fitted into place. One of the last was a single humerus (upper wing bone) which was indistinguishable from the same bone from the Hoopoe of Africa and Europe (but see below).

There was also a small group of fragmentary bones from Sugar Loaf (including two collected earlier by Norman Kerr) which turned out to belong to a pigeon. It was, however, a very odd pigeon, having relatively larger legs and smaller wings than modern pigeons: the implication was that it was an endemic species which lived mainly on the ground.

Another batch of non-seabird bones – from the Prosperous Bay deposits – also had large leg bones associated with relatively small wing bones, and were clearly from a large rail (a Moorhen-like bird). This was obviously a new species, and Philip asked

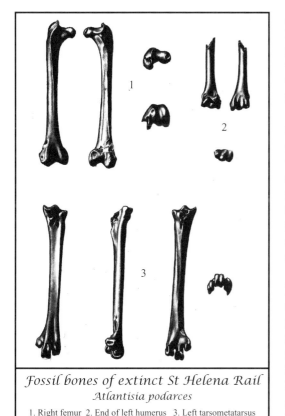

Fossil bones of extinct St Helena Rail
Atlantisia podarces
1. Right femur 2. End of left humerus 3. Left tarsometatarsus

Figure 15   From photograph in A. Wetmore (1963), *Ibis*.

Alexander Wetmore – then head of the Smithsonian Institution in Washington and the doyen of avian paleontologists – to study the bones. He concluded that this was a strong-footed bird almost the size of a small chicken, though not so heavily built, and with wings so reduced that it was evidently incapable of flight.

In the eventual report on the bones, Philip showed that thirteen species of seabirds had bred on the island in the past, compared with the 6 8 species present in 1959.[27] On land, whereas there was now only the Wirebird, at least three additional species had been resident in the past. These results provided a dramatic demonstration of the disastrous effects that human beings – and the mammals they brought with them – could have on island bird populations, and showed the danger of depending solely on historical records in documenting island bird communities.

Douglas and Philip had only a short time on the island and lacked experience with bird fossils, so the work was inevitably only preliminary; it was 1971 before a young American paleontologist, Storrs Olson, arrived in St Helena to carry out a more definitive study. As well as revisiting the known sites he found an additional one at Sugar Loaf and two near Sandy Bay beach. During his six week stay he collected 4,600 subfossil bird bones representing 21 species. These included all the extinct landbirds that we had found, together with one more. This was a second species of flightless rail – hardly larger than the Wirebird – which Olson named *Porzana astrictocarpus*.

Olson confirmed Philip's opinion that the extinct pigeon was ground living and pointed out that among all known pigeons, this was the only one besides the extinct Dodo and Solitaires (from islands in the Indian Ocean) that had become strongly adapted for terrestrial life, with relatively large size but disproportionately small wings.[28] He considered it as representing a new genus and species, *Dysmoropelia dekarchiskos*.

The Hoopoe proved more interesting than Philip had thought, since although the wing bones were similar in size to those of the African species, the leg bones found by Olson were larger; he became convinced that this bird – like the pigeon – could barely fly. He named it *Upupa antaios* and noted that even the African Hoopoe is particularly easily caught by cats; the St Helena bird, unaccustomed to predators and incapable of rapid escape by flight, was probably exterminated within a few years of the introduction of cats.

Olson's work on the flightless island birds – and especially on the rails of Ascension and St Helena – led him to think hard about the evolution of flightlessness. It had long been realized that rails on continents would render themselves vulnerable to mammalian predators if they lost the power of flight. On islands where such predators

[27] N.P. Ashmole (1963c). The list of seabirds breeding in the past was augmented by later finds.

[28] Another fossil pigeon with reduced wings and heavily constructed legs has recently been described from Henderson Island in the Pacific: G.M. Wragg & M.I. Weisler (1994).

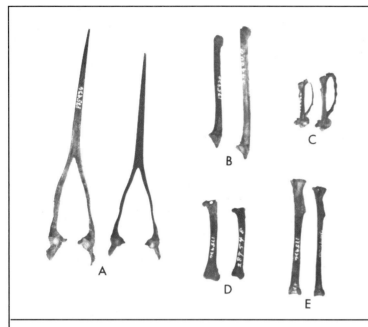

*Fossil bones of extinct St Helena Hoopoe (left)
compared with ordinary Hoopoe from Africa (right)*

A. Lower beak B. Middle wing bone C. Outer wing bone
D. Thigh bone E. Middle leg bone

Figure 16
From photograph in S.L.
Olson (1975), *Smithsonian
Contributions to Paleobiology*

are absent, however, the balance of the forces of natural selection is different. Flight muscles have high energy demands and reducing them saves resources that can be used for other purposes, including increased reproductive effort. In the absence of predators, therefore, individuals with genes conferring reduced wings and flight muscles will tend to outcompete more normal individuals and leave more offspring, thus leading to progressive reduction of flying ability over successive generations.

Olson also threw some light on the genetic mechanism that might bring about such changes. He invoked the theory of 'neoteny', which is the slowing down of some aspects of bodily development so that the animal reaches sexual maturity while retaining some juvenile characters. Well developed legs and running ability are needed by young rails as soon as they hatch, but flight feathers – because they are dead structures of fixed size – are usually developed only when the body is nearly full grown. Young rails thus resemble adult flightless rails. All that is required to evolve flightlessness in adults is a genetic change retarding the development of the flight apparatus relative to the age of sexual maturity. Research shows that such changes in rate of development are often genetically simple, requiring only minor changes in the DNA. It is easy to understand, therefore, why so many island birds have become flightless over relatively short periods.

Apart from the landbirds with reduced powers of flight, the only extinct landbird known from St Helena was found in the year before Olson's visit by the late John Bailey. Both he and Arthur Loveridge had continued to collect bones in the period after the BOU visits in 1958-59 and had sent them to the Museum of Comparative Zoology at Harvard, where Loveridge had worked for much of his life. Among these, Olson found a damaged wing bone of a cuckoo. He named it *Nannococcyx psix*, meaning dwarf cuckoo represented by a crumb (Greek *psix*) of bone. Olson was aware that the size of the St Helena Cuckoo was not established, since it too might have had relatively reduced wings. Cuckoos tend to have a varied animal diet, and the rich invertebrate fauna would have given the St Helena bird plenty of opportunity. The most plausible ancestors are the small green African cuckoos (genus *Chrysococcyx*) which are migratory and have also reached two islands in the Gulf of Guinea. However, they are 'brood parasites': this means that like the European Cuckoo *Cuculus canorus* they lay their eggs in the nests of other small landbirds.

It seems, therefore, that unless the ancestral cuckoos that reached St Helena long ago built their own nests, or were large enough to have parasitized the St Helena Hoopoe, they must have had some other hosts. In spite of the tenuous nature of the evidence, we are inclined to think that in the prehistoric forests of St Helena, an insectivore niche was occupied by a small cuckoo and that it parasitized at least one other extinct forest bird, so far undetected in the fossil deposits.

Olson's collection also included bones of three more species of seabirds. Most significant was a second and larger species of frigatebird, probably the Great Frigatebird (whose scientific name, perversely, is *Fregata minor*). In the oldest deposits Olson also found two bones (possibly from a single individual) apparently belonging to the Sooty Shearwater, a species typical of much cooler waters. Finally, there was a single bone of an unidentified gull.[29]

An important aspect of Olson's work was his analysis of the changes in the bird populations of the island over long periods of time. Climate changes during the millions of years of St Helena's existence have inevitably led to considerable changes in the ocean temperature and its productivity. The food of seabirds comes from the ocean, and its abundance and the distance that birds have to fly to find it determine which species can breed on any particular island. Olson distinguished three periods of bone deposits.[30] Sugar Loaf Site 1 represents the oldest period, Dry Gut and Sugar Loaf Site 3 are examples of the middle period and Prosperous Bay and Sugar Loaf Site 2 are from the most recent period. Although no absolute dates can be given, the middle one was evidently within the last 2-3 million years, when strong global fluctuations in climate gave rise to a series of ice ages in regions further from the equator. The most recent sites were presumably occupied by seabirds – and visited by some of the landbirds – until the time of arrival of humans.

The strange ground living pigeon *Dysmoropelia* occurred only in the oldest deposits. This seems to be a case of a strong-flying ancestral species reaching the island naturally, evolving towards a more terrestrial way of life – and probably losing the power of flight – and then becoming extinct long before discovery of the island by humans. The reasons for the extinction are obscure, but it may be relevant that two species of palms and at least one other plant are also represented in fossil deposits but have not survived to the present day. The extinction of the pigeon could have been caused directly by ancient climatic or volcanic events or have been linked to consequent changes in the vegetation.

Attempts to use series of assemblages of fossils to reconstruct changes in ancient communities are inevitably tricky, since one is unlikely to get a full picture of the animals present during each of the periods concerned. For the seabirds of St Helena the problem is especially great because of the drastic changes in the space available for nesting caused by fall or rise in sea level at the start or finish of ice ages. During periods of low sea level some kinds of seabirds may have abandoned the high parts of the island to nest closer to the sea. However, the changes in the fossils noted by Olson are based on large samples and seem convincing.

---

[29] The gull found by Olson was assumed to have been a straggler, but the collection that we made in Dry Gut in 1995 included a complete and well mineralized humerus that is also of a gull. It is 132 mm long and is closely similar to that of a male Herring Gull *Larus argentatus* from Shetland, which is 136 mm. Although Olson (1975) pointed out that gulls seldom establish populations on tropical oceanic islands, the finding of a second gull bone on St Helena suggests that a small population was established at some time in the past. We have not yet compared our specimen with other species, but the best candidate appears to be the Kelp Gull *Larus dominicanus*, which is the right size and which breeds from the subantarctic almost to the equator on the guano islands off the coast of Peru.

[30] To obtain a rough chronology, Olson obtained information on the percentage of nitrogen and on the ratio of carbon to nitrogen in bone samples from several of the deposits. Since nitrogen gradually leaches out of bones, this gave an estimate of their relative ages.

101

In particular, Olson analyzed the changing fortunes of the petrels or tubenoses (including shearwaters, gadfly petrels and storm-petrels). Most consistent through all periods were the White-faced Storm-petrel, a long-legged, subtropical species now lost from the island, and the Madeiran Storm-petrel, which was always present in fairly low numbers and still survives on offshore islands. In the earliest period the extinct large gadfly petrel *Pterodroma rupinarum* and the smaller *Bulweria bifax* were abundant, and there were smaller numbers of Audubon's Shearwater. The shearwater *Puffinus pacificoides* was present at this time but apparently then became extinct. In the middle period the large gadfly petrel had increased enormously, comprising four-fifths of the bones collected, but *Bulweria bifax* had declined. In the most recent deposits another swing was apparent, with the large gadfly petrel much reduced and Audubon's Shearwater now very abundant.

Olson attributed the latest changes to a decrease in richness of the ocean surrounding St Helena and a warming trend in the surface waters. During the last ice age St Helena was probably surrounded by relatively cool waters enriched by strong upwelling off the coast of southwest Africa, but after about 15,000 years ago it gradually became more tropical. The recent bones, therefore, some of which may be little more than 500 years old, represent a largely warm water petrel community.

The other seabirds represented in the recent deposits also reflect the proximity of tropical waters. Frigatebirds, Masked Boobies and Sooty Terns all became abundant only in the recent deposits. These are species heavily dependent on flying fish for food and may only be able to maintain populations on St Helena in periods when ocean temperatures are high enough to bring large numbers of flying fish within reach of the island. A hint that the status of some of these species on the island is marginal at present comes from our observation that Masked Boobies did not breed successfully on Shore Island in the 1994-95 summer, although a few flying juveniles evidently raised in the previous year were still around.

During our recent visit to St Helena we found or were shown several additional fossil bone sites, including those in sand deposits above Lot's Wife's Ponds and other places nearby.[31] These deposits are similar to the more recent of the ones at Sugar Loaf; like these, they have many bones of storm-petrels and shearwaters. They also include some eggshells, occasionally almost intact (Plate 18); evidently these birds chose the sandy deposits for breeding because it simplified the excavation of nesting burrows. We found smaller numbers of bird bones at Castle Rock and at Mundens; Nick Thorpe showed us some in flood deposits near the bottom of Sharks Valley and Evie Bailey took us to a place on Donkey Plain where there were many bones on the surface (Plate 3). The latter site was where in 1988 Neil McCulloch had found a single bone recognised by Storrs Olson as belonging to a wader (shorebird) larger than the Wirebird; we omit it from the list in Chapter 15 since it has not yet been identified even to family level.

We also found two new bone sites on Prosperous Bay Plain, which are especially intriguing in relation to work that we did on the white powdery deposits present in many parts of the island, some of which represent old guano.[32] In 1995 we looked at

---

[31] In the symposium St Helena Natural Treasury held at the Zoological Society of London in 1988 (P. Pearce-Kelly & Q.C.B. Cronk 1990), Storrs Olson commented: "With so much more still to be learnt, the natural treasury of fossils on St. Helena deserves to be more fully exploited. For in this case, not to collect specimens means only that they will be disintegrated by sun and rain or washed into the sea." It was with this in mind that in 1994-95 we collected many more fossil bird bones from several different sites. We shall soon be studying these in cooperation with Storrs Olson, and have prepared a labelled set for use by people on the island.

[32] The phosphates on Prosperous Bay Plain were first noted by R.A. Daly (1927), who commented that they doubtless represented an ancient bird rookery. Linda Brown (1981), who studied soils on the island, later noted that an area on the northern part of Deadwood Plain had particularly high levels of phosphate in the soil, and made a similar deduction.

the aerial photographs in the Agriculture & Forestry Department and transferred to our maps the areas that showed up as pale patches; we then collected samples from the surface of the ground whenever we were walking in relevant places. We concentrated on Prosperous Bay Plain, but other noticeable pale deposits were just to the south of it as far as Stone Top ridge, near Sugar Loaf, Ruperts Valley, around Castle Rock Plain and north of Sandy Bay Beach. Looking at them in the field, some were obviously shell sand deposits but others were powdery rather than sandy, and in a few places there were substantial deposits that we felt sure were guano from old seabird colonies.

With the help of Godfrey Fitton of the University of Edinburgh, we have now been able to obtain an index of phosphorus levels in 32 samples by X-ray fluorescence spectrometry, comparing our samples with a basalt standard. The results confirmed our expectations for some sites and clarified the rather confusing situation around Prosperous Bay Plain. Very high levels of phosphates were present in three deposits which we had recognized as old bird colonies. One was a few hundred metres inland in Banks Valley; (Plate 4) another was behind the bulk fuel store in Ruperts and the third near the coast in Breakneck Valley.

On Prosperous Bay Plain the situation was complex. At the end of the track leading to the southeast corner of the main depression all the spaces between the rocks are filled with a white powdery deposit, but this proved to have negligible phosphate content. This suggests that a mineral rich lake occupied the low part of Prosperous Bay Plain at various times; whenever it dried up, minerals derived from the surrounding rocks were precipitated. Moderate phosphate values sufficient to indicate old guano were found on the ridge between the eastern part of Prosperous Bay Plain and the coastal cliffs, and in a gully at the southwest corner of the plain, near the track to Woody Ridge. Extremely high values came from two sites on the summit of the low ridge connecting these two areas, which separates Prosperous Bay Plain from Dry Gut.

This information suggests that the low rocky and arid ridges to the south and east of the plain were the sites of major bird colonies. These ridges were probably some of the most open areas on St Helena in its pristine state (Plate 5). We did not find bones near the summits of these ridges, but in a shallow gully in the northwest of the plain (close to the track to Cooks Bridge) the commonest bones were of the large gadfly petrel *Pterodroma rupinarum* (Plate 18). In the southwest corner, near the track to Woody Ridge, we found bones of the White-faced Storm-petrel. On the surface between these two sites Myrtle found two wing bones of the extinct St Helena Hoopoe. Bones of the two petrels have also been found in Dry Gut itself, but we now think that they may have been washed down from colonies on the high land above.

Table 5A. Summary of land and freshwater animals with wild populations on St Helena, now or in 1502

This table includes extinct species that were probably present on the island when it was discovered but omits species thought to have become extinct before then.

Vagrants and non-breeding visitors (and their parasites) are omitted.

GROUP Scientific and English names	Total species	Endemic species	Endemic genera	Comments on status
VERTEBRATES				
MAMMALIA (mammals)	c.7	0	0	All introduced
REPTILIA: CHELONIA (turtles)	2	0	0	Two marine turtles may breed
REPTILIA: SQUAMATA (lizards)	1	0	0	Introduced gecko
AMPHIBIA (amphibians)	1	0	0	Introduced frog
OSTEICHTHYES (bony fish)	2	0	0	Introduced; more information needed
AVES (birds)	30	7	0	10 endemic/indigenous breeding birds; 11 others probably breeding in 1502; 9 introduced land birds
INVERTEBRATES: not Arthropoda				
TURBELLARIA (free-living flatworms)	c.6	3+	1	High endemic diversity; more information needed
NEMERTINA (ribbon worms)	1	0	0	Status doubtful
NEMATODA (nematode worms)	c.21	?	?	More information needed
MOLLUSCA: GASTROPODA (snails & slugs)	c.35	c.20	c.5	High endemic diversity, but endemic species almost all extinct
ANNELIDA: OLIGOCHAETA (earthworms)	c.21	?1	0	Introduced; one possible endemic
ARTHROPODA: not Insecta				
SCORPIONES (scorpions)	1	0	0	Introduced
PSEUDOSCORPIONES (pseudoscorpions)	8	5	3	High endemic diversity
ARANEAE (spiders)	c.99-100	45-46	12-13	High endemic diversity
ACARI (mites & ticks)	c.86	c.42	?1	High endemic diversity; more information needed
CRUSTACEA (crustaceans)	30	6-10	0	Moderate endemic diversity; more information needed
DIPLOPODA (millipedes)	15	0	0	All introduced
CHILOPODA (centipedes)	12	2-3	0	Mostly introduced
SYMPHYLA (symphylans)	3	0	0	All introduced
ARTHROPODA: INSECTA (insects)				
COLLEMBOLA (springtails or collembolans)	21	?0	0	More information needed
DIPLURA (diplurans)	4	0	0	All introduced
THYSANURA (thysanurans)	5	1	0	Mostly introduced
ODONATA (dragonflies)	1-2	1	0	One species endemic but extinct; one perhaps now naturally established
ORTHOPTERA (grasshoppers & crickets)	11-12	5-6	3	High endemic diversity
DERMAPTERA (earwigs)	4	1	0	Endemic Giant Earwig probably extinct; one other species probably indigenous

Table 5A. Continued

GROUP Scientific and English names	Total species	Endemic species	Endemic genera	Comments on status
ISOPTERA (termites)	2	0	0	Probably both introduced
BLATTODEA (cockroaches)	8-9	0	0	All introduced
EMBIOPTERA (web-spinners)	1	0	0	Introduced
THYSANOPTERA (thrips)	10	2	1	One or more non-endemic species may be indigenous
HEMIPTERA: HETEROPTERA (bugs)	36-37	20-21	13	High endemic diversity, especially in mirids
HEMIPTERA: HOMOPTERA (hoppers, aphids, scale insects)	c.74	18-19	c.9-10	High endemic diversity of hoppers; aphids & scales almost all introduced
PSOCOPTERA (psocids)	14	5	0	High endemic diversity
PHTHIRAPTERA (lice)	9	0	0	External parasites of birds: some species introduced with their hosts
COLEOPTERA (beetles)[33]	c.257	c.148	32	Extraordinary endemic diversity, especially of weevils
NEUROPTERA (lacewings)	5	2	0	Moderate endemic diversity
HYMENOPTERA (parasitic wasps, ants, bees & wasps)	c.60+	c.13-18+	2-4+	Moderate endemic diversity; more information needed
LEPIDOPTERA (butterflies & moths)	c.104	c.51-53	0	High endemic diversity, especially in tineids & pyralids
SIPHONAPTERA (fleas)	6	0	0	All introduced
DIPTERA (flies)	c.116+	16	3	Moderate endemic diversity
TOTALS	**c.1129-1134**	**c.413-430**	**c.84-89**	

---

[33] About a dozen introduced beetle species included in the total probably failed to establish themselves.

Table 5B. **Birds of St Helena**

*Sections A and B together show the approximate composition of the bird communities at the time of the discovery of the island by humans in 1502. * indicates an endemic species, and † an extinct species.*

More information on species in group E can be found in the systematic treatment. Records of many other occasional visitors are listed by B.W. Rowlands et al. *(1998).*

English and local names	Scientific name	Comment
A. Endemic and indigenous breeding birds		
Madeiran Storm-petrel (Pickering)	*Oceanodroma castro*	
Red-billed Tropicbird (Trophy Bird)	*Phaethon aethereus*	
Masked Booby (White Booby, Gannet)	*Sula dactylatra*	
Brown Booby (Duck)	*Sula leucogaster*	
Moorhen (Water Bird, Water Duck)	*Gallinula chloropus*	Indigenous resident
* Wirebird	*Charadrius sanctaehelenae*	Surviving endemic
Sooty Tern (Wideawake, Egg Bird)	*Sterna fuscata*	
Brown Noddy (Black Bird, Egg Bird)	*Anous stolidus*	
Black Noddy (Noddy Bird)	*Anous minutus*	
White Tern (White Bird, Sea Bird)	*Gygis alba*	
B. Additional endemic and indigenous birds breeding in 1502		
*† St Helena Bulweria	*Bulweria bifax*	Fossils throughout
*† St Helena Petrel	*Pterodroma rupinarum*	Fossils throughout
Audubon's Shearwater	*Puffinus lherminieri*	Fossils throughout
White-faced Storm-petrel	*Pelagodroma marina*	Fossils throughout
Red-footed Booby	*Sula sula*	Fossils recent
Great Frigatebird	*Fregata minor*	Fossils recent
Lesser Frigatebird	*Fregata ariel*	Fossils recent
*† St Helena Rail	*Atlantisia podarces*	Fossils throughout
*† St Helena Crake	*Porzana astrictocarpus*	Fossils middle-recent
? Kelp Gull	*Larus dominicanus*	Fossils middle; possible breeder, 1502
*† St Helena Cuckoo	*Nannococcyx psix*	Fossil recent
*† St Helena Hoopoe	*Upupa antaios*	Fossils middle-recent
C. Endemic birds extinct before the time of discovery		
*† St Helena Shearwater	*Puffinus pacificoides*	Fossils ancient
*† St Helena Dove	*Dysmoropelia dekarchiskos*	Fossils ancient
D. Introduced breeding birds		
Chukar Partridge (Partridge)	*Alectoris chukar*	
Ring-necked Pheasant (Pheasant)	*Phasianus colchicus*	
Feral Pigeon (Pigeon)	*Columba livia*	
Peaceful Dove (Dove)	*Geopelia striata*	
Indian Myna (Miner Bird)	*Acridotheres tristis*	
Madagascar Fody (Cardinal, Red Bird)	*Foudia madagascariensis*	
Java Sparrow (Sparrow)	*Padda oryzivora*	
Common Waxbill (Amadavat, Averdevat)	*Estrilda astrild*	
Yellow Canary (Canary)	*Serinus flaviventris*	

Table 5B. Continued

English and local names	Scientific name	Comment
E. Other birds of special interest		
Bulwer's Petrel	*Bulweria bulwerii*	Possible breeder
? Murphy's Petrel	*Pterodroma ultima*	Doubtful status
Cattle Egret (Cattle Bird)	*Bubulcus ibis*	Frequent visitor
Lesser Gallinule	*Porphyrula alleni*	Vagrant
American Purple Gallinule	*Porphyrula martinica*	Vagrant
Arctic Skua	*Stercorarius parasiticus*	Summer visitor
Pomarine Skua	*Stercorarius pomarinus*	Summer visitor

Chapter 6

The major habitats on land today

In earlier chapters we have described the original vegetation of St Helena and discussed the native plants and animals. Later, we give an account of the destruction of most of the original habitats and the loss of many of the native plants and animals. Here we focus on the island as it is today, ecologically transformed by the impact of humans and of the animals and plants that they have brought, but still scenically beautiful, biologically diverse and fascinating to visit. We discuss the major habitats found on the island, and describe some places where they can most easily be appreciated. We also mention many of the characteristic plants and animals, both native and introduced.

Stacks and islands

Around the coast of St Helena there are some 24 offshore outliers varying from rocks that barely emerge from the sea, to substantial islands such as Egg Island with an area of more than 3 1/2 hectares, and dramatic pinnacles such as Speery Island with a height of about 135 m. Islands are most numerous in the southwest, but two – George and Shore Islands – are at the eastern extremity of St Helena and can be seen when approaching the island by sea from South Africa (Plate 6).

In geological terms these islands are merely rocky features of the St Helena volcano that have resisted marine erosion more effectively than the surrounding rock. They are of immense significance for conservation because they are free of feral cats and other introduced mammal predators, and so provide nesting places for seabirds that are prevented from breeding successfully on St Helena itself. Nonetheless, seabirds on the islands have been subject to human predation ever since the discovery of St Helena. The following is a clockwise list of the stacks and islands where seabird were breeding in the 1990s.[1] Those where only roosting birds have been found are omitted:

George Island: Madeiran Storm-petrel, Masked Booby, Sooty Tern (Wideawake), Brown Noddy (Blackbird) and Black Noddy (Noddy Bird).

Shore Island: Masked Booby, Brown Booby (very few), Sooty Tern, Brown and Black Noddies, White Tern (Sea Bird; probable), Red-billed Tropicbird (Trophy Bird) and Madeiran Storm-petrel (Pickering).

Speery Island: Black Noddy (a large colony), Brown Noddy, White Tern (probable), Sooty Tern, Madeiran Storm-petrel (probable) and Red-billed Tropicbird (probable).

Salt Rock: Black and Brown Noddies.

The Needle, Upper Black Rock and Lower Black Rock: Black Noddy.

Black Rock (Thompsons Bay): Black and Brown Noddy.

Thompsons Valley Island: White Tern (probable).

Peaked Island: Black Noddy, Brown Noddy (few).

Egg Island: Black Noddy (large colonies), Brown Noddy (c.800 pairs), Sooty Tern (?), Madeiran Storm-Petrel.

Lighter Rock: Black and Brown Noddies (few).

---

[1] The current status of the seabird populations has recently been carefully assessed by the South African ornithologist Beau Rowlands (1995, and in B.W. Rowlands et al. 1998).

Bridled Dolphin Stenella attenuata

Figure 17
From A. Edwards (1990)

A good way to see some of the seabirds is to go by boat southwestwards from James Bay as far as Egg Island. Landing here is not recommended, because of the disturbance to nesting birds, but from a boat one can get excellent views of the Brown Noddies which lay their eggs in flat places on the rocky slopes of the island. On the cliffs here and on the mainland nearby are dense colonies of the smaller, darker and more delicate Black Noddy with its well-defined white cap.

During the trip one is very likely to see Bridled Dolphins (locally called Porpoise). The local population of more than a thousand individuals makes a regular daily circuit near the northwest coast. Between Lemon Valley and Egg Island they are usually within half a kilometre of the shore in the morning, tending to move northeast and going further out to sea later in the day. Although these beautiful sea mammals have sometimes been killed by people, they have probably been less affected by human discovery of the island than any other native vertebrate.

Off the southern tip of St Helena is Speery, the most spectacular of the offshore islands (Plate 1), with almost vertical cliffs all round. Even more difficult of access, however, are George and Shore Islands on the east coast between Great Stone Top and King & Queen Rocks. Visiting ornithologists have apparently landed on George Island only three times, in 1925, 1952 and 1992.[2] Shore Island is the most interesting seabird island to view from the coast. By walking down to Gill Point, the site where Wideawakes were evidently breeding until about a decade ago, most of the breeding birds can be seen.

Shore

For visitors and most residents only a few parts of the shore are easy to reach. Access by car is possible only to James Bay, Ruperts Bay and Sandy Bay beach. Lemon Valley Bay is a popular destination and can be reached by boat from Jamestown. The more adventurous can – ideally with someone to guide them – walk down to Lemon Valley Bay, Banks Valley Bay, Turks Cap Bay, Prosperous Bay, Stone Top Bay, Potato Bay, Lot's Wife's Ponds, Manati Bay and a few others.

Very few beaches now have significant amounts of sand but there was substantially more in relatively recent times. There are changes, however, even within single years. Ruperts Bay, for instance, can vary from having enough for a game of football to having none at all. Sand is still dredged from James Bay for use in the building industry. Sand extraction, coupled with the construction of sea walls long ago, here and elsewhere have probably combined to reduce the chance of successful breeding of turtles, which used to lay their eggs in pits in the sand behind the beaches, as they still do on Ascension.

Sandy Bay beach still has sand, composed mainly of particles of black volcanic rock; it is a good place to search for stranded pleuston,[3] animals characteristic of the surface layer of the open ocean that float and drift with the current and wind, in this case from the direction of South Africa. Examples are the By-the-wind Sailor, a small member of the jellyfish group, and its larger relative the Portuguese Man-of-war. The former has an elliptical gas-filled raft carrying an oblique, vertical sail and the latter has a swollen blue

---

[2] Philip well remembers waiting in vain for three weeks in 1959 for the boatman to be satisfied that the weather would permit a landing; he and Douglas Dorward had to be content with overlooking the islands from Gill Point. Graham Sim landed there in 1968 and confirmed the establishment of the Masked Booby colony.

[3] From the Greek word meaning 'to float'.

float; both these species have stinging tentacles trailing in the water and the Portuguese Man-of-war is capable of capturing quite large fish. Other animals often washed up on this beach are the floating marine snail *Ianthina* which support itself on a raft of air bubbles, and the goose barnacle *Lepas* attached to flotsam or kelp. The seeds of several plants adapted to dispersal by floating can also be found, including the spectacular sea bean, which is the seed – 6 cm across – of the vine *Entada scandens*.[4] Sandy Bay beach is one of the places where lucky beachcombers can still – at least until recently – find sea worn pieces of St Helena Ebony wood, reminding us that these were once substantial trees.

The other places where one can easily reach the shore are mainly rocky, and at most of them it is possible to explore a short distance along a wave-cut platform at low tide, for instance at Prosperous Bay and north of Ruperts Bay.[5] On the rocks close to the water's edge are the ubiquitous and agile red shore crabs *Grapsus grapsus*, making their living as scavengers. In rock pools the conspicuous animals include sea urchins, starfish, anemones, corals, octopuses and a variety of small fish. You are likely to see gobies, one of which, *Priolepis ascensionis*, is endemic to St Helena and Ascension, and the endemic wrasse called the Greenfish. Other fish of the rock pools are the Five-finger or Sergeant Major (a damselfish) and the young of the Shitty Trooper (a surgeonfish that is said to eat excrement). Among rocks in shallow water several species of moray eels (locally known as congers) are fairly common; they normally stay in crevices but can sometimes be aggressive towards people.[6]

Along the rocky shore, above the tide mark, is likely to be a good place for adding to the faunal list for the island, since invertebrates in this habitat have not been well studied. Recent discoveries at Birddown, north of Ruperts Bay, include the ant *Paratrechina longicornis*, previously not recorded from St Helena, and a new species of mouse spider (Gnaphosidae). At Potato Bay recent finds include a nocturnal cricket, a new species of aquatic crustacean *Platorchestia ashmoleorum* and the hitherto unrecorded woodlouse *Halophiloscia couchii*.[7]

Larger animals that can be seen on the rocky shores include rats and mice on land, the occasional turtles and dolphins just offshore and a wide variety of seabirds. The birds are not only those that breed on St Helena. They include, for instance, skuas (which Americans call jaegers) that breed in the far north of Europe and America but migrate across the equator; in the summer (the northern winter) a hundred or so Arctic and Pomarine Skuas can be seen in mixed groups off Jamestown.[8]

---

[4] Seeds of *Entada scandens* have been known to germinate here, but this species is a forest plant adapted to climbing on trees, so it has not been able to establish itself in the arid volcanic terrain of coastal St Helena.

[5] It cannot be overemphasised that extreme caution must be taken when walking or fishing close to the shore. Exceptionally large waves cannot be anticipated and fatal accidents - as well as injuries - occur from time to time.

[6] Occasionally the boundary between the terrestrial and marine environments on these rocky shores becomes unexpectedly blurred: we were told by friends of an occasion when they were fishing at 'the Dockyard', below Flagstaff Hill, and a group of flying fish that were being chased by 'porpoise' dashed themselves onto the rocks on land, in efforts to escape. From the description we suspect that these fish belonged to the family Hemiramphidae, a group not mentioned in Edwards' book on the fishes of St Helena but recorded from Ascension Island.

[7] It is well worth searching special kinds of microhabitats for invertebrates. We found the woodlice by pulling off flakes of mineral deposits at a place where water was seeping out of the rocks above the beach at Potato Bay. This species - though not endemic - is likely to have reached St Helena naturally, since it is characteristic of the seashore and could have arrived on driftwood.

[8] Distinguishing these species from each other (and from the Long-tailed Skua, which might also be present) is a job for the serious birdwatcher.

Cliffs

The cliffs of St Helena are up to 400-500m high in several places and are impressive even on the relatively sheltered northwest coast of the island around Jamestown. They are some of the most inhospitable places imaginable, most of them being composed of layers of eroding rock and loose volcanic ash that make the establishment of plants difficult and access by humans hazardous. In spite of this, shore-fishermen have traditional routes to many sea-level rock ledges that on first sight appear to be totally inaccessible. In a few places fixed ropes or old electrical cables provide a little assistance, but many paths simply disappear over the edge of the cliff and are not for the uninitiated.

The dry western cliffs are now almost devoid of native plants and may always have been relatively barren. The eastern and southern cliffs, however, are influenced by condensation as the winds rise over the land, and as a result often have lichen growing on them. These cliffs evidently had much more vegetation in the past, at least towards the top, and although goats have managed to remove most of this, a few pockets of endemic flowering plants and indigenous ferns have survived in particularly inaccessible places. In conservation terms the cliffs are of thus of great importance, with some endemic plants that are extinct elsewhere managing to maintain tiny populations on the cliffs. Scattered sections of cliff provide – along with the Peak Dale Gumwood grove – almost the only examples of semi-natural habitat that can be found on the island away from the Peaks.

Survival on steep cliffs has been possible, of course, only for those species that are able to cope with the exposure and lack of soil, especially Scrubwood, Old Father Live Forever and St Helena Plantain. The Scrubwood can hang on in precipitous places (Plate 6) and is a good interceptor of mist; when growing on more level ground it assumes a domed shape which gives it great wind-resistance. Old Father Live Forever is easy to overlook since it can spend months as a grey-brown leafless rootstock in a cleft of the rock, putting out leaves and flowering only after rain. The ridge leading down to Turks Cap is one of the places where it can be seen, at least from a distance.

The same ridge offers a chance to see a few St Helena Tea bushes close-up (Plate 28) and a substantial group on a broad ledge on the southern face of the ridge; this species grows well on loose rubbly slopes but is not really a plant of steep cliffs. Similarly, the Salad Plant, although it is now entirely confined to ledges on cliffs, is probably there only by default: in the past it evidently grew in more accessible places in the dry parts of the island, but it is very susceptible to plant-eating mammals (including people).

The St Helena Plantain is visible on cliffs in several areas (Plate 30), for instance below Flagstaff, and may actually survive on a good many cliff faces that cannot be overlooked. It is probably too much to hope, however, that there might still be surviving individuals of the Dwarf Ebony somewhere around Sugar Loaf, Flagstaff or the Barn.

Grazing pressure is now reduced, and although there are still rabbits, Scrubwood is regenerating in several places. One of the most impressive examples is in the valley southeast of Distant Cottage, but our favourite area is at Man and Horse Cliffs. Joan Hill, the highest point on these cliffs at 579 metres, ranks with Flagstaff, the Barn and Great Stone Top as one of the most impressive cliffs on St Helena – or perhaps anywhere in the world. The Tea Plant grows near the top, and on the cliffs below are some of the most luxuriant patches of Scrubwood to be seen on the island. In a few places, blue-green foliage signals the presence of the Salad Plant, but none of the groups are readily accessible, suggesting that rabbits may destroy any that grow in places within reach (Plate 25).

A vanished habitat

In Chapter 3 we pointed out that the changes in sea level during the ice ages of the last three million years had dramatic effects on the shape of St Helena. During most of this period there was a broad apron round the island, sometimes more than doubling its area. This formed an enormous habitat that is hardly represented on the island today: relatively level arid land, much of it exposed to wind and salt spray, and largely lacking shelter or shade. Soil was washed down from the higher part of the island and accumulated in gullies, mixed with sand blown across the flats. In the lowest areas - the fringe exposed only when sea level was close to its minimum - there may have been sheets of fine clay formed earlier by accumulation of silt on the sea floor, surviving in places which were sheltered from wave action as the sea receded and left them exposed.

A number of the native plants will have been well adapted to conditions on the platform. We can imagine extensive areas covered with Babies Toes, Salad Plant, the trailing Hogweed and *Tribulus cistoides*, and also the convolvulus *Ipomoea pes-caprae*, now probably extinct on the island; Boneseed was doubtless also present locally. Samphire will have formed low thickets on the silt in the gullies as it does close to the shore today, with French Grass forming delicate mats in sandier areas. The endemic grass *Eragrostis saxatilis* and the two endemic sedges in the genus *Bulbostylis* doubtless also occurred in places. The presence of shrubs is less certain, although the Dwarf Ebony, Tea Plant and perhaps Scrubwood may have managed to live in some parts of this low desert zone.

Endemic land-snails, almost all now extinct, will have formed a key part of the animal community on the exposed platform, feeding on the mainly low-growing plants and using the calcareous shell sand as the raw material for their heavy shells. New snail species were doubtless formed when populations were marooned on islets by fluctuations in sea level, or isolated by changing distribution of mobile sands unfavourable for occupation by snails. A rich community of other invertebrates of arid land, now confined to Prosperous Bay Plain and a few other places such as Broad Gut, will have had major populations on the platform. They were doubtless preyed on by the Wirebird, whose total population would have been very much greater than during the last few thousand years, when rising sea level confined it to the few unwooded places on the high part of the island.

During long periods the waves broke on gently shelving rocky shores rather than against the base of the cliffs. The action of the waves ground up the calcareous skeletons of the marine molluscs, barnacles and sea urchins living on the rocks and in the pools, producing white shell sand which accumulated on the sloping shores. The beaches formed in this way doubtless provided perfect nesting grounds for a large population of Green Turtles, as well as easy places for seals to haul out and breed. It also seems likely that many of the seabirds would have nested on these sandy flats rather than flying on inland to the high parts of the island.

Although certain native plants have been able to escape from grazing animals by taking refuge on the cliffs, some of them may still be under threat from competing introduced plants. At Flagstaff and other places nearby the cliffs are being invaded by species such as Wild Coffee and Creeper. In the south and west Tungies (prickly pear cactus) sometimes spread down from the cliff top, though not colonising the steepest parts. The Nargy Plant has become dominant on steep slopes in Breakneck Valley and some other places nearby, and the small mallow *Sida cordifolia* has become abundant on cliff paths near Jamestown.

The surviving groups of endemic plants have diverse communities of insects and other invertebrate animals associated with them. Some of these are introduced, but others are endemics which have a chance of becoming widespread again if the host plant populations are allowed to recover.[9]

Three species of seabirds nest on the cliffs – the White Tern (Sea Bird) is sparsely distributed, but there are large colonies of the Black Noddy (Noddy Bird) on vertical cliffs at low levels, especially southwest of Horse Pasture. The Red-billed Tropicbird (Trophy Bird) breeds in loose groups: courting birds can often be seen circling high beside the cliff near Ladder Hill Point, but the biggest colony is probably that on the seaward face of Great Stone Top. The cliffs are also favourite roosting places for Averdavats, Mynas and Pigeons.

Semi-desert zone

Where there are not substantial cliffs the arid lower part of St Helena is occupied by a badly eroded semi-desert with steep rocky slopes and gullies and only scattered plants; rainfall is less than 300 mm per year. This habitat extends from near sea level to about 250 m in a few places in the west and higher in some areas in the east and south. It includes the badlands so conspicuous from the Sandy Bay road and covers much of the area of the Crown Wastes (see Chapter 7) on the eastern flanks of the island.

We have a special interest in the invertebrates of barren volcanic land and subterranean habitats, which tend to be neglected by most entomologists. We therefore put out traps at several sites in the eroded dry zone, in Broad Gut, below the Gates of Chaos and at Gill Point. Although some of the animals found in these sites were clearly introduced (eg cockroaches and scorpions) there were also a number of species that seem to represent the original fauna of the dry, eroded outer fringes of St Helena. These include a cricket of the subfamily Mogoplistinae (family Gryllidae) which had not previously been found on the island, and an endemic spider *Zimirina relegata* belonging to the family Prodidomidae, an obscure group typical of desert habitats. There was also an abundant thysanuran *Ctenolepisma sanctaehelenae* which we regard as endemic although the Belgians thought it might turn out to be an introduced South African species.

A number of indigenous plants still have a foothold in this zone. They include three species of tufted grass in the genus *Eragrostis*, the spreading grey-green Samphire and locally the fern *Ophioglossum polyphyllum*. The endemic Boneseed (Plate 27) can be found with persistence and luck, and Babies' Toes occurs in several places, for instance just above Sandy Bay beach. Two locally common introduced plants are the creeping

---

[9] When shaking insects off clumps of Scrubwood our first find was the elegant, long-legged stilt bug, not seen since 1879 and thought to be extinct; there were also several kinds of planthoppers, including one that represents a new endemic genus. On some bushes of St Helena Tea Plant on Turks Cap ridge we found a new species of bug in the family Miridae - a tiny pale species, with bright red eyes; more than a century ago the entomologist Wollaston discovered two bugs related to this species, living respectively on Gumwoods and the Tree Fern.

Ice Plant with succulent leaves apparently frosted with minute droplets of liquid, and Venus Rose with showy pink flowers. Another important species is Saltbush, probably spread mainly by Pigeons which eagerly eat the tiny red fruits.

The walk from Sandy Bay beach to Lot's Wife's Ponds provides a memorable experience of this habitat. French grass, an endemic *Euphorbia* with delicate pink stems, can sometimes be found growing prostrate among rocks in the floor of the gut at the start of the path, and as you climb to a steep ridge you will pass a number of wild tomato bushes with tiny edible fruits. In a sandy depression near the ridge you may find the prickly, yellow-flowered *Tribulus cistoides* growing on the sand; this plant was found by Burchell and is probably indigenous (Plate 27). The descent towards the coast is spectacular and gradual. In a gully there are several plants of Hogweed, a rambling, vine-like plant which is probably indigenous; it dies back to a few woody stems in the dry season but puts out vigorous shoots and white (sometimes purple) flowers after rains (Plate 29).

Lot's Wife's Ponds themselves are on a wide wave-cut platform protected on the seaward side by a dyke. Another dyke forms an impressive pillar known as the Chimney (Plate 6). Just above the ponds is one of the well known high level shell-sand deposits (Plate 4). This one has some remarkable wind-sculpted shapes and contains numerous subfossil bird bones, mainly of petrels; in some places one can even find more or less intact eggshells (see Chapter 3 and Plate 18).

Another good way of getting a feel for these eroded wastes is to walk up Broad Gut from Sandy Bay Beach and then veer left up the gut leading towards the Gates of Chaos. The slopes are almost entirely barren, but in the gut itself there are scattered individuals of introduced plants that are widespread in the Scrub Zone above. The succulent New Zealand Spinach (Plate 25) grows in places where there is occasionally running water, and the spindly Wild Tobacco gets its roots down into the damp silt in the gut bottoms. The sedge *Scirpus prolifer* (possibly native) and the introduced Wild Celery (Plate 7) grow higher up where there is more nearly permanent water, and we also found a just-surviving plant of Wild Brinjal (Plate 31). Other commonly encountered introduced plants in this gut are Prickly Poppy *Argemone mexicana* (Plate 30), Venus Rose and *Lantana*.[10]

The eroded valleys cutting down from the uplands through the Crown Wastes to the sea are one of the most conspicuous features of the St Helena landscape (Plate 7). In some places, looking from above, one can see a green ribbon of vegetation winding down a valley between brown, eroded slopes; Broad Gut viewed from near Peak Dale is one example. The greenery in these valleys is often composed mainly of Wild Mango (Plate 25). The water in the streams tends to be loaded with dissolved mineral salts; in many cases it trickles gradually away into the gravelly stream-bed, disappearing entirely underground before reaching the sea.

It is in the northwestern sector of the great Sandy Bay amphitheatre that the Semi-desert zone extends furthest up the slopes – to 600 m at Blue Point, which can be reached by a spectacular walk along the ridge from near Distant Cottage. On inland cliffs near here are the two surviving wild specimens of Ebony (Plate 8), and the Scrubwood population that also survived on the cliffs is now spreading on to the eroded land above. The Salad Plant and St Helena Plantain can also be seen on the cliffs here.

---

[10] It was apparently after walking up Broad Gut nearly two hundred years ago that the botanist W.J. Burchell discovered the endemic shrub *Heliotropium pannifolium*; since that day, no sign has been seen of this plant, which evidently originated from floating seeds of an ancestral species that drifted to the island with the currents.

Continuing south, one can climb down to Castle Rock Plain, where it is still possible to find fragments of Ebony root or wood. Even further down there is a spot labelled on old maps as Man o'War Roost, which is evidently the place frequented by the last survivors of the St Helena Frigatebird or Man o'War Bird, after their breeding grounds were made untenable by the influx of introduced predators, especially feral pigs and cats. In this area there are skeletons of many large bushes of the St Helena Tea Plant, and nearby are some live ones, perhaps the biggest still present on the island. This is at a height of about 150 m, showing how the native scrub in the past managed to grow far down into what is now an almost entirely unvegetated zone.

In the extreme east of the island, north of Stone Top Bay, is a remote and barren area where the raw volcanic landscape is reminiscent of parts of the much younger Ascension Island. The impression is strongest near Gill Point (Plate 6), which overlooks Shore and George Islands. The fairly level area at the top of the cliffs is known locally as the Bird Ground and it is clear that Wideawakes nested there fairly recently.[11] Masked Boobies from the colonies on Shore and George Islands regularly glide close past the Bird Ground, riding on the updrafts along the cliff-tops and peering down in curiosity. It seems likely that if cats could be kept out of the area, breeding colonies of boobies, petrels and Wideawakes would soon become established there. As it is, a visit to this area provides a wonderful birds-eye view of the seabird colony on Shore Island.[12]

Prosperous Bay Plain - a unique animal habitat
Prosperous Bay Plain (Plate 6) is a special part of the dry zone and one of the largest areas of relatively level ground on the island. It was formed about eight and a half million years ago by massive outpourings of basalt and then trachyandesite lava from vents on the northeastern flanks of the Southwest Volcano, which dominated St Helena at that time. These lavas flooded out to cover a large area, from Longwood in the west to Horse Point in the north and Bencoolen in the south. It seems, however, that in the east they did not reach the sea, but were penned in by older rocks. We suggest that they may have formed an enormous pond of lava, which then solidified to produce a relatively level tract of land. Successive flows over a period of a few months or years gave rise to irregularity in the surface without destroying the basic saucer shape.

This depression, lying in a part of the island with low rainfall, persisted for millions of years without the development of major gully drainage patterns. After the occasional heavy rains a lake formed: one such occurrence was noted in the St Helena Records in March 1787. During some periods a different climatic regime doubtless rendered the lake a more persistent feature. It will always have been rich in dissolved

---

[11] We were given two independent accounts of Wideawakes nesting here. One was from an islander, aged 77 in 1995, who had collected Wideawake eggs there in his youth. He said that clouds of birds were present, and his wife recalled that the eggs were excellent for 'caking'. More surprisingly, a much younger man had also collected eggs in this area, only about a decade previously (the mid 1980s). He took us to the place and showed us egg-shells, as well as masses of feathers and bones that were evidently from Wideawakes that had been killed by feral cats. The bleached skeleton of a cat was lying in the open a short distance away, and digging among the mass of feathers on the floor of a small cave at the cliff top, we uncovered the mummified body of a kitten. Although most of the bones found at Gill Point were of Wideawakes some were from Madeiran Storm-petrels, suggesting that this species also bred there in the relatively recent past (it still evidently does so on the nearby islands). More surprising was our discovery there of four wings of Bulwer's Petrel, discussed in chapter 5.

[12] At first light on 23rd February 1995 Philip counted 150 Masked Boobies there. Five of these were apparently fledged young from a previous breeding period, but although we saw many adults courting, we are fairly sure that there was no successful breeding in summer of 1994-95. A handful of pairs of Brown Boobies also breed on Shore Island (we once counted 10 adults and one downy chick), as well as noddies and sometimes a few Wideawakes.

mineral salts, as a result of leaching of the volcanic rocks and of guano from the seabird colonies on the low ridges nearby. Whenever it began to dry up, the least soluble minerals (especially gypsum, hydrated calcium sulphate) crystallised out, gradually building up the white deposits that we see in the lowest part of the plain today. Sometimes it overflowed, flushing out the more soluble nitrates and phosphates from the guano and returning them to the sea.[13]

Viewed as sterile and forbidding by many, Prosperous Bay Plain was a place which Myrtle always wanted to visit again and again, during our time on the island. Like other deserts where we have worked, the plain provides a view of nature at the edge. The environment is hostile, and the animals and plants that live here must have special adaptations for coping with it.

There is no proper soil on the plain, and the arid dusty ground is largely saturated with mineral salts. Plants are few, scattered and low growing; it is not clear that the area ever supported much more extensive vegetation. However, there may have been a few Boxwood, Scrubwood and Tea Plant in favoured places, perhaps with patches of the Salad Plant, Boneseed and Babies' Toes. On the ridge just south of the plain where there is an exceptional level of phosphates we found French Grass, a tiny, prostrate, endemic *Euphorbia* that also occurs in Broad Gut, and a charming puffball fungus about 2 cm across, probably in the genus *Bovista*. Other indigenous plants still present on the plain include Purslane (Plate 30), and Samphire in some silty gullies.

In ancient times the plain was the site of sea bird colonies (see Chapter 5). Although there are no historical records of these, they may have still been occupied in 1502: the plain is in a remote part of the island which even now is rarely visited except by fishermen and people collecting rocks for construction work. In the days before settlement it would have been ignored by passing seamen anchored off Chapel Valley, while the inevitable toll of the birds by previously introduced pigs, dogs, cats and rats would have eventually eliminated the colonies. Fossil bird bones, mainly of seabirds but including those of the extinct St Helena Hoopoe (Figure 16), can be found on the surface in shallow water-worn channels.

The rough track that leads into Prosperous Bay Plain from Bradleys crosses Fishers Valley at Cooks Bridge where there is sometimes water; this is a good place to see Moorhens, as well as Wirebirds and coveys of Partridges. It is the endemic invertebrates, however, that provide the main biological interest, and for species adapted to dry habitats, the plain is probably the most important place on the island. Almost nothing was known of these animals until the work of the Belgians in 1965-67. The plain was one of their 80 study areas, and they apparently collected at four sites. The results were truly remarkable. Their collections included 55 endemic species (out of an island total of just over 400); of these, 22 were found nowhere else on the island, and several more occur only on the plain and in immediately adjacent areas. Of the 22 species restricted to the plain, five were the sole members of endemic genera.

Few people, looking out over the unprepossessing expanse of the plain, would imagine that these two square kilometres or so held the entire world populations of 22 species and five genera of animals. We cannot be sure, however, that they are still present. The Belgian expeditions were more than three decades ago and no one else has seriously investigated the fauna of the plain.

---

[13] The floor of the lowest part of the plain is now between 300 and 310 m and drainage is northwards into Fishers Valley, but in the past the main overflow may have been over the southeast corner at a level of c.315 m, into the unnamed gully leading down to Gill Point.

Among the most notable invertebrates are the pseudoscorpions. Two of the five endemic species known from the island have been found here. *Hemisolinus helenae* is the only member of its genus, which is thus endemic to the plain. *Sphallowithius excelsus* is also confined to the area, but a related species is known from Peak Dale. Fourteen endemic species of spiders occur on the plain; five of these were found nowhere else, and one is in an endemic genus (*Bonapruncinia*) known only from the plain.

Beetles show even higher diversity. Twenty endemic species have been found, five of them being found nowhere else. Most notable are the tenebrionids, a group characteristic of dry habitats throughout the world, including the coast of Namibia. One of them – *Helenomelas basilewskyi* – is the sole species in an endemic genus, and has been found only on the plain, where many individuals were collected by the Belgians. *Tarphiophasis* is another endemic genus of tenebrionids with five species; two of these have been found only on the plain, a third there and at Holdfast Tom nearby, and a fourth there and in several other parts of the island, including Sandy Bay beach.

Another interesting species is the tachinid fly *Atlantomyia nitida*, which is the sole member of an endemic genus; it has been found only on the plain and is probably a parasite of the endemic grasshopper *Primnia sanctaehelenae* which also occurs there. Prosperous Bay Plain is also the sole locality for St Helena's only endemic soil centipede, *Tuoba benoiti*. The plain is not one of the places where the Belgians found Giant Earwigs, but we found the long-dead remains of a female under a rock overhang in the southeastern corner.

Prosperous Bay Plain is a major centre of endemicity, and the reason is fairly clear. For more than half the life of the island, the area has been open, with only sparse vegetation. It offered quite different ecological and evolutionary opportunities from the lush and humid Peaks, and developed a distinctive community. However, many of the animals now entirely or almost confined to the plain may have had larger ranges at some times in the past. The platform of arid land that was present round the island during the Pleistocene ice ages offered conditions rather similar to those on the plain, 300 metres above. It is no accident that several of the common species on the plain have also been found at Sandy Bay beach; the low, dry land behind the beach in Broad Gut doubtless provides a refuge for populations that expand on to the platform whenever sea level goes down.

Today, the plain is a threatened habitat. Although some animals live on or under the scattered plants, most of them hide under rocks during the daylight hours, emerging to forage by night. Since all the underground cracks are filled with mineral salts, loose rocks on the surface are a crucial resource. The uncontrolled collecting of rocks as building material, which has been going on for many years, has led to devastation of the habitat of the endemic species. Many animals may also have been affected by introduced predators, of which the most important is the large centipede *Scolopendra morsitans*; this is an aggressive carnivore against which the endemic species may not have effective defences. We fear that many of the special animals may have already become extinct, and suggest that a detailed study of the ecology of Prosperous Bay Plain should be given high priority, especially if there are still plans for the construction of an airfield in the area.

Scrub zone
Inland from the northwest-facing shore of the island, along most of its length and between about 200 m and 400 m in altitude, is an extensive zone covered with scrub,

made up almost entirely of introduced species. At higher levels this grades in many places into woodland, some of it planted, some developing with little human interference but again dominated by alien species. In the south and southeast the scrub zone is poorly differentiated from the extensive areas of semi-desert lower down, and in the easternmost parts of the island its place is largely taken by Creeper waste.

The difficulty in generalizing about the vegetation in this zone partly reflects the highly dynamic situation. Intensive grazing by goats and donkeys has been controlled for only a few decades, and even in 1995 we saw a few donkeys in a remote area near the Gates of Chaos and saw cactus pads nibbled by donkeys at Horse Pasture. Some effects of reduced grazing are now apparent. The endemic Scrubwood is spreading back into areas that it would formerly have dominated (with the Ebonies and Tea Plant), and a number of introduced shrubs and trees are spreading downwards in some areas.

Quentin Cronk described several sub-divisions of the scrub zone according to the dominant species of shrubs. By visiting different parts of the island it is easy to see these various types, although the separation between them is not clear cut. The first part of our account is based on Cronk's analysis, and this is followed by a discussion of some special areas – Ruperts Valley, The Heart Shape Waterfall and Jamestown.

Lantana dominated scrub

Lantana (sometimes referred to as Wild Currant or Black Sage) is a dominant component of the scrub in many areas on the western flanks of the island, from Thompsons Valley northwards to Horse Pasture and also in some places near Sandy Bay. *Lantana* is poisonous to stock and this may have been one reason why it spread so widely on the island when there was intense grazing by goats and donkeys. It is now declining in some places where reduced grazing pressure allows other plants to compete; it has also been the target of a fairly successful biological control programme.

Tungies (*Opuntia* species) are also important in this type of scrub, but generally less dominant than in the areas mentioned below. One native shrub, Samphire, is sometimes also present here as well as in the semi-desert lower down, but most of the other plants are introduced. They include Saltbush, Wild Tobacco, Blue Weed, sedges and grasses and a number of herbs; in some places one can also find Silk Cotton, Wild Pepper, Kei Apple, Wild Brinjal, Spoor and Wild Coffee. The latter species, and the agave known as English Aloe, become important towards the upper limit of this type of scrub.

Many of these plants can be seen on a walk down to Ebony Plain, just north of Thompsons Valley. As the name indicates, the native Ebony once grew here, and in 1985 there was an attempt to re-establish it. However, the trees seen growing there now are Rebony *Trochetiopsis x benjamini*, a hybrid between Ebony and the Redwood which has proved more successful under modern conditions than the Ebony itself.

Tungy dominated scrub

Scrub dominated by Tungies occurs in the far north and northwest of the island, sometimes developing close to the top of the cliffs. This scrub has relatively low diversity but as well as *Opuntia* it often includes *Lantana*; other species present are Silk Cotton, the composites Blue Weed, Everlasting, and *Conyza bonariensis*, and two grasses, *Vulpia bromoides* and Kikuyu Grass; other noticeable but patchy plants include species of agave, especially the Fence Aloe.

Tungies have been abundant on the north side of the island for more than a century and have interfered with agriculture in some areas. Several decades ago the moth

Cactoblastis cactorum was introduced in an attempt at biological control; this does not seem to have been very successful, but the gregarious black and orange caterpillars of the moth can be found inside discoloured pads of tungies in various parts of the island (and also on Ascension).

Scrub dominated by Wild Coffee, Poison Peach and Black Olive

This type of scrub occurs east of the central ridge, in a roughly north-south band at 300-400 m centred on Levelwood. Larger trees found in some places are Wild Mango and Cedar; smaller plants may include *Lantana*, Blue Weed, Everlasting, and Wire Grass, while Cape Grass often occurs in the open spaces. Above this scrub type there is mainly agricultural land; its lower border is often Creeper waste. In Sandy Bay the scrub is spreading downhill, presumably as a result of relaxation of grazing pressure, coupled with the presence of Mynas and Pigeons, both of which are responsible for dispersing seeds. Wild Coffee and Black Olive appear to be gaining ground, and with other introduced trees such as Spoor and Cedar they may gradually transform the scrub at these levels into a low forest of alien tree species. In many of the valley bottoms Wild Mango is already dominant, turning them into almost impenetrable thickets, which from above look like green ribbons traversing the brown and barren Crown Wastes. Since the valleys also tend to be precipitous, it is now rarely possible to walk down along them towards the coast.

Animals of the scrub zone

All the land birds, except Moorhen and Pheasant, may be seen in the areas of scrub zone discussed so far, and Rabbits, Rats and Mice are all widespread. The invertebrates of the scrub zone are numerous and diverse, although the majority of the species are introduced. The spectacular Diadem Butterfly is perhaps the most exciting: displaying males can sometimes be seen along the Pipe Path on Banks Ridge and also on the roadside at Bottom Woods. This species is almost certainly native but because of its patchy distribution it has been recorded only rarely. The male is velvet black, with a large circular white patch on each wing (Plate 24). He chooses an open area and makes frequent flights, apparently patrolling it; he attempts to drive off other males and even sometimes flies at a person who intrudes into his territory. The female Diadem is quite different from the male: she is orange-brown with black borders to the wings.[14]

The African Monarch is the other conspicuous butterfly likely to be seen. It is large, with orange-brown wings with black borders and white markings (Plate 24). These butterflies are poisonous because the caterpillars feed on plants in the family Asclepiadaceae (Milkweed family) that produce toxic compounds as an evolutionary response to herbivore attack.[15] The caterpillars have a striking black, white and yellow pattern; they can often be seen on Silk Cotton in the scrub zone – for instance in Thompsons Valley – and also on Milkweed (Plate 24).

---

[14] The female Diadem is a mimic of the African Monarch butterfly, and we found it very hard to distinguish between them. This type of mimicry evolves when one species (termed the model) is poisonous and has bright colours (often red or yellow and black) that warn potential predators and often deter them from attacking. The mimic is another species which evolves similar coloration to that of the model and thus gains protection by bluff, without being poisonous. In some cases, as with the Diadem, it is only the female who becomes a mimic. This may be because an evolutionary change in the colour pattern of the male would make him less attractive to females.

[15] The Monarch caterpillars, however, have breached this defence by evolving immunity to the toxins; furthermore, they store them for their own protection and retain them when they become adult. Accordingly, both caterpillars and butterflies show warning coloration.

Also of interest are the introduced Honey Bees, which apparently became extinct several times in the 19th century and had to be brought in again. There are some bee-keepers on the island, but bees sometimes also go wild, and their nests can be found among rocks in the scrub zone. A spectacular insect associated with bees is the large Death's Head Hawk-moth (Plate 24). A moth of this weight has high fuel consumption, and the Death's Head goes straight to the source, crawling into bee-hives or wild nests to feed on the honey. This species probably could not maintain a population on the island in the absence of bees, and it is also possible that it is implicated in the periodic extinction of bees mentioned above. The enormous caterpillars of the Death's Head can feed on a variety of plants.

Ruperts Valley

Some broad valleys, especially in Sandy Bay and the western flanks of the island, have damp habitats produced by permanent or intermittent streams, which form distinct parts of the scrub zone. Ruperts Valley is a special case. Ruperts was noted by the Belgians as having an unusual fauna, with many species associated with humans or buildings. Doubtless many insects and other invertebrates arrived here since it was a landing place much used by the early visitors and settlers, and later by the Royal Navy who brought in intercepted slave ships. The valley is rather well separated from the adjacent valleys by the barren rocky hills inland and on either side, so it is not surprising to find there a number of clearly introduced species that have apparently not spread to other parts of the island. They include, for instance, the web-spinner *Oligotoma saundersi*, a member of an obscure order of fragile insects that look a little like stoneflies. This is a particularly good place to watch Canaries, Averdavats, Cardinals, Mynas and Doves and, with luck, the Diadem Butterfly.

Jamestown and the Heart Shape Waterfall

The Jamestown valley itself, the centre of human activity on the island for several centuries, has also been a busy port of entry for alien animals and plants. It differs from Ruperts, however, in giving relatively easy access to other parts of the island, climbing along a permanent stream into the moist uplands. Among the most impressive features of the valley are the Heart Shape Waterfall and Cat Hole below Francis Plain. The waterfall plunges almost 100 m from its lip at 400 m, but now carries only a trickle because water is held back by the dam in the gut above. The cliffs here provide inland refuges for at least two endemic plants, Scrubwood and St Helena Plantain (Plate 30). The latter species grows only on small ledges on the nearly vertical rock face, and can be conveniently compared with the introduced Ground Plantain that is growing on the slope at the foot of the fall.

Getting to the waterfall can be hard work, since the path is heavily overgrown. However, the scramble is well worth while. The final approach through a grove of large Thorn trees is particularly interesting, though it is unwise to hold on to branches or trunks as the thorns are fierce. Around the foot of the fall is an area that is kept permanently damp by the fine spray from above, which wanders in the wind, making different noises as the drops fall on grass, rocks or leaves. The characteristic animals of this area are discussed with those of other freshwater habitats.

At Cat Hole, near the waterfall, one can see the possibly native *Polygonum glabrum*, a tropical species whose fruits are eaten and seeds dispersed by birds. On St Helena it apparently survives in the wild only here; it can be seen from above – draped over a cliff ledge – by walking from the Briars along Barnes Road. There is a vigorous cultivated specimen growing at Scotland.

Lower down James Valley are gardens with a variety of large trees such as Mangoes and Figs, which grow well but do not regenerate naturally. In this area and Jamestown itself one can see nearly all the land birds of the island without any extensive walking. The quarry opposite the Jamestown hospital is an easily accessible place to see White Terns, Java Sparrows, Pigeons with noticeably varied plumage, Mynas, Doves, Cardinals, Canaries and Averdavats. In the upper part of The Run in James Valley there is fair chance of seeing – or at least hearing – the Water-bird or Moorhen. At night, the evergreen trees in Jamestown hold communal roosts of both Mynas and Java Sparrows.[16]

Creeper waste
A special habitat found mainly in the far east of the island is Creeper waste. This is the term applied to large expanses of relatively level, somewhat saline and often heavily eroded land that are now dominated by spreading mats of the introduced Creeper, *Carprobrotus edulis*; this is a prostrate, succulent relative of the Ice Plant (Plate 3). Creeper waste occurs especially between Bottom Woods and Horse Point, and in some parts of Prosperous Bay Plain. Apart from the badlands and scoured valleys that are so prominent in the modern landscape of St Helena, Creeper waste is perhaps the most striking of the degraded habitats. It is a wholly artificial habitat which often also has some Saltbush, another successful but probably introduced plant; *Lantana* generally does not thrive, perhaps because the areas are too exposed, but it is present in some places along with occasional Poison Peach and Everlasting. In one part of this zone, between Horse Point and Bradleys, the Endemic Section of the Agriculture & Forestry Department has established plantations of endemic trees, especially Scrubwood and Gumwood. The eventual hope is to arrest the gully erosion and to restore at least semi-natural woodland in some parts of this degraded part of the island.

Much of the area now covered with Creeper, at an altitude of about 325-425 m, would in the past have had dry Gumwood woodland or Scrubwood scrub. The higher areas – dominated by Gumwood – formed part of the Great Wood (see Chapter 7). This area was the main habitat of the Giant Ground Beetle and Giant Earwig, which may both be extinct. Mice are now common in the area, as is the large introduced centipede *Scolopendra morsitans*, and both of these animals are thought to have been important predators on the endemic beetle and earwig. Ecological devastation of this area has not stopped with destruction of the forests; there is now a great scarcity of the superficial rocks that used to provide refuges for a variety of invertebrates including the Giant Ground Beetle. Use of rocks for walling during the attempts to preserve the Great Wood and rock collection for construction work (which continues to the present day) has undoubtedly contributed to the decline of some of the endemic invertebrates. To see the animals, which include woodlice, spiders, bristletails, crickets, scorpions, cockroaches, beetles and ants, as well as a small species of earwig, it is best to turn

[16] Intrigued by the number of Mynas dropping in to the roost at dusk, we did a rough census on 7th March 1995: between 5.35 and 6.45 pm we counted 646 arriving birds; obviously there was room for error, especially when birds circled before settling in the trees, but it is clear that Mynas from a wide area above Jamestown commute to and from the roost every morning and evening. Two weeks later, on 21st March, we watched Java Sparrows coming in to roost in the trees in the public garden close to the Castle. Between 5.05 and 6.40 we counted 2,860 arriving birds, although the smaller size and larger numbers of the Sparrows made this a rougher count than that of the Mynas. We saw or heard signs of other Myna and Sparrow roosts in several parts of the island, and suspect that both these species generally roost communally in thick vegetation, at least when they are not breeding.

over only one or two rocks, and only in places where they are abundant; afterwards, they should be gently replaced in their original positions.[17]

Looking underneath plant debris, especially around the scattered clumps of flax that occur in some places, is a particularly good way to find the red-brown scarab beetles *Mellissius adumbratus* and the rarer *M. oryctoides*. Both species are restricted to the area around Deadwood and Horse Point, together with Prosperous Bay Plain. It is mainly the remains of dead adults that accumulate under the plants, and even now they are occasionally accompanied by blackish wing-cases (elytra) of long-dead Giant Ground Beetles; these can be recognized by their great size: they are about 17-23 mm in length (the animals as a whole were 29-38 mm).

The larvae of *Mellissius* – fat white grubs with reddish heads, known as Hogworms – eat plant roots, and can be found by digging under Creeper plants. Mouse holes are often conspicuous where the hogworms are present, implying they are preyed on by mice. A third species of *Mellissius* has apparently sometimes caused serious damage to pastures in the moister regions in the central part of the island. Melliss reported that:

> *"It is said that the only way of destroying these creatures is to turn a herd of swine for a few days into the field where they are; they destroy both grass and grubs, but of the two evils they are the least."*

Arable land, pasture and New Zealand Flax

Between 450 and 700 m the interior of the island is almost entirely devoted to agriculture and forestry; there is much pasture and woodland, and substantial areas are still occupied by abandoned plantations of New Zealand Flax. Small areas of land are arable, mainly at Longwood, near Broad Bottom and at Cleughs Plain; there is small-scale market gardening in several places, potatoes being an important crop.

The pasture is of several types. At lower elevations (especially between about 430 m and 530 m near Longwood) there is low productivity grassland in an area receiving rainfall of about 400 mm/year; here pasture has replaced the original dry gumwood forest. The main grasses are *Pennisetum clandestinum*, the possibly indigenous *Cynodon dactylon* and *Digitaria ciliaris*. Careful management is needed as these areas are easily affected by overgrazing, which can lead to severe problems of erosion. Similar pastures are found at Woody Ridge and also at the other end of the island above Man and Horse. In the latter area there is a comparable rainfall regime, but immediately to the east the land rises and the rainfall increases. This results in a transition above Botleys to richer pasture in which there is much *Stenotaphrum secundatum* along with the *Pennisetum*; this continues up to the ridge at an elevation of more than 700 m. In the centre of the island, however, in even wetter conditions, *Agrostis tenuis* becomes important, together with *Pennisetum*, *Paspalum scrobiculatum* and *Anthoxanthum odoratum* (Hay Grass). Rocky places among the pastures are good places to see the Small Bellflower, which is almost the only one of the upland endemic plants that can still be found away from the Peaks.

Over the centuries there have been serious problems with invasion of pastures by alien shrubs. Blackberry was a particular menace early in the 19th century, but *Lantana* and the Tungies (*Opuntia* species) and Furze have recently been troublesome in some areas. Furze is no longer used as fuel, but it is probably the most important food-plant for one of the few butterflies of St Helena, the Long-tailed Blue (Plate 24).

---

[17] When searching for animals, we found ourselves tempted to turn over the few remaining loose rocks, but soon became aware that other people had been moving the same rocks and that this was causing disruption of the relatively moist cavities so important as retreats for small invertebrates.

This butterfly is a well-known migrant and may have reached the island naturally. However, it probably could not have established itself before discovery of the island by people, since its caterpillars seem always to feed on plants of the pea family, and none of these are native to the island.

At higher elevations many pastures are bordered with Thorn trees, largely because cut branches of this tree take root easily and so provide a convenient way of demarcating boundaries. In these situations they are also useful in another way, since they are regularly lopped to provide leaves as forage for stock, especially from November to March; they are said to contain up to 18% protein. Thorn trees have spectacular scarlet flowers with nectar that appears to be attractive to Mynas, and doubtless other birds too. Thorn trees and some other kinds of large trees provide breeding sites for the White Tern or Sea Bird. They make no nest, but place their eggs in a slight depression on a branch; as a result, accidents to eggs and chicks are common.[18]

The drier and relatively level grasslands are now the primary habitat of the endemic Wirebird (Plate 21), a small plover which catches prey by sight and thus needs ground with scanty or low vegetation and plenty of insects and spiders. One of the easiest places to watch Wirebirds is the golf course at Longwood, but they are also abundant on Deadwood Plain and often visit the wet areas in Fishers Valley.

Substantial parts of the uplands are still covered by plantations of New Zealand Flax, although there has been no commercial use for flax in the last few decades and all the flax mills are derelict. Flax plantations are gradually being turned back into pasture, usually leaving some flax as erosion control. Dead flowering stems of flax are favourite perching and displaying sites for the Cardinal and the Averdavat, and accumulated debris around the flax plants holds moisture and provides a rich microhabitat for a variety of invertebrates. From the point of view of conservation, however, flax is a menace, because of its tendency to invade and outcompete native vegetation.

Woodland

Woodlands consisting of a variety of introduced trees cover relatively small areas in the uplands and at middle elevations (700 down to about 400 m); tongues of woodland extend further down valleys in many places. The woods are on both private land and public land managed by the Agriculture & Forestry Department. About 450 hectares are in timber production and 650 ha producing fuelwood; there are also about 200 ha considered as conservation forest.

The most important species in terms of production are pine (mainly *Pinus pinaster*), *Eucalyptus* species, Australian Blackwood and Cedar; both Pine and Cedar regenerate naturally, and the latter species may well become dominant in some drier areas in the long run. One of the finest stands of Pine can be seen at High Hill, where the mature trees give almost the impression of a natural forest. Some of the most conspicuous trees on the island are scattered Norfolk Island Pines, which have reached a height of 40 m and a diameter of 5 m. An attempt is now being made to increase the establishment of high value timber species, with the emphasis mainly on Silky Oak and Cape Yew. Other trees and shrubs that are widespread in woodlands at the higher levels include China Date, Elderberry, Ink Bush, White Flower, Moonflower, Ginger, Buddleia, Bamboos and White Olive.

---

[18] We were startled one day to find a downy chick on the road near Bishops Bridge, but soon realized that it had fallen off a Thorn tree by the roadside. We were able to climb part way up and put the chick on a strongly sloping branch a few feet below the nest site. It quickly scrambled up, using its sharp, hooked claws to give it a grip on the bark, and was reunited with a waiting parent. After this, we looked out for it whenever we passed, and were pleased to see it being fed and eventually reaching fledging age (Plate 21).

Many of the woodlands at relatively low levels, including some classified as scrub on the land use map, result from programmes of erosion control in the Crown Wastes. These have employed a variety of species of Acacia (especially Port Jackson Willow and Australian Blackwood) and also the Dry Land Tree *Eucalyptus lehmannii*. Some low level woodlands also include Pine and Macrocarpa, and there are increasing numbers of Cedar, Black Olive, Wild Mango, Wild Pepper Tree and Spoor; China Date and White Olive also occur. At about 500 m at Peak Dale is the largest remnant of Gumwood woodland; another small group of these trees survives in Deep Valley.

In the uplands of St Helena there are numerous wet guts (gullies); some of these peter out in the semi-desert – at least during the summer – but a few form perennial streams that reach the sea. The guts are densely vegetated at all levels, but the components change with altitude; endemic flowering plants are hardly ever represented. Yams – though no longer extensively cultivated – can be found beside the streams from near sea level (for instance in Sharks Valley) up to about 600 m. Many other introduced plants grow in the guts, some of the most successful being Thorn, White Flower (especially around 500-600 m), Elderberry, Blue Weed and Ginger; locally one can find Moonflower, Giant Fuchsia and a variety of other aliens.

The central ridge

The central ridge of St Helena forms a huge curve around Sandy Bay, from Hoopers Rock (>700 m) in the west, northeastwards via the Depot (>670 m), High Peak (798 m) and Mount Vesey (>740 m), on to Casons Gate (>690 m), east along Sandy Bay Ridge (747 m), then across the road to Stitch's Ridge; this leads to the summit ridge itself – often referred to as the Peaks – which trends south-southeastwards and has three peaks. The first summit reached when walking from the west up Cabbage Tree Road (a track, not a drivable road) is Cuckold's Point; it is just over 800 m and has a Norfolk Island Pine on it, and nearby is a large Cape Yew tree. The next summit – at 820 metres the highest point on the island – is Diana's Peak, which has no landmark tree. The southernmost extension of the ridge, where it still exceeds 780 m before dropping to Long Ground Ridge, is Mount Actaeon; it also has a large Norfolk Island Pine.[19]

The central ridge has much higher rainfall than elsewhere on the island, and for much of the time it is shrouded in mist. This zone – containing fragments of the original cloud forest – is extraordinarily rich biologically and desperately endangered. The trees and their attendant invertebrates, unique to the island, are a grave responsibility for the people and government of St Helena because they are part of the heritage not just of St Helenians but of all humans; we shall all be the poorer if they cannot be saved. We cannot tell how many of the species described from the central ridge in the past still survive today. Furthermore, there is no way of knowing how many more species have still to be described.[20]

---

[19] The names of these peaks have been the subject of controversy for many years. We accept the authority of the official Diana's Peak National Park Guide published in 1996, with the names used by St Helenians such as George Benjamin, which were also used on the Ordnance Survey maps as recently as 1948. This usage, however, does not conform to that on the current Ordnance Survey maps.

[20] The small amount of work that we did at this level on the island included an investigation of two tiny caves at High Peak. They were really only overhangs, partly caused by erosion but perhaps partly excavated by people; they proved to contain several endemic invertebrates, including the Spiky Yellow Woodlouse and a species of centipede that may prove to be new to science. A closely related centipede was found by the Belgians on the Peaks, and we found what may be a third species at Coles Rock, providing confirmation that even this group of relatively inefficient dispersers - given so much time - eventually managed to cross the ocean to St Helena at least once during the prehistory of the island.

Pasture, flax and forestry plantations extend the whole way up the slopes in many places along the western section of the central ridge, eliminating the native vegetation, but small areas have survived near High Peak. Among the Black Cabbage on the exposed southern face of this hill there is a good stand of Lobelia; small groups of this shrub occur in several other places on the central ridge, but it tends to be crowded out by introduced species. High Peak also has the only remaining plants of the Large Bellflower (Plate 26); the Small Bellflower is relatively common, both here and elsewhere on the ridge. Dwarf Jellico also grows here on a rocky outcrop (Plate 32).[21]

It is in this area – around High Peak and Mount Vesey – that the Endemic Section have been making some of their most serious attempts to re-establish endemic vegetation. Young Redwoods have been planted out, but are not particularly vigorous. Ebonies, and especially the hybrid "Rebony" do well, however, and looking down from High Peak one can see a grove of young trees that begins to give some idea of what an Ebony forest on St Helena would have been like (Plate 8).

The northernmost (middle) section of the ridge is of little ecological interest, but in the eastern section, starting at Cabbage Tree Road, are the only surviving substantial remnants of the original cloud forest of St Helena.[22] At around 700 m and for about 100 m downwards this would originally have been largely Cabbage tree woodland, growing on richer soils than those on the crest of the ridge. Black Cabbage trees are still locally abundant, and evidence for the downward extension of the Cabbage tree woodland is provided by the presence of a small group of She Cabbage which have survived between two fields in Swampy Gut at a little over 600 m. The He Cabbage , another component of this woodland, can still be seen in a few places along Cabbage Tree Road at about 720 m. Both She Cabbage and He Cabbage are short-lived trees, adapted to establishing themselves in "light-gaps" formed by small landslips or the fall of a large tree. They grow fast into the canopy and produce seed that has a chance of being dispersed to another gap when one becomes available. Such trees are especially vulnerable when the total forest area is much reduced, so special measures are needed for their conservation.

The Redwood and the False Gumwood, which were originally major components of the Cabbage tree woodland, are now almost extinct. Two shrubs, Roxburgh's and Burchell's Bellflowers, were lost over a century ago. The understorey plant Lobelia, however, can still be found growing wild in a few places. Perhaps more dominant previously and even now abundant is the endemic Black Scale Fern, a vigorous species growing to two metres high which has tended to take over spaces at high levels left vacant by the removal of Tree Ferns.

Both Lobelia and the Black Scale Fern also occurred at the highest levels, where the Cabbage tree woodland originally gave way to Tree Fern thicket; this community still survives around Cuckold's Point, Diana's Peak and Mount Actaeon, though in much modified form. It was a rich community, in which long-lived Tree Ferns and Black Cabbage played a major role but a number of other endemic trees, shrubs, herbs and ferns were also important.

---

[21] When staff from the Endemic Section placed plastic bags over some of the inflorescences in order to collect seed for propagation, they inadvertently captured an interesting range of invertebrate animals, including aphids, weevils and endemic woodlice of the species *Littorophiloscia alticola*.

[22] The guide to the Diana's Peak National Park makes suggestions for walks on the Peaks. However, since searching for scarce endemics in the rain and mud on the exposed ridge is not everyone's cup of tea, it should be mentioned that an easier way to see the special plants is at the George Benjamin Nature Trail at Casons Gate. Here many of the surviving species of endemic flowering plants and ferns characteristic of the Peaks have been planted and labelled; interpretation is provided in an information hut at one end of the trail.

There have already been permanent losses of flowering plants from the Tree Fern thicket. The beautiful Stringwood became extinct in about 1865, and the St Helena Olive is now teetering on the brink (Plate 30). Also at risk are the Whitewood (Plate 27) and the Dogwood (Plate 31), two ancient relict species of particular evolutionary interest (see Chapter 7); these are the subject of current research efforts aimed at ensuring their survival. One surviving species is Jellico (Plate 32), a giant endemic umbellifer that used to be eaten like celery; stands of Jellico can still be found around wet flushes in a few places. Another endemic plant found in this habitat is Diana's Peak Grass, a sedge with long, strap-like leaves forming a shallow V-shape in cross-section (Plate 27).

The misty environment of the Peaks is ideal for ferns, and most of the rich array of endemic species that would have been abundant in the Cabbage tree woodland and Tree Fern thicket in the past can still be found there without too much difficulty. Apart from the Tree Fern and Black Scale Fern already mentioned, they range from the large species of *Pteris*, *Dryopteris* and *Pseudophegopteris*, with graceful, broad and much subdivided fronds, to the small species of *Elaphoglossum*, with strap-like or twig-like leaves, which often grow as epiphytes (Plate 32).

None of the known endemic ferns of the Peaks have become extinct, but many now have extremely restricted ranges and must be considered seriously endangered. The worst plight is that of one of the Buckshorns, *Lycopodium axillare*, which is apparently reduced to a single individual growing epiphytically on a tree on the ridge. The other Buckshorn, *Lycopodium cernuum*, can still be seen along the path up from Cabbage Tree Road.

The frequent incidence of mist on the central ridge provides ideal conditions for the growth of epiphytes.[23] Epiphytic growth also plays a part in the natural regeneration of some of the endemic trees. This is because neither the Tree Fern nor other plants can regenerate on the thick mor humus.[24] However, both Black Cabbage and Whitewood seedlings can establish themselves as epiphytes on the trunks of the Tree Ferns. When the trunk falls, they can put down roots through the mor humus and have a chance to take over the space that had been occupied by the Tree Fern.

Once individuals of Black Cabbage, Whitewood or Dogwood become established a 'mull humus' begins to form. In this the leaves are decomposed mainly by animals and the crumbly residue becomes mixed with the mineral soil, with no clear boundary. This is a medium in which seedlings – and also sporelings of the Tree Fern itself – can develop. It is obvious that this situation must lead to a highly dynamic and patchy community in which both soil type and vegetation is continually changing.

The native plant community which evolved on the highest part of the central ridge of St Helena has survived more intact than any at lower altitudes, largely due to the poor soils and the inconvenience of the steep slopes for agriculture. However, almost all the endemic species are endangered by the relentless invasion of this relict habitat by New Zealand Flax and other introduced plants. Flax has now reached the ridge in many places, and can even be seen growing epiphytically on a Cape Yew tree – itself exotic – near Cuckold's Point[25] (Plate 7). Flax, however, is not the only threat to the native vegetation on the Peaks. Most

[23] Epiphytes are plants growing on the trunks or branches of other species.

[24] Mor humus is a compact blanket of organic material, separate from the mineral soil below, which builds up underneath established Tree Ferns.

[25] Quentin Cronk recently pointed out that the Peaks are like an island in a sea of flax, and when the flax flowers it sheds a great wave of seed, windblown up the Peaks. Dr Cronk was on St Helena in 1983 and again in 1995, and noted that the flax had advanced into the Tree Fern thicket at a rate of about 5 metres per year during the interval; he calculated that some 10% of the native forest had been lost between his two visits.

of the gullies running up to the ridge are choked with a tangle of introduced shrubs and herbs, often dominated by the Bilberry *Solanum mauritianum* (Plate 31). Other invasive species found at high levels include Blackberry, Fuchsia and Quinine.

A great many endemic invertebrates inhabit the highest part of the central ridge. These include the Blushing Snail (Plate 22), the Spiky Yellow Woodlouse and the Golden Sail Spider, all of which have been featured in recent publicity relating to conservation on St Helena; there are also a great many other less well known species such as the endemic ground beetles that live mainly in rotting trunks of the Tree Fern.[26] Among the non-endemics, one of the most conspicuous is the Painted Lady Butterfly (Plate 24); we have seen individuals defending territories on the footpath at the very summit of the island.

The animals just mentioned are generalists, typical of the humid habitat of the central ridge but not tied to particular kinds of plants. Many insects, however, have evolved in parallel with particular plant species (or groups of related species) on which they feed, so that each of the endemic plants has a set of herbivorous endemic insects associated with it; in some cases, the plants also have associated insect pollinators which depend on them. Extinction of a plant species may therefore cause extinction or serious threat to the survival of a number of endemic insects. Let us hope that this very special habitat, with its extraordinarily high diversity of endemic species, will at last be given adequate protection and the sophisticated management that it needs if the biological communities are to avoid further decline in diversity.

Freshwater

There were no substantial bodies of standing water on St Helena before people arrived and began constructing water tanks and reservoirs. However, natural freshwater habitats included streams, muddy places in gut bottoms, damp areas below waterfalls and the pools left behind for a while after storms or seasonal rainfall. These damp situations are now good places to get a glimpse of the Moorhen, and the sharp, repetitive call of the Grass Frog is a constant accompaniment to walks; this amphibian was brought to the island in about 1880, and evidently spread quickly through all the watercourses on the island.

It is well known among zoogeographers (biologists who seek to understand the distribution of animals) that indigenous species restricted to freshwater environments are absent or scarce on oceanic islands. The few species that are present pose intriguing questions as to their mode of arrival. Have they evolved from marine species capable of dispersing in ocean currents? Could they have floated to the island on driftwood, or flown or drifted in the wind? Or do they have eggs or minute resting stages that could have travelled in mud caked on the feet of waterbirds? All these modes may have played a part on St Helena.

The endemic St Helena Dragonfly, whose ancestors doubtless flew to the island long ago, has not been definitely seen for many years. However, there have been recent records of a well known migratory tropical dragonfly, *Pantala flavescens*; it would be of great interest to prove breeding of this species on the island. Most other groups of insects that breed in freshwater are absent; for them, the vast expanse of salt water between Africa and St Helena has evidently proved an insuperable barrier. One exception is the blackflies (Simuliidae), which managed to reach the island and have undergone intriguing evolutionary modifications that are discussed in Chapter 15.

---

[26] If one reads through the reports of the Belgian expeditions - or of Mr and Mrs Wollaston who studied the beetles and moths of the island a century earlier - one finds continual references to endemic species restricted to the central ridge,

Equally remarkable, however, was the discovery by the Belgians of several kinds of tiny freshwater crustaceans and flatworms in special freshwater habitats, mainly in Lemon Tree Gut, Peak Hill, and on the central ridge. We call these seepage pools; they are small pools formed from streamlets percolating through the rock fissures and collecting in shallow depressions at the bases of the rocks. Their significance is mainly that they mark places where flows of subterranean groundwater emerge to form surface streams. The animals in them, therefore, may be mainly representatives of populations that live primarily underground.

Apart from *Iais aquilei* (see box) several other animals were found in these habitats; one of them is equally remarkable, but on account of its distribution rather than its

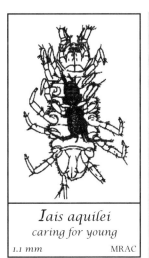

Iais aquilei
caring for young

1.1 mm   MRAC

Figure 18

Parental care in a freshwater crustacean

One of the most exciting discoveries made by the Belgians was a crustacean related to the woodlice but fully aquatic, which they found in seepage pools at the Briars and nearby in Lemon Tree Gut above Cat Hole. This animal, called *Iais aquilei*, is in the isopod family Janiridae. It is less than one and a half millimetres long and would be barely worthy of mention if it were not for its extraordinary life history.

The curious feature of this animal is that almost all its relatives - which have worldwide distribution - live attached singly to other isopods in a different family (Sphaeromidae), feeding on scraps of food dropped by their larger hosts. The family Sphaeromidae, however, does not occur on St Helena, and here the *Iais* live independently. This situation is not quite unique, since *Iais pubescens*, a relative of the St Helena species that occurs around the Southern Ocean, is said to live independently on Gough Island in the Tristan group and on the west coast of New Zealand.

Whenever one kind of animal exploits another by living on it or in it, a critical stage in the life history is when the young of the exploiting species need to find new members of the host species to live on. We do not know at what stage the young *Iais* in other places find their own sphaeromids, but the reproductive biology of the independent St Helena species provides fascinating clues. As in some other isopods, the female has a 'brood pouch' in which she keeps her three or four fertilized eggs during the early stages of development. When the St Helena males were examined, however, it was found that many of them had a single larger juvenile firmly attached to their underside, held in position by a specially adapted pair of the male's legs. Presumably, therefore, the female either passes one juvenile to the male, or the juveniles are released by the female and actively search for a male. Since the male positively clasps the juvenile it seems likely - viewed in evolutionary terms - that he is caring for one of his own young, until it grows large enough to start independent life.

Other species in the genus *Iais* live mainly on coasts or estuaries, on submerged or floating logs. We suspect, therefore, that the ancestors of *Iais aquilei* reached St Helena on driftwood, but that if they were already associated with sphaeromid hosts, these either did not survive the sea crossing or failed to establish themselves on the island. The *Iais*, however, made the transition to independent life in freshwater, and evolved into the modern endemic species.

biology. This is another crustacean, a tiny freshwater shrimp *Tanais stanfordi* (family Tanaidae). On St Helena it has been found in springs and seepage pools below cliffs on the central ridge, and in Lemon Tree Gut. Some individuals are dark brown and others pale, the former probably living in the light and the latter underground. The puzzle is that this species has been found in about ten places scattered right around the world: for instance, the head of the Red Sea, Ceylon, New Guinea, Galápagos Islands, eastern South America and St Helena. Th. Monod, who wrote the account of the Belgians' specimens, concluded that the distribution of the species as known at that time was clearly without any plausible explanation! We imagine – like Monod – that the species is really more generally distributed, and we guess that it has been transported by birds.

This mode of dispersal is more clearly implied for one of the species in another group, the ostracods. These are crustaceans in which the whole body is enclosed by a pair of valves, like a tiny pea-shaped mussel. The endemic *Herpetocypris helenae*, found in springs near Napoleon's grave and on the central ridge, is a member of a family in which dessication-resistant eggs are produced. There is thus obvious potential for occasional transport of eggs on the legs of water birds such as the Moorhen and the other rails that reach St Helena from time to time.

Another aspect of the biology of this ostracod is also relevant. No males have ever been found, and in both this and some other members of the family it is suspected that reproduction may be 'parthenogenetic'. This is a process in which a female can produce young without the intervention of a male. Not surprisingly, parthenogenetic species are relatively common on isolated islands: a single female has the potential to found a new population, rather than requiring the simultaneous arrival of both male and female individuals.

Many evolutionists believe, however, that there is often a long-term penalty for doing without sex entirely. Sexual reproduction is a remarkably efficient way of shuffling the genes, thus producing an enormous range of characteristics in each generation of offspring. It is the action of Darwinian natural selection on this variation that leads to most evolutionary change. In a species where sex does not occur, the offspring are 'clones' of the parents: that is, they are genetically almost identical to them. The result is that the species may not be able to take advantage of all the evolutionary opportunities offered by an island where many vacant ecological niches are available; it may also be vulnerable to parasites and to environmental change.

The only other freshwater ostracod recorded from St Helena is the endemic *Xestoleberis potamophila*, recorded from springs in Lemon Tree Gut and higher up on the island; it is much smaller than the previous species and both males and females are found. It also belongs to a different family, whose members are almost entirely marine, with only one species in a brackish lake on the Galápagos Islands. Furthermore, the eggs are not resistant to dessication and the young larvae are brooded by the female. Transport of the ancestors of the St Helena species by birds is therefore implausible; presumably they reached the island in marine currents and then made the transition to brackish and eventually freshwater habitats.

Our late colleague Jan Stock and other biogeographers have suggested that at least for some other types of aquatic crustaceans that live in cracks and crevices in the rocks, this transition from salt to fresh water normally takes place only if submerged land is uplifted by geological processes, or if sea level drops (for instance as a result of an ice age). As discussed in Chapter 3, both of these things happened during the prehistory of St Helena.

One other group of planktonic crustaceans - the copepods - have colonized freshwater habitats on St Helena, with three species found in Lemon Tree Gut and one also at Oakbank. All three belong to widespread species and it is not clear whether they reached the island naturally.

Apart from crustaceans, the most diverse invertebrates in freshwater on the island are free-living flatworms known as turbellarians; these are flattish, unsegmented worms that are easily overlooked. One group on St Helena includes two endemic species, *Dinizia sanctaehelenae* and *Tryssosoma jennyae*, the latter so distinctive that a new genus has been formed for it. Both of these tiny worms are found in freshwater, but the group as a whole is primarily marine; like one of the ostracods mentioned above, they presumably evolved on the island from marine ancestors. Unfortunately no-one has looked for their relatives around the coasts of St Helena, but their general relationships seem to be with species on various islands and coasts in the southern hemisphere.

Caves and underground spaces

St Helena is not rich in caves and cavernicolous animals are not easy to find. The shallow erosion caves along the coast and the numerous cave-like overhangs in the sides of some of the valleys do not contain true cavernicoles, which need spaces which are continually dark and moist, and which are insulated from the strong temperature fluctuations of the outside world.

However, things were very different in the distant past. We know this because we have worked on many younger volcanic islands which have extensive systems of cracks and underground spaces; on St Helena, these have mostly been eroded away during the seven million years since volcanic activity ceased, or have been filled with silt washed down by the occasional violent floods. Furthermore the results of our investigation of underground spaces on Ascension – along with work by many other biologists – has shown that vagrant invertebrate animals can cross vast expanses of ocean and colonise the subterranean environments even on a mid-ocean island. St Helena, with a similar degree of isolation, has existed for so much longer that there must have been time not only for colonisation but also for evolutionary changes adapting the colonists to subterranean life. Therefore, knowing that a specialised underground fauna existed on St Helena in the past, the relevant question was whether this fauna still survives.

During our visit we searched extensively for places which might enable us to gain access to the remaining subterranean spaces. Because of the lack of proper caves, the most promising type of underground habitat was the complex set of narrow spaces between small rocks in scree slopes and rock falls and in accumulations of rubbly rocks, where they have not been filled in by silt.[27] In the Canary Islands and elsewhere this type of site has often proved to contain specialized cavernicoles. Again and again, however, we found that the animals living in these spaces on St Helena were not part of the indigenous underground fauna but were well known soil-dwelling species that have been carried around the world by people. They include woodlice, millipedes, centipedes, pseudoscorpions, spiders, mites, diplurans, symphylans, springtails, cockroaches, booklice, beetles and flies. In addition, there is a large array of introduced earthworms.

[27] One technique that we used on St Helena was to drive a perforated steel pipe deep into loose rock or scree slopes, and then place insect baits in small jars in the pipe. The other technique involved digging a horizontal hole, for instance in a road cutting, in rocks where there seemed to be plenty of cracks and spaces where animals could live.

We did, however, find a few cavernicolous animals in this type of habitat. One of these was a minute white spider with much reduced eyes from a slope covered with a jumble of large rocks at the foot of Lot. Another interesting species was a cricket that we first found in cavities in the rocky bank along the road to Prince Andrew School. It remains to be seen whether this cricket is endemic, but intriguingly, it belongs to a subfamily not previously recorded from St Helena, though represented by three species on Ascension.

What we really wanted to find, however, were lava tubes. St Helena does have a few, but we found only two short ones that we could actually get into. One of these – the Needle's Eye Cave – opens out near the sea close to Jamestown harbour and is easily reached by boat, but it proved uninteresting from the zoological point of view.

The second lava tube at first seemed equally unpromising. We called it Ruperts Battery Cave (Plate 4). The opening is about 50 m above sea level beside the path traversing the cliff between Ruperts and James valleys. The cave descends steeply towards the sea, but has been largely filled with lava rubble, probably because it was regarded as dangerous. We found few animals in this cave, but among the specimens was a strange, minute, colourless and wingless insect which we thought must be one of the booklice (psocids). Four years later, the psocid specialist Charles Lienhard found time to examine it and immediately realized that it was not only a new species but the first blind psocid known: the eyes are entirely lacking.[28] The significance of this find is that it demonstrates that St Helena did indeed have a fauna of invertebrates highly adapted to subterranean life. This species of psocid may or may not be the sole survivor of that fauna, but its complete lack of eyes clearly implies a long evolutionary history of underground life on the island.

We have not given up hope of finding more kinds of true cavernicoles on St Helena. Apart from further investigation of the Ruperts Battery Cave, the place we would now try is the barren clinker area near Gill Point. This is the site of some of the most recent volcanic activity on the island, and the very dry conditions have minimized the effect of weathering. We think there may be underground cavities in this area that could harbour specialized animals.

---

[28] C. Lienhard & N.P. Ashmole (1999).

Chapter 7

Ecological history of St Helena since 1502

We have referred in earlier chapters to the devastating effects of introduced mammalian predators on the native birds of St Helena, and of goats and other herbivores on the vegetation. Here we provide a more systematic historical account of the gradual disappearance of the natural forests of St Helena, under the impact of humans and the domestic and other animals that they brought to the island.

Processes of ecological deterioration have rarely been documented in detail on a timescale of centuries. The meticulous records of the East India Company relating to St Helena provide an instructive example of the inexorable progress of 'the tragedy of the commons'. This phrase, with its implication of the inevitability of a Greek tragedy, was introduced by Garrett Hardin in a seminal article published in 1968. It refers to the remorseless destruction of a potentially sustainable resource – such as common grazing for animals – by a number of independent exploiters following their own self-interest. Each individual gains in the short run by attempting to increase his share of the take, even though the result in the long run is disaster for everyone. The tragedy can be seen in progress in many modern human activities, most clearly in the exploitation of world fish stocks and timber resources. The concept does not apply, of course, to an effectively regulated commons in which people have rights to graze a limited number of animals (or harvest limited quantities of a resource) in a sustainable system.

For a century and a half after the discovery of St Helena in 1502, the alien herbivores introduced to the island by mariners were the prime agents of ecological destruction. The animals concerned were mainly goats and pigs, though cattle also played a part; they were used by people through unsystematic harvesting by ships' crews, mainly early in the southern autumn when the winds were most favourable for return voyages from the Indies.[1] Subsequently, however, humans played a more direct role in the devastation of the island ecosystem. The year 1659 saw the arrival of the settlers with their insatiable hunger for grazing, timber and firewood. Much of the subsequent history of St Helena is the working out of a variation on the tragedy of the commons. The resources for which people competed were in the main not strictly commons, but comprised the natural vegetation of the island (on government and private land), which provided grazing for livestock and wood for building, cooking, heating, tanning, distillation and burning in the production of lime. The records provide a chronicle of a long but spasmodic struggle on the part of the authorities (and occasionally by the settlers working cooperatively) to prevent over-exploitation and ultimately destruction of the natural assets of St Helena.

Before this struggle came to an end (or at least to a pause) with the killing of the wild goats and the rapidly increasing use of imported fuels in the middle of the twentieth century, natural vegetation had vanished from almost every part of the island except the steepest cliffs and the summits of the highest ridge. Many endemic plants and trees had become extinct, while the populations of several others had been reduced to single

---

[1] N.M. Wace (1999).

figures before efforts began to bring them back from the brink and give them another chance of survival. Most of the other endemic plants survive only in small groups, threatened by competition from introduced invasive plants and a variety of insect pests. The effects on native animals are less well documented (because most of the species are small and inconspicuous) but have undoubtedly also been severe.

The progressive devastation of St Helena did not go unnoticed, and some of the 18th century environmental initiatives on the island can provide inspiration for today. Their failure, however, provides a simple, salutary message: even the most enlightened attempts at conservation and sustainable management are of little value unless continuity of policy is assured on a timescale of centuries.

The devastation of the native vegetation

We here provide a chronological account of the process by which the pristine vegetation of St Helena became transformed by human influences commencing in 1502. We quote extensively from the official St Helena Records, which started in 1678, barely two decades after settlement of the island by the East India Company in 1659, and continued until the handing over of the island to the British government in 1834. For the earlier period – from the island's discovery until settlement – we refer to the sparser and less systematic accounts by early travellers;[2] for the brief treatment of the most recent period (in the final section of this chapter) we use a variety of sources, including the studies by Linda Brown and her colleagues in the late 1970's.[3]

The first party of Portuguese explorers, led by João da Nova and reaching St Helena in May 1502, made little immediate impact on the island. They gathered wood to make fires, killed sea-lions (and perhaps also seals), seabirds and probably turtles for food, and collected seabird eggs. The direct impact of these and other early visitors was slight, but when they departed they left behind both deliberate and accidental legacies.

The early visitors intended that when other Portuguese ships stopped at the island they should be able to obtain fresh meat, fruit and herbs; they therefore introduced animals and plants likely to provide a sustainable resource for the future. The animals included goats, pigs and several kinds of edible birds. The plants included a variety of fruit trees,

Tree planting on St Helena and the green movement of two centuries ago

Although the natural vegetation of St Helena was almost entirely destroyed during the three and a half centuries after the island's discovery, the spectacle of despoliation and its obvious economic costs may have had influence far beyond the island. In a recent book which includes extensive discussion of St Helena, Richard Grove has suggested that the history of environmental concern in the western world has been strongly influenced by the experience of the colonial powers in the tropical countries they governed, as well as by attitudes to nature encountered in India and other non-western cultures.

---

[2] See also Q.C.B. Cronk (2000).

[3] Summarized in L.C. Brown (1981, 1982).

Grove also argues that tropical islands - sometimes viewed as analogues of the Garden of Eden, as potential Utopias or as symbolising the world ecosystem - often changed within a few generations after colonial occupation from a state close to paradise to devastated deserts. He suggests that it was on islands such as St Helena and Mauritius in the late seventeenth century that general critiques of environmental degradation were first formulated, and understanding of the limitations of natural resources and the need for conservation emerged.

On St Helena the lack of continuity of policy between governorships often contributed to failure of conservation initiatives, but the wide overseas experience of governors and other administrators was sometimes beneficial. Professional scientists also played a part; they were often medical men or were in charge of botanical gardens, and were in close communication with academic societies and groups in their home countries, so that new ideas moved fast.

The latter part of the 18th century was a period in which prominent thinkers and colonial administrators in Britain and various parts of the empire were becoming aware of the potential links between deforestation and climatic change. Both agricultural improvement and tree planting schemes were under consideration or in course of implementation in several parts of the world. Environmental protection policies instituted in Mauritius and the Caribbean and based on coherent philosophical and scientific ideas, were evidently partly responsible for the renewed attempts by the Directors of the East India Company to organise forest conservation measures on St Helena. These ideas were widely accepted in influential circles, but the forests had already largely disappeared, despite the strenuous and far-sighted efforts of several governors half a century earlier.

The botanist W.J. Burchell, whose role in the discovery of the plants of St Helena has already been discussed, was clearly influenced by these ideas relating to conservation and by contemporary aesthetic approaches to landscape. Pondering on the deforestation of the island in his journal for 1807 (quoted by Grove) he wrote that he felt...

> "...the demolition of one of these ancient gum trees with a superstitious concern, and the feeling of a fellow creature; for in all probability, unless St Helena should be deserted, these trees would never again be suffered to attain so great an age, and (as this tree is peculiar to the island) this was sacrilegiously destroying the largest of the kind that would ever again be in the world".

By the middle of the 19th century the destruction of tropical forests had become a public issue in England, with clear realisation - for instance by members of the British Association - of the deleterious ecological and economic effects of the elimination of forests in many parts of the world, together with concern about possible ensuing changes in climate. Writing at the start of the new millennium, we find Grove's analysis depressing; with forest destruction rampant and global climate change already impinging on human welfare in several regions, we are shown how intelligent people nearly two centuries ago were alert to the dangers of large-scale interference with natural ecosystems. Grove sees the roots of modern environmentalism in those early times, but growth of the tree was stunted for an inordinately long time, and it has yet to reach its prime.

vegetables such as radishes and pumpkins, as well as a number of herbs. The accidental introductions included rats and cats, whose effects will be discussed later.

Goats and pigs may have been introduced on the first visit, although a date of 1513 is generally quoted. These animals had enormous ecological effects in the centuries that followed. Goats evidently multiplied rapidly, since Captain Cavendish, who came in 1588 in command of the first English ship to visit the island, wrote:[4]

> "There are in this island thousands of goats,which the Spaniards call cabritos, which are very wild: you shall see one or two hundred of them together, and sometimes you may behold them going in a flock almost a mile long. Some of them are as big as an ass, with a mane like a horse and a beard hanging down to the very ground. They will climb up the cliffs which are so steep that a man would think it a thing impossible for any living thing to go there. We took and killed many of them for all their swiftness, for there be thousands of them upon the mountains."

Anyone with experience in Mediterranean countries will be able to imagine the impact of thousands of goats on vegetation which had been evolving for millions of years on St Helena in the absence of vertebrate herbivores. Not a single one of the native plants has thorns or other physical protection against browsing. Furthermore, the seedlings of many species lack the capacity to regenerate if they lose the leading shoot. During the occasional droughts, almost all the edible and accessible plant material must have been consumed in most parts of the island. Survival of the endemic species depended on individual plants being able to live in places inaccessible or unattractive to goats and pigs.

The pre-settlement accounts are not consistent enough to chart the fluctuations in the goat population. The Cornish traveller Peter Mundy,[5] visiting in 1634, reported that the island was: *"abounding in Goates, of whome you may see many flocks of great numbers every Foote"*. Although the animals were hunted by visiting sailors, their numbers were doubtless determined primarily by the balance between reproduction and starvation. When periods of drought with consequent mortality were followed by periods with good rainfall, the plant populations evidently gained a respite and some regeneration occurred. On his second visit in 1638 Mundy wrote:

> "For by report off Diverts off our company that had bin sundry tymes at this Island, They Never saw More store Nor better water than Now ran in every valley, Never saw itt More greene and Flourishing in grasse and trees then Now att present (I meane aloft)." ..."The Cattle allsoe Never in better case: all this alofft as afforesaid." ... "the higher the land the better ground; here and there groves and woodes off small trees, in other places thicketts off Shrubbes, weedes and Fearnes, harbours For hogges as the rockes for the goates; all the rest yeilding good grasse; allsoe some Mints, Malloes, purcelane, a kind of Camomill smelling very sweet are here to bee Found." ... "The goates For the most part blacke, some white or party coulloured."

On his third visit, in 1656, Mundy reported that:

> "Neither did I, nor any of our company (for ought I could heare), see soe much as one goate: supposed to be devoured by dogges, which have mightily encreased here."

Mundy is generally a good witness, but it is clear that he and his companions did not visit all parts of the island. Only a couple of years later, John Nieuhoff visited the island and commented:[6]

---

[4] T. Cavendish, quoted by P. Gosse (1990).

[5] R.C. Temple (1914, 1919), R.C. Temple & L.M. Anstey (1936).

[6] In a translation reproduced by P.L. Teale (1978, 1981).

"Wild goats are here in vast numbers, but are very difficult to be taken, by reason of the many Rocks."

There was no regular human population on St Helena during the first half of the 17th century. When the English East India Company settled the island in 1659 goats were a dominant feature of the ecosystem, and the records of the company provide ample evidence of the preoccupation of the authorities with them and their effects. At first, the Company and its employees on the island were possessive about goats. In 1678 the Records say:

"It is therefore Ordered that from the day of the date hereof noe person whatsoever on the said Island doe presume on any pretence whatsoever to Hunt, Kill, or Destroy any of the Said Wild Goates without leave first had in writing from ye Govr. of the Said Island."

By 1698, however, the Company had changed its attitude to wild goats, as indicated from the report of a Consultation:

"Although the Right Honourable Company by their former orders doth stile all wild Goates on this Island, to be their owne, However considering that since ye time – the case is quite altered, cheifly four years since, where there are so many tame goates, that the Islanders desired very often the Governor and Councill to advise a means to destroy greater part of them, because – hardly finding food on the rocks (that is the uttermost parts of this Island) were forced by a natural necessity to come nigher inland, and so theire plantations and cattle endangered by a totall ruine. Joynt to this, that having ships coming here, but very seldome, the owners thereof, had no wayes to dispose of them, but was spent amongst theire families. Insomuch that this great plenty made them neglect pounding of them: and consequently the most part thereof did runn wild."

The somewhat disjointed statement went on to describe the evils of unregulated shooting of goats, and finally ordered that to avoid quarrels, neighbours should hunt goats together, and only on Wednesdays.

The idea of fencing woodland against grazing animals soon arose. A law was said to have been enacted in about 1682 requiring planters to fence in part of their land, but it was ignored and a quarter of a century later the planters denied all knowledge of it. There is no doubt, however, that the East India Company not only encouraged the planters to conserve trees, but also tried to ensure its own future wood supplies. When allotting land to the original settlers the Company had kept part of the island for its own use; one such area was the Great Wood (see below).

Shortage of timber on the island was noted remarkably soon after the settlers arrived, with indications of the decline of Redwood and Ebony – two of the most important native trees – before the end of the 17th century. In 1694, for instance, the records state: *"Timber growing very scarce in the Island. Ordered that none of the companies Timber trees (Redwood) be sold for private use."* It has been plausibly suggested that timber shortage became apparent so quickly because browsing by goats had been killing the young trees for 150 years, so that the more accessible parts of the forest were in a senile state when the settlers arrived. The old trees close to settlements would have been quickly felled for use in buildings or barked by the tanners, and there would have been few saplings to take their place.

The appointment of Governor Roberts in 1708 initiated three decades in which there was greater continuity in efforts to control goats and preserve woodland, than at any other time in the four centuries following discovery of the island. Three governors during this period – John Roberts, Isaac Pyke and Edward Byfield – were notably interested in conservation and had support from London.

Three months after Roberts became Governor, a letter was sent to the Directors: *"In answer to your 27 para. about Wood we do apprehend there can be no want this fifty year, but we shall be encouraging the people to plant for their necessary uses about their plantations."* Roberts was as good as his word, and within a few months not only re-promulgated the old forgotten law about fencing, but also used his leverage to bring about action. According to T.H. Brooke, writing in his *History of St. Helena* in 1808, many of the inhabitants had made a considerable income by hiring out their slaves to the Company, as labourers, at the rate of one shilling and sixpence per day, but the Council now resolved that no black should be hired by the Company until his proprietor could certify that his land was fenced and planted with a due proportion of wood.

At this time thirty-six of the *"principle inhabitants"* made a series of propositions to Governor Roberts, one of which asked for access to the 'Great Wood', and in the accompanying address said:

> *"And whereas your Worship and Councill having Represented to us thee Necessity we are in for the Good of our Selves and Successors To use means for the preservation of Wood, which grows very Scarce, and will inevitably be at Last the undoing of the Island, and the Inhabitants of it, if due Care is not taken for the Maintaining of wood, in Planting ye Same, Wee making Serious Reflections on this Account, Came to this Conclusion Viz: That Every Planter Possessed of Twenty Acres of Land, Shall be obliged to Enclose one Acre and plant it with wood, and so Proportionably for more or Less, and to take that Care that no Cattle or Hoggs, shall come to Graze on the said Land, that the said wood so growing may not be Spoiled ..."*

Roberts agreed that the planters could make use of the Great Wood, but only on condition that they made a law requiring them to plant one acre of wood in each ten (rather than twenty) acres they possessed, either freehold or leasehold. The law – which was accepted by the petitioners and duly enacted – not only stated the requirements for fencing, but also specified the maximum planting distance for trees of seven foot from each other, and made provision for restocking after felling *"with wood of the same nature"*. It then continued:

> *"The Intent of this Law is that every Person shall have a Sufficient quantity of wood to Supply their own Occasions, and always keep standing the full Quantity of one Acre in Ten which shall be Continued Established and Maintained Live Acres of wood for ever."*

A period of two years was allowed for compliance, after which all land would be seized by the Company, unless the owner could prove that difficulties in the supply of seeds or plants was responsible for the delay.

In 1710 Roberts wrote to the Directors in London expressing extreme dissatisfaction at the failure of Governor Poirier (who had been in office for most of the previous decade) to undertake adequate fencing, and commented: *"indeed had he done anything to prevent the Island going to Rack and Ruine we should have the less need of hands and our labour and time been employed to much better service."*

The records from the same period state: *"The Redwood and Ebony trees ... are most of 'em destroyed by the Tanners that for laziness never took the pains to bark the whole tree but only the bodies."* Ebony was used not only for tanning, but after 1709 also for burning limestone to make lime. Many of the trees were conveniently already dead – killed by goats or the tanners – and in the same entry in the Records there is the comment:

> *"We do find that Ebony wood will burne Lime and being informed that there is huge quantities of that wood which lies dead on the hills near Sandy Bay the Gov. and Capt.*

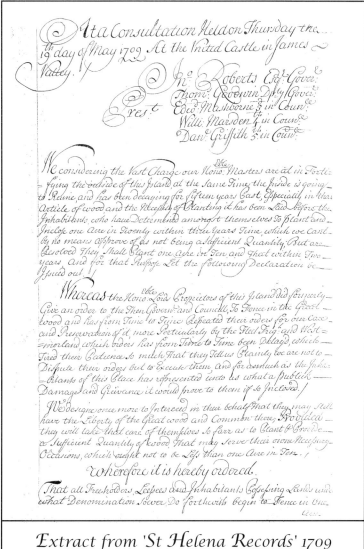

Extract from 'St Helena Records' 1709

Figure 19

Mashborne went there to view it and found the report true for that there is abundance indeed and just by that place where the wood lies is mountains of extraordinary Lime Stone."

Governor Roberts used official resources in forestry enterprises, including fencing of some of the Company's land to protect the trees from goats and other grazing animals. The records in 1709 report the planting of five thousand and twenty nine Gumwood trees and five hundred Lemon Trees in Plantation Valley. Roberts also began actively enforcing an old regulation requiring: *"the owners of every beast to pay the Company twelve pence per head, for being suffered to graze one year upon the Company's waste land."*

Such an active governor was bound to make enemies, and some of Roberts' initiatives were soon undermined. For instance, shortly after his resignation in 1711 the Directors wrote to his successor, Benjamin Boucher, in the following terms:

> *"... our late Governor Roberts says in his Letter that the goats destroy all the young Wood and that the Island will be speedily ruined if the Law for planting Wood is not put in Execution. That therefore he proposes it as a generall Benefit to the Company and all the Inhabitants to kill all the Goates, unless they cou'd be kept from brousing on the Young Trees. Consider you of this, and give us your Opinion what we shou'd direct therein and in such general Concerns consult with the Islanders, and lett them make such Laws in these and such like Cases they judge best; But if you are well assured that Particular Peoples Interest and not the General Benefit of the whole hinders the making of good Laws, then interpose your Authority."*

In the response from the island, Roberts' suggestion about killing goats was discounted:

> *"... we dont think this feasible or beneficial either to your Honours or the inhabitants for that goats generally range in the out parts of the Island next the sea where nothing else can, or few Trees grow except Shrubs which is of no use, and they live with lesser care than anything else and is very ready meat and saves the killing of Cattle."*

The writers of this letter also mentioned that:-

> *"... as to those Trees being barked for tanning leather ... they never grew in or near the Great Wood but under the Main Ridge called Redwood Trees the best and most proper for building houses of which theres but very few now the nature of those Trees seldom producing any young ones although enclosed whereas Gumwood doth."*

In their response, the Directors picked up the last point, taking a long view:

> *"This Seems very Strange to us, do you try to raise more, and if one peice of ground is not kindly, try another, for it is very Necessary to have usefull Timber and in Quantity on St. Helena because of the great Charge in Sending Supplys."*

After three years of selfish rule by Boucher, Governor Isaac Pyke was appointed in 1714. He commented that the island was: *"in a declining state and in some parts constantly decaying being every year in a worser state than the former"*. Governor Pyke immediately embarked on a series of positive measures. One of these was the importation of Furze, which came to be a crucial source of fuel on the island as the native trees were progressively destroyed, and was also used for hedging. Pyke also started the planting of imported pines, as well as of native trees and various fruit trees. In one month in 1716, for instance, the Records show that 1,860 plants were put in, including: *"800 Gum Wood Trees and 650 Figg Trees."* It is not clear, however, how much was achieved in the long run, since towards the end of this first period during which Pyke was Governor, a Letter from England exhorted: *"Remember our orders for planting and fencing our lands they have seemed of late to lie asleep or to be dead revive them."*

On about 1st May 1719 there occurred one of the major storms that occasionally affect the island, and the account in the Records strongly suggests that the severity of the erosion that it caused was related to the extensive destruction of the trees whose roots would have held the soil together. The flood:

> *"carried away the soile in an incredible manner with both grass, trees, yams, and stone walls before it. It brought down rocks of a mighty bulk and covered abundance of fruitful land with stones, the fine earth being washed away in such great quantity that the sea for a great way round about the island lookt like black mudd."*

Another comment from 1717 shows clear recognition of the deleterious effects of deforestation:

".... those things that used to flourish under the lee of such a shade are blasted and destroyed by the high winds so that not the mountains only but the plains and valleys too have been destroyed by cutting up the wood from the upper ground."

Edward Byfield became Governor in 1727 (he had earlier been acting Governor for a while) and the Records immediately start to reflect his concern about planting and fencing, with a series of exhortations to the inhabitants. Even when planting was done, however, unpredictable weather sometimes caused problems of survival. In the year of Byfield's appointment a letter to England said:

"Redwood Trees excellent Timber of a good colour and fine scent and much resembles a Red Cedar. Yet it was nearly lost to the island, but about five years ago the Govr. got a couple of young plants neither of them above an inch high set them in his garden, took great care of them and they now produce seed in great abundance."

It appears that the Governor referred to was Edward Byfield, who at the relevant time was superintendant to the plantations, and his action on behalf of the St Helena Redwood in about 1722 must be one of the earliest cases anywhere in the world of a positive effort to conserve a species in danger of extinction. It is particularly intriguing to find that 30 years later, the island was apparently able to export Redwood: in 1757 the Records state that the *Queen Sophia* was: *"loaded with bale goods, pepper, salt petre, and redwood, bound for Copenhagen."*

Byfield energetically enforced the law requiring fencing and planting of wood, and imposed so many fines on delinquents that the inhabitants themselves realized that drastic action was required. In 1729 the Records record the following Petition:

"To the Worshipfull Edward Byfield Govr & Council. The humble petition of the inhabitants assembled at the country church most humbly sheweth, that whereas your petitioners to their great concern have considered the ill state and condition of this island in the great want of wood and its daily going to decay which if not prevented will inevitably be the ruin of this place, that notwithstanding the great care & diligence of your petitioners in planting and setting wood in the proper season their labours are entirely lost by the goats and sheep (which are now very numerous) by breaking in upon their lands and destroying the Woods as well as being destructive to all the young wood that comes up yearly in the out parts of this island your petitioners therefore humbly pray that all the goates & sheep upon this island may be destroyed for the term of ten years from the time they are all destroyed in which time your petitioners hope their island will return to its primitive covering of wood, and to allow two years time for the destroying of the goates or sheep..."

"Furthermore your petitioners request that those people that have ranges of goats and they may be entitled to them by being registered and to have the privilidge of those ranges at the expiration of the time in order to raise fresh stocks of goates & sheep again ..."

The Records list the 41 persons who approved and the 11 who either refused to sign the petition or opposed the killing of goats and sheep (the latter group included Thomas Greentree, of whom more later). They then continue:

"The said petition being read Mr. Alexander & Mr. Goodwin who have each of them large stocks of goates were asked if they were willing they should all be killed & they very readily consented being sensible that no other way or means would be effectual to raise wood in sufficient plenty & as wee are perfectly convinced that this of all methods that

can possibly be contrived likely to answer the end for which it is designed is the best wee have agreed thereto & as an encouragement to others to bear with a present inconveniency which in all probability be attended with great advantage to the present as well as future generations we have determined to kill all the Honourable Company's stock of goates & sheep except such same sheep as are kept in pasture with the cattle & in lieu thereof we will endeavour to raise stocks of other sorts of provision sufficient for their use ..."

This episode brings out the curious status both of the goats and of the steeper and more eroded fringes of the island, which as early as the 1680s were referred to as: *"the Company's waste land"* and which are now known as the Crown Wastes. Although hunting of goats had been prohibited in 1678, planters could obtain permission from the Governor and Council to appropriate flocks of goats to their own use, and to maintain them on parts of the Company's waste lands. By the late 1720s ownership of goats was evidently well established, and the arrangements for their destruction included provision for registration of 'goat ranges'. Subsequently these ranges were bought and sold in a formal way, and although goats wandered freely and intermingled, they were marked and could be sorted out when pounded.

The major cull of the goats on St Helena in 1729, after deleterious effects of the high populations had become apparent, is an intriguing early example of an attempt at ecological restoration of devastated land. Writing in Scotland in the year 2000, we find irony in the fact that it was late in the 20th century before steps were taken to remedy similar effects of excessive populations of deer on natural vegetation of the Highlands.

Credit for the St Helena initiative must go primarily to Governor Edward Byfield, and even though the law requiring destruction of goats (and sheep) provided for the ranges to be resumed after ten years, it did have a beneficial effect. An inhabitant who died in 1805 at the age of eighty-three, informed T.H. Brooke that many parts of the island where no trees had grown for many years before, became covered with wood after the enforcing of the act.

The fundamental problems persisted, however, and surfaced again shortly after Byfield had resigned and Isaac Pyke had returned to hold a second term as Governor. The Records for 1732 include the following passage, the end of which would serve as a summary of Hardin's article on the 'tragedy of the commons' referred to at the start of this chapter. Pyke and his colleagues on the Council wrote:

"In Several Letters from hence to your Hons. you have been acquainted that the scarcity of wood was then such in all parts of the island that the people could hardly get fuel for their necessary purposes. The mater since has daily grown worse & worse for notwithstanding they are all sensible of what great consequence the encrease of wood is to them and that their own and the fortunes of their children after them & that even the preservation of the island itself depends upon the speedy encrease thereof yet hardly one of them has taken the necessary care about this matter but quite the reverse has happened they have wastfully cut down great numbers of grown timber ..."

"... if effectual care be not immediatly taken of this matter this place before the end of the next generation will become a desert & so do this to purpose We humbly propose to your Honours as the most likely if not only expedient that can be offered that you would be pleased to give us leave to lett all the common wast land of which there is an abundance that at this time has neither {bush?} or grasse growing thereon the most of it fit for wood at rates in proportion to the value of it, some of it being worth only 12p some 18p and some perhaps 2 or three shillings & are to be fenced & always set apart for the sole purpose of raising wood & for no other use whatsoever for as long as it lies common no care will ever be taken of this matter every man thinking that he has as good to cut wood

off the common as his neighbour and so they all agree to cut down & destroy & never think of planting or raising other trees in lieu of those they fell."

Governor Pyke, ruthless but effective, died in 1737. In the following decade, it was partly conflict between the local administrators and the Directors in London that rendered conservation efforts futile, as is shown by an episode in 1744-45, in which a serious attempt was made to curb the destructive effects of common grazing. The first relevant entry runs:

"The Governor reports that he has been informed there is a place called Peak Gutt which hath heretofore produced great quantities of Ebony and would still produce the same but the goats allowed to go in that range bark the growing trees and hinder their increase."

As a result of this information, and also reports that some of the goats in question were infected with the mange, it was decided that all the goat ranges contiguous to Sandy Bay should be visited and the goats pounded for examination. It was also pointed out, however:

"that it would be greatly for the Honble Company's interest, that the growth of Ebony should be encouraged, they and others concerned in the said range, were desired to meet & consult among themselves, upon what terms they would consent to give up the said range for that purpose, and that if they could not agree among themselves, their severall interests sho'd be appraised by some of the neighbouring planters, and the money of such appraisement should be paid them within 2 or 3 Years, or be again putt in posession of the said ranges."

Two of the relevant owners, Messrs Thomas and James Greentree, were therefore instructed to pound their goats for inspection on a specified date:

"... to which written order each of them returned for answer, that they had something else to do, & they would pound their goats when they wanted them."

The reaction of the authorities was immediate:

"...the said Greentrees were this day ordered to attend, and having been heard in their own defence their excuse appeared so triffling, that their crime and contempt of authority were rather aggravated than otherwise; for all of which they were severely reprimanded ... & to deter them & others from daring to offer the least contempt for the future, they the Govr. & Councill unanimously ordered, that each of the said Greentrees should be fined £10 Sterling..."

The Greentrees attended and paid their fines, and the Govr. & Council made full use of the occasion:

"at the same time told the said Messrs. Thomas & James Greentree that they ought to look upon this fine as a very mild punishment for soe great a crime that disobeying lawfull authority was much the same as resisting it, and resisting authority was the beginning of rebellion which was a capital crime."

They did not, however, have the last word, since a few months later a letter from the Directors in England stated:

"The two Mr Greentrees having applied to us for relief we would have you repay them the fines levyed upon them for disobeying the orders as to their goats. These cattle being of much more use to us and the poorer sort of planters than the growth of ebony, herefor they should not be destroyed upon that account."

The island Records for July 9th, 1745 tersely state:

"We have repaid the two Messrs Greentree their fines according to your orders, as you are of opinion that the goats are of more use here than ebony they shall not be destroyed for the future."

Those with long memories must have smiled cynically in 1778 when a letter was received from England which included the passage:

"We are of the opinion that encouraging the growth of wood is of the utmost consequence to this island not only from the advantages to be derived from it as fuel but because it is well known that trees have an attractive power on the clouds especially when they pass over Hills so high as those on your Island and we are inclined to believe that the misfortunes the Island has been subject to from drought might in some measure have been averted had the growth of wood been properly attended to ..."

"... we lamented the want of attention not to say total neglect that has prevailed for more than 70 years past with respect to an object of the highest importance to the welfare of the island, namely the cultivation of wood, and if a steady perseverance is not observed to promote it in the future the present inhabitants will afford their posterity as just a reason for condemning their conduct as they have now to deplore that of their ancestors."

The authorities on the island at this time and during the next few decades were receptive to the advice from London. Governor John Skottowe made substantial efforts at preserving native woods, while the Huguenot Daniel Corneille, who succeeded him, renewed contact with the eminent botanist Sir Joseph Banks. New planting schemes were initiated, and continued during the governorship of Colonel Robert Brooke, who received extensive advice from Banks on tree planting and other matters. The efforts met with some success, and in 1794 oaks planted at Plantation House about seven years previously were reported to be 30-40 feet high. Brooke also undertook an ambitious scheme to conduct water from springs below Diana's Peak to Deadwood, which saved many of the company's cattle during a subsequent drought. This example encouraged some of the farmers to make similar watercourses, enabling them to convert several acres of barren ground into good grazing.

At this time there was not only an able Governor in the person of Brooke, but also a Lieutenant-Governor, Francis Robson, who really cared about trees. He responded to questions from London with a long explanation of the difficulties involved in promoting the growth of wood on the island. He confessed to: *"being naturally a Scientific Person"* and made a number of acute observations. For instance, in response to a suggestion that part of the very limited fenced area should be reserved for hay, he pointed out that:

"...its annually being mowed would inevitably cut off any young tree plants that may have casually come up there, and they are of such a nature, that if once cutt off, the same plants will not shoot again."

Robson may have been the first person to note the lack of defensive adaptations in the endemic plants against browsing herbivores (which were absent from the island during the whole evolution of its plant community).

A separate report sent to the Directors at this time discussed both European and indigenous trees likely to succeed at Longwood, and a detailed response was given to a question about tree planting; it suggests that considerable skill and care were used in the planting carried out around this time:

"Being requested by the Board to give our opinion respecting the proper time for planting the Hon'ble Company's grounds called Long Wood with Gum Wood plants; in compliance therefore with this wish, we have to observe that we conceive a more eligible or happy

144

time cannot occur than the present, particularly if plants of a proper size and strength can be procured, not only on account of the present rains, but from observation the spring of the year is always favourable for transplanting these as well as most other plants – the size we would recommend as most likely to take is from nine to twelve inches high should they be set where the grass is high; if otherwise plants from six to nine inches..."

In spite of the tree planting activity and ecological concern of the late 18th century, Governor Robert Patton, arriving in 1802, found an island largely denuded of trees. Although each tenant – since about 1709 – had been required by a clause in his lease to grow and protect trees on a tenth part of his land, compliance had not been ensured. Patton instigated a new regulation entitling each proprietor to a renewal of his lease, on the terms of his existing tenure, provided he had reared to a certain height a specified number of trees. This number, however, was only six trees per acre, providing a depressing contrast with the 1709 law, which required planting of trees on a tenth of the land at a minimum distance of seven feet (over 800 per acre).

The comments by the botanist W.J. Burchell from the same decade show his dismay at the degraded state of the island.[7] On a trip along Stone Top Ridge from the Bellstone to Boxwood Hill he recorded shrubs of Scrubwood and Boxwood and commented:

"I have noticed that all the way we have come is strewed with the decayed remains of trees and shrubs which must formerly have covered all these hills .... the soldiers and inhabitants have been suffered barbarian-like to cut down the trees with a wanton waste, only making use of the stems and thick branches, leaving the brushwood behind. Almost everyone can tell me they can remember thick and almost impassable groves of trees growing on these hills, which now offer to the eye nothing but a cindery bareness."

Alexander Beatson, who took over as Governor in 1808, was an innovative agriculturalist and prolific writer. In his efforts to educate the landholders in good husbandry, he made use of the fact that printing had been introduced to St Helena in 1806. One of his schemes was to develop an initiative taken two decades earlier by Governor Robert Brooke, relating to the burning of Samphire (a salt-tolerant plant then known as 'salsola') to produce barilla or soda-ash, an impure alkali. A local merchant was already using this procedure in the making of soap, but Beatson started up a substantial export operation. He found that the plants grew back rapidly after cutting, and also showed that they could be grown from seed. One eventual outcome of this sensible initiative shocked Charles Darwin on his visit to the island in 1836; he wrote:

"Partridges and pheasants are tolerably abundant; the island is much too English not to be subject to strict game-laws. I was told of a more unjust sacrifice to such ordinances than I ever heard of even in England. The poor people used to burn a plant, which grows on the coast-rocks, and export the soda from its ashes; but a peremptory order came out prohibiting this practice, and giving as a reason that the partridge would have nowhere to build."

Governor Beatson was well aware of the destruction caused by both goats and people, and made serious attempts to protect the remaining native forests. In 1813 he noted that:

"If the goats are not exterminated and the Sheep tamed there is but too much reason to apprehend that those animals will be a constant source of vexation and loss to those who have really a desire to contribute their efforts to the general good of the Island."

In a Proclamation issued a few weeks later Beatson addressed a different issue:

---

[7] Quoted by L.C. Brown (1982).

"Notwithstanding the various regulations which have been promulgated to prevent the destruction of trees particularly on the interior heights of the island – yet such has been the disregard to those regulations that some Proprietors of Cabbage Tree Lands have lately complained of being daily robbed of whole trees that would be even useful in building and that blacks are frequently seen carrying Cabbage Tree wood to James's Town for fuel altho' furze is to be obtained. To put a stop therefore to so injurious a practice the Governor & Council do hereby positively prohibit Cabbage Tree of any description being used as fuel in James's Town under the penalty of £5. to be incurred by any person in whose house or premises such wood shall be found: the whole amount of the penalty will be paid to any informer who shall convict the offender or offenders. A reward also of 40s/ will be paid from the police fund to any person who shall convict another of carrying to James's Town, either the stems, branches or roots of Cabbage Tree wood, green or dry whether with or without the permission of the proprietor of the land from which they shall have been taken: and the person so convicted shall be liable either to a fine of £5. or corporal punishment not exceeding 200 lashes to be awarded by any two magistrates.

Beatson's Proclamation was rescinded after his departure, but was reinstated in 1816 after the arrival of Napoleon and of Hudson Lowe as the new Governor. The new version implied that the proprietors of the Cabbage Tree lands were sometimes themselves guilty parties:

"Whereas it has come to the Knowledge of the Governor and Council that certain Landholders without regarding the mischievous consequences of divesting the interior heights of the island of wood, but intent only on present advantage are in the habit of cutting down growing trees and selling the same for fuel – Such practice is hereby positively prohibited in future..."

These proclamations provided at least theoretical protection for the endemic cabbage trees, which evidently still survived in substantial numbers near the central ridge. Other native trees had suffered more severely, and the forests of Ebony, Redwood and Gumwoods which had originally covered so much of the island had evidently almost disappeared by the early 19th century. Ebony was considered 'almost extinct' as early as 1771; Redwood – seriously threatened as early as the 1720's – was reduced to only a few individuals in the wild by 1807. Gumwood had fared slightly better, but was patchily distributed and rapidly declining. In 1824 the Proceedings of the Agricultural and Horticultural Society of St Helena, quoted by Linda Brown, noted that: *"the practice of tethering goats upon the green patches of wire grass on Ladder Hill"* was destroying: *"the young gumwood growing in many parts"*. A Proclamation dated 22nd July 1833 and signed by R.F. Seale, Secretary to Government, commented on continued destruction of Gumwoods at Longwood:

"whereas the cutting of wood upon the Company's enclosed or waste lands without permission from the Governor, or upon the property of individuals without leave of the proprietors, is already prohibited by law: Notice is hereby given, that any person upon whose premises any green or dry gum wood shall be found without such person being able to account satisfactorily for the same, will become liable to be prosecuted for theft."

This was the last attempt by the East India Company administration to conserve the native trees of St Helena. Like almost all previous initiatives, this one was evidently ineffective, since by 1868 Melliss estimated that there were fewer than 2,000 Gumwood trees remaining. Thus ended nearly two centuries of intermittent and ineffective attempts by the East India Company to protect the native trees and woodland of the island from the effects of self-centred and short-sighted exploitation.

Within a year of Seale's Proclamation, attempts at conservation on St Helena were overwhelmed by a political earthquake. In April 1834, with hardly any warning, responsibility for the island was transferred from the East India Company to the British Government. The change was an economic disaster for the island, with drastic reductions in the scale of government employment and remuneration. Seale himself eventually lost his job, many families were thrown into poverty and within a few years substantial emigration occurred.

There was thus a situation on St Helena, by the middle of the 19th century, in which the economic motive for conservation of native trees had almost disappeared, and at the same time, agriculture was probably close to its nadir. An entry in the St Helena Almanac of 1862 reads:

> "The greater part of the island is now bare of trees and verdure, many mountains having little upon them beyond samphire and a few scrubby weeds, which alone save them from absolute sterility, especially in the dry season when the shallow soil is utterly parched up. Other mountains are capable of affording a very limited supply of food for sheep, which traverse their loftiest peaks and most intricate paths in search of their scanty fare."

The continuing effect of agriculture on the indigenous vegetation is shown by a report on the agricultural resources of St Helena written in 1884 by Mr. D. Morris, then Director of Public Gardens and Plantations in Jamaica. He estimated that the area of forest was by this time reduced to around 400 acres: *"both of indigenous and introduced trees, in detached and struggling patches"* and he noted that since the land on the higher slopes afforded good hay grass there was a tendency: *"to cut down in every possible locality the indigenous trees"*. Morris continued, however, with a suggested conservation measure analogous to the restoration initiatives under way at the start of the 21st century:

> "I would suggest that a boundary be marked from the top of the central ridge, extending, say, 500 yards down the slope to the northward, and this should be permanently maintained in forest; and where at present denuded, that it be carefully and systematically replanted."

> "This belt might begin at the Old Picquet House [just above Old Luffkins], *the eastern* [he meant western] *termination of the central ridge, and extend to the westward* [eastward], *under High Peak, Old Telegraph, Sandy Bay Ridge, Stitches Ridge, the Three Peaks, to High Ridge and Long Ground Ridge. The high road running under the northern slope of the central ridge might form a convenient boundary for this belt; but in cases where it comes close to the ridge, as at Telegraph and Sandy Bay Ridge, the boundary might fall below the road."

The writings of 19th century scientists who visited St Helena indicate varied degrees of concern about the loss of the native vegetation. More eloquent but less practical than Morris was the coleopterist T. Vernon Wollaston, who had made a six month visit in 1875-76. In discussing the likely early extinction of beetle species associated with lost endemic plants such as the Boxwood, Wollaston wrote in 1877:

> "...the fast-disappearing asters and gumwoods, around which a whole tribe of Cossonids may be said to cluster, tell a tale of what a few more generations may accomplish, — unless the inhabitants should become sufficiently alive, even yet, to their own interests (which, however, I can scarcely venture to anticipate) to put a stop to the pernicious practice of destruction which has already reduced a considerable portion of the island to a well-nigh hopeless state of arid and chaotic sterility."

He continued in a footnote:

> "... it is not so much for the sake of the trees themselves that I am pleading as for the conditions of the country which their presence in large masses could not fail to imply; for

147

where forests exist (and no forests, in any region, are equal to those of nature's own planting), there also exists, inevitably, moisture; and without moisture, and well-filled streams, what are the chances of successful cultivation?"

Wollaston went on to point out the problems of soil erosion caused by loss of trees:

"The light and friable soil which a mass of herbage will slowly but steadily accumulate in the course of a few centuries, and which becomes thicker and more persistent as time goes on, would be held together, in situ, as above mentioned, so long as the vegetation is left untouched; but when the latter has been so far tampered with that the roots and fibres perish, and there is no foliage left to break the violence of the tropical rains when falling upon the ground, the soil will be gradually washed down into the river-beds below and be carried bodily away."

More than 50 years later came an equally impassioned plea from Philip Gosse – traveller, doctor, naturalist and prolific writer – who visited the island in 1937 while writing his book on the history of the island. Gosse was appalled by the continuing influence of goats, in spite of the fact that the role of these tough, agile herbivores in destroying vegetation and promoting erosion had been understood for at least two centuries. In a formal letter to the Colonial Secretary he wrote:

"Almost everyone "keeps" goats. They roam at large and where they will, eating up all the seedling trees; so that amongst others, the famous Ebony Wood tree is extinct, and there are at this moment only seven living specimens in the whole island of the beautiful and unique flowering Redwood... The Agricultural Officer surely should grow seeds of these survivors in the Government experimental garden..."

"The Islanders are jealous of their goats and resent any suggestion that the island would be better without them. Goats appear to give their owners some sort of social status, certainly they give him little else. The St. Helenians scarcely ever eat goat's flesh, although meat with them is a rare luxury. Nor was I able to hear of a single case of a goat being milked and cows' milk is a luxury."

"I suggest that ruthless measures be taken to settle once and for all the goat problem."

It was to be several more decades before the island authorities were ready to adopt the necessary 'ruthless measures'. We do not know whether the goats in the 1930s were really as useless domestically as Gosse implied, but there is no doubt that they still exerted their malign influence on the native vegetation, and this was officially recognised in the 1950s.

In 1957 Norman Humphrey, Agricultural and Forestry Officer, estimated the land use on the island as follows:

Barren	20,100 acres
Pasturage	4,650 acres
New Zealand Flax (*Phormium tenax*)	3,350 acres
Established forests	1,000 acres
Cultivated land	500 acres
New forests	400 acres
Total	30,000 acres

At that time the two thirds of the island considered barren (the Crown Wastes) had a scattering of introduced herbs and shrubs, but the endemic vegetation had almost entirely disappeared from all those parts of it that were accessible to goats. In 1960 C.R.

Wallace, the government entomologist whose remit was the control of agricultural pests, summarised the state of the economy as follows:

> "The population of the island at the time of the 1956 census was slightly under 5,000. The standard of living is kept up by substantial grants of Colonial Development and Welfare Funds from the United Kingdom. Directly or indirectly, this money supports free public services and enables the employment of hundreds of inhabitants in Government service or relief work. ....The Colony's chief export is Phormium fibre (hemp, tow, rope and twine) and there is also a small export trade in vegetables, bananas and other rural produce. Flour, rice and other cereals, dairy produce, canned meat, fresh fruit, onions, seed potatoes, and various stock feeds, including maize, are imported: even peanuts, which were formerly grown in St. Helena, are now imported. There is a chronic shortage of meat. Dairying is on a very small scale, the officially estimated sales of fresh milk averaging less than 1 gallon of milk per head of population per year."

The vanishing Great Wood – a case study

In the preceding section we have attempted a general account of the ecological despoilation of St Helena between its discovery in 1502 and the 20th century. We now take a closer look at a particular piece of land, known as the 'Great Wood', the history of which exemplifies many of the problems of the island, and also of natural habitats elsewhere suffering exploitation by human populations. When St Helena was settled in 1659 this wood had already suffered one and a half centuries of browsing by goats and rooting by swine, and was doubtless very deficient in young trees. It was still, however, a Gumwood forest covering the largest tract of relatively level ground at high altitude on the island: it included the areas now known as Deadwood Plain, Longwood and Bottom Woods. It was the primary habitat for two of the most spectacular endemic invertebrates, the Giant Ground Beetle and the Giant Earwig, both of which are now feared extinct, and was a stronghold of many other species.

We tell the story of the destruction of the Great Wood mainly through direct quotations from letters between the Governor and his Island Council on the one hand and the Directors of the East India Company in London on the other; additional passages are from the official records of proceedings of the Island Council. The repetitive nature of the exchanges is fundamental, as is the evident frustration of the Directors at their inability to ensure a consistent line of action on the island. Our first quotation dates from just two decades after settlement.

1679. Records, August 11th:

> "Whereas several persons of this island have several times turned many swine into the Great Wood and parts adjacent lying in common, many of which swine they have not bin able since to find, and soe they have turned wild, and thier encrease hath not bin marked whereby persons are not able to distinguish thier own from other mens, but now all are mingled and running in droves and herds one amongst another, soe that everyone thinks that all unmarked swine may bee as well his as anothers; whereupon many have endeavoured to seaze kill and convert to thier own use as many as they can catch: which hath occasioned sundry complaints of looseing both stock and encrease.
>
> For ye preventing of which inconveniences, it is ordered, that all persons whatsoever doe forthwith cause all thier swine old and yong to bee marked with thier own usual and proper marke; and that noe sort of swine bee turned into the said Great Wood and parts adjacent without being soe marked; unlesse he or they shall be able to make it appear that they are thier owne proper goods and chattells."

1683. Letter from England, August 1st:

"We think ye Great Wood is ye fittest place to be first enclosed for the Company use if you can run your enclosure so by straight lines as to take in some convenience of water this works will be prop. for ye negroes to be employed about. We would have you fence in the full extent of the Great Wood which we understand is near two miles square."

A rebellion on the island in 1684 doubtless diverted attention from the fencing project. 1708. Letter to England, November 23rd:

"If the Great Wood was fenced in it would be wood enough for the whole island. But it will be a great work it being about five miles round and stone very scarce in that place, and could not be done for less than one thousand pounds. But shall when the necessary fortifications are done take in some of it and take necessary measures to provide for the next generations."

1709, June 14th. Propositions and address to the Governor and Council, 18thly:

"They desire liberty to make use of the Great Wood and comon otherwise they will be ruined."

The Governor and Council responded:

"Provided you will agree to make a law to plant one acre of wood in every ten acres of land you possess; otherwise you shall have no benefit of our wood or common, as our published order."

The group representing the inhabitants responded:

"Agreed to and Sattisfied."

1710. Records, March 7th:

"..should the law of planting prove abortive the Island in twenty years time will be utterly ruined for want of wood, for no man upon St Helena can say there is one tree in the Great Wood, or other woods less than twenty years old, consequently it will dye with age...".

1710. Letter to England. Referring to the earlier intention to fence in the Great Wood:

"but never was a stone laid ... nor can we give you any estimate as yet what your charge will be to fence in ... the Great Wood because the digging for stones is so uncertain, for the charge will be so much the more or less according to the distance the stones must be brought for fencing."

1711. Letter from England:

"Take care our own plantations, and the Great Wood be all fenced in, and as there is opportunity that new trees be planted to supply those which have been unaccountably destroyed for the sake of the bark to tann leather with, but coud never have been done, had our own people been watchfull & by now & then surveying the wood & finding when any standing trees had been barked, had thereupon yssued out orders proper to have prevented the like in future."

1713. Letter to England:

"Its impossible to fence the Great Wood and had we never so many hands the charge of doing it would be more than the advantage to your honours ..."

1713. Letter from England:

"... what is wrote about fencing in our Great Wood that it will not quitt Cost; consider of it and do what is best for us ..."

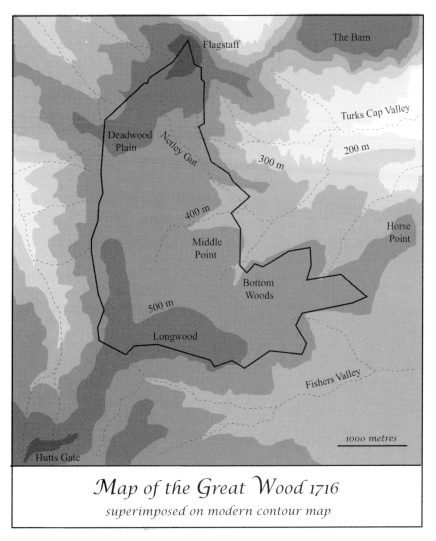

Map of the Great Wood 1716
superimposed on modern contour map

Figure 20

1716. Letter to England:

"We could fence in the Great Wood which unless it be fenced in will not have a tree upon it in twenty years more, because the old trees are now of long standing and some always falling down and dying and the small trees which arise are all destroyed by the cattle which go there as if a common."

1716. Records:

"We find the place called Great Wood is in a flourishing condition, full of young trees where hoggs (of which there is a great abundance) do not come to root them up, but the Great Wood is miserably lessened and destroyed within our memories, and is not near the circuit and length it was, but we believe it does not contain less now than 1,500 acres of fine woodland and good ground, but no water but what is salt or brackish."

"If wells could be sunk we should think it the most pleasant and healthiest part of the island. But as to healthiest we don't think twill hold so, if the wood that keeps the land warm were destroyed for then the rains which are violent here would carry away the upper soil and it being a clay marl underneath would produce but little."

151

The 'Wood's End' was mentioned as being formerly at the Hutts:

"but the Wood is so destroyed that the beginning of the Great Wood is now a whole mile beyond that place, all the soil being washt away."

An outline plan of the Great Wood was inserted in the records in 1716. This can be transferred to a modern map without much difficulty, and effectively delimits the upland plain of northern St Helena above the 400 m contour. It has a perimeter of 13.7 km (8.5 miles) and is some 1400 acres (570 hectares) in area.

The main attempt to fence (with a stone wall) the Great Wood was made in the period 1723 to 1727, mainly under Governor John Smith. The area actually fenced was much more modest than that indicated on the 1716 plan, and it is not clear that effective protection of the fenced area was achieved, even in the short term:[8]

1727. Records, November 14th:

"Whereas the Honble Company have been at a very great Charge and expense in fencing the Great Wood in Order to preserve it for the gen.l. good of the island, yet several persons in contempt & defiance of the ancient Laws made for the preservation thereof have nevertheless lately felled and carried away several young trees from that part called the Flagstaff and Dead Wood, which if not speedily prevented will destroy all the young Wood there grown by cutting down some and exposing the rest to the bleakness of the winds and weather".

It was ordered that all blacks should be sent via Hutts and thence through the Great Gate only and should return the same way and not to:

"carry or take with them any bill or hatchet upon any account whatever nor are they upon any pretence to fell, pluck up, destroy or cutt down any young wood or other trees, but are to take such decayed wood, such only, as is already fallen."

Soon after the main work on the wall was carried out, the tide of opinion on the island began to turn away from using the Great Wood primarily for wood production. Cronk mentions that in 1728, four acres at Longwood were tried for crops, and despite the acute timber shortage the settlers saw more promise in the Great Wood for crops and pasturage. T.H. Brooke, writing his history of the island in the early nineteenth century, said that:

"In the year 1728 [we think actually a little earlier], *about one hundred and fifty acres were completely enclosed, sixty-four of which, on that part called Horse Point, were appropriated to wood.[9] The remainder was divided into three pastures, and was found, for nine months in the year, to be capable of maintaining the Company's whole stock of black*

---

[8] Signs of the 18th century fencing are still evident. A bank and ditch along the side road from the Meteorological Station continues southwards before turning sharply to the west on the ridge above Fishers Valley; there was an associated stone wall within living memory, but it was taken down in recent years for building. Hardly any stones are left, but in places where the subsoil has a firm consistency it has been cut into a straight edge to form the foundation for the wall. In the other direction the wall continued to the north of Bottom Woods, across Bilberry Field Gut and then to an enclosure west of Netley Gut. The remains indicate that it was of drystone construction and was designed to be 2 feet thick and 6 feet high (Plate 8).

[9] Q.C.B. Cronk (1986b) in his account of the decline of the Gumwood, comments that the Horse Point enclosure was immediately successful, as many seedlings sprang up after the rains and subsequently the saplings had to be thinned. We suspect, however, that the 'Horse Point' referred to is not the place marked as such on the modern map (near Bryans Rock), which is clearly excluded from the 1716 map of the Great Wood. The natural vegetation near the modern Horse Point may have consisted mainly of Scrubwood rather than Gumwood; Burchell (quoted by L.C. Brown, 1982) recorded the presence of the 'dwarf gum shrub' or scrubwood between Bottom Woods and Holdfast Tom, and a single large Scrubwood survived there into the 1980s. No trace of enclosure at the modern Horse Point is shown on an 1811 map which clearly indicates the rest of the wall, and there is no sign of any substantial bank or ditch. The name Horse Point in some old records evidently refers to the area around and to the south of the Meteorological Station (west of the modern refuse dump). We have been told that even now the name is used to refer to this area, just east of Bottom Woods.

cattle, which, by Mr. Byfield's care, was increased from about two hundred and ten head to nearly double that number."

Consequently, in 1733 an idea for parts of the common to be enclosed for tree planting was opposed and it foundered. Preservation of the trees was no longer the sole objective, and in the decades that followed, the destruction of the unfenced parts of the Great Wood continued. Eventually, however, the tide of opinion turned again, and the local people realized what they had lost.

1777. Letter to England, July 20th:

> *"The Long Wood which has hitherto yielded a constant supply of fewel for this valley (as well as several of the out forts, and inhabitants in the country) being in a state of decay and going off very fast, from the great consumption of that article, and there being no succession as all the young trees are immediately upon their sprouting out of the ground destroyed by the black cattle, sheep and goats, which it is impossible to prevent in its present state without a fence round it."*

> *"We think it our indispensible duty, to acquaint you with the great detriment the loss of this useful commodity will be to Your Honors in particular and the inhabitants in general, as the produce of the whole island in this article, is inconsiderable when compared with Long Wood alone, which it is imagined by all will not last above twelve or fifteen years, and when that is gone will put the inhabitants who have posessions in the country, upon securing their property of fewel which will be barely sufficient for their own consumption and reduce the rest of the inhabitants who have no land to the greatest distress."*

The letter went on to suggest: *"the necessity of putting an impregnable fence about this place which we judge may be compleated at an expense not exceeding three thousand pounds."* The writers argued that in 10 or 12 years it would be so successful that thinning would be necessary, and that within twenty years the Company's ships would be able to obtain wood there. However, the reply from England was sharp.

1778. Letter from England, January 23rd:

> *"In your letter of 20th July last, wherein you recommend a fence to be made round the Long Wood, in order to prevent the cattle from destroying the young trees, you allege that their destruction in process of time might occasion a scarcity of fuel on the island, and have also set forth that such fence might be completed for a sum not exceeding £3000."*

> *"But here referring back to your general books from the years 1723 to 1727 inclusive, we find a charge entered of £5401.9.7 for fencing the above-mentioned wood which charge appears to have been disapproved of by the Court of Directors for the time being; and notwithstanding so large a sum was then expended a considerable part of the fence remained unfinished, and as that part which was compleated is now in a ruinous state, by which we have sustained the loss of upwards £5000. We disapprove at present of so expensive an undertaking on the uncertainty of an estimate which sets down the whole at so far less a sum than was before expended on the unfinished work – but as we consider this as an object of consequence, we desire you will obtain another estimate taken by men of experience and with the utmost exactness; for having been already deceived by one estimate, we think it necessary to give you this caution because a second deception will call for our severest censure. And we also recommend to your consideration whether a bank thrown up with two rows of furze will not answer the end at a much less expence than walling."*

> *"To prevent however as much as possible any difficulties that may arise from a scarcity of fuel we direct that the vacant ground of that part of the Long Wood called Horse Point (which is already secured by a good fence) be planted with Gum Wood Trees, that the trees*

Burchell's drawing of the Great Wood in 1809

Figure 21

be from time to time properly thinn'd, and that the wood for fuel be not too soon cut down. We likewise direct that furze be planted upon all waste land in the vicinity of James's Valley... and we direct that such lands when so planted be not, as heretofore, let out to private persons upon lease; but reserved entirely for fuel for the general use of the Inhabitants."

A decade later Governor Robert Brooke reopened the matter of the use of the land where the core of the Great Wood had stood; his comments evoked some puzzlement in London. 1789. Letter from England, 16th December:

"We have attended to Governor Brooke's observations respecting Long Wood. The large sums of money that have been expended for enclosing this place and the flattering advantages that were held out on the completion; gave us reason to suppose, there could have been but one opinion on the utility of this measure; we are surprised to hear the Governor speak of the unplanted parts, as we gave our positive directions for planting trees in every part, as soon as the fence was compleated; if you are fully convinced of the benefit to be derived from putting cattle on the grassy parts, and can prevent them from doing any injury to the other parts of the Wood, we have no objection to your adopting this proposal of the Governor's.

Before the end of the eighteenth century wood production was no longer seen as the primary land use for the area, apparently because when the trees went, a wire grass invaded the area and provided the best grazing on the island. T.H. Brooke, in his history of 1808, commented:

"But even had the orders of the Company [to plant the whole of the enclosure] been carried completely into effect, it may nevertheless be questioned how far the promised advantages would have compensated for the diminution of the number of cattle which must have been the consequence of converting so large a tract of excellent pasturage into a plantation. Other less valuable spots might have been fixed on for planting wood ..."

We know little of the final stages in the loss of the Great Wood, although much destruction of trees doubtless occurred as a result of Napoleon's confinement within its boundaries as well as the consequent establishment of a military camp on Deadwood Plain. The East India Company's farm manager, Thomas Breame, was judged – by a committee set up by the Governor, Sir Hudson Lowe – to have illicitly sold Gumwoods to Longwood, presumably for firewood, although he claimed that the felling had been done by the carpenters of HMS *Northumberland* when adapting the house for Napoleon's use.

The continuing ineffectiveness of attempts to preserve the remnants of the Great Wood is shown by a Proclamation dated 22nd July 1833 and signed by R.F. Seale, Secretary to Government, which stated:-

154

"The depredations upon the Gum Wood Trees at Longwood, are becoming so frequent as to threaten a speedy destruction of the whole of that plantation".

Four decades later Melliss reckoned that there were still 700-800 Gumwoods scattered in the area once occupied by the Great Wood. Now, the pathetic row of half a dozen old Gumwoods near Piccolo Hill – probably planted early in the 20th century – provide the only living reminder of the Great Wood. However, a long section of the wall – the controversial, expensive and abortive project of the early 18th century – still winds over the barren slopes around Middle Point. It was near the wall in Bilberry Field Gut that we found in 1995 a piece of decayed wood that was probably Gumwood.

It is, however, premature to draw a line under the story of the Great Wood. In the dawn of the new millennium, a brave attempt at restoration is getting under way (see Chapter 8).

The rise of the alien plants

The introduction of alien trees and plants to St Helena started with the discovery of the island in the early sixteenth century and continued after settlement in 1659. Tree seed was imported at least as early as 1714, but for several more decades most planting on the island was mainly of native species and it was not until the 19th century that the trickle of introductions became a flood.

The Victorian botanist Joseph Hooker, who visited St Helena twice, was one of the first naturalists to emphasize the ecological significance of introductions of alien species. Writing about St Helena in 1867, he commented that: *"by far the greater part of the vegetation that exists, whether herbs, shrubs, or trees, consists of introduced European, American, African and Australian plants."* Hooker suggested that because many of these exotic plants were now overrunning the island, it was: *"in all probability impossible that the native plants will ever again resume their sway."* He mentioned – among other alien plants – *"Cape of Good Hope Bushes* (Cape Gooseberry), *Broom, Gorse* (Furze) *and Brambles."*

'Scotch fir', 'Spruce fir' and oaks were planted with some success in the 1740s, and in 1758 the 'Stone pine' was introduced. This was followed in 1787 by the tree now known as Maritime Pine, of which the scientific name is *Pinus pinaster*; it was referred to on the island simply as 'the Pineaster'.

From the time of Governor Beatson in the early 19th century timber production on the island was primarily by means of plantations of introduced trees, and one of Beatson's last acts as Governor in 1813 was publication of directions for rearing plantations of Pineaster and other trees, based on his observations during the previous five years. He argued that the best trees for St Helena were Pineasters, together with Stone Pine, Cypress, Botany Bay Willow, indigenous Redwood and the large species of Morgossa, *Melia azedarach* (which he recommended as 'underwoods' for fuel because they reproduced after being cut down). He thought that the Blackwood (recently sent by the Governor of the Isle of France) might also be useful.

Beatson noted that some 11,000 Pineasters from the Plantation House Garden had been planted out in various parts of the island during the years 1811-13. He also mentioned that Redwood trees planted three and a half years previously were: *"from 6 to 8 feet high, with fine strait stems now in red blossom."*[10] Pineasters sown at the same time had achieved somewhat greater growth.

---

[10] This observation is of particular interest since it suggests that the deleterious effects of inbreeding, so apparent in Redwoods surviving in the 1990s (R.E. Rowe 1995) had not reached serious levels in the early 19th century.

The planting activity continued after Beatson's departure; for instance, 27,000 Pineasters were planted in 1816. In 1822 we see an early example of substantial financial incentives for private tree planting. A Proclamation on May 30th read:

> "It is hereby notified that the following premiums will be given for the planting of forest trees. The landholder who between this date and the 1st October next, shall form the largest Plantation of forest trees, effectually secured from mishap, provided such plantation shall not be less extent than 2 acres and contain not fewer than 5000 trees being about 4 ft apart, provided the trees shall be in a thriving state on the 1st January 1823, such landholder shall be entitled to a premium of £150."

The owner of the next largest plantation was to receive £30, a very considerable sum. Although the timescale for establishment seems short, Beatson had earlier noted that Pineasters typically grew about two feet in a year. This species was extensively planted and proved to be capable of natural regeneration on the island; it soon became a valuable timber tree.

Other species brought in about this time included Cape Yew, Wattles (*Acacia* species) and some species of *Eucalyptus*. By the latter part of the 19th century many other trees that now play major ecological roles on the island had been widely planted. They included Cedar (from Bermuda) which was introduced in the 1860s and is spread by Mynas, as well as Spoor, Thorn, Privet and Olives (*Olea* species).

Most of the trees and other plants introduced to St Helena during the 19th century and earlier were brought in with a particular role in mind, and some generated significant economic benefits. Perhaps the most important of the early introductions were yams, which were in cultivation within a few years of settlement. A number of different types were grown, some for animal feed and others for human consumption. Yams were grown in damp conditions and suffered during the periodic droughts. They are no longer cultivated, but still grow wild in many of the guts.

Some of the introduced plants quickly spread out of control and either caused problems with agriculture or threatened native species. Invasive species included Furze, 'Elderberry' *Solanum mauritianum*, Buddleia *B. madagascariensis*, White Flower and Common Blackberry. The Furze, imported in the 18th century, rapidly became invasive and still causes problems on pasture land. The Blackberry provides a good example of an economically significant invasive plant. It was apparently introduced in 1775 from Madeira and quickly became a menace, overrunning pasture land in the higher areas. By 1806 it was realized that drastic action was required. Soldiers from the garrison were made available to clear brambles from pasture land; landowners paid the soldiers for this work, and were afterwards responsible for keeping their land clear. This seems to have overcome the immediate crisis, but in 1875 Melliss commented that the Blackberry still had to be kept carefully in check on pasture land, and that it was swamping the indigenous vegetation along the high ridge.

The continuing destruction of the native vegetation even in its refuge on the crest of the central ridge was clearly indicated in Morris' 1884 account of attempts to produce quinine on the island in 1869-71. More than 5,000 *Cinchona* plants had been planted out on the slopes above Newfoundland or on Mount Actaeon. Those on the slopes did not thrive, and cultivation was ultimately confined to the narrow ridges of Mount Actaeon and Diana's Peak, where some plants can still be seen today.

Commenting a decade later, Morris concluded that there was no chance of the cultivation of quinine being a commercial success. He continued: "*and on other*

156

grounds it would be very undesirable to cut down any more of the indigenous forest, which already is reduced to such a small extent".

An alien plant that has had pervasive effects on the ecology of St Helena is New Zealand Flax *Phormium tenax*. This was introduced in the first half of the 19th century, probably by an American whaler or by a ship returning from delivering convicts to Australia. Flax was already growing wild in December 1852, when Fred. Moss wrote to the *St. Helena Advocate* suggesting that it could be developed into an industry. The first substantial planting was of 100 acres in 1870. The Colonial and Foreign Fibre Company set up a mill in Jamestown in 1874, but the enterprise soon failed because of a sudden drop in the price of fibre and the high cost of transporting the leaves – mainly by donkeys – for processing. At the time of Morris' visit in 1883 the flax was unused, but he reckoned that it could be economic if the processing machinery was placed close to the plants.

In 1907 a government mill was started at Longwood under supervision of New Zealand experts, and planting proceeded rapidly, stimulated by the high prices paid for fibre during the First World War. During the early 1920s five private fibre mills were in operation as well as the government one, and a decade later the number of mills had risen to nine. A rope and twine factory was also established and the industry as a whole directly employed some 300 people. At its maximum around the time of the Second World War and the Korean War more than 3,000 acres of flax were under cultivation.

However, the flax industry brought only very limited benefits to the ordinary inhabitants. Some 70% of all privately owned land on the island was in the possession of three families, who controlled most of the growing and processing of flax. The trade was really profitable during the First World War, but wages remained low. Furthermore, the flax industry continued to be at the mercy of the world fibre market. In 1932 all the flax mills closed as a result of a drastic fall in the price of fibre, and only reopened later that year when the government provided a subsidy.

The flax industry went into decline after the Second World War, surviving only with government support. It finally collapsed in the mid 1960s, when the introduction of synthetic fibres was severely depressing the natural fibre market. The *coup de grâce* came in late 1965 when the government almost doubled the wages of their own employees (to £5 per week) but did not introduce a proportionate increase in the guaranteed price for fibre. The private mill owners, unable to afford comparable wage increases for their employees, all closed their mills during 1966. Clearance of flax has since been undertaken in some places, the land being converted to pasture or planted for forestry.

During the expansion of the flax industry no attention seems to have been paid to conservation of the native plants. The land used for flax extended up into areas just below the central ridge where fragments of Cabbage tree woodland and Tree Fern thicket still survived. Along most parts of the ridge, only the most precipitous areas were left unplanted, these being mainly on the south side, overlooking Sandy Bay. Furthermore, the flax gradually spread upwards into unplanted areas, reaching the ridge itself in some places and crowding out the natural vegetation. It has been pointed out that flax inhibits erosion on the steep slopes around the central ridge, but this is of small comfort since the endangered native species that it displaces would anyhow control erosion if left undisturbed.

Philip Gosse, during his visit in 1937, was outraged by what he viewed as the ruthless behaviour of the landowners who controlled the flax industry. His anger emerges clearly in a long statement that he sent to the Rt. Hon. W.G.A. Ormsby-Gore,

Secretary of State for the Colonies, on his return to Britain, and also in the last pages of his book on St Helena. In the latter, while describing the Peaks, he wrote:

> *"The upper part of this ridge is still clothed by the primeval forest of the island ... but now it has all disappeared except this last vestige. On both the steep sides of the Ridge the ruthless and rapacious flax growers have hacked down and grubbed up the wild olive, tree ferns, cabbage trees, lobelia, and everything else which God planted there, in order to grow their flax, which would grow just as well in many other parts of the island."*

Gosse may not have been entirely fair to the flax growers, but they were undoubtedly tough businessmen. They belonged mainly to families who had become prosperous as merchants during the 19th century and had bought land cheaply after the social and economic structure of the island was thrown into turmoil by the departure of the East India Company. The flax industry for a while offered both prosperity to the landowners and employment – though under tough conditions – to many St Helenians; it also helped the government to balance its books.

In the early decades of the 20th century, when flax cultivation was rapidly destroying the relict native forests on the peaks, no significant voices seem to have been raised on behalf of conservation. A century earlier Beatson's edicts would have protected the forests – at least in theory – and the environmentally aware governors in the early decades of the 18th century would have been acutely conscious of the issues involved. The lack of interest in the native plants on St Helena in the early 20th century shows how unsafe it is to assume that awareness of environmental issues in one period will be maintained indefinitely. At present, however, serious attempts are being made to halt the advance of the flax on the peaks, and other initiatives are being taken to protect the surviving native plants.

We end this sad chronicle of the decline of St Helena's native vegetation with a quotation from the opening passage of a 1956 report by the island's Agriculture and Forestry Officer, Norman Humphrey, in which he gives a concise diagnosis of the ecological problems of the island:

> *"St Helena has had a long history of land misuse through ignorance and indifference, inconstancy of purpose, neglect and the adverse effects of external events. As a result, over two-thirds of the Island have been reduced to useless waste lands and most of the remainder has suffered great losses of both soil and soil fertility. Sporadic efforts over the years have been made to arrest the decline and bring back a measure of prosperity to the people whose home it is but with only limited success and that all too often evanescent.*

Chapter 8

Caring for the wild life of the island

In this chapter we describe 20th century initiatives relating to conservation on St Helena and look forward to the opportunities for ecological restoration on the island. We start, however, with a brief discussion of the motivation of conservationists. In documenting the ecological history of St Helena we saw how concern about destruction of the forests was an early and recurrent theme at meetings both of the Island Council and of the Directors of the East India Company in England. The motives for this concern were at first purely practical and economic. There were recurrent efforts to protect economically useful woodland from grazing and other destructive forces, and to plant additional trees for future use as timber or firewood. Similarly, pasture land used for rearing domestic animals needed to be protected from overgrazing by wild ones. Nesting gamebirds needed to be protected, so that there would be young to shoot later in the year. Seabird colonies needed freedom from disturbance at the start of the breeding season, so that the birds would settle and lay eggs in maximum numbers in accessible places. Even some kinds of introduced songbirds, useful because they could be sold to people on passing ships, were given protection in order to maintain the stocks.

We have also noted that experience of ecological devastation associated with colonial enterprises on St Helena and elsewhere, was partly responsible for an early rise in environmental awareness in the western world as a whole. This concern, however, was almost always linked to potential economic costs of ecological damage. In the literature on St Helena prior to the mid 20th century there are few pleas for conservation that imply concern for the plants or animals for their own sake.

Even today, when the desirability of maintaining biodiversity is widely accepted and it is normal to deplore destruction of tropical forests, the arguments are often based on economics or on practical human welfare. In the St Helena context it would be natural to argue for conservation of the local dolphin population on the grounds that the animals are an attraction to visitors, bringing money to the island. Similarly, the recent progress in re-establishing endemic trees in various parts of the island could be cited as an element in promotion of the island as an interesting place to visit.

Arguments for conservation are also now often made on grounds of scientific interest. For example, conservation of Chimpanzees, closest relatives to humans, is often promoted on the grounds that their study is of fundamental scientific importance. From this it is only a short step to the idea that seeing and learning about the variety, beauty and elegant adaptation of plants and animals in natural ecosystems is an enriching and inspirational experience, and that it should be available to each of us whether we live in Britain, South Africa or St Helena.

Many people now go further, taking a fundamentalist view of conservation. They argue that given our great power, we have a moral duty of stewardship over all the living things with which we share this planet, irrespective of their economic value. Acceptance of this view, coupled with a perceived need to repair some of the environmental damage that the human race has caused over the centuries, is at least partly responsible for the startling rise in support for environmental organisations such as Greenpeace, Friends of the Earth and the World Wide Fund for Nature (WWF).

Although this view had clear antecedents two centuries ago (see box in Chapter 7) it was less in evidence by the start of the 20th century. In 1938, however, we hear an eloquent harbinger of modern attitudes to conservation in Philip Gosse's book on the history of the island. After deploring the destruction of the *"primeval forest"* by the flax growers he went on to say:

> *"Let us hope that at this eleventh hour the Government of St. Helena will forbid, once and forever, a single tree, shrub or fern to be destroyed in this wanton manner. The Ridge should be inviolate. It should be in the safe keeping of the island for all time, and not one square foot of it should belong to a private individual or company."*

With the second world war looming, Gosse's plea seems to have gone largely unheeded, but it may have exerted its influence through some of the people mentioned in the next section.

Conservation of the endemic plants

Here we focus on the conservation and restoration initiatives taken during the second half of the 20th century. In the early part of this period the most influential people were Norman Humphrey and Norman Kerr. The former, working in the 1950s, put agriculture and forestry on St Helena on to its modern footing, while the latter, over the same period, was renewing the efforts at conservation of the endemic plants that had been largely abandoned after the time of Beatson in the early 19th century.

In 1956 Governor James Harford wrote a foreword to Norman Humphrey's landmark review of agriculture and forestry on the island, pointing out that Mr Humphrey played an important part in: *"a crucial phase of the transition in the sphere of land use from* laisser faire *to reasoned control."* Although Governors Roberts, Pyke and Byfield from more than 200 years earlier might bridle at the implication that they did not exert reasoned control, the subsequent failures were all too clear and the actions of the 1950s mark a real turning point.

Norman Humphrey played a key role in the moves against feral goats that were to lead eventually to the effective ending of the devastating onslaught of these animals on the island ecosystem, which had continued for four and a half centuries. The first step had been taken in 1940, when the Goat Range Rules were established. A 'goat line' was established and marked with cairns, running close to the 1500 foot (c.460 m) contour and dividing the relatively fertile uplands from the eroded exterior of the island. Above this line goats could be destroyed on sight; below the line were the goat ranges which had their origins in much earlier times but which were now more tightly regulated.

Writing some 15 years later, Humphrey noted that natural regeneration followed these measures, but all the trees he mentioned (Pine, Port Jackson Willow, Cedar and Spoor) were introduced rather than native species. The endemics in the Crown Wastes below the line remained under pressure, and the surviving cabbage trees and other endemics of the central ridge were threatened more by invasive exotic plants than by the alien herbivores.

Humphrey took further action against the goats, establishing a programme for progressive closing of all of the goat ranges over a period of some ten years. The Levelwood area was closed first, in about 1955, followed by Ruperts Valley and the area above Jamestown and progressing eventually to the last areas in Blue Hill and Sandy Bay. By 1962 most of the feral goats had been eliminated.

The establishment of Hardings and Casons National Forest, planned and started in the 1930s and completed shortly after the second world war, represented the first serious attempt in the 20th century to establish forests on Crown land. Planting of introduced tree species (in the early years mainly Maritime Pine, Eucalyptus species, Australian Blackwood and Bermuda Cedar) has proceeded almost continuously since then, and now results in substantial supplies of firewood and timber.

Action to protect the endemic trees has been slower to take effect. A Forestry Ordinance was enacted in 1937, with the purpose of creating forest reserves. It was replaced by a new ordinance in 1954, which was later amended to provide more effective conservation measures and is still in force. Three areas of indigenous vegetation were declared reserves under the earlier ordinance, but they remained the property of their original owners and no adequate measures were taken to protect the endemic plants.

A voluntary scheme brought in under the later ordinance led to dedication of some areas that had endemic vegetation, and subsequent management by government. One of these was part of Diana's Forest, on the crest of the central ridge. Norman Humphrey negotiated its dedication in 1956/57, and in his 1956 report stated that this forest should be cleaned of invading exotics as soon as possible. He pointed out, however, that the task would be slow and difficult. A footnote indicates that a start was made on this work by 1957, but we do not know for how long the programme was maintained.

Norman Kerr seems to have been the first person in the 20th century to focus on the welfare of particular endemic plant species. He was on St Helena from 1953 to 1956, serving as Headmaster of the Secondary School, Education Officer and Information Officer. He was a qualified botanist and spent much time studying the native plants; among his finds was a group of ten specimens of the False Gumwood on a cliff on the north side of Mount Vesey.[1]

During his time on St Helena, Norman Kerr also sowed the seed for longer term action to protect the native flora, since he introduced George Benjamin to the identification of the endemic plants. We guess that it was also Kerr and Humphrey who were largely responsible for establishing explicit legal protection for named indigenous plants. The Forestry (Indigenous Trees and Plants Preservation) Rules, 1959 made it an offence to *"cut, gather, burn, carry away or otherwise damage or destroy any tree or plant belonging to a kind indigenous to St. Helena without first obtaining a permit in writing from the Forestry Officer."* The original schedule listed nine species of trees and plants that were deemed indigenous, and it was subsequently amended several times.

This legal move and the start of action against invasive exotics on the central ridge in the 1950s was – as far as we are aware – the first official action to help the endemics since the end of the East India Company's rule in 1834. However, in a scenario sadly reminiscent of the conservation efforts of 250 years earlier, efforts seem to have flagged in subsequent decades. Even in the 1980s, losses of key habitat on the Peaks occurred as a result of invading flax, although action is now again being taken to halt the advance of this plant.

One of the foundations for recent attempts to preserve the native flora and fauna of St Helena was provided by Linda C. Brown, whose work on the island was financed by

---

[1] Kerr returned in 1970 and wrote a short article on "The endemic plants of St. Helena". He also prepared a longer manuscript on the "Endemic flowering plants of St. Helena" and also a "Monograph of the vegetation of St. Helena", but neither of these was published. A few years later a comrehensive compilation of the plants was made by R.O. Williams (1989), but this was never published.

the Overseas Development Administration. She provided check-lists of both plants and animals, with useful discussions of the indigenous vegetation and its destruction.

The latest chapter in the saga of the endemic plants of the island really began, however, with George Benjamin's finds of rare endemics in the mid 1970s, and Quentin Cronk's arrival on St Helena in November 1980, initiating modern scientific investigation of the flora. Cronk, aged 21, had recently graduated in botany from Cambridge University. At the Agriculture & Forestry Department he was introduced to George Benjamin, who was then a forest guard, and it was arranged that George should work with Quentin during his stay. Thus began a partnership that laid the foundations for the efforts to save the endemic plants now being carried forward by a new generation of conservationists.

George Benjamin   Plate 8

No contemporary book discussing the environment of St Helena can be complete without paying tribute to the single-minded determination of George Benjamin. He has devoted his life to the endemic plants of St Helena in a way that must evoke envy among concerned people on other islands of the world, where expert 'home-grown' conservationists are often lacking.

George was born in 1935 and started work in Solomons flax mills at the age of 15, moving in 1958 to the Agriculture & Forestry Department, where he worked until his retirement in 1995. Initially employed as a labourer, he later became a forest guard, and in this position made notable discoveries of surviving endemic trees. In 1984 he was promoted to Forestry Assistant to work full time on the conservation of the endemics, and in 1985 was sent for six months to the Royal Botanic Gardens at Kew to learn propagation and conservation techniques. He completed his career as Conservation Officer in A&F.

At the time of his retirement, Quentin Cronk wrote in the St Helena News:

"Every biologist or endemic specialist who has come to St Helena from the UK or elsewhere agrees on one thing: George Benjamin is an inspiration to work with. His almost unbelievable long distance vision for spotting out plants, his instinctive feel for plants, his fieldcraft (knotting a flax rope in a trice to get to that tricky spot), his encyclopedic knowledge of St Helena and its endemics and his deep appreciation and concern for the unique flora and fauna of this island: all these things have contributed to the opening of new possibilities for the environment of St Helena."

George's contribution to endemic plant conservation has been recognized by the award of the British Empire Medal.

George Benjamin had previously made striking contributions to knowledge of the status of some of the endemic plants. By the mid 1970s the She Cabbage was considered almost extinct, but then George found a group of trees between two fields above Osborne's Cottage (Plate 27); seedlings were subsequently planted out in a number of places. A more dramatic discovery came in August 1977 when George was counting Dogwoods near Diana's Peak and recognized a specimen of the St Helena Olive (Plate 30) – sole member of an endemic genus – which was previously thought to be extinct; despite intensive efforts, this special species of tree is still hovering on the brink.

During Quentin Cronk's short visit in 1980, he and George Benjamin put in long days visiting remote parts of the island. When looking along the inland cliffs facing out towards Lot's Wife, they saw two bushes with white flowers on a crag (Plate 8). Improbably, these proved to be specimens of the St Helena Ebony, the first that had been seen for over a century.[2] George's brother Charles Benjamin was lowered on a rope to collect cuttings and these were successfully propagated. In the following years, several thousand cuttings and seedlings have been planted in various parts of the island. The rediscovery of this beautiful species, which played a key role in the ecology and history of the island, provided a powerful stimulus and a foundation on which subsequent species conservation efforts on St Helena have been based.

The triumph of the rediscovery of the Ebony was quickly followed by the finding by Stedson Stroud in 1982 of a single Bastard Gumwood (Plate 26). A year later a mature specimen of a closely related tree – the False Gumwood – was found on a cliff above Coles Rock, although a decade elapsed before the rediscovery of the group of the same species on Mount Vesey that had been noted by Norman Kerr in the 1950s.

In parallel with more intensive searches for surviving individuals of rare tree species, steps were taken to increase the chance of the survival of their populations. In 1983 Simon Goodenough came from the Royal Botanic Gardens at Kew to direct the setting up of a propagation unit and to advise on habitat restoration, and in the last two decades several islanders have benefitted from training at Kew. Propagation from surviving individuals in the 1980s and 1990s has kept several endemic tree species alive up to the present time, though prospects for the future are variable (see Chapter 16).

Cronk had returned to St Helena in 1983 to do the field work for his doctoral thesis, which constituted the most thorough analysis of the island's flora since the treatment by Melliss more than a century earlier.[3] In 1995 Cronk visited the island more briefly, to undertake field studies of the Dogwood (Plate 31). As he pointed out, this is one of St Helena's commonest endemic trees, with a world population of 132 adult individuals!

Directly relevant to the conservation of plants whose numbers are so drastically reduced is another doctoral study, recently completed by Rebecca Rowe. She came to the island to investigate the genetic basis of the problems involved in attempting to maintain populations of Redwoods and Ebonies. The Redwood has been on the brink of extinction since the early 18th century and in the words of a recent publication on the endemic plants, the few surviving individuals: *"are most unthrifty and even with the best care, will not miss an opportunity to die."*[4]

The basic problem is one of inbreeding, as discussed at the end of Chapter 1. As many as half of St Helena's thirty or so surviving endemic plants may now have populations so small or so fragmented that significant ill effects of inbreeding are likely in the long term. In trying to save fragmented populations one strategy is to link isolated groups of individuals by replanting in between them. When raising stock for this, further inbreeding can be minimized by using unrelated individuals as parents of the next

---

[2] J.C. Melliss had vainly "searched the whole Island over" for surviving trees in about 1870. See also Q.C.B. Cronk (1986a).

[3] Cronk was helped extensively by George Benjamin. He subsequently published modified versions of several sections of the thesis, dealing with the decline of the Ebony, Redwood and Gumwood, as well as more general topics, and also a book on the endemic flora (Q.C.B. Cronk 2000).

[4] M.D. Holland (1986).

generation. Ideally, one should try to arrange pollination between plants from different places. Failing this, one can collect seed or cuttings from different places and establish a population of mixed origin, so that the subsequent generation will be relatively outbred.

In extreme cases arranging crosses between two different but related species may be the only hope, since this is an extreme form of outbreeding. A dramatic demonstration occurred by accident at Scotland in 1982, when an Ebony planted next to one of the few surviving Redwoods set seed which evidently resulted from pollination by the Redwood. The resulting hybrid, known as Rebony, is a vigorous and beautiful tree that clearly has a future on the island and elsewhere.

In 1990 increasing awareness of the importance of the endemic plants led to the creation of a special Environmental Conservation Section within the Forestry Division of the Agriculture & Forestry Department. This unit, sometimes referred to as the Endemic Section, has a substantial budget and is responsible both for Crown Waste rehabilitation (using mainly exotic trees) and for the endemics programme. The links with the Royal Botanic Gardens at Kew have been maintained, and support has recently been obtained from WWF for conservation work on several of St Helena's most endangered plants.

Soon after the establishment of the Environmental Conservation Section the focus of attention shifted to the Gumwood, St Helena's National Tree, which has a wild population of less than 1000 trees. The Gumwood seems not to have suffered significantly from inbreeding but is vulnerable to a different kind of threat. In the early 1990s the only remaining substantial fragment of Gumwood forest, at Peak Dale, became seriously endangered when the trees were attacked by an introduced homopteran bug, *Orthezia insignis*, known locally as the Jacaranda Bug. This insect probably arrived sometime after 1973 and was first noted on Gumwoods in 1991. Six trees had died by 1992 and 108 by June 1993. The stand might have been essentially destroyed if it had not been for the work of Simon Fowler, a biological control specialist, who organised the introduction of a predatory ladybird, *Hyperaspis pantherina*, to control the bug.[5]

The effect was dramatic and the immediate threat to the mature Gumwoods seems to have been removed, but the situation will require careful monitoring for a long time, since renewed attack by the Jacaranda Bug on Gumwoods or on related species such as False and Bastard Gumwoods, Scrubwood and even He Cabbage is still a possibility. It is hoped that any such outbreaks can be dealt with by the local Integrated Pest Management Team, who are able to multiply up the ladybird in the laboratory for release in particular places if natural control seems inadequate. Planting of seedling Gumwoods is now being carried out, with the eventual aim of linking the two existing stands of Gumwoods at Peak Dale with young trees, so as to form a substantial piece of woodland comparable to that which covered so much of the island in the past.

Cuttings have also been taken from the Gumwoods in Deep Valley. Whereas the trees at Peak Dale have apparently hybridised with the otherwise extinct subspecies known as Burchell's Gumwood, with the result that they are highly variable, those in Deep Valley are the pure Gumwood. The plan is to establish an orchard or 'field gene-bank' in a place where seed can easily be collected. Seedlings will then be planted back in Deep Valley to boost the population there. The existence of the second group will also safeguard the stock in case anything should happen to the original trees in Deep Valley. Similar

[5] R.G. Booth et al. (1995).

164

approaches are being used in relation to other endemic plants, with seed orchards being established for more than a dozen species. In managing these, great care will be taken to minimize loss of genetic variation, so as to maintain the vigour of the stocks.

During recent years some progress has also been made in habitat preservation and restoration. Management and planting of endemics started on High Peak in 1984, and this was soon followed by the planting of Ebony and hybrid 'Rebony' at Ebony Plain, and of Scrubwoods and Gumwoods at Horse Point Plain (Plate 8). The latter initiative is now being taken further, with the inauguration by the Advisory Committee on the Environment of the *Millennium Gumwood Forest Project* at Horse Point, which was once part of the Great Wood (see Chapter 7). All the people of St Helena now have an opportunity to plant their own Gumwood trees, thus establishing the Millennium Forest as a community effort and eventually transforming a degraded site into an attractive woodland.

Equally important is the development of a programme for removal of flax and other invasive weeds from some areas on the Peaks. Work of this kind, attempted under Norman Humphrey's direction in the late 1950s, was subsequently allowed to lapse and the advance of the alien plants resumed. The main emphasis of the current programme is on halting the spread of flax into Tree Fern thicket.[6] Experimental plantings of endemics are also being carried out to see which is the best way of re-creating Tree Fern thicket on areas that have previously been flax plantation.

The spread of flax and other weeds onto the ridge clearly represents an environmental emergency, as recognized by Philip Gosse more than half a century ago. As well as being the last refuge for a number of endemic plants, the patches of native vegetation are the sole remaining habitat for a large number of endemic insects and other invertebrate animals to which little consideration has been given during formulation of conservation plans. We applaud the action that is now being taken against the alien weeds: the work of flax control is laborious and expensive, but it is the only way in which the unique fauna and flora of the central ridge can be given a chance of survival. Consolidation of the gains made, and commitment to a long term strategy for ecological restoration of the central ridge, can be considered the highest of all the conservation priorities for the island.

Conservation of dolphins, turtles and birds

St Helena has no native land mammals, land reptiles or amphibians, and of the landbirds only the endemic Wirebird and indigenous Moorhen survive. Perhaps as a result of the lack of a larger set of extant endemic vertebrates, the important populations of native but non-endemic species of seabirds, turtles and marine mammals have received rather little attention.

Although in this book we have considered only terrestrial habitats, it is encouraging to hear that a start has recently been made in development of a marine conservation programme for St Helena waters. Dolphins (locally known as Porpoise) have traditionally been caught by fishermen, but in 1979 the harpooning of dolphins from boats was prohibited, with potential penalties including heavy fines and revocation of fishing licences.[7] Passage in 1996 of the Endangered, Endemic and Indigenous Species Protection Ordinance now provides complete protection for dolphins.

---

[6] D. Smith (1996).

[7] W.F. Perrin (1985).

Sea turtles and turtle eggs have been protected since 1984. However, turtle conservation, treated as a critical issue in many parts of the world (including Ascension) has not been given priority on St Helena; this is perhaps because few people realise that marine turtles are part of the natural fauna of the island. Green Turtles are known to have bred at Sandy Bay in the past, and turtle eggs have been found recently at Turks Cap Bay. Green Turtles are regularly seen in James and Ruperts Bays, and since individual turtles normally return to their natal islands to breed, it is conceivable that some or all of these individuals were born on St Helena long ago.

It seems evident that Green Turtles could still be restored as a breeding species here, if they could be given access to a sandy beach and protected from disturbance. This is not easy on an island where almost all the beaches have disappeared, but it might be possible to arrange for the western edge of the Sandy Bay beach to be made more suitable for turtle nesting. A few days work with a bulldozer moving sand, accompanied by removal of rocks by hand, should be enough to establish a small area within which a few turtles could lay their eggs. Although this beach is used by many people, we believe that all St Helenians would be enthusiastic about an attempt to restore a population of such a key member of the fauna of the island, and that the turtles and their nests would soon be looked after with the same enthusiasm and care that is provided for the Ebony and Gumwood now.

The Wirebird – the one surviving endemic bird – has managed its own conservation in the last few centuries, maintaining a substantial population in the face of drastic habitat change and the predation that it presumably suffers from cats and rats. A major study carried out by Neil McCulloch in 1988-89 indicated that there were about 500 Wirebirds and suggested that the species was not threatened at present. There was a decline in the early 1990s, but numbers seem now to have stabilised. In the period 1998-2000 a grant under the Darwin Initiative has permitted more detailed work by McCulloch on the ecology of the Wirebird. In his earlier report, McCulloch outlined a conservation strategy for the species, including control of grazing and management practices on the Deadwood Plain/Flagstaff area, which has much the largest concentration of birds. The Wirebird is now fully protected and as McCulloch has pointed out, it is regarded with considerable affection by the islanders, so that measures necessary for its future welfare are likely to be readily accepted.

The situation of the surviving breeding seabirds is much less favourable. Colonies are restricted to offshore islets and mainland cliffs; the White Tern also nests on the branches of large trees inland (Plate 21). The presence of feral cats and rats prevents seabirds from breeding successfully in accessible places anywhere on the main island. Because the offshore islets have such a limited area of even moderately level ground, populations of several seabird species are severely limited by lack of safe space for breeding.

Another initiative now under discussion has the potential to improve this situation. The plan is to enable seabirds to recolonise mainland St Helena at Gill Point, where Sooty Terns have laid eggs within the last decade or so. Gill Point is immediately opposite Shore and George Islands where there are now crowded colonies of boobies and other species (Plate 6). The relatively level ground near the cliff top could be fenced against feral cats, which are probably the main factor preventing breeding at this site by Sooty Terns, Madeiran Storm-petrels and Masked Boobies. This area is evidently also used by resting (or possibly breeding) Bulwer's Petrels, since wings of two of these birds were found on the cliff top in 1995, as explained in Chapter 5.

The Royal Society for the Protection of Birds has provided funds to enable the Environmental Conservation Section to carry out surveys of the birds on Gill Point and the offshore islands every three months, to establish a basis for further conservation measures.

Seabirds have enjoyed little legal protection in the past, and landing on the offshore islands where most of the seabirds breed is still not restricted. However, George and Shore Islands (both of which have booby colonies) are distant from Jamestown and hard to land on. Speery Island is precipitous, but Wideawake eggs have been taken there in the past. Egg Island and the other islets southwest of Jamestown have been subject to intermittent disturbance.

The Birds Protection Ordinance 1996 makes it an offence to kill or injure any bird or to destroy eggs. Named native seabirds are now also protected under the separate Endangered, Endemic and Indigenous Species Protection Ordinance 1996 and an associated Protection Order, which also covers turtles, dolphins and named endemic plants. Licences may be issued for killing of pest species, or of birds for scientific purposes, and also of game birds, for which shooting seasons are fixed each year.

Conservation of insects and other invertebrates
More than 400 endemic species and 80 endemic genera of invertebrates have been described from St Helena in the last two centuries (see Chapter 5). This diversity in such a small area ensures the status of St Helena in the first rank of islands in terms of importance for animal conservation. However, little relevant action has been taken until recently.[8] Very little research on invertebrates has been done since the major Belgian expeditions 30 years ago, and no-one has any idea how many of the known endemic species are now extinct, or how many remain to be discovered. Research is needed in order to formulate worthwhile invertebrate conservation policies. For example, our own pilot work showed that even tiny surviving groups of endemic plants have some undescribed insect species associated with them.

The lack of proper analysis of information obtained by earlier naturalists has also had negative effects. It prevented, for example, the recognition of the conservation importance of Prosperous Bay Plain. This tiny area represents a biodiversity hotspot of global significance, with an array of invertebrates endemic at the generic and species level (see Chapter 6). Their habitat has deteriorated drastically as a result of removal of rocks over a long period, and major additional disruption would ensue if a decision was taken to build an airfield on the plain.

While Prosperous Bay Plain is a centre for animals of arid habitats, the Tree Fern thicket on the Peaks is a stronghold for endemic insects and other invertebrates adapted to humid conditions. A tiny fragment of this habitat has survived relatively intact, and as explained above, a serious attempt is now under way to guard it against further invasion by flax and other alien plants. There is a chance, therefore, that some of the surviving endemic animals may now have a more secure future.

Increase in the awareness of the importance of invertebrate conservation on St Helena is mainly the result of visits to the island by two expeditions from the Invertebrate

[8] This lack of attention to animal conservation is reflected in the official vagueness about the number of endemic species present. The UK Biodiversity Action Plan, published in 1994 as a result of the signing of the Convention on Biological Diversity in Rio de Janeiro, lists St Helena as having "about 300" endemic terrestrial invertebrates. Since more than 400 have been described it is not clear whether the apparent 'loss' of a quarter of the endemic fauna represents a guess about possible recent extinctions or is simply a result of the accidental omission of several taxonomic groups from a formal check-list included in a previous report on sustainable development on the island (see later).

Conservation Centre at the London Zoo. The first, in 1987/88, was led by Dave Clarke and the second, in 1993, by Paul Pearce-Kelly. During the second expedition Pearce-Kelly, together with Graham Drucker of the World Conservation Monitoring Centre, provided the stimulus for the formation of the St Helena Nature Conservation Group, which is likely to play a key role in future conservation efforts on the island.

The group is made up of local people whose aim is to foster awareness and conservation of flora, fauna and the environment of St Helena, both terrestrial and marine. One of their earliest activities was taking part in the production of an attractive poster promoting conservation, entitled *Invertebrate wonders of St Helena*. This focused mainly on a few 'flagship' species of invertebrates whose habitats are severely threatened. There can now be few islanders who have not heard about – for instance – the endemic Giant Earwig, Spiky Yellow Woodlouse and Blushing Snail.

By drawing attention to these striking animals, and by working with school children and other groups, the conservationists have been able to help people to understand that almost all the endemic animals are threatened by habitat destruction and the onslaught of alien species such as centipedes, ants and mice. It is now necessary to build on this public awareness and to develop a coherent conservation strategy for the invertebrates, based on appropriate research.

Broader issues

In this chapter we have been concerned primarily with actual, physical measures taken to conserve the native plants and animals, rather than with the many plans and reports that have been produced from time to time. It would be unjust not to mention, however, a few particularly noteworthy initiatives.

The first was a symposium held on 9th September 1988 at the Zoological Society of London under the title of *St Helena: Natural Treasury*, organised by Paul Pearce-Kelly and Quentin Cronk. This meeting called attention to the need for conservation action on the island, resulted in a useful publication and led to later action by the St Helena Working Group (now the South Atlantic Working Group) of the UK Overseas Territories Conservation Forum..

A second initiative was the *Sustainable Environment and Development Strategy and Action Plan for St Helena*, or SEDS, an Overseas Development Administration (ODA) project managed by the Conservation Unit of the Royal Botanic Gardens at Kew.[9] A group of consultants went to the island and produced a comprehensive report in 1993. The island community formed a SEDS Response Committee which decided to concentrate on certain aspects of the SEDS proposals, particularly conservation. An early outcome of the SEDS initiative was the stay on the island from 1994 to 1996 of Douglas Smith, who was funded by the ODA. He initiated a regular *Endemic Bulletin* in the *St Helena News*, helped the Environmental Conservation Section with a number of projects, and planned the flax removal programme discussed above.

With the retiral of George Benjamin in 1995 there was a need for new leadership of the Environmental Conservation Section, and Rebecca Rowe (now Cairns-Wicks) – who had done her doctoral research on the Redwood – was appointed as Environmental Conservation Officer and later as Environmental Coordinator. The latter role involves work with the Advisory Committee on the Environment, which comes under the Office of the Chief Secretary but has partly independent

---

[9] Government of St Helena 1993.

168

membership. This committee inherited from the SEDS Response Committee the remit of fostering the concept of sustainable development on the island.

Another important step was taken on 11th March 1996 when Diana's Peak was declared a National Park, realising part of the vision of D. Morris in 1884 and of Philip Gosse in 1937. The park has an area of 64 hectares, including 15.7 hectares of Tree Fern thicket. It is thought that in 1502 there may have been about 133 hectares of this type of vegetation, which was always confined to the highest ridges. The management plan for the park includes the diagnosis of various ecological problems and appropriate prescriptions for solving them.

In a seminar on the island in 1995,[10] Quentin Cronk had suggested a more ambitious scheme which – if executed – would provide an excellent complement to the park on the Peaks. Cronk proposed that the whole of the wild southwest corner of the island from Peak Dale down to the coast between Sandy Bay and South West Point should be made into a National Park (private land and areas used for grazing could be excluded). We developed this idea in a talk to the Heritage Society and Nature Conservation Group in 1995, and the discussion that followed the talk continued as an extensive correspondence in the *St Helena News*.

The basic idea is that this area – amounting to more than one tenth of the surface of the island – could become the site of an ecological restoration project exciting enough to gain international recognition and support. The area is of no economic value, has relatively few invasive alien plants and has surviving populations of most of the endemic plants (and many animals) typical of the drier zones. Over the long term, it might be possible to re-create approximations to most of the original vegetation zones of the island that were described in Chapter 4. This area is not the only one deserving attention. The case for protection of Prosperous Bay Plain was explained above, and the restoration projects at High Peak, Ebony Plain and near Horse Point have been mentioned previously.

One of the most significant aspects of the plans for Diana's Peak and other conservation measures on the island is the degree of public awareness and involvement. There are regular environmental bulletins in the island newspaper. Volunteers are recruited for planting projects and surveys and the whole population is kept continually aware of the unique flora and fauna, and of the progress in conserving it. When the last remaining St Helena Olive tree died, its passing was given the prominence of an obituary of a leading citizen. (Three seedlings outlived it, but the future for the species is bleak).

With many conservation projects already in progress and others under consideration, there is now perhaps more activity relating to conservation on St Helena than at any time in its history. Goats and pigs are prevented from roaming freely over the Crown Wastes and even the donkeys are tenuously under control. Diana's Peak National Park has been established, and invasive alien plants are being weeded out of endangered areas of Tree Fern thicket. Endemic plants are being propagated and planted in appropriate places. Laws have been passed to protect seabirds, turtles and dolphins, and there is widespread awareness of the plight of some of the endemic invertebrates.

This activity results partly from worldwide recognition of the need for decisive action to slow the rate of degradation of our planet. Since the 'Earth Summit' held in

[10] Agriculture & Forestry Department (1995).

Rio de Janeiro in 1992, concern about the destruction of wildlife is now relatively high on the political agenda, and states have accepted an obligation to protect the biodiversity of their natural environments. There is an increasing sense of human responsibility for other forms of life, along with realisation that a healthy environment is a real asset to any community, in terms of the quality of life of the inhabitants as well as in specific areas such as fisheries and forest resources, education and tourism.

One reflection of this increased awareness of environmental issues was the publication by the Joint Nature Conservation Committee in 1999 of a profile of the biodiversity of the United Kingdom's Overseas Territories.[11] Another was the organisation – jointly by the Foreign & Commonwealth Office and the UK Overseas Territories Conservation Forum – of a conference under the title *"A Breath of Fresh Air"* in London in June 1999. This provided an opportunity for representatives of governments and non-governmental organisations from all the United Kingdom's Overseas Territories to share their experience in dealing with environmental issues. A short time previously it had been announced that the UK government was making available a substantial sum of money for environmental action in the Overseas Territories. The momentum is being maintained by the organisation in Gibraltar in autumn 2000 of an international conference on environmental conservation in small territories, *"Calpe 2000: Linking the Fragments of Paradise"*.

We wholeheartedly welcome the energy and practical support now being given to environmental initiatives on St Helena and elsewhere. The challenge for the future is to develop a clear and consistent – though flexible – conservation and restoration policy for St Helena, and to apply it vigorously on a timescale of centuries. This is not an easy goal on an island where administrators and consultants come and go, and the funds required for the island community to function are often subject to the vagaries of political decisions in London.

The formulation of a Sustainable Environment and Development Strategy for St Helena, the designation of a National Park, the Millennium Forest initiative and the other measures discussed above are impressive first steps towards fulfilment of the international responsibility to restore the natural habitats of St Helena, and to care for her endemic and indigenous species. The test of effective stewardship will come in the long term. It will be demonstrated if, in ten, a hundred and a thousand years time, St Helenians are living in harmony with a beautiful, productive and diverse restored natural environment, in company with almost all of the native plants and animals that have managed to survive the vicissitudes of the last half millennium. Success will be most likely if the impetus comes from local people, supported by conservationists elsewhere, and with secure long-term funding from government and external environmental organisations.

---

[11] D. Procter & L.V. Fleming (1999).

Part III

Ascension Island

"Att evening we arrived att Ascention and anchored on the NW. side of the iland. On our rightt hand was a faire sandy bay and on our leftt were multide of rarreg, craggy, sharpe pointed hard rocks for many miles along the shoare, and up toward the land, appearing white with the dung of sea foule, of which were innumerable of severall kinds. The most desolate, barren (and like a lan thatt God had cursed) thatt ever my eies beeheld (worse than Kerne Ky, etts. in Cornewall). I coceave the whole world affoards nott such another peece of ground: most part of the collour of burnt bricke, reddish, the substance stones, somwhat like pumice stones; the rest like cinders and burnt earth. The hills, of which there are many, were meere heapes of the same. It may bee supposed thatt the fire in former ages hath consumed the substance therof, hath made it incapable of producing any vegetalls. Only the topps of the high mountaines in the middle appeared somwhatt greene, there beeing a kind of rushes and spicy grasse."

Peter Mundy, writing in 1656 (see R.C. Temple & L.M. Anstey 1936)

Exploring Ascension in 1501

Admiral João da Nova was sailing with all haste to India with three ships, on a mission to relieve the Portuguese garrison in Calicut. On 25th March 1501, quite unexpectedly, he came in sight of an unknown island, later named Ascension.

The discovery of Ascension was later overshadowed by that of St Helena which da Nova made on his return voyage, and it may be that he and his crew did not even land on Ascension on that first day. We choose to imagine, however, that they took a brief walk through the western desert of the island, and we speculate on their reactions.

Vivid impressions of Ascension were formed even before the sailors set foot ashore. As they worked their little ships round the forbidding coastline, looking for a landing, they were met and followed by thousands of seabirds. Most appealing were the dove-like White Terns, with snow-white plumage showing the shadowy outline of bones through their wings, dark eyes enlarged by a ring of minute black feathers, and straight black bills. They were so curious, and hovered so close, that a few were caught by hand. There were also several kinds of multi-coloured boobies, which the sailors were later to see breeding on land, and which perched inquisitively on the rigging and rails.

All around the ship were Ascension Frigatebirds, long-winged and fork-tailed; they kept station in the wind, all facing to the southeast, but peeling off from time to time to chase a booby or pick up with grapnel bills a scrap thrown overboard by the sailors. Low over the water flew Madeiran Storm-petrels, playing to and fro and chirping like Swallows, but with white rumps reminiscent of House Martins. Every now and then a flock of black and white Wideawakes flew gracefully past on their way to distant feeding grounds, while dense groups of Brown and Black Noddies worked over a school of Steenbrass, dipping to the water surface to catch fry.

Eventually the ships reached the sheltered westward coast of the island, where beaches of pale gold sand interrupted the stark expanses of barren black lava. As soon as they dropped anchor they were surrounded by hundreds of Blackfish: deep-bodied, slow-swimming triggerfishes, silhouetted in the clear blue water against the bright sand below, which eagerly grabbed scraps thrown overboard and nibbled the weed on the ships' hulls.

Landing was not difficult, since there were no rollers that day, but walking on the loose sand of the steeply shelving beach was surprisingly tiring. The sailors were puzzled by the enormous tracks, leading from the tideline to the wide sandy area at the back of the beach, which was entirely filled with large conical pits. At dusk, however, the riddle was solved, when Green Turtles more than four feet long emerged from the breakers and lumbered up the beach. Soon those that were not disturbed began laboriously digging pits in the sand to lay their clutches of a hundred or so white, leathery, spherical eggs. From time to time during the night, the beach would come alive with hatchling turtles scurrying down into the surf and instantly swimming out to sea. Some were intercepted by the enormous yellow, purple and brown landcrabs that lurked in burrows around the fringes of the beach, and the few that were still on land at daylight were quickly taken by swooping frigatebirds.

Showing off by teasing and riding on an adult turtle, one young sailor put a hand too close to the massive jaws and came away minus a finger. His friends managed to stop the flow of blood and applied a makeshift bandage, and he made his way back to the ship. Then someone remembered that turtles – as well as their eggs – were good to eat: within a few minutes the Ascension rookery suffered its first losses at the hands of man.

Some of the sailors went off fishing from the rocks, baiting their hooks with crabs killed with stones. The catch was rich and varied, with many speckled Congers (moray eels) and purple-spotted Jack (a seabass), both of which made good eating; a few people were lucky enough to catch Longlegs lobsters.

While the beach held interest and the promise of food, the sailors were appalled by the view of the desolate hinterland. It appeared to consist entirely of jagged black rocks and barren red hills, reminding them of clinker from a furnace. Most important, there was no sign of freshwater.

As they explored inland from the beaches, the sailors found walking difficult, since they were barefoot or with makeshift sandals and the rocks were jagged and too hot to touch. Some parts were really dangerous, with huge blocks of rock liable to crash down the steep slopes after an incautious touch. The sun was fierce and the heat was thrown back by the rocks, so the water they had brought with them was soon exhausted.

They were pleased when they found themselves in what looked like a dry stream-bed. It was floored with fine cinders that provided relatively easy walking, so they now made rapid progress inland. Occasionally locusts whirred off, though it was hard to see what plants they could have found to eat. On the left the sailors could see the spectacular skyline of one of Ascension's most recent volcanoes –

later to be named Sisters Peak – fronted by a jagged expanse of black lava that was perhaps only a few hundred years old. Soon they began to hear an increasing noise of seabirds, and found themselves on the edge of an enormous booby colony: they would never forget the experience.

The noise was deafening and the cindery plain was here covered with dazzling white guano and occupied by hundreds of pairs of nesting Masked Boobies, called Gannets by the sailors from their resemblance to the European species: the size of a goose, creamy white with black on the wings and tail and with feet and beaks in shades of yellow and grey. A few were incubating a pair of eggs, but at this time many pairs were being pestered by fully feathered grey-plumaged young, well able to fly but not yet independent. On rockier slopes pairs of Brown Boobies were defending level spaces carpeted in the centre with small pebbles brought by the solicitous males, who whistled wheezily in answer to the raucous honks of their mates.

Nearby was a field of particularly jagged rock, which a sailor who had been to Italy realized was solidified lava formed by a volcano. On the rough ledges in the most precipitous parts of the lava there were twig nests – with single eggs or chicks – belonging to Red-footed Boobies, confusingly present in two quite different colours: their bodies were either pure creamy white, or coffee-coloured, but in all of them the wing tips were black and the tails white, the webbed feet scarlet and the bills pink and blue.

Most spectacular, however, was a colony of frigatebirds on a rocky slope. Some were quietly incubating, but at a few sites a male was displaying alone. When a female – readily identified by her red feet – hovered or flew past, the male leant back on his tail with body almost upright, beak pointing vertically in the air and wings fully extended along the ground; throwing back his head to show his grotesque inflated scarlet throat sac, throbbing rhythmically and shaking from side to side, he vibrated his wings and clattered his bill noisily; all of this often with no apparent effect on the passing female.

Picking their way cautiously round the fringes of the colony were a couple of long-legged Ascension Night Herons, on the look out for regurgitated fish or recently hatched booby chicks. Also to be seen were speckled brown Ascension Rails with brilliant red eyes, about the size of moorhens but unable to fly, running about freely on dry and dusty land, turning over corpses of seabird chicks to look for beetles.

Leaving the birds and the crabs behind, the sailors pushed on towards the base of the central mountain, hoping that its greenness high up and its cap of cloud implied that streams could be found near the base. In this they were disappointed, finding only a spurge with milky sap, some sedges and grasses in the gullies, masses of purslane and also a few specimens of a strange flowering bush that they had never seen before – the nearest approach to a tree that Ascension seemed to offer.

They were by now so thirsty that they turned back towards the coast without reaching the cool upper part of the mountain, where they would have found acres of ferns shrouded in swirling mist. This forbidding island – apparently lacking freshwater – was not one that they would recommend as a port of call for following ships.

Chapter 9

The island and people

Location and administration

Ascension is an extremely isolated and relatively young oceanic island. It lies at latitude 7°57'S and longitude 14°22'W, 1,300 km northwest of St. Helena. The nearest continental land is Cape Palmas (Liberia) 1,504 km to the NNE. Recife on the coast of Brazil is 2,232 km to the west. The coast of Gabon is just over 2,600 km to the east and that of Angola and northern Namibia is further south at a distance of about 3,000 km. The island is roughly triangular, 11.5 km from north to south and 14 km from west to east. It has an area of 97 km², with extremely rugged volcanic terrain. The western part of the island is relatively low and dry while the eastern end is higher and moister, rising to the Peak of Green Mountain at an altitude of 859 m (Plate 9). Just north of the eastern end of the main island lies Boatswainbird Island, with an area of about 5 ha; there are also a number of rocky stacks around the coast.

Confusingly, Ascension is described as a Dependency of St Helena, but it is a quite separate British Overseas Territory with its own Governor.[1] However, the Governor by convention is also the Governor of St Helena, where he resides. The Administrator of Ascension, who is appointed by the British Secretary of State for Foreign and Commonwealth Affairs, reports both to London and to the Governor in St Helena. He holds all the public offices including that of magistrate and is responsible for the Post Office, Savings Bank, police, immigration, conservation and the environment. He also chairs the Ascension Island Management Group, made up of representatives of the various British and American 'user organisations'. At present these comprise Merlin Communications who manage the British Broadcasting Corporation's World Service transmitting station, Cable & Wireless (who also run a European Space Agency Ariane tracking station), the Combined Signals Organisation, the Royal Air Force and their contractors Turners, Serco, Eurest and Maersk Shipping, and the United States Air Force and their contractors Computer Sciences Raytheon. In addition the Administrator chairs an Advisory Forum made up of representatives from the user organisations. The US government have an agreement with the UK for the use of some land on the island for their installations; they also run the airfield, although this is also used by the RAF.

At the time of writing (early 2000), common services on the island (apart from those taken on by the United States authorities and the Royal Air Force for their own installations) are provided by Ascension Island Services (AIS), a British firm set up for the purpose. These arrangements are currently under review with the aim of introducing a more normal form of democratic government.

Ascension Island is unusual in that land is vested in the Crown and all the buildings are owned by the organisations operating on the island. There is no permanent

---

[1] We are indebted to Mr Roger Huxley and Mr Geoff Fairhurst, successive Administrators on Ascension, for this explanation of the status of the island. The complexity of the arrangement sometimes leads to confusion, as we discovered when we looked up St Helena on the on-line gazeteer database of the United States Central Intelligence Agency (CIA). There we found that St Helena had a high-specification airfield. This, of course, would be news to the inhabitants of St Helena, one of the largest island communities that lacks any form of airfield. The entry doubtless referred to Ascension Island, 1300 kilometres away!

population: everyone on the island is there on contract (or is a dependant of a person with a contract) and if a job ends, the employee has to leave. However some St Helenian families have lived on Ascension for decades. Workers come mainly from St Helena, with smaller numbers from Britain and the United States. The current population is about 920. The main installations are towards the west of the island, with the workers and their families living at Georgetown, Two Boats village, the RAF camp at Travellers Hill and the US base between Georgetown and the airfield. The eastern part of the island is entirely uninhabited.

Discovery and occupation[2]

Credit for the discovery of Ascension Island on 25th March 1501 goes to the Portuguese Admiral João da Nova, on his way to India using the newly developed route round the Cape of Good Hope; on the return voyage he discovered St Helena. Da Nova named the island Ilha da Concepção, but on Ascension Day 1503 it was rediscovered by Affonso d'Albuquerque – another Portuguese commander – and named accordingly. It was the second name that stuck. In 1539 Ascension was given a charter by King John III of Portugal, recognising it as part of the Portuguese Empire.

The island remained uninhabited for three centuries. It would have been much more popular with mariners if it had provided freshwater. Ships on their way back to Europe from the Indian Ocean and beyond, typically stopped at St Helena, where they could obtain water and also fruit, herbs and fresh meat. Ascension was at first visited mainly by ships which had either overshot St Helena or needed to stop for repairs. Gradually, however, visits became more frequent, as word spread among the seafaring community of the abundant turtles which could be captured on the beaches at certain times of year.

Ascension had no settled population until 1815. On 22nd October of that year, only seven days after the *Northumberland* had reached St Helena with Napoleon, the Royal Navy occupied Ascension to preempt any attempt by the French to use it as a base for a rescue mission. Shortly afterwards the island was established as HMS *Ascension*, sloop of war. After Napoleon's death in 1821 it was maintained as a depot and sanatorium for the African Squadron of the Royal Navy, but control was transferred from the navy to the marines. The original camp, Regent Square, was renamed Georgetown in 1829 in honour of King George IV (Plate 10).

The first Royal Marine Commandant was the formidable Lt. Col. Edward Nicholls. He supervised an ambitious building programme, using massive blocks of local volcanic rock. A pier, houses and fortifications were built, roads constructed and later, miles of iron piping were laid. This required a substantial labour force and in the early days there were repeated requests for more hands; some were acquired from intercepted slave ships. In 1826 the Commandant wrote to the naval Commodore saying:

> *"The black men.... are clean and well conducted. They are getting very useful, but poor fellows they are continually asking me to get their wives here from Sierra Leone. I hope you will be so good as to have them sent. We are really in want of some of the fair sex, having only six in the Island which is by far too few. Those of them that have not wives at S.L. request you will send them some. They wish them young under 25."*

The organisation of a secure freshwater supply and the establishment of a farm on the mountain were key aims of the marine garrison. At first water was taken

---

[2] Our brief account of human activities on Ascension is based on a number of sources, especially J.A.K. Thompson (1947), B. Stonehouse (1960), D. Hart-Davis (1972) and J.E. Packer (1968b, 1974, 1983).

mainly from Dampier's Drip. A detachment of marines was established there with their families, in caves cut into the rock. They collected the water in casks and transported 60 or 70 gallons daily to the garrison almost eight kilometres away, on the backs of mules and donkeys. Since well over 100 people lived in the garrison, this can have been none too much for personal needs in a hot climate. By 1829 about 360 gallons were being transported daily; this was about three-quarters of the total output from Dampier's even outside periods of drought.

The obligation to provision the ships of the African Squadron led to great efforts to increase the supply of water and production of stock and vegetables; there was also concern about the military security of the island. Captain H.R. Brandreth, Royal Engineers, was sent to assess the situation on the island in 1829, and with much advice from the Commandant he produced a comprehensive report and recommendations.

A substantial water tank was soon built at Dampier's, and in 1831 a four-inch pipeline was completed from there to Georgetown. In the meantime Brandreth located a new source of water, sinking a well near the head of Breakneck Valley. This was on the other side of the Peak, the water being piped through the mountain via a 300 metre tunnel dug through the compacted cinders and then on down to join the original pipeline at Dampier's. This was not the end of problems with water supply. Brandreth's Wells failed after some years and were abandoned for a while, but reopened with temporary success in 1877. A paved rainfall catchment area on the peak was constructed in 1881, but around this time distillation was also being used, although the equipment tended to break down; even when it was working, the water ration to the garrison was only two gallons a day per person; even in 1956 it was only 6 gallons.

The farm on Green Mountain (Plate 10), established in 1817, was soon able to provide a wide variety of vegetables and fruits, as well as pigs, goats, sheep and oxen. During the next century and a half its output was evidently extremely variable, depending largely on the priority given to it by the authorities and the energy of the successive farm managers.

Natural products of the island were also utilized from the early days, and included seabird eggs and cured fish. Most important, however, were the Green Turtles. The sporadic exploitation of these during the previous three centuries now gave way to a systematic and intensive harvest. The economic importance of turtles is indicated by the fact that members of the garrison – at any rate later in the century – received half a crown for every turtle captured.[3] The work apparently occupied 19 men for about four months from the middle of January. As a conservation measure they were required to let the turtle lay its eggs first.

During the heyday of the operation in the 19th century turtles not only provided food on Royal Navy ships, but were sent to England, where turtle soup became a feature of banquets given by the Lord Mayors of London and at the Admiralty. Turtles were also used to barter for other goods on a substantial scale. In the archives for the early decades of occupation there is a record of a visiting French ship which provided – in return for 300 turtles – a list of supplies including:[4]

> "55 *Wether sheep (which shall be kept for the African Squadron), 25 Chauldron of most* *excellent Coals, sixty Casks of Beef, ten of Tongues, One Dozen of Hams, twelve Barrels* *of Pitch and Tars, three Barrels of Flour, eight Tons of Oat Straw with the grain in, One*

---

[3] A.B. Ellis (1885).

[4] Quoted by D. Hart-Davis (1972).

Cask of Wine, Fifty Bushels of Oats and Barley, Two Casks of Bread, five Bolts of Canvas, five Coil of Rope, One Hundred Deals, Nails, Paints, Oil, etc, etc."

Because of the restricted season of availability, a sea-water pond for holding turtles alive until needed was built soon after 1815 and later enlarged. A second pond was built in 1829, a year in which it is recorded that 1500 turtles were collected (Plate 13). Data are patchy thereafter, but suggest a decline during the second half of the 19th century; 1506 turtles were caught in 1845 and between 500 and 1000 in most years of the following decade, but only 160 in 1867 and 122 in 1886.[5]

Between 1924 and 1934, the Eastern Telegraph Company had a concession to take turtles. Records are incomplete, but in 1930 the company sold 106 turtles out of 141 caught. There were various problems, however, with parasites, shipment and falling demand, and the enterprise was barely economic. The concession was not renewed in 1935 and in the ensuing years only a few turtles were taken for local consumption. In 1942, however, large numbers of United States troops arrived on the island and the Government of St Helena issued licences to collect up to 50 turtles to supplement their diet. It appears the meat was not popular and in 1943 only small numbers were used by the US and British communities. As far as the records show, no turtles were turned after 1943.

However, this was not the end of commercial use of the Ascension Green Turtle population. In 1969 a commercial hatchery, Mariculture Ltd of the Cayman Islands, was given permission to start collecting and exporting turtle eggs. In all but one year between 1969 and 1975 about 25,000 eggs were taken. Of these, 20,000 were exported and 5,000 were hatched on Ascension; at least some of the hatchlings were kept in the turtle ponds and fed for several weeks before being released into the sea. The idea was that the locally hatched young would have increased survival and so compensate for the removal of the other eggs.

Throughout the 19th century it can be assumed that fish was a valued supplement to official rations for members of the garrison. However, fishing was probably mainly an individual pursuit and there is little information about it, although dried and salted eels were added in the 1820s to the list of products available to visiting ships.

The island's early function as a sanatorium for the African Squadron brought with it serious health hazards. Only two years after the marines took over in 1821, the island was visited by HMS *Bann*, a sloop with a crew of 135. A virulent infectious fever – presumably picked up from a port on the African coast – had established itself on board, and after sick men were brought ashore it spread quickly in the local community. Eventually about 26 of the crew died, but also more than 50 of the garrison.

After this catastrophe strict quarantine regulations were established. When HMS *Bonetta* arrived in 1838 with yellow fever on board, and on similar occasions with other ships, sick seamen were brought ashore at Comfort (now Comfortless) Cove, 2 km north of Georgetown. Food was left for them at an agreed place, after which the garrison party fired a musket and withdrew without any personal contact. Sentries were posted on Long Beach to ensure that no-one from Comfort Cove visited the garrison. Those who died were buried in the 'climper' near the cove; several small cemeteries can still be found, and a number of the graves have been cleaned and painted in recent years.

---

[5] Information on the exploitation of turtles comes from J.A.K. Thompson (1947), D. Hart-Davis (1972), R.C. Huxley (c.1998), and other sources.

In spite of the precautions and the apparently healthy nature of the climate, infectious disease was a continuing problem on Ascension. Captain William Bate, an energetic officer who commanded the garrison for the decade commencing in 1828, was one of the many who died during a severe epidemic of influenza in 1838; Bate's successor died after 21 months tenure, and his successor after only seven months.

Nonetheless, for several decades after the death of Napoleon the island was used as a relatively healthy base providing support for the ships involved with the suppression of the slave trade. The expense was harder to justify later in the 19th century, and in 1888 the island establishment was reduced. However, mid-ocean islands tend to reassert their strategic significance and during the Boer War communications with South Africa became of paramount importance. In 1899 the Eastern Telegraph Company (later Cable & Wireless) brought ashore a submarine telegraph cable in Comfortless Cove, initiating the 20th century role of the island as a communications hub.

Human activities in the 20th century
The connection of the Royal Navy with Ascension terminated in 1922. For most of the next fifty years the manager of the cable company administered the island and served as Resident Magistrate. Until the second world war, life must have been very quiet on the island, punctuated mainly by the arrival every few weeks of a Union Castle liner on the South African route.

In 1925 the island was visited by collectors from the Cleveland Museum of Natural History in the schooner *Blossom*. They collected seabirds on Boatswainbird Island, turtles on the beaches and also camped in a cave at Dampier's while working on the mountain. No scientific account of the expedition was published, but the leader George Finlay Simmons wrote a travelogue in the *National Geographic Magazine* under the title *Sinbads of science*.

The 1920s also saw renewal of the exploitation of guano deposits on Ascension, an activity that had first occurred in the middle of the 19th century. We know little about the early operation, but John Packer records that in 1851 a Scottish firm sent two brigs to collect guano from Boatswainbird Island, and import statistics show that 1116 tons of Ascension Island guano reached Britain in 1851 and 1852.[6] There may also have been some exploitation around 1880.

The Ascension Island Phosphate Company was formed in the 1920s to work the phosphate deposits on the main island and also the guano on Boatswainbird Island. The latter had been accumulating in the bird colonies for at least four decades and a later report suggested that the yield in the 1920s was about 1,000 tons.[7] After this time, guano was collected from Boatswainbird Island intermittently at least until the end of the 1950s, for use on the mountain farm, but the quantities concerned were small.

The phosphate deposits exploited in the 1920s were around English Bay. Facilities including a number of buildings and a light railway from English Bay to Porpoise Point

---

[6] G.E. Hutchinson (1950).

[7] In 1995 we talked on St Helena with Ernest Roberts, who worked for the phosphate company in the 1920s. We were surprised to learn from him that the guano collectors on Boatswainbird Island returned each night to a camp on the mainland. In 1924 an exceptional storm flooded the campsite at Spire Beach and washed the tents into the sea, stranding the men in two groups on either side of the precipitous gully. Roberts had to go by boat to Georgetown through lightning and thunder to get help. After this about 26 labourers camped on Boatswainbird Island for up to a month at a time. During the period when Roberts was working there a couple of ships were loaded with guano.

were established in 1923.[8] By late 1925 the company was employing six Englishmen and more than 100 St Helenian labourers in the phosphate operations. The deposits are in the form of a leached white powder, mainly in narrow crevices between the jagged rocks; extracting them must have been a laborious and unpleasant job, carried out in the intense heat of the lava flows. The operation was abandoned in 1931.

After the second world war, however, phosphate extraction was considered again. The agricultural officer from St Helena, J.A.K. Thompson, obtained samples of the deposits in the English Bay area during a visit in 1947. Analysis showed these to contain 7-10% phosphate and <1-14% nitrogen. However, samples from the lava flow east of Mars Bay had much more phosphate (27-42%) though again highly variable nitrogen (<1-5%). For comparison, two samples of relatively fresh guano from Boatswainbird Island contained 12-15% phosphate and 9-20% nitrogen. Thompson seems to have considered that exploitation of the guano on Boatswainbird Island would be a viable commercial proposition. With regard to the mainland phosphate deposits, he clearly felt that the economics were marginal, but suggested that:

> "it should however leave sufficient margin not only to recover all costs but to allow for some profit, however small; from this point of view it would prove worth while if only to provide employment for a part of the surplus labour in St Helena."

This idea was apparently not put into practice, but John Packer recounts how a mining engineer from a company interested in re-opening guano workings visited the island in 1958, but concluded that exploitation would be uneconomic with modern equipment. The engineer reluctantly agreed with Packer's view that a hundred men with teaspoons would be more suited to extracting the scattered small pockets from the rocks than two or three bulldozers.

Activities of a quite different kind had occurred during the second world war, with the construction of Wideawake Airfield (and a camouflaged tank farm for fuel) on Waterloo Plain, inland from South West Bay. The work was completed by American army engineers in less than six months in 1942, with the objective of providing a refuelling point for American aircraft crossing the Atlantic to join the military campaigns in Africa and the Far East. From 1943 until the end of the war some two thousand servicemen were stationed on the island. Though they doubtless caused disturbance to the Wideawakes (see Chapter 11) and to the turtles nesting on the beaches, and also shot the remaining feral goats, their impact on the ecology of the island was otherwise rather slight.

After the end of the war the garrison was rapidly reduced and in 1947 the last servicemen left. The human population fell to about 170 and administration was again in the hands of Cable & Wireless Ltd, who were the only users of the island.

Less than a decade later, however, saw the opening of the modern phase of Ascension's history as a multi-purpose British and American mid-ocean facility, with frequent comings and goings of a variety of organisations, mainly concerned with communications. In 1956 the US Air Force, by arrangement with the UK Government, began preparing for the establishment of a tracking station for missile trials on the Eastern Test Range, stretching from Cape Canaveral in Florida across the Caribbean and on towards South Africa.

---

[8] This activity resulted in the grounding of a Union Castle liner in 1926 after its captain mistook the lights of the guano company for those of Georgetown. Subsequently, official sailing directions for this part of the Atlantic included a special warning of the hazard.

In October 1957 the British Ornithologists' Union expedition, of which Philip was a member, established themselves in Mars Bay to study the seabird populations (see Plate 11 and box in Chapter 12). By this time the American camp, known as Miracle Mile, had been established by Pan American for the US Air Force, the Volcano Club was open and *Snark* guided missiles were occasionally splashing into the sea offshore.

The British Broadcasting Corporation (BBC) became involved with the island in 1961, although major construction of technical facilities near English Bay and of accommodation near Two Boats did not commence until 1964 and the station became operational only in late 1966. In 1964 the administration of the island passed from the manager of Cable & Wireless to an appointed Administrator. Ascension continued, in effect, to be a closed island; with very few exceptions, only people directly connected with one of the resident organisations were permitted to visit

In 1965 the airstrip was considerably lengthened, and in the following year the American National Aeronautics and Space Administration (NASA) organised facilities for tracking satellites and spacecraft, including the *Apollo* missions and – in 1975 – the launch of the *Viking* spacecraft setting off for Mars. The South African Cable Company established facilities on the island in 1968-9, and at about the same time the Composite Signals Organisation (CSO) joined the list of user groups on the island.

The last visit of a Union Castle liner on a scheduled passenger service was in 1977; the first such visit had been in 1863. The service was taken over by the RMS *St Helena*, a ship which had previously seen service in Alaskan waters.[9] The year 1982 saw major disruption of life on the island by the Falklands War. The Royal Air Force built up a large presence on the island, and in the following year – after the end of the war – construction of a permanent camp was undertaken at Travellers Hill. In 1984 Ascension Island Services was established to run the common services on the island.

During the 1990s Ascension began to lose its importance in global communications, although it still plays an important role as a staging point for people *en route* for the Falklands and St Helena. The authorities have recently begun to encourage tourism as a way of enhancing the economy and generating jobs for St Helenians. Ascension is no longer closed to the public, although intending visitors must ask the permission of the Administrator to come to the island. Cruise ships already make occasional visits and access by air is likely to become easier in the future. As we enter the new millennium, this remote island is facing fundamental change.

---

[9] She was replaced in 1990 by the present 'RMS', but there were substantial teething problems.

Chapter 10   # The physical environment

Landforms and geology

The volcano and the island
The origin of Ascension Island has been described in Chapter 1. Like St Helena, Ascension is the tip of a large conical volcano with its base on the floor of the deep ocean; as in the case of St Helena, the island represents only a tiny fraction - perhaps 1% - of the total volume of the volcano. However, while St Helena is about 14 million years old, Ascension is much younger. The oldest subaerial rocks (those above sea level) that have been checked for age are roughly one million years old. We take this as the approximate age of the island, while realizing that the estimate may be increased by discovery of somewhat older rocks.[1]

Ascension is geologically active, and the arriving visitor sees a raw landscape, a picture of an island in the construction phase. It is only a little smaller than St Helena, but is quite different in profile. Whereas St Helena is a heavily eroded cliffed remnant of a larger island, with the form of a flat cake, Ascension is a basically conical and potentially growing island: erosion on the exposed eastern coasts may be more than balanced by future lava flows expanding the island in the west. Although no eruptions have been recorded in historical times, some of the flows are thought to be less than a thousand years old and further activity is likely.

The complex landscape has been produced by a long series of eruptions, those in the east producing dramatic white steep-sided hills and cliffs, while the more recent ones in the west involved massive outpourings of black lava, covered in places by a layer of fine cinders, forming volcanic deserts sloping gradually down to the sea. Superimposed on these wide expanses is a random array of spectacular red brown 'parasitic cones', volcanic hills formed around the eruptive vents on the flanks of a large volcano.

The rocks of Ascension
The rocks of the island are volcanic (extrusive) in origin, having been erupted either as lava flows or as pyroclasts (meaning 'fire-broken' and referring to any particles ejected from a volcano into the air) which then fall to the ground to form pyroclastic deposits (also known as tephra). The main types of volcanic rocks on Ascension have characteristically different proportions of silica. Basalt and hawaiite have about 45-50% (hawaiite having a higher content of alkali elements), mugearite is 50-55% silica, benmoreite 55-60%, trachyte 60-70% and rhyolite 70-75%.

In Figure 22, for simplicity, we label the rocks with less than 60% silica as basalt and those with more than 60% as trachyte. The first group are dark coloured, even black, though

---

[1] Barry Weaver tells us that some of the estimated ages of rocks given by C. Harris et al. (1982) are now considered too high. The first serious account of the geology of Ascension was by Charles Darwin (1844), and was followed by a comprehensive treatment by R.A. Daly (1925). Modern brief accounts are by F.B. Atkins et al. (1964), J.E. Packer (1983) and M.S. Rosenbaum (1992), and a fuller one by D.L. Nielson & B.S. Sibbett (1996); technical aspects are discussed by A. Kar et al. (1998). A detailed treatment of the geology of both Ascension and St Helena is provided by B.L. Weaver (1999).

183

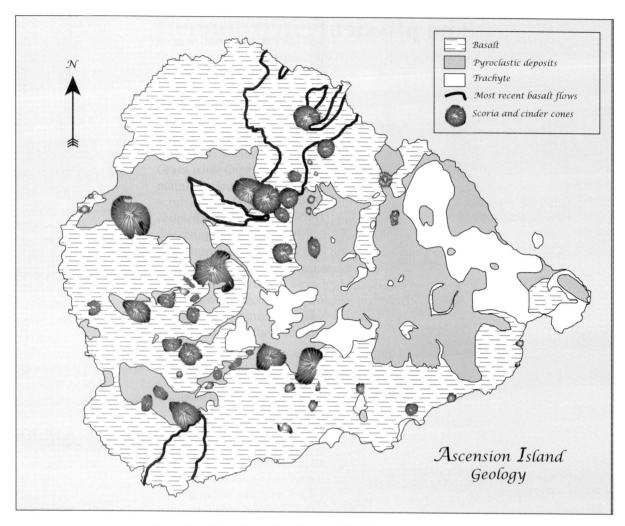

Figure 22   Adapted from F.B. Atkins et al. (1964), with permission of *Nature*.

benmoreite tends to be less dark than basalt, and basalt may be red brown as a result either of weathering or of 'hydrothermal' alteration by steam during its eruption. These dark volcanic rocks contain relatively high proportions of the minerals pyroxene and olivine (a silicate of magnesium and iron) and are sometimes termed 'mafic' (a contraction from magnesium and ferric). In contrast, trachyte is a pale grey rock composed mainly of feldspar, an aluminium silicate mineral that forms white crystals; rhyolite also consists largely of feldspar, along with quartz (silica). Trachyte and rhyolite together are often referred to as felsic volcanic rocks (with a derivation from feldspar and silica). Felsic lavas, when altered hydrothermally or by weathering, give rise to a friable, whitish, sandy rock in which the original minerals have gained water or oxygen. Erosion of trachyte often gives rise to honeycomb patterns, or to the formation of 'platy' fragments, well seen on Ascension at the Devil's Riding School.

The silica content of the magma (molten rock formed by partial melting of materials from the earth's mantle) partly determines the character of the erupted lava, which is relatively fluid if silica content is low, and progressively more viscous with greater proportions of silica.

Viscosity is also affected by temperature, hotter magma being less viscous. Since the eruption temperature of low silicate (mafic) lava is higher than that of high silicate (felsic) lava, temperature tends to enhance the effect of differences in composition, so that felsic lava is enormously more viscous than mafic lava. As magma moves towards the surface during an eruption, the reduction in pressure brings gases out of solution. If the magma is very fluid, the gases (mainly steam) can boil off fairly steadily during an eruption, but if the magma is viscous they are impeded and the eruption is more likely to be explosive.

Explosive eruptions of viscous felsic magma may lead to the formation of pumice, pale coloured pyroclasts consisting of a light frothy glass which are thrown high in the air and then settle on the land, often in great drifts, or on the sea where they may float, forming pale patches on the surface and sometimes travelling for hundreds of miles. If the magma contains less gas the eruption may be passive, trachyte lava spreading out laterally in a thick flow with an almost level surface, behaving much like thick porridge poured out of a pan. If the magma is even more viscous it behaves more like bread dough, forming massive domes hundreds of metres across and up to 100 metres thick.

A geothermal exploration well more than 3000 metres deep has shown that the undersea base of the Ascension volcano is largely mafic in composition, and it is possible that mafic eruptions were involved in the emergence of the island. However, the old rocks in the centre and east of the island are mainly felsic (trachyte and rhyolite) and they include the oldest rock yet found on Ascension, a rhyolite from east of Middleton ridge dating from just one million years ago. Felsic activity in the central area continued for almost half a million years, and built up the main mass of Green Mountain. Daly's Crags represent a trachyte outlier in the northwest that is 750,000 years old, and the Devil's Riding School is another in the southwest, 660,000 years old (although it is a complex of trachyte and basalt, as explained by Barry Weaver). In the east, Weather Post is a trachyte dome that may be about the same age. Its formation was preceded by a massive trachyte flow from the area of the Devil's Cauldron (which is an explosion crater), forming the cliffs south of Spire Beach and the cliffs and hinterland at the Ariane site near North East Bay. The curious formation called Bears Back, near the road to North East Bay, may have resulted from an intrusion of trachyte beneath older rocks, doming these upwards but failing to pierce them.

There are no secure dates for other conspicuous felsic domes on Ascension such as trachytic Ragged Hill, White Hill and Letterbox and rhyolitic Little White Hill, but it seems likely that felsic activity in the east occurred over a similar period or somewhat later than that in the centre. Little White Hill is fringed with older mafic scoria that also form the wig of Wig Hill. Boatswainbird Island is also capped with mafic material, which in some measure protects the softer trachyte from erosion and has resulted in the cake-shaped form of the islet.

The dark rocks in the lower western and southern parts of the island represent a wide variety of mafic lavas. Only a few have been dated, and all appear to be less than 500,000 years old, suggesting that mafic activity has been mainly subsequent to the felsic eruptions. However, in the walls of Cricket Valley, east of Green Mountain, are basalt lava flows that must be older than the trachyte dome of Weather Post which cuts through them; these flows may be the oldest mafic rocks exposed on Ascension and dating them seems a high priority. (The origin of Cricket Valley, however, is still a puzzle to geologists.) Relative dating by study of lava flow patterns is possible in some groups of cones; in the southwest, Dark Slope Crater is old and South Gannet Hill the youngest, with Command Hill intermediate.

Most of the mafic flows are of 'aa', the Hawaiian name for lava that was just liquid enough, when erupted, to spread out from the vents and move across the country in broad sheets a few metres thick. Such lava solidifies with extremely jagged, clinkery rock on the surface and with deep cracks (formed by contraction during cooling) that penetrate into the more massive centre of the flow; these cracks are typically between half a metre and two metres apart. The lower surface of the flow tends to be rubbly, including many fragments that have solidifed and then been rolled forward with the continuing flow. It is this vertical structure that generally makes it easy to count a series of flows when a section through them is exposed by erosion, forming a cliff.

In a few places, however, the flows are of 'pahoehoe': basalt that has emerged from the vent very liquid and highly gasified. It flows rapidly, spreads into thin sheets and cools with a relatively smooth surface, often showing ropy forms reminiscent of thin cooling porridge, and 'toes' a foot or so across where a small part of the flow has stopped. Pahoehoe can change into aa lava as it cools or loses gas rapidly (for instance when flowing over a cliff), but the reverse change cannot occur. Pahoehoe can be seen in some places just north of the northwest end of the runway, and in an unusual situation at the 'lava lake' south of the base of Sisters Peak, where liquid lava has been impounded and has solidified with a roughly level surface. Pahoehoe is the type of lava that sometimes forms the volcanic caves known as lava tubes, which are discussed below.

On Ascension the basaltic lava has generally been erupted from cylindrical vents, rather than the long fissures that were common on St Helena, and has taken the form of both flows and lava fountains. The 50 or so cones and craters scattered over the plains of Ascension were created by a mildly explosive type of eruption in which lumps of molten rock are flung into the air from a vent, forming a lava fountain, and fall back to earth close by, solidifying during flight or shortly after impact to form the irregular rubbly chunks of clinker so characteristic of Ascension (technically they are scoria, a term referring to all pyroclastic deposits of basaltic composition). Sometimes the scoria become welded together on impact, forming agglomerate. Some lava fountains produce clots of magma which are fluid enough to be shaped during flight and which remain airborne long enough to harden and so retain their form on impact. They are then called volcanic bombs, which may be spindle-shaped, ropy, long-tailed, or reminiscent of cannonballs. Scoria normally contain 'vesicles', which are gas bubbles frozen into the solidifying rock; these also occur in basalt lava flows, especially near the upper surface.

The scoria produced by fountaining vary in colour according to their state of oxidation: they are normally blackish when first deposited, but are reddish if the rock surface is oxidised by steam escaping from the vent at the same time; alteration at a lower temperature by water can give a yellow colour. Over longer periods, weathering leads to reddening of all basalt rocks, as the iron in the minerals is progressively oxidised. It is the combination of these processes that has given rise to the wonderful variety of colours in the landscape, which is especially dramatic at sunset.

Scoria cones formed by lava fountains normally rise to a summit crater. The outside walls have slopes determined by the angle of rest of the loose rocks; this is typically a little over 30 degrees from the horizontal. Because the prevailing winds are from the southeast the scoria generally accumulate more on the northwest (leeward) side of the vent, while the southeast (windward) wall is steeper and thinner. Perfect Crater (east of Sisters) is almost symmetrical, presumably because it formed in the shelter of Green Mountain.

Fountaining is typical of the early stages of an eruption when the magma is most highly gasified; if lava flows are produced at this stage they may be of the pahoehoe type. Observations elsewhere suggest that the fountaining that forms scoria cones typically lasts less than a year. Fountaining may be succeeded by calmer eruption of less highly gasified, more viscous lava. It is at this stage that a large quantity of lava may well up in a crater and breach it, flowing out to form an aa flow. One of the most recent eruptions of Sisters produced an enormous northward flow of aa which reached the sea on a broad front, forming the coastline east of English Bay. Surrounded by this flow is East Crater, locally known as Broken Tooth, where the crater wall has been ruptured by a massive stream of aa which flowed northeastwards to form Porpoise Point. Another large and probably recent aa flow arose from South Gannet Hill and reached the coast east of Mars Bay to create the southernmost point of the island.

Although fissure eruptions have been rare on Ascension, there is a dramatic example in the Devil's Inkpot flow on Letterbox, thought to be one of the latest eruptions on the island. It came from three fissures (less than 10 metres wide) in the trachyte dome, and is of dark brown benmoreite which looks like chocolate icing on the white trachyte cake.

As well as massive volcanic rock, Ascension has large areas (around 45% of the surface) covered by pyroclastic deposits or tephra (synonymous terms covering accumulations of all types of particle expelled into the air during eruptions). Pyroclasts are classified by size. Those less than 2 mm in diameter are termed ash, those between 2 mm and 64 mm are cinders (or lapilli), while larger ones are referred to as blocks and bombs. Non-explosive eruptions can produce airborne ash, which may travel far, but explosive or at least fountaining eruptions are normally required to distribute larger particles over the landscape. In Figure 22 we do not distinguish felsic from mafic pyroclastic deposits. The former are typically of pumice, the latter of blackish basaltic cinders. Cinders form most of the cones on Ascension, but Broken Tooth and Hollow Tooth are formed of blocks. Most of the cones appear red brown as a result of oxidation of the cinders, but on many (such as South Gannet Hill) buried cinders are still black; in a few, steam emitted during the eruption oxidised all of the cinders.

Felsic eruptions on Ascension have produced voluminous but patchy pyroclastic deposits in a broad band extending from the Devil's Riding School in the southwest, around the north of Green Mountain and on to the northeast coast. This is in general the area where the underlying rocks are also felsic in nature. Some of the deposits are of air-fall pyroclasts, resulting from an upwardly-directed explosion that blew particles high into the air; they are sand or gravel sized, somewhat rounded, full of vesicles and thus very light and weak. A good example is exposed in the road cut on the NASA road north of Spoon Crater. In some places around Green Mountain, however, there are deposits formed by pyroclastic flows, occurring when a dense and turbulent eruption column of pyroclasts suspended in hot volcanic gas collapses at the source vent under the force of gravity. It then behaves as a fluid as it moves in an avalanche down the side of the volcano, eventually settling to form a block and ash flow deposit.

Basaltic pyroclasts are more obvious to the visitor, who will see them forming a blanket over large areas of blackish lava, especially southeast of the mountain, northwest of South Gannet Hill and west of Sisters as far as Long Beach. The deposits are many metres thick in places, for instance at the foot of Daly's Crags (Plate 9), where they have been quarried; further west (and more distant from the source) the layer is much thinner. Basaltic cinders and ash also contribute to the Green Mountain massif, forming a large accumulation near the summit and blanketing parts of the eastern and southern flanks.

In some places on Ascension, 'xenoliths' have been found. These are pieces of coarse-grained rock that crystallized slowly at great depth in the volcano, but were then torn off the sides of the fissure through which magma rose to the surface during an eruption, and were ejected from the volcanic vent without melting (though sometimes altered by the heat). Xenoliths of gabbro (the intrusive equivalent of basalt) 10-20 cm across occur among scoria near the rim of Dark Slope Crater; they have crystals up to 5 mm long of white feldspar, green pyroxene and red-brown olivine. Xenoliths of granite with crystals of quartz and other minerals were noted by Charles Darwin in 1836. They are up to 30 cm across and are associated with deposits of trachytic pyroclasts on the left of the mountain road at about 470 m; they have been shown to be about a million years old, and are thus as old as any of the rocks formed on the island itself. Other granite xenoliths occur on the southern slope of Middleton ridge.

Both basaltic and trachytic lavas are fine-grained rocks that have cooled too rapidly for large mineral crystals to form. Some of them, however, contain phenocrysts, crystals that have formed slowly in a subterranean magma chamber over long periods prior to eruption. One example is the basaltic flow from Command Hill that spread over much of the land to the west, from the US base to Portland Point; it contains large crystals of olivine and feldspar in a fine-grained matrix.

The most attractive rock type found on Ascension is obsidian, a volcanic glass formed when rapid cooling of molten trachyte at the surface leaves too little time for crystallization of the minerals. It is somewhat unstable and chemically reactive, tending to crystallize in the long term. It occurs in layers at the base of some rhyolite flows, for instance at Sharp Cliff west of South East Bay and at the bottom of Middleton ridge opposite Travellers.

Other geological features

Dykes, which are common on St Helena, are rare on Ascension, but there is a good example on the western slopes of Spoon Crater. Others can be seen below Middleton's and between Northeast Cottage and North East Bay.

A non-volcanic rock that can be found near low tide mark in many places is beach rock or cemented sand. This is produced when crystals of calcium carbonate (of the form known as aragonite) are laid down between the grains of sand on a beach. Rock formation can occur in as little as ten years in a warm climate such as that of Ascension.[2]

In a few places on the island there are deposits that seem to have been laid down in freshwater. In the level area sometimes called Sandy Plain, between Perfect Crater and the southern part of Bears Back, there are thin beds of pumice and ash which are finely stratified and were probably deposited in a shallow temporary lake. Some of the craters on the island hold water for a few days after heavy rain: we have been told of this happening at Perfect Crater within recent years; another place that sometimes holds water is Cricket Valley, and this may partly account for its relatively level floor (Plate 14).

---

[2] During the last century men quarrying the beach rock about 100 yards from the sea in the northwest of the island found a group of turtle eggs fossilized in the hard rock. Sir Charles Lyell in his classic book Principles of Geology described the fossils: "The eggs must have been nearly hatched at the time when they perished; for the bones of the young turtle are seen in the interior with their shape fully developed, the interstices between the bones being entirely filled with grains of sand, which are cemented together."

The Devil's Riding School probably contained water for a substantial period. Charles Darwin first noted the possibility of this after sending samples of deposits to a German colleague who said that they included mineralized remains of plants. A few years ago John Packer examined under high magnification some samples that he collected in the Devil's Riding School in 1997, and found that those from one layer - which was about 10 cm thick - included roughly one third organic material.[3] Much of this consisted of the silica skeletons of diatoms, microscopic plants that occur in both salt and fresh water. There is no reason to suppose that the Devil's Riding School was ever below sea level, so it seems clear that it must have been a persistent lake.

Crater lakes are common on volcanic islands, but the climate of Ascension is now too hot and dry to make the persistence of a lake plausible. It seems likely that the freshwater deposits in the Devil's Riding School were laid down at a time during the last half million years when – under the influence of one or more of the Pleistocene ice ages – rainfall at Ascension was higher than at present.

Rare but violent floods have led to the formation of water channels by erosion in various parts of Ascension. There is no permanent running water on the island today, but in the past Dampier's Drip seems to have run continuously. In 1828 a visitor described it as producing "*a stream of water that might pass through an ordinary sized goose quill*".[4]

Changes in sea level

We saw in Chapter 3 that lowering of sea level during the Pleistocene ice ages led to a massive increase in the land area of St Helena, adding an enormous apron outside the present line of cliffs. On Ascension the effect was to produce a relatively narrow shelf below the cliffs in the east of the island, but a broader extension of the shelving coastal areas in the west. Off Clarence Bay, where the shelf was widest, the edge of the sea when sea level was lowest must have been more than 4 kilometres further west than the present shoreline; overall, the area of Ascension was more than 50% greater than it is now.

A point of particular interest is that Boatswainbird Island will have been joined to the main island during periods of lowered sea level, including the last ice age. When the world became warmer and sea level rose, Boatswainbird Island became isolated, perhaps around 8000 years ago; the animals living on it were thus protected from the impact of introduced species that had such large effects on the main island.

Caves

Several types of volcanic caves are found on Ascension. Little was known about them until a British potholer, Rob James, went to the island with the Royal Air Force in 1984 and undertook a systematic survey.[5] Sea caves are commonest on the western coasts where basalt lava flows are subject to erosion by the sea. Water enters by joints in the rock and gradually hollows out weaker sections of the flow. One cave near Comfortless Cove is 14 metres long and has its seaward entrance under water; further in there are two air bells, the second of which can be entered from the land. Like most sea caves, this one is dangerous to enter in rough weather.

There is a large tidal sea cave near White Bluff, southwest of Cocoanut Bay. At low water it is possible to enter from the seaward end and to follow the tunnel - which is

---

[3] J.E. Packer & L. Packer (1998) p.50.

[4] James Holman, quoted by B. Stonehouse (1960).

[5] R. James (1985).

up to 11 metres high - inland for 60 metres. A fine group of stalactites hang from the roof about a third of the way in. At high water even the back of the cave is flooded.

The best known caves on Ascension are those called the fumaroles north of Sisters Peak, where sub-fossil bird bones have been found (see Plate 12 and box in Chapter 12). They are hollow spatter cones, built from scoria derived from from clots of basaltic lava blown out of a vent. The caves inside them have relatively narrow shafts descending about eight metres but broaden out below into a number of short passages and chambers; the overall depth is 22 metres.

Near the fumaroles is Packer's Hole, which has an overall depth of 18 metres (Plate 12). It seems not to be a lava tube or volcanic vent but rather a complex narrow cleft, presumably formed by rock movements; cinders have trickled in from the surface and carpet parts of the cave floor. We found interesting endemic invertebrate animals in this cave.

In the southwest of Ascension are some lava tubes, which are formed during particular kinds of eruptions. During an eruption of pahoehoe or very hot aa lava, the flow is fastest where the slope of the ground is greatest, slower on nearly level ground and at the sides of the spreading sheet. The lava solidifies first where it moves slowly, so that sometimes a 'river' of lava is left flowing between banks of newly solidified rock; if the flow then ceases, an empty channel may be left. On Ascension, formations of this kind are particularly clear in the area between Spoon Crater and South Gannet Hill. Sometimes, however, the upper surface of the lava may also solidify while the flow continues underneath. If the eruption stops and the last of the lava flows right through, an empty lava tube is left. The largest lava tube on Ascension is Command Hill Cave, which follows the southwest slope of the hill and has a total length of 74 metres. It is a large-diameter tunnel with an easy entrance towards the top and a final chamber which is roughly nine metres high and nine metres across, with a sandy floor.[6]

A little more tricky of access but perhaps more interesting is Chapel Grotto Cave, behind the chapel on the west of the road from the Command Hill cross roads to the American base. The messy entrance is an eight metre roughly vertical shaft leading into a passage with a sand floor. By crawling under an arch about 30 cm high one can reach a chamber nine metres wide and a lava tube passage with a blind end. The low arch inhibits air movements and results in inside temperatures exceeding 32°C, accompanied by high humidity, so that one emerges dripping with sweat. We found particularly interesting bird bones in this cave (see Chapter 12).

Another cave of interest is one that we found in 1990 and called Ravine Cave (Plate 14). It is on the north side of a ravine half a kilometre south of Spoon Crater, and at a height of about about 200 metres above sea level, making it the highest cave that we have located on the island. It is a lava tube partly exposed by erosion of a cliff face and is most easily reached by climbing down from the fairly level area above, which gives the impression of being partly hollow.

Climate

The climate of Ascension Island is dry, tropical and oceanic, with little seasonal change; it has the same general controls as St Helena. Ian Mathieson has pointed out that the apparent difference in climate of the two islands is exaggerated by the fact that a greater proportion of people live and work at high levels on St Helena, and thus tend to encounter

---

[6] On some volcanic islands - including Tenerife - such tubes extend for many kilometres underground.

cool and cloudy weather. Close to sea level, the annual average maximum temperatures are relatively similar; at a given level, rainfall is about 30% higher on St Helena than on Ascension.[7]

Ascension lies in the path of the South-East Trade Winds; winds from the southeast and east blow for more than half the time in every month and have an average speed of about five knots (9 km/hr). The trade wind inversion is usually at a height of about 1000-1500 metres over Ascension; it stabilises the climate, acting as a strong cap which inhibits vertical cloud development and thus ensures generally low rainfall. It also reduces the chance of thunderstorms, which are very rare on the island.[8]

The temperature on Ascension is strikingly constant throughout the year. In Georgetown, just above sea level, the average daily maximum temperatures vary only between about 31°c in the warmest months (March and April) and 27°c in the coolest (September).[9] The daily temperature range at sea level is typically about six degrees. There is also a roughly six degree difference between temperatures at sea level and at 660 m on Green Mountain. Relative humidities at sea level are around 70%.

Although rain in the lowlands of Ascension is rare, the winds rising over the eastern end of the island frequently bring cool and misty conditions to the ridge of Green Mountain, and the mean annual rainfall at an altitude of 660 m is about 680 mm. Rainfall is about half as great at Two Boats, northwest of the mountain at an altitude of 290 m, and averages only about 130 m on the western coast. Coastal rainfall has a strong peak in April and March (means respectively 27.9 and 17.7 mm) and is lowest in December (2.5 mm) although there is much variation. In some years there are spells of several days with drizzly showers, and at irregular intervals there are torrential rains that are quickly followed by rapid growth of grass and other short-lived plants in normally barren areas. [10]

These very heavy and often destructive rains have generally occurred in the period March-May, sometimes lasting for two or three days. Some of them seem to be associated with southern hemisphere 'easterly waves', disturbances originating in central equatorial Africa and moving westwards across the tropical Atlantic.[11] These give rise to strong easterly high level winds and probably provide the best chance for aerial immigration of animals to the island.

The exceptional rains that occurred on Ascension in 1963 and 1984/85 (and doubtless many of the earlier events) were associated with a remarkable periodic phenomenon called El Niño (the child) which affects both the oceans and the atmosphere (see Chapter 3).

Surrounding sea

Tides are relatively unimportant on Ascension since the total range is less than 1 m. However, this apparent stability of sea level can be misleading, because of strong wave

---

[7] Available weather data up to 1989 have been summarized by I.K. Mathieson (1990).

[8] Nonetheless, in 1896 the Captain's steward was knocked to the floor in Georgetown while talking on the telephone, when the overhead line was struck by lightning.

[9] The higher figures sometimes quoted probably result from an error in conversion from Fahrenheit.

[10] The following is a list of some occasions on which exceptional rains have occurred, though there are many gaps in the records and the rains listed varied substantially in their severity: 1831, 1841, 1859, 1876, 1886-87, May 1899, April 1909, February-April 1924, April 1934, March 1963, April 1964, March 1974, March 1984 (4th March had 317 mm, the highest daily fall ever recorded), April 1985; 1995 was also a very wet year, but with the rain spread over the period Feburary to July.

[11] B.A. Hall (1989).

action on the windward coasts and the intermittent occurrence of 'rollers', violent breakers that approach the island without warning from either the northwest (occasionally the southwest) and persist for a few days. Similar rollers occur on St Helena.

Our own interest in the sea around Ascension relates mainly to its use by the seabirds of the island. Before Ascension was disturbed by humans, it was a major site for breeding and roosting seabirds; their numbers are now much depleted, but they remain a key component of the ecosystem of the tropical South Atlantic. The productivity of the sea varies enormously from place to place and this variation is reflected in the availability of food for the seabirds. Some of the species - for instance the Brown Booby - feed close inshore, on prey that spend time in shallow waters at some stage in their life cycles; other seabirds commute long distances to and from the island on a daily or longer basis, exploiting distant and patchy sources of food.

Ascension is situated on the northern edge of the enormous zone of low productivity occupying the central part of the South Atlantic; this is effectively a great marine desert (see Figure 9 in Chapter 3).[12] Around Ascension the upper layer of the sea - down to 50-100 m - is at a temperature of more than 23°C throughout the year. Below this layer of warm water is a permanent thermocline: a layer within which temperature drops sharply with increasing depth. This situation is inherently stable because the warm water is less dense than the cooler water below. The resultant lack of vertical mixing prevents enrichment of the surface layer - where the light is bright enough for photosynthesis to occur - by nutrients present in the cooler waters of the deep ocean. As a result, away from the immediate influence of the island we see clear blue waters with little plankton and sparse populations of fish and other marine animals. Biological productivity in the surface layer is low and depends largely on rapid recycling of the limited nutrient supply, for instance when fish-eating birds defaecate while flying over the ocean.

However, features of the marine currents in the area may lead to higher productivity in certain areas (Figure 3). Ascension lies in the path of generally westerly surface currents for most of the year. The cold Benguela Current, enriched by upwelling near the coast of southern Africa, initially flows northwestwards. The nutrients are gradually depleted as the current warms and then turns westwards in a broad band between about 25°S and the equator, forming the South Equatorial Current. Oceanographic research in recent decades has complicated this picture, showing that between 7° and 9° South (Ascension being at 8°S) there is an *eastward-flowing* current - the South Equatorial Countercurrent - below the surface throughout the year.[13] At the surface the flow is generally westward in the southern winter when the South-East Trade Winds are strongest, but even this may be eastward - at any rate in the area west of Ascension - in the southern summer.

Anything that creates turbulence in the currents is likely to increase productivity. When the subsurface current encounters the submerged cone of the Ascension volcano, some mixing doubtless occurs between the impoverished shallow layers of water and the richer, deeper ones.[14] Furthermore, as well as the Ascension volcano, there are a number

---

[12] J. Scullion (1990).

[13] C.W. Brown (1990).

[14] Increased productivity resulting from this process is known as the 'island mass effect' and has been demonstrated elsewhere, for instance around Hawai'i and the Scilly Isles. Probably there is an effect of this kind around Ascension, improving the food supply of the inshore-feeding seabirds.

192

Green Mountain and Bears Back (right) from the sea off North East Bay

Sisters Peak beyond a lava field where seabird guano can still be seen; only Wideawakes now breed on the main island in places accessible to cats

PLATE 9

ASCENSION ISLAND

Boatswainbird Island from near Spire Rock

View down to Sisters from Elliotts Path on Green Mountain

Dew pond at the summit of Green Mountain, 1958

The Red Lion in 1958, when the farm was under the management of Peter Critchley

A 19th century gun stands guard over Georgetown

PLATE 10
ASCENSION ISLAND

Members of the expedition relaxing on the mountain during their 18 months stay on the island studying the biology of seabirds (Douglas Dorward, Philip Ashmole, Sally and Bernard Stonehouse)

BOU outpost on Boatswainbird Island. Bernard watching departure of *Ibis*, marooning expedition members on the island for up to a week

The BOU camp in 1958. There were no shops in those days and everything needed for 18 months (including food, huts, Land Rover and boats) had to come on board a Union Castle liner

Leaving Boatswainbird Island in *Ibis*

Transferring stores by dinghy to *Ibis*, previously a ship's lifeboat, at anchor in North East Bay

Philip's hide for observing the Wideawakes

PLATE 11

ASCENSION ISLAND – THE BOU CENTENARY EXPEDITION 1957-59

Top left Americans from the Pan Am base in 1958 helping the BOU party to collect bird bones from the 'fumarole' where the first skull of the extinct Ascension Rail was found

Top right Collections of bones from under rocks have yielded information on the vast extent of Ascension's seabird colonies prior to the arrival of cats; this site was excavated in 1958

Centre left Philip and Myrtle estimating the density of Wideawake nests in 1990

Centre right Myrtle with pipe traps specially designed for sampling underground invertebrates, ready for shipment in 1994

Bottom left Myrtle searching for invertebrates in Packer's Hole – site of the discovery of an endemic species of blind spider *Catonetria caeca*

Bottom right Brian and Paul Bell working on rodents trapped during the feasibility study for eradication of feral cats and rats. Myrtle's broken wrist attests to the dangerous nature of the Ascension clinker

PLATE 12

ASCENSION ISLAND

Top left Sooty Terns and Ascension Frigatebirds in flight

Top right View to north East Bay with American Aloe
Agave americana and Yellow Boy *Tecoma stans*

Centre left The turtle ponds near Long Beach, used in the
past to store live turtles before shipping

Above White Hill from Letterbox in 1995 with Ascension
Spurge *Euphorbia origanoides*

Left South East Bay, once the site of a booby colony, with a
pair of Masked Boobies (barely visible in the foreground) at
their nest in 1990, before its loss to a feral cat

PLATE 13
ASCENSION ISLAND

Top left The path from Bell's Cottage in 1959

Top right Cricket valley in 1958

Centre right Cricket valley in 1995

Above Castle Hill and the Peak in 1958, with Bermuda Cedar, Screwpine and low-growing Guava

Right View from Ravine cave – site of the discovery of a new species of pseudoscorpion *Apocheiridium cavicola*

PLATE 14

ASCENSION ISLAND

Left A donkey enjoying the seed pods of the invasive Mexican Thorn *Prosopis juliflora*

Below left After the meal, well fertilised Mexican Thorn seedlings growing along the donkey path

Below centre Cat larder with remains of Frigatebirds; any seabird landing on the main island is at risk from feral cats

Below right In 1995 Wideawakes were still being killed in large numbers by feral cats

Bottom left Tracks of cats patrolling for hatchling turtles at English Bay

Bottom right This cat, photographed in 1995, had been 'adopted' (and probably sterilized) and wore a pink ribbon to indicate its status to the pest control personnel

PLATE 15

ASCENSION ISLAND

Colony of Masked Boobies *Sula dactylatra* on Boatswainbird Island, where seabirds can breed in safety

Frigatebirds on the cliff at Spire Beach, just out of reach of cats

Shelly Beach at the eastern extreme of Mars Bay Nature Reserve

White Rock and White Bluff (foreground) in Cocoanut Bay. The stacks are safe refuges for some species of seabirds

Hummock Point and its hinterland was designated a nature reserve in 1997 to protect the pristine volcanic landscape and the Ascension Spurge

Waltheria indica in the Mars Bay Nature Reserve, where it and other alien plants threaten the endemic Ascension Spurge *Euphorbia origanoides*

PLATE 16

ASCENSION ISLAND

of other submarine volcanoes or seamounts which could cause some disturbance and therefore local enrichment of the surface waters. A seamount to the west is steep and isolated, but along the Mid-Atlantic Ridge to the southeast is a cluster of seamounts including one - known as Grattan - which rises to within 72 m of the surface at a point about 250 km from Ascension, and must cause substantial turbulence in the current.[15]

In general, however, the waters to the south of Ascension are impoverished, while productivity increases northwards towards the equator. In the area from 2-4°S (more than 400 km north of Ascension) higher concentrations of phosphates - one of the key nutrients - are found near the surface in the cool season, when enrichment by upwelling occurs. As discussed in Chapter 12, the increased productivity in this area is probably of great importance to the seabirds of Ascension.

---

[15] J.M. Brozena (1986).

Chapter 11

The animals and plants:
a historical view

Animals on the pristine island

Our imaginary account of what the sailors might have seen, if they had gone ashore on that first human visit to Ascension in 1501, is based on evidence of various kinds. Up to the end of the 15th century Ascension Island had developed untouched by human hand. Its short existence of around one million years had been punctuated by episodes of cataclysmic volcanism, the effects of which were still largely unobscured by either weathering or by the mantle of vegetation that covers the rocks in so many parts of the world. The American geologist Reginald Daly pointed out that:

> "Ascension presents an ideal case of a complex volcanic island in its constructional stage".

We have come to realize, however, that the island also presents a unique and fascinating stage in the development of a natural ecosystem. In 1501 Ascension was an isolated pile of rock so remote from continental land that it had been colonised by only a few kinds of plants and animals; the evolutionary processes that give rise to the complex biological communities of older islands such as St Helena had only just begun.

For about 150 years after its discovery in 1501 Ascension was visited only in emergency. The Dutch traveller Jan van Linschoten, anchoring offshore on 28th May 1589 in a fleet with a leaky ship, commented that:[1]

> "there commeth not a ship in twentie yeares into that Iland, because there is nothing in it to be had."

Peter Mundy, passing Ascension in 1634, commented:[2]

> "...by report there is not soe much as fresh water upon it, verie bare and nothinge to bee had there but Sea Fowle and fish, of which there is aboundance. Noe shipp would willingly touch there, except [it] put by St Hellena, which if they overshoote, It is hard or noe fetching it againe, by reason of wynde and Currant settinge to the N.W."

Even the occasional early visitors, however, tended to notice the birds, for this was one of the great seabird breeding stations of the tropical oceans (Table 11A). The only endemic species was the Ascension Frigatebird *Fregata aquila*, distinct from the various related frigatebirds occurring on Trindade, in the Caribbean and on the Cape Verde Islands, and probably from both the species known as fossils on St Helena. The other seabirds of Ascension are all relatively widespread species, breeding elsewhere in the Atlantic and in many cases also the Indian Ocean and Pacific, although several of them were first formally described and named on the basis of specimens from Ascension.

The island has all three species of 'pantropical' boobies, which occur in warm waters around the world: Masked Booby *Sula dactylatra*, Brown Booby *Sula leucogaster* and Red-footed Booby *Sula sula*. It also has two out of only three existing species of tropicbirds, the large Red-billed Tropicbird *Phaethon aethereus* and smaller White-

---

[1] P.A. Tiele (1885).

[2] R.C. Temple (1919).

tailed (or Yellow-billed) Tropicbird *Phaethon lepturus*. Petrels are poorly represented, with only the Madeiran Storm-petrel *Oceanodroma castro* breeding in numbers, but a small shearwater in the *Puffinus assimilis/lherminieri* assemblage was probably also present in the past. In contrast, the island is rich in terns, with enormous numbers of the Sooty Tern or Wideawake *Sterna fuscata* and good populations of three other widespread tropical species: Brown (or Common) Noddy *Anous stolidus*, Black (or White-capped) Noddy *Anous minutus* and White (or Fairy) Tern *Gygis alba*.

Knowledge of these birds accumulated only slowly. The Portuguese discoverers of the island did not land in 1501, but it was reported that their ships were visited by large birds that clambered about and allowed themselves to be taken by hand.

Linschoten gave a fuller account of his visit in 1589:

> "... in it there are no beastes at all, onely by reason of the great quantitie of Fishes ther are so many Birds in it yt. it is strange, and they are of the bignesse of young Geese, & came by thousands flying about our ships, crying and making great noyse, and ranne up and downe in the shippe, some leaping and sitting on our shoulders and armes, not once fearing us, so that wee tooke many of them, and wrung of their neckes, but they are not good to eate, because they taste morish [fishy]. I think the cause they are so tame is, because they see but few men".

It was not until 7th June 1656 that scientifically useful information on the birds was obtained, by Peter Mundy. His ornithological observations are worth quoting in full:[3]

> "Of sea fowle, as I said before, are a numberlesse number; some of them would, by hovering over our heads, seeking to lightt on us, soe near thatt wee strucke them downe with sticks, especially a smalle sort, very white, of the shape and bignesse of a white turtle dove; and like turtle doves, they are seene either single, or two and two, roosting on the rockes. Another bigge russett gannett would lightt on our ships yards and suffer themselves to bee taken by hand like boobees, another sea foule of the same quallity. There is another sortt called hewers, because they ly hovering over the water to descry their prey, as our country hewers in the West stand on the hills to discerne the pilchard. They are long-winged, close-footed, forcke-tayled. They soare exceeding high and steddy. We saw of them outward bound, when wee were near Trinidado, an iland on the coast of Brazill: allso near Christopher Iland by Saint Lawrence. Allso a bigge sortt of gulls, like mangas de veludo [velvet sleeves]; their bodies white, the tops of their wings blacke, with a black list round about them. Pittrells flying and playing two and fro, chirping like swallowes, beeing aboutt the same bignesse, shape and collour, soe thatt they may more fittly bee termed sea-swallowes; many of them together. Here were of other sortts, here omitted, generally feeding on fish, but the greatt ones on smalle tortoises att their season."

This account of the seabirds was unrivalled for 100 years, but of even greater interest was Mundy's description of the Ascension Rail *Atlantisia elpenor*, an extinct species whose existence was - until 1958 - known only from his brief description and tiny sketch. Although he seems not to have gone far inland himself, some of the crew did, and Mundy reported:

> "Some of our company went up and broughtt downe six or seven goates, doubtlesse att first left there by the Portugalls: alsoe halfe a dozen of a strange kind of fowle, much bigger then our sterlings ore stares: collour gray or dappled, white and blacke feathers intermixed, eies red like rubies, wings very imperfitt, such as wherewith they cannott

Peter Mundy's Rail

Figure 23

---

[3] R.C. Temple & L.M. Anstey (1936).

196

raise themselves from the ground. They were taken running, in which they are exceeding swift, helping themselves a little with their wings (as it is said of the estridge), *shortt billed, cloven footed, thatt can neither fly nor swymme. It was more than ordinary dainety meatt, relishing like a roasting pigge."*

Afterwards, Mundy pondered on the puzzle of how a bird that could neither fly nor swim could exist on such a remote island; his journal entry includes one of the earliest references to the possibility of evolutionary change in animals.

"I have heretofore asked the question concerning Mauritius henns and dodos, thatt seeing those could neither fly nor swymme, beeing cloven footed and withoutt wings on an iland far from any other land, and none to bee seence elce where, how they shold come thither? Soe now again concerning the Ascension birds allsoe, thatt can neither fly nor swymme. The iland beeing aboutt 300 leagues from the coast of Guinnea and 160 leagues from the iland of St Matheo, the nearest land to it, the question is, how they shold bee generated, whither created there from the beginning, or thatt the earth produceth them of its owne accord, as mice, serpents, flies, wormes, etts. insects, or whither the nature of the earth and climate have alltred the spape and nature of some other foule into this, I leave it to the learned to dispute of."

There is no mention of the Ascension Rail in later accounts, but three hundred years later, bones of this species were found in a cave near Sisters and in old guano deposits near South Gannet Hill. Subsequent work in the caves showed that the island once had a population of another landbird, the Ascension Night Heron, which seems to have been noted by none of the early travellers, perhaps because small herons forage on beaches in so many parts of the world. The investigations that led to the discovery of bones of these extinct birds are described in the next chapter.

In spite of Mundy's evidence of human predation on the Ascension Rail, the population is unlikely to have been significantly affected until the arrival of rats early in the 18th century; this crucial event is discussed later.

Seabirds were doubtless intermittently exploited by the sailors. Colonies of Wideawakes (perhaps Mundy's "*bigge sortt of gulls*") would have been conspicuous from the sea, and egg-collecting parties were doubtless landed on the nearest beach. Other species were also utilised, perhaps especially when the Wideawakes did not have eggs: several travellers wrote of wringing necks or knocking down seabirds, presumably to eat. Boobies are often mentioned, but tropicbirds would probably also have been taken by sailors who went ashore.

Nonetheless, the impact of these visits on the seabirds was not severe. Removal of large numbers of Wideawake eggs at random intervals will have had little effect on the population of these long-lived birds, and we doubt that enough adult birds were killed to have had a significant effect on these or other species. Certainly there were still massive seabird colonies on the mainland of Ascension in the middle of the 18th century.

The best account of the birds from this period came from Peter Osbeck, a chaplain in the Swedish navy who visited Ascension in 1752. It included a careful description of the white phase of the Red-footed Booby, which is important evidence that this species - which everywhere else in the world nests in trees - had become adapted to nesting on ledges on the chaotic piles of lava present in many parts of Ascension.

The Abbé de la Caille, a French priest, traveller and naturalist who visited the island in April 1754, also commented on huge numbers of frigatebirds, boobies and tropicbirds on the lowland plains. Similarly, J.G. Forster, who came in 1775, commented that the black lava was:

*"the rendezvous of numberless men of war birds and boobies, which sat on their eggs and
suffered us to come close to them."*

Although the seabirds were of interest to some visitors and they and their eggs were
sometimes eaten, the major attraction of Ascension for passing ships was a major
rookery of Green Turtles, whose remarkable life history is discussed in Chapter 12. In
1634 Peter Mundy saw no reason why any ship should want to stop at Ascension, in
spite of the abundance of seabirds and fish, but by 1656 he was clearly aware that the
island offered an important resource in the form of Green Turtles. We have seen one
significant comment from the intervening years; a message referring to the ship *Mary*
in 1644 said: *"she has gone for Asention to turtell."* Presumably the word had spread
among sailors that turtles nested in large numbers on Ascension and were an ideal
source of fresh meat for the last leg of the voyage home to Europe. Peter Mundy's
shipmates obtained only five turtles during one night late in the season (7th June), but
any ship that could put sailors ashore earlier in the year would be able to obtain as
many as they could cope with.

At least from the middle of the 18th century the turtles made the island a popular
stopover point. The practice of ships' captains leaving messages at a particular place
on shore and receiving news of the previous visitors was well established by 1673; it
was still in use in 1769 and probably continued until settlement of the island in 1815.

Peter Osbeck, visiting in 1752, commented that:-

*"The European ships on their return from the East Indies seldom sail by this island
without going on shore to catch as many turtles as they want; but they never come in
sight of it on their going to those parts."*

The turtles coming up the beach at night were turned on their backs and collected
in the morning with a ship's boat. It cannot have been an easy task, since they were
up to 4 1/4 feet long by 3 1/4 feet broad and weighed around a quarter of a ton, but
ships' crews were skilled in handling awkward objects. Once on board, the turtles
could be kept alive for five or six weeks, until needed as food, merely by shading them,
sluicing them with sea water four or five times a day, and turning them sometimes on
their backs and sometimes on their bellies. Osbeck mentioned that one turtle could
provide a meal for up to 130 men.

Apart from the vertebrates - turtles, birds and fish - Ascension had hardly any native
animals of interest to the visiting sailors. The indigenous land invertebrates are almost
all inconspicuous, mainly nocturnal insects and arachnids living in the barren lava
and cinders of the desert lowlands (see Chapter 12). The one exception is the landcrab
Gecarcinus lagostoma, an omnivorous terrestrial crab that lives in burrows in most
parts of the island but which has to return to the sea to breed. Its large size and bright
coloration must have attracted attention, but we guess that the sailors' commonest
response to a landcrab was to lob a rock.

Native vegetation and the impact of goats

In Table 11B we provide a list of flowering plants and ferns that are endemic or apparently
indigenous to Ascension Island. It is extraordinarily short. Among the flowering plants
there are only four endemic species plus some 3-10 species that may be indigenous. Ferns
comprise five endemic species and about eight that are probably indigenous.[4]

---

[4] The only formal modern accounts of the endemic plants are by Q.C.B. Cronk (1980, 2000). A student expedition from
Edinburgh University visited the island in 1998 and produced a status report on the endemic species (in press).

One of the first, slender clues to the original vegetation of the interior of Ascension Island was provided by Peter Mundy, who commented in 1656 that:

> *"Only the topps of the high mountaines in the middle appeared somwhatt greene, there beeing a kind of rushes and spicy [? spiky] grasse."*

The earliest systematic botanical work on Ascension was done by James Cunninghame, who visited the island in 1698 and recorded his observations in an early volume of the Philosophical Transactions of the Royal Society, which had been founded in 1660. Cunninghame gave descriptions of three clearly identifiable plants: the endemic Ascension Spurge *Euphorbia origanoides* (Plate 28) which is still present on the island, though apparently not so widespread as in the past; a grass *Aristida adscensionis* (Plate 28) which is widespread elsewhere in the tropics and which still grows locally in drier areas, but used to occur also on the mountain; and the convolvulus *Ipomoea pes-caprae*, which originally grew on the beaches and on dusty plains inland and is well known as a pioneer on beaches in many parts of the tropics. A fourth species, referred to by Cunninghame as *"purslane"*, was presumably *Portulaca oleracea*, a widespread tropical species. Cunninghame also described a plant that has been provisionally identified as *Hibiscus trionum*, but which we suspect might be Hogweed *Commicarpus helenae*; this species still grows very locally in dry areas on Ascension, as it does on St Helena (Plate 29).

Three years later Ascension was visited by William Dampier, navigator, explorer, pirate and writer, who was one of the few people to explore the interior of the island. Indeed, he had little alternative, having been stranded with his crew when his ship the *Roebuck* foundered while at anchor on 22nd February 1701. Dampier's party were on the island until about 8th May, and were lucky in their timing, which coincided with the breeding season of the turtles. Freshwater was of course also crucial for the survival of the marooned seamen, and Dampier found a source of water. Although his name is attached to the drip or spring (now dry) northwest of the peak and below the Administrator's residence, a much more plausible suggestion is that he found the stronger spring at the head of Breakneck Valley, immediately to the west of the peak.

In Dampier's account of his stay on the island he also mentioned the presence of a shrub, large and old enough for a sailor to have carved the date 1642 on it, presumably sixty years previously. This shrub was probably the species found in April 1752 by Peter Osbeck, who collected a specimen from the single bush that he saw, which was growing *"on a plain"*. This was promptly described by his compatriot Carl Linnaeus, the great taxonomist, who was in the process of establishing the modern system of classifying plants and animals and referring to them using two-word Latin names. Linnaeus named Osbeck's shrub *Sherardia fruticosa*, but for complex reasons it is now officially called *Oldenlandia adscensionis*. It probably used to grow mainly at middle altitudes on the mountain, with scattered individuals germinating and growing for a while in watercourses in the lowlands after rain.

Osbeck was much affected by the heat, but during his walk he also found four of the plants mentioned by Cunninghame: *Aristida Adscensionis* *"on a mountain"*; *Convolvulus* (now *Ipomoea*) *pes-caprae* *"on the shore"*; *Euphorbia origanoides* *"between the stones, the food of the goats"*; and young individuals of wild Purslane, *Portulaca oleracea* (which he considered the most common plant) *"among the stones"*. Osbeck also recorded green and yellow lichens inland and several kinds of seaweeds on the shore, but he evidently did not go up Green Mountain.

One of Osbeck's comments has caused some confusion; he wrote:

> "The climate in itself is hot, being so near the line; but it would be tolerable if there were
> only some trees under whose shade one could take shelter. The island has formerly had
> woods, as appears from several perfect petrefactions of branches of trees, and pieces of
> wood; but in particular from a large petrified stump."

Later in the same account Osbeck gave further details of these specimens. It seems
certain, however, that he was misled by the appearance of fresh lava, which may have
been unfamiliar to him. 'Petrifaction' of wood is not normal in geological settings such as
that of Ascension, and no-one since has been able to find any evidence of ancient trees.

In May 1775 Captain Cook visited the island in the *Resolution* at the end of his
second expedition. On board was the German naturalist Johann Georg Forster, who
made a number of botanical observations. He mentioned that the *Aristida* covered the
sides of Green Mountain, and commented that the goats were browsing on *"a
prodigious quantity of purslane"* at the foot of the mountain. In this area Forster also
discovered an endemic fern now known as *Pteris adscensionis*.

Most of the other plants now thought to be native to Ascension grew only on Green
Mountain; the baked cinder plains between the anchorage and the foothills made a
formidable barrier, and none of the botanically-inclined early visitors seem to have
made it to the summit. It was not until the 19th century, when a track was established
and a water supply organised, that the vegetation of the mountain was described. The
botanist Joseph Hooker, visiting in 1843, mentioned that:

> "the green peak is clothed with a carpet of ferns and here and there a shrub allied to but
> different from any St. Helena one. There are nine ferns, of which no less than six differ
> from those of St. Helena, and three of them are entirely confined to the island."

Apart from the ferns and many species of moss, discoveries on the mountain
included two endemic grasses: *Sporobolus durus*, which used to occur on Green
Mountain but may now be extinct, and the tiny *Sporobolus caespitosus*, which is
adapted to the cool misty conditions on the east side of the mountain and survives in
very low numbers.

The native vegetation of Ascension Island suffered its first human-induced
disruption as a result of the introduction of goats. The second major influence was the
massive introduction of alien plants, which took place mainly after settlement of the
island in 1815; this is discussed later.

The date of introduction of goats to Ascension Island is uncertain. Linschoten,
whose visit was in 1589, explicitly stated that: *"in it there are no beastes at all"*.
Although he did not go ashore, there was evidently no knowledge among the seamen
of goats being present on the island, and it is at least possible that they were not
introduced until early in the 17th century. Peter Mundy, writing in 1656, implicates
"the Portugalls" as being responsible for the introduction of goats, while Osbeck, who
visited a hundred years later, said that French mariners were responsible.

Irrespective of the precise time of the arrival of goats, their impact was much less
obvious than on St Helena, because Ascension was anyhow a desert landscape, with
only sparse native vegetation. The numbers of goats in the past can only be guessed.
Dampier found them to be very common in 1701, and in 1798 there were *"great herds"*.
In 1828 the population was thought to be 600 and in 1896 the farmer's estimate was
600-700. A good many goats must have been shot by early visitors like the crews of
Mundy's and Dampier's ships, but without any lasting effect on the population.

Waterloo Plain (the airfield) photographed in the 1920's

Figure 24

Shooting doubtless continued throughout the period of human occupation; it probably intensified early in the 20th century and in 1922 only about 55 goats remained. The last individuals seem to have been shot by servicemen in about 1944.

In general, the goats would have found little to eat. As mentioned above, Osbeck commented that the Ascension Spurge was *"the food of the goats"*, but we do not know whether goats will in fact eat this plant, which is protected by a poisonous milky latex; some related species can be lethal to goats. If they did eat the Ascension Spurge, this could provide an explanation for its curiously patchy modern distribution.

Probably more important for the goats was the purslane *Portulaca oleracea*, as indicated by Forster's observation. Today, this plant occurs only in widely scattered places. We have found it just east of Mars Bay, where the jagged nature of the lava probably gives it some protection from sheep and donkeys (Plate 30). The goats also ate the convolvulus *Ipomoea pes-caprae* that bears their name. This now grows mainly at middle levels, especially around Two Boats village and the old NASA site, and by the road through Grazing Valley. Originally, however, it seems to have been a plant of the coasts and lowlands. It can still be found near South West Bay, and a photograph probably taken in late 1925 shows a Wideawake colony on the dusty Waterloo Plain that later became the airstrip, studded with luxuriant spreading *Ipomoea* plants (Figure 24).

Another food for the goats was the sedge *Cyperus appendiculatus*, which still grows in normally dry watercourses in the plains and on Green Mountain; it was probably more abundant on the lower parts of the mountain in the past. Several grasses seem to be

201

indigenous to Ascension and two - *Aristida adscensionis* and *Digitaria ciliaris* - were probably important to the goats, both being widespread on the island. The two endemic grasses in the genus *Sporobolus* were never significant in the lowlands but were doubtless eaten by goats in the higher parts of the island.[5] The ferns may have been largely ignored by the goats.

It is certain, however, that the goats browsed on *Oldenlandia adscensionis* - the only substantial shrub native to Ascension - and they may have had a drastic effect on it within a century or so of their introduction. Quentin Cronk has noted that many of the early specimens collected by botanists showed a compact growth form that could have resulted from browsing by goats. This shrub is now thought to be extinct, though it was still present about a century ago.

The arrival of rats and mice
William Dampier's shipwreck in 1701 was a crucial event in the island's history, since it was probably from the *Roebuck* that rats first came ashore on Ascension. The evidence for this timing is that Dampier himself did not mention rats in the brief account of his stay on the island, though he was an acute observer and commented on turtles, goats, land crabs, Men of War Birds and Boobies. Rats were noticed, however, by the Abbé de La Caille during his visit in April 1754. The species of rat on Ascension is *Rattus rattus*, known as the Tree Rat on St Helena. This also supports the arrival of rats with Dampier, since it has been shown that although *Rattus rattus* was the usual species on ships in the 16th and 17th centuries, its dispersal was already curtailed very early in the 18th century, with *Rattus norvegicus*, the Brown Rat, taking its place on ocean-going vessels from then until about 1850.[6] House mice may have reached the island at the same time as the rats or shortly afterwards; they were also noted by La Caille in 1754.

Although rodents doubtless had some effect on the native plants, their ecological impact must have been primarily on the animals. House mice can devastate populations of island invertebrates, as shown on Marion Island in the southern Indian Ocean, where mouse eradication is now being considered as a conservation measure. We shall never know how many insects and other invertebrates native to Ascension became extinct as a result of predation by mice and rats.

It is almost certain, however, that the flightless Ascension Rail was exterminated by the rats.[7] There is no record of this bird after that of Peter Mundy in 1656, and it evidently became extinct before the middle of the 18th century. Another species that may have been lost from the island at this time is the Ascension Night Heron.

The rats probably flourished by scavenging on the bird colonies. Rat teeth are often found when searching for bird bones in the old guano deposits. The effect of rats on the colonies of the larger seabirds was probably confined to disturbance and the killing of some young birds. The small Madeiran Storm-petrel, however, which was clearly described and mentioned as abundant by Peter Mundy in 1656, quickly declined as a breeder on the main island after the arrival of rats. The breeding success of the

[5] Grasses - like the sedges - grow from the base, and are thus well adapted to survive grazing. Indeed, they owe their worldwide success partly to the evolution of large mammalian herbivores, which tend to produce grassland in some areas that might otherwise be covered by trees.

[6] Ian Atkinson (1985) has argued convincingly that records of *Rattus norvegicus* from Ascension are incorrect.

[7] A small flightless rail on Henderson Island in the Pacific manages to coexist with rats, but the species concerned is the the smaller Polynesian Rat *Rattus exulans*. (G.M. Wragg & M.I. Weisler 1994).

Wideawakes may also have been affected by rat predation on eggs, but experience elsewhere shows that this cannot be assumed.

When the island was occupied in 1815, rats and mice immediately became a pest around the settlements; it was apparently this that led to the prompt importation of cats by the Royal Navy. The rats quickly became less abundant, the change doubtless brought about partly by the cats and partly by better arrangements for food storage as the navy settled in. Later in the century considerable resources were used in attempts to control rats, mice and also cats and land crabs, with measures including the employment of vermin killers and the offering of bounties. In the single year of 1879, for instance, the bounty system produced a 'bag' of pests comprising 7,683 rats, 4,013 mice, 66 cats and 80,414 land crabs.

A basic change in the distribution of rats on the island may have occurred when breeding colonies of all seabird species except Wideawakes were eventually eliminated from accessible places in the lowland. At this point the rats were deprived of a continuous supply of food (and the water that it contained) and they may have largely disappeared from the lava deserts of Ascension.

In 1965 R.A. Davis of the British Ministry of Agriculture visited Ascension to investigate the problems of rats, feral cats and donkeys. He found that rats were numerous all over the mountain, down as far as the level of Two Boats and around Dampier's Drip. They were, however, uncommon in the lowlands except around buildings. In contrast, mice were present all over the island, from the mountain down to the sea-shore. Davis attributed the difference to the ability of mice to exist without free water, provided that the water content of their food is not too low; rats are more dependent on access to free water.

The current status of rodents on Ascension is probably similar to that described by Davis. However, it was shown by Brian and Paul Bell during our joint work on the island in 1995 (see Chapter 14) that some rats live with larger numbers of mice in the rough lava close to the Wideawake fairs (for instance near Mars Bay).

Seabird decline and the feral cats

The historical records show that major seabird colonies existed on the main island of Ascension before the arrival of humans. Further evidence is provided by the extensive white deposits in the lowland deserts, especially in the northwest of the island and east of Mars Bay. Mike Blair and his colleagues on the RAF Ornithological Society expedition in 1987 looked at the distribution of these deposits, and in 1990 we did some more work on them. Those around English Bay have been exploited as fertilizer, and most (but not all) of our samples of whitish powder from other parts of the island proved also to be rich in phosphates, which could only have come from the food of seabirds.

We shall never know how many of these areas were occupied by seabirds at the same time, or whether the pattern changed substantially between 1501 and 1815. It is clear, however, that the 19th century saw fundamental changes in the ecology of Ascension, especially affecting the seabird populations and the vegetation. In 1815 human activity changed from frequent short visits to the bays on the western coast by ships' companies occupied in harvesting turtles, seabird eggs and fish, to a resident community occupying Georgetown, Dampier's Drip and later also Green Mountain. As already indicated, the Royal Navy also imported cats.

Bernard Stonehouse, studying the early naval records, was surprised by the absence of references to seabirds or their exploitation. Accounts by several visitors, however, show that large seabird colonies still existed during this period. For instance, a painting by Admiral Sir Jahleel Brenton, dating from about 1819, clearly shows boobies and tropicbirds in the area between Georgetown and Sisters Peak.

In 1838 the island was surveyed by Lt. George Bedford, and the original manuscript copy of his chart - examined by Bernard Stonehouse in the Admiralty Archives - shows the locations of 'South Gannet Fair' in the southwestern corner of Ascension, 'Booby Fair' a mile to the east of it, and 'North Gannet Fair' on the eastern slopes of Sisters Peak.[8] Bedford also recorded Wideawake fairs near Dark Crater, South Red Crater and South-west Bay Red Hill.

It is not known how many adult birds were taken for food, but we suspect that the families in the garrison soon learned to appreciate tropicbirds, which are heavy-bodied, muscular birds eaten by islanders in all the tropical oceans. The Wideawakes may also have provided a change in diet, although one 19th century visitor commented that they: *"are not very tempting even when disguised by the most skilful chef."*

There is no doubt about the heavy exploitation of Wideawake eggs. In the early 1830s H.R. Brandreth recorded the taking of 120,000 in a single week, with a collecting season lasting between one and two months.[9] In a naval establishment such records are likely to be accurate; they suggest a harvest of around half a million eggs per breeding period. As late as the 1870s F.G. Penrose noted that a single collector could take about 200 dozen in a morning. Human use of the eggs subsequently decreased, and by the late 1950s Stonehouse estimated that not more than 8-10,000 eggs were taken in each breeding period for local consumption, while just a few gross were exported to St Helena. The collecting of Wideawake eggs was prohibited in the mid-1960s.

It is not easy to know how much effect the intensive egg collecting of the 19th century had on the Wideawake population. It was assumed at the time, by people on the island and even by the noted ornithologist J.P. Chapin writing in 1954, that almost all Wideawakes, if deprived of one egg, would replace it within the same breeding period. Chapin, after recommending smashing of eggs close to the airstrip in 1943 to safeguard planes against the risk of hitting birds (see later), commented:

> *"I had good reason to suppose that they would lay again elsewhere that same season; indeed it might mean only a delay of a few weeks in bringing off a nearly normal number of young."*

Chapin's view, however, was developed before the recognition of the difficulty experienced by seabirds in obtaining food in impoverished tropical oceans (see Chapter 12). Wideawakes lay only a single egg, but it is relatively enormous: about 19% of the weight of the female. Producing it requires a large input of fish and squid, mostly obtained by the female but some probably provided by the male in 'courtship feeding'. Philip's experiments with marked birds in 1958 indicated that less than a fifth of Wideawake pairs replaced eggs that were taken while fresh, and took an average of almost three weeks to do so. It is clear, therefore, that egg collecting has a major effect on the production of young, and may have affected the size of the adult population.

Losses of adult birds, however, have a more immediate effect, and the importation of cats by the naval garrison in 1815 had profound consequences for the Wideawakes and other seabirds. Some of the cats quickly established a 'feral' population: one that

---

[8] 'Fair' is the term used on Ascension for colonies of ground nesting seabirds - now only those of the Wideawake.

[9] In J. Sabine (1835).

was derived from domestic animals but was now more or less independent of humans. Within a few years the cats had increased enormously and were reported as being a pest to gamebirds and poultry. As early as 1823 the Commandant of the garrison, Lieut. Colonel Nicholls, reported that:[10]

> *"...we are overrun by wild cats as bad if not worse than the Island formerly was by rats. A rat is scarcely to be seen now and I hope soon to put down the cats by the assistance of my dogs."*

Nicholls mentioned killing 16 cats in a day, but failed to eradicate them. As already mentioned, later historical records include numerous references to attempts to control the numbers of cats as well as other vermin. However, while the cats had a year-round unlimited supply of seabirds available as prey, there can have been little chance of keeping numbers down for long.

The destructive effect of the cats on the young of the seabirds was noted as early as 1825 by the French naturalist Lesson. Since that time, cats have been the dominant factor in the composition of the seabird community on Ascension and thus in a huge expanse of the tropical Atlantic Ocean.

The main seabird decline probably occurred during the fifty years following 1815, although the picture is far from clear. For instance, the Red-footed Booby, clearly described by the traveller Osbeck in 1752 as nesting on the lowland plains of Ascension, seems not to have been recorded breeding subsequently until the latter part of the 20th century, when only a handful of birds survived.[11] The decline of the other species of boobies, the frigatebirds and the tropicbirds was probably rapid. However, a photograph taken about 1907 shows Masked Boobies nesting between White Hill and Weather Post, and there is also evidence of nesting by both this species and the Brown Booby on the mainland in the early 1920s. Nonetheless, it seems that towards the end of the 19th century only Wideawakes were breeding in large numbers in the more accessible parts of the main island.

Although Wideawake colonies persist, the population has declined drastically. In the late 1990s the breeding population was estimated as betwen 175,000 and 200,000 pairs (see Chapter 15) and in the colonies today one could not approach the egg-collecting feats of the 19th century. We suspect that several million individuals may have bred on the island in the past.

A key question is why the Wideawake population - though reduced in size - has survived the depredations of the feral cats, while the other ground-nesting seabirds have been eliminated from accessible places on the main island.

On Ascension, Wideawakes are probably preferred prey of the cats, being relatively defenceless and nesting in dense colonies on level ground. However, they are absent from the island and thus unavailable to the cats for two to three months in each breeding cycle. Tropicbirds also leave the island after breeding and moult far out at sea, but because their breeding is not synchronised there are always some vulnerable individuals. Boobies and frigatebirds are available year-round, even when not breeding, and doubtless also suffered heavy predation, especially when the Wideawakes were absent.

---

[10] Quoted by B. Stonehouse (1962a).

[11] K.E.L. Simmons (1990). The possibility that large numbers of Red-footed Boobies might have survived until relatively recently was raised by an observation of J.N. Tomlinson, the British Government Representative on the island in 1946. He was shown thousands of Red-footed Boobies roosting on the high inaccessible rocks between Powers Peak, Weather Post and White Hill, and was told that the birds came there every year. It was later suggested that they might have come from Fernando de Noronha or Trindade (see N.P. Ashmole et al.1994). By the late 1950s the visits had ceased, although the B BOU party found three skulls of this species on the slopes of White Hill.

When the cats first became established, seabirds of some kind were present all year round, providing a superabundant food supply; accordingly, the cat population evidently underwent a population explosion. The larger seabird species, suffering human predation as well as losses from cats, declined and were eventually eliminated from accessible places on the main island. The Wideawake population, which was almost certainly larger than those of the other birds, suffered heavily, but was still substantial when the accessible colonies of the other species were destroyed. At this point, the cat population must have declined drastically, as a result of starvation in the intervals between the Wideawake breeding periods.

It is likely that this critical stage was reached sometime in the latter part of the 19th century, although there were probably intermittent subsequent attempts at breeding by Masked Boobies on the main island, as mentioned above; indeed, such attempts still occur today. The other seabirds of Ascension can now breed only on inaccessible cliffs, tiny offshore stacks, or on Boatswainbird Island. This situation is further discussed in Chapter 14.

Since the elimination of most of the other seabirds, the nesting Wideawakes have remained vulnerable to the cats, which take both adults and young. In 1958-59 Philip counted nearly 1300 corpses of Wideawakes killed by cats at one large fair over a period of 15 months. It was hard to extrapolate the rate of predation to the whole population, but it seemed likely that between one and five percent of the adults were taken in each breeding period. Counts of corpses by members of British Army ornithological expeditions in the 1990s show that losses of adult Wideawakes to cats are still substantial. The cats probably also take many small chicks, although these losses are much harder to measure than those of adults, because there are no inedible remains to be found. Near the end of the breeding period the cats also eat many of the nearly-fledged young.

The nesting Wideawakes were subjected to more drastic disturbance during the second world war when the American airfield was constructed on Waterloo Plain, inland from South West Bay. The eastern end of the site - north of South Gannet Hill - was a traditional Wideawake nesting area and probably by far the largest colony on the island. The strip was constructed very rapidly in early 1942; in August, just after it was completed, the birds started laying in enormous numbers. The pilots were worried about the possibility of hitting Wideawakes on take-off or landing, so the American ornithologist James P. Chapin was flown to the island to advise on the problem.

Chapin recommended that eggs laid close to the air-strip should be broken while fresh, in the expectation that the birds would lay again elsewhere (but see earlier in this chapter). More than 40,000 eggs were smashed and the birds left the site for the time being. Writing after the war, however, Chapin admitted that although his advice had been simply to repeat the process in each breeding period when the birds returned, he had heard that sometimes adult birds were also being killed. Over the long term the Wideawakes abandoned the area immediately around the runway as a breeding site, but continued to occupy relatively level areas in the lava near Mars Bay and near the coast east of South Point.

Feral cats are now the most important predators on the Wideawakes, and are particularly serious because they kill so many adult birds. The Wideawakes do, however, also suffer some natural predation of young chicks by frigatebirds; it is hard to be sure how important this predation was before the island was discovered, but it is obviously much increased by human disturbance of the colonies. The chicks are vulnerable to frigatebirds mainly in the few days after hatching, and a parent normally broods the chick during this time. If the parent is disturbed and takes off, the chick is left exposed and helpless, and may be snatched up by a swooping frigatebird.

Thousands of pairs of frigatebirds breed on Boatswainbird Island but only small numbers frequent the Wideawake fairs, mainly around the time that the eggs are hatching. The plumage of frigatebirds is variable, and in the 1950s Philip showed - by compiling a photographic database of the birds over the fairs - that the same individuals returned day after day to catch Wideawake chicks (Plate 13). Most of the frigates depended on finding stray chicks, swooping down and snatching the chick with a downward flick of the long, hooked bill. Wideawakes normally brood their chicks for several days after hatching and chicks that stayed out of sight under their parents were relatively safe. A couple of easily recognizable adult frigatebirds, however, had mastered a neat trick: they chose an adult Wideawake that was brooding a chick rather than incubating an egg (probably indicated by greater restlessness), swooped down and grabbed the bird by the head, lifting it a few feet in the air before letting go and swooping again to snatch the defenceless chick.

There are no precise data on trends in the Wideawake population over the last century, but as indicated earlier, the evidence suggests a massive decrease. A particularly worrying feature of the situation is that the smaller the Wideawake population gets, the higher will be the percentage of birds taken by cats in each breeding period. This could lead to accelerating decline and rapid extinction of the population, if the current plans to eliminate the feral cats are not successfully implemented (see Chapter 14). At present, we think there are fewer than 1000 feral cats. They probably tend to congregate around the Wideawake fairs during breeding, but in the intervals eke out a living around the coasts or on the mountain, eating crabs, young turtles, lizards, mice, rats and rabbits, along with the occasional unwary White Tern or frigatebird.

The other introduced animals

Although it was the cats introduced soon after establishment of the garrison that led to the most fundamental changes in the island ecosystem, a number of other alien animals have been introduced - intentionally or by mistake - mainly in the early part of the 19th century. Accounts of these introductions have been given by Eric Duffey in his study of the ecology of the island, and by Duff Hart-Davis.

The establishment of the mountain farm in the 19th century was soon followed by the arrival of invertebrate crop pests, doubtless transported on plants for cultivation or in the soil around them, and with imported fruits and vegetables. Some pests, however, may have reached the island naturally, either before or after human occupation: likely candidates include several noctuid moths. The only early and intentional insect introduction was of honeybees, brought to the island in 1827 and again in about 1935; there have been none on the island in recent years.

Introductions of land birds were made mainly in attempts to control the depredations of caterpillars and other pests. Thirty six Starlings were imported in 1852 and survived for several years. In the decade following 1879 unsuccessful introductions included more Starlings, thrushes, Barn Owls, Rooks, Jackdaws and 'cardinal birds'. The Indian Myna, however, imported in several consignments from Mauritius, established itself and is still abundant. Other successes were the Common

Waxbill (Averdavat) and the Yellow Canary, apparently imported in 1860 and certainly established by 1878; both have survived to the present day. The only recent introduction of songbirds is of House Sparrows, which followed the arrival of one individual late in 1985, presumably on a ship. Six more individuals were brought to the island in early 1986, and a small breeding population has now become established, though confined to a tiny area in Georgetown.

Introduction of game birds for sport probably started soon after occupation, but we do not know the precise dates. Guineafowl were flourishing by 1828; by 1865 they had been joined by pheasants and partridges, and the three species were said to be plentiful and to be helping in controlling harmful insects. These species all subsequently died out, but the Red-necked Francolin, possibly introduced from northern Namibia as early as 1851, survives in the eastern uplands to the present day.

A number of mammal introductions were made in connection with agriculture or for transport purposes. Donkeys, brought in shortly after 1815, first escaped in the 1830s; by 1839 it was reported that 37 were running wild. A new importation was made from Mozambique and Zanzibar in 1858 and a feral population is referred to in the 1870s. In 1935 there were about 100 and by 1958 probably more; 50 were put down in 1994 by local police, and there are probably about the same number left. Sheep, also introduced around the time of occupation, now roam at will, but are periodically rounded up and have been an important source of meat. The current population estimate is 1600-1800. Cattle and pigs were also brought in for the farm in the early years, but have not established independent populations.

Rabbits were introduced by about 1830, probably from the Cape of Good Hope. They soon became a menace both to agriculture and to attempts to establish trees, and there is a record of them being killed in thousands in 1874. Four years later an epidemic reduced their numbers drastically, and consideration was given to transferring the disease to Australia to control the rabbit population there. They were again causing problems on the farm early in the 20th century, when ferrets were used to control them; they have since been relatively scarce.

The influx of the additional herbivores, in addition to the continuing effects of the goats, doubtless made further impact on the native vegetation. However, the introduction of alien plants had more fundamental effects in the long run.

Plant introductions and transformation of the vegetation
Portuguese mariners - mindful of potential future visits - introduced edible plants and fruit trees (as well as animals) to many of the islands that they discovered. We are doubtful, however, whether they brought plants to waterless Ascension, which in the early days was not viewed as a worthwhile place to stop. Thus although the vegetation of Ascension may have soon been affected by the feral goats, the effects of alien plants have been largely restricted to the period since settlement of the island in 1815.

Extensive plant introductions started with arrival of the first garrison and establishment of the market garden on Green Mountain; as well as vegetables, an assortment of weeds doubtless quickly arrived. In 1843 the influential botanist Joseph Hooker visited the island in the course of a circumnavigation of the globe on the Antarctic Expedition of Sir James C. Ross. Hooker later advised the Admiralty to appoint a gardener on Ascension and to import a variety of trees, grasses, fruits and vegetables (see below). Intriguingly, he thus set in motion a chain of events that led at the end of the century to Hedley Cronk's tenure as farm superintendent (the later title for the official gardener), and thus perhaps indirectly to the botanical research on Ascension and St Helena by a modern representative of the Cronk family, a century and a half later.

Hooker was intensely interested in plant distribution, and in his 1866 lecture on insular floras he described the "*catastrophes*" caused by man on various islands by fire, the ravages of goats and the introduction of exotic plants. On Ascension two decades earlier, however, Hooker seems to have been unconcerned about possible effects of introduced plants on the sparse and species-poor native vegetation. His proposals amounted to a systematic attempt to transform one of the most barren islands in the world into a more productive and attractive environment for human occupation: we do not know of a more striking case of a plan to 'green' an island. A clear account of Hooker's advice and its implementation was given by Eric Duffey in his article on the ecology of Ascension Island; this forms the basis of the following summary.

Hooker's first proposal was to plant the higher levels of Ascension with trees of large growth, with the aim of increasing the rainfall. The second was to clothe the steep sides of the valleys to help soil formation and conserve moisture condensed on the mountain. The third was to plant the most promising spots in the lower valleys with trees and shrubs adapted to dry soil conditions. Finally, Hooker suggested the introduction of a greater variety of tropical and European crops to the mountain gardens.

As a result of Hooker's advice in 1844, a gardener, John C. Bell, was appointed with instructions to obtain as many suitable plants as possible from St Helena and elsewhere. An early batch of imports arrived in 1845 from (or at least via) Buenos Aires. The scale of the operation soon became impressive: in October 1847 seven hundred packets of seeds of herbaceous plants were dispatched from Kew Gardens and in November eight cases of plants included bamboos, grasses, *Acacia* (which may actually have been *Leucaena* species), *Eucalyptus*, *Tabernaemontana*, *Bougainvillea*, *Ficus*, *Opuntia*, *Agave sisalana* and *Aloe*. Until 1850 consignments of seeds and plants were sent to Ascension every month, and for a number of years thereafter plants came from England each November and from the Cape of Good Hope each May.

These first systematic introductions had fundamental effects: a species of bamboo became dominant on the peak of Green Mountain around the end of the nineteenth century, *Eucalyptus camaldulensis* is common at intermediate levels, species of *Acacia* and of *Opuntia* (prickly pear) cover large areas, while agaves are widespread on the lower mountain slopes. Furze (Gorse) *Ulex europaeus* was introduced in 1850 as browse for cattle and horses, and is still present in the lee of the mountain.

Imports from Africa were also extensive. In 1858 a consignment from the Botanic Gardens at Cape Town included 228 species, of which a number soon became established; these include *Cassia occidentalis*, *Vitex trifolia* and *Clerodendrum fragrans*. *Pandanus* was also sent, but must have also been brought in earlier since one was over 30 feet high in 1859. The Cape Yew *Podocarpus elongata* was also established by 1859 and may have been brought from South Africa at the same time.

Many fruit-trees were imported, of which the Banana was most successful, still growing today in moist ravines, especially on the north slopes of the mountain. The Cape Gooseberry *Physalis peruviana* must have been brought in very early since it was said to be covering all the higher parts of the mountain by 1828; the fruit was apparently much sought after by the inhabitants. Similarly, according to a nineteenth century botany manual the berries of Black Nightshade *Solanum nigrum* were used by members of the garrison to make pies (the unripe fruits are poisonous). Blackberry *Rubus pinnatus* and Guava *Psidium guajava* were established by 1859 and were doubtless also used for food.

A number of the trees now established on the island were already present by the end of the 1850s. These included *Juniperus bermudiana* and *Casuarina equisetifolia*, which are both now spreading in some areas, and Margossa *Melia azedarach* and Mulberry *Morus* species, which survive near the farm and in some other places.

Both the Coconut Palm *Cocos nucifera* and Date Palm *Phoenix dactylifera* must also have been brought in quickly, since a group of the former was established at Cocoanut Bay as early as 1859 and Date Palms were already growing near the farm at the same date. Much effort was expended on afforestation in the following years, with more than 5,000 trees planted, for instance, between 1862 and 1874.

Some species were also brought from Australia around this time. They include Silky Oak *Grevillea robusta*, which is quite common around the farm, and the creeping grass *Cynodon dactylon*, introduced in 1875, which can be found in a few exposed areas. Other grasses were brought from Australia as late as the first decade of the 20th century.

An interesting snapshot of the effects of this massive programme of plant introductions is provided by A.B. Ellis, writing in 1885 about a visit to Ascension which he had made some three years earlier. Ellis was evidently no botanist and his list of plants said to be indigenous to Ascension includes a number of imported weeds; however, he seems to have been observant and well informed about the island. He commented on the absence of a single plant or blade of grass on the way from Georgetown towards the mountain, but continued:

> "At about 1,000 feet of elevation [presumably near Two Boats] *a few sickly-looking prickly-pears and aloes may be perceived, a little higher a scanty growth of grass and bushes clothes the earth, and finally the gardens cover that shoulder of the mountain on which the houses are built."* .... *"The hospital has a fairly good garden ...; and in the kitchen gardens a few vegetables are raised. The whole cultivated area, however, is little more than an acre, and trees, as distinguished from shrubs, are certainly under twenty in number; but some three thousand acres of the mountain is sparsely covered with Bahamas grass, gorse, wild ginger, blackberry, castor-oil shrubs, and the indigenous plants, among which the nasturtium is the most common .... After long-continued drought this area of vegetation becomes greatly circumscribed, and has been known to be reduced by one half."*

The visit by Ellis may have been at a rather low point in the horticultural enterprise. Under the direction of Hedley Cronk, farm superintendent from 1896 until 1922, the operation was efficiently run and expanded in scale. Cronk also organized the introduction of many additional plant species, including the Norfolk Island Pine *Araucaria excelsa*, which seems to have been brought in somewhat belatedly as a source of timber for ships' masts.

A later view of the mountain farm is provided by J.A.K. Thompson, Agricultural and Forestry Officer in St Helena, who wrote a report on Ascension Island in 1947 after a visit lasting 17 days. He calculated that the gardens at the mountain farm amounted to some 6.5 acres, of which 1.75 were not currently under cultivation; there were also around 90 acres of pasture. At this time the main objective of the farm was the rearing of pigs to produce fresh pork; sweet potatoes were grown to provide them with food.

During the century preceding Thompson's visit several of the more invasive plants had gradually extended their hold on Green Mountain and high land to the east. Guava soon became dominant in enormous areas, especially on the eastern and southern slopes of the mountain, and by about 1900 ineffective attempts were being made to control it; in 1947 it was found to be seriously threatening pasture land.

Other introduced shrubs against which action was taken around the turn of the century included *Opuntia*, *Buddleja* and Venus Rose *Catharanthus roseus* (Plate 25). In an attempt to prevent recolonisation, cleared areas were planted with a tropical African grass, *Melinis minutiflora* (Plate 29). This was already abundant by 1886, especially between 1500 and 2500 feet and it is still dominant in many areas. The prickly pear *Opuntia* continued to spread in spite of the efforts at control a century ago, and in 1974 the moth *Cactoblastis cactorum* - whose caterpillars eat away the pads from the inside - was introduced to Cricket Valley in the hope that it would exert biological control. We found caterpillars near Spoon Crater in 1995, but the prickly pear is still abundant in the drier parts of the middle zone, to the south, west and northwest of the island.

Some other introduced species are successful in the arid parts of the island, though their ranges may be highly dynamic, extending after the occasional rains and contracting during long dry periods. Castor Oil *Ricinus communis* (Plate 28) which was well established by the early 1880s, is certainly affected in this way. Similarly, Duffey's account includes a map that he drew in 1958 showing several square kilometres around Georgetown covered by dead *Acacia* bushes, which had grown most thickly in the broad erosion channels. These had presumably become established after a previous episode of heavy rainfall, perhaps as early as 1934.

Duffey also found a smaller area south and west of the American base that was covered by dead bushes of the low, spreading shrub *Waltheria indica* (Plate 16). This may have undergone its main expansion during the present century; it can now be seen, for instance, on the slopes of South Gannet Hill, along with the endemic Ascension Spurge and the introduced yellow prickly poppy *Argemone mexicana* (Plate 30). The poppy also grows in dry water courses, and was already established as early as 1828. We do not know the date of introduction of the Wild Tomato, but it was well established in the late 19th century, when it was recorded as growing luxuriantly in Cricket Valley. The creeping passionflower *Passiflora suberosa* was present at around the same time, but may have spread recently (Plate 30).

A much later introduction is Yellowboy *Tecoma stans*, probably brought in by H. Cronk around 1900 (Plate 13). It is now dominant in extensive areas on the western foothills of the mountain, mainly above 200 m, and also around Cricket Valley (Plate 14). Another species that has spread recently is *Bryophyllum pinnata*, already common in 1956 when first noted by Packer; it is widespread on the mountain.

An even more recent and much more troublesome introduction is that of the Mexican Thorn or Mesquite *Prosopis juliflora* (it is possible that two closely related species or hybrid forms are involved). This thorny leguminous tree was apparently brought to the island in the 1970s and is now probably the most actively spreading plant on Ascension; in January 1996 it was already present in 56 of the 97 one km map squares covering Ascension.[12] It spreads rapidly because the seed pods are eaten by donkeys and the seeds are then distributed in their dung. Up to 60 seeds can be excreted in each dropping and rows of seedling trees can be seen lining donkey paths in otherwise barren cindery areas in the western lowlands (Plate 15). This invasive shrub poses major threats to the environment of Ascension, and is further discussed in Chapter 14.

---

[12] R. Prytherch (1996), S.V. Fowler (1998), A.R. Pickup (1999).

There are, of course, also a large number of agricultural weeds that have been introduced unintentionally and have established themselves, and many ornamental species that have not spread widely. A new batch of ornamentals were introduced in the area of Two Boats village in the 1960s by horticultural officer D.N. Stokes. It seems likely that a number of these will spread and become naturalised in time.

One and half centuries after Hooker formulated his programme for transforming the vegetation of the island, his vision has been largely fulfilled. The importation of a multitude of alien plants, together with the accidental introduction of other species, has resulted in dramatic changes in the character of the vegetation which are still proceeding. It seems certain that the trees and shrubs on the mountain intercept moisture and increase effective precipitation (see discussion in relation to St Helena in Chapter 3); soil formation at lower levels has doubtless been accelerated by the luxuriant growth of the introduced vegetation; and some plants adapted to dry conditions - especially the Mexican Thorn - are spreading in the desert lowlands. The overall effect has been the greening of a substantial part of the island.

Table 11A. **Birds of Ascension Island**

*Sections A and B together show the approximate composition of the bird communities of the island at the time of discovery of the island by humans in 1501. * indicates an endemic species and ✝ an extinct species.*

Records of many other vagrants and seabird visitors are listed by Bourne & Simmons (1998).

English and local names	Scientific name	Comment
A. Endemic and indigenous breeding birds		
Madeiran Storm-petrel	*Oceanodroma castro*	
Red-billed Tropicbird	*Phaethon aethereus*	
White-tailed Tropicbird	*Phaethon lepturus*	
Masked Booby	*Sula dactylatra*	
Brown Booby	*Sula leucogaster*	
Red-footed Booby	*Sula sula*	
* Ascension Frigatebird	*Fregata aquila*	Surviving endemic
Sooty Tern (Wideawake)	*Sterna fuscata*	
Brown Noddy	*Anous stolidus*	
Black Noddy	*Anous minutus*	
White Tern	*Gygis alba*	
B. Additional endemic and indigenous birds breeding at the time of discovery		
Audubon's Shearwater	*Puffinus lherminieri*[13]	Fossils ?date
*✝ Ascension Night Heron	*Nycticorax new species*	Fossils recent
*✝ Ascension Rail	*Atlantisia elpenor*	Fossils recent
C. Introduced breeding birds		
Red-necked Francolin (Francolin)	*Francolinus afer*	
Indian Myna (Myna)	*Acridotheres tristis*	
House Sparrow (Sparrow)	*Passer domesticus*	
Common Waxbill (Amadavat, Averdavat)	*Estrilda astrild*	
Yellow Canary (Canary)	*Serinus flaviventris*	
D. Additional birds of special interest		
Cattle Egret	*Bubulcus ibis*	Frequent visitor
Lesser Gallinule	*Porphyrula alleni*	Vagrant; one subfossil?
American Purple Gallinule	*Porphyrula martinica*	Vagrant
Moorhen	*Gallinula chloropus*	Vagrant

---

[13] This species may still breed on the island in tiny numbers: see Chapter 15.

Table 11B. **Endemic and indigenous flowering plants and ferns of Ascension Island**

Species are listed alphabetically by family, genus and species scientific name, but with the ferns separate.

FAMILY and scientific and English name	Status	Comments
FLOWERING PLANTS		
AIZOACEAE		
Tetragonia tetragonioides, New Zealand Spinach	Probably indigenous	
CONVOLVULACEAE		
Ipomoea pes-caprae, Camel's-foot Creeper	Indigenous	
CYPERACEAE		
Cyperus appendiculatus	Indigenous	
EUPHORBIACEAE		
* *Euphorbia origanoides*	Endemic species	
GRAMINEAE		
Aristida ascensionis	Indigenous	
Digitaria ciliaris	Possibly indigenous	Identity needs confirmation
Enneapogon cenchroides	Possibly indigenous	
Polypogon monspeliensis	Possibly indigenous	Identity needs confirmation
* *Sporobolus caespitosus*	Endemic species	
* *Sporobolus durus*	Endemic species	Perhaps extinct
MALVACEAE		
? *Hibiscus trionum*, Bladder Ketmia	Conceivably indigenous	Identity doubtful; now absent
NYCTAGINACEAE		
Commicarpus helenae, Hogweed	Probably indigenous	
PORTULACACEAE		
Portulaca oleracea, Purslane	Probably indigenous	
RUBIACEAE		
* *Oldenlandia (ex Hedyotis) adscensionis*	Distinctive endemic species	Extinct

Table 11B. Continued

FAMILY and scientific and English name	Status	Comments
FERNS		
ASPLENIACEAE		
Asplenium erectum	Indigenous	Endemic variety *A. erectum* var. *ascensionis*
DENNSTAEDTIACEAE		
Histiopteris incisa	Indigenous	
Hypolepis rugosula	Possibly indigenous	Perhaps introduced from St Helena
DRYOPTERIDACEAE		
* *Dryopteris ascensionis*	Endemic species	Perhaps extinct
GRAMMITIDACEAE		
* *Xiphopteris ascensionense*	Endemic species	Sometimes treated as a form of *X. trichomanoides*
LYCOPODIACEAE		
Lycopodium axillare	Probably indigenous	Recorded only once, long ago; present on St Helena
Lycopodium cernuum, Buckshorn	Indigenous	Also on St Helena
MARATTIACEAE		
* *Marattia purpurascens*	Endemic species	
NEPHROLEPIDACEAE		
Nephrolepis hirsutula	Indigenous	Possibly endemic form
OPHIOGLOSSACEAE		
Ophioglossum species	Possibly indigenous	Identity not clear
PSILOTACEAE		
Psilotum nudum	Indigenous	
PTERIDACEAE		
* *Anogramma ascensionis*	Endemic species	Perhaps extinct
* *Pteris adscensionis*	Endemic species	

Chapter 12

Turtle migration, bird biology and animals of the clinker

Scientists working on Ascension have made significant advances in several fields of biology. Studies of the marine green turtles have brought together several distinct scientific disciplines – geology, oceanography, satellite telemetry, traditional zoology and molecular biology – in attempts to throw light on their remarkable migrations; recently there has been intensive work on aspects of their nesting behaviour. Members of the British Ornithologists' Union Centenary Expedition in 1957-59 carried out pioneering long-term studies of tropical seabirds, using new methods and developing a number of influential ideas relating to their ecology and evolution; this was followed up by important work on the controls of breeding in boobies. More recently, work on the fauna of the clinker and caves has contributed both to theories of how animals establish themselves on isolated islands and to understanding of the evolutionary processes that follow colonisation.

Turtle migration, plate tectonics and molecular biology

The first scientific observations on the Ascension population of Green Turtles were made in 1656 by Peter Mundy, who applied his customary curiosity and powers of observation when his shipmates captured five females during their 24-hour visit.[1] Mundy noted that:

> *"The shee-tortoise may have 7 or 800 eggs att one tyme in her belly; some tell of 1000 and 1300. I conceave they lay them att severall tymes, aboutt 100 or 200 at once, for they had a greatt many ready and perfitted, for which they came on shoare to lay them. They have a tough filme or skynne instead of a shell, having yolke and white like henns eggs, and aboutt thatt bignesse, butt these perfitt round. They lye in a long filme or gutt one by another, like beads, in which are a greatt number of those that are ready and a greatt number of a lesser sort, beeing butt yolkes as yett and unperfitt, butt all of one size; and then a greatt number of a lesser sort againe. All these severall sorts questionlesse ar laid att severall times."*

Nearly three hundred years later the scientists on the *Blossom* expedition provided more precise counts but less interpretation, mentioning that a female they caught had 263 eggs together with 586 globular yolks.

Peter Mundy was also well informed about the nesting process:

> *"Aboutt this iland are many sandy baies and coves, where the sea-tortoises com on shore to lay their eggs, which they doe by nightt, and scraping a pitt in the sand, doe lay their eggs in itt, and soe covering them againe, leave them to bee hatched and broughtt forth by the heatt of the sun. The yong ones, as soone as they are hatched, run toward the sea by instinctt of nature, and thatt by nightt alsoe, by reason of foule thatt watch to devour them on the land, as fishes doe waite for them in the sea, beeing ordained living food for both."*

Much of the modern research on the Ascension turtles has been concerned with the breeding migrations. It is now known that the turtles spend most of their adult lives feeding on seaweeds along the coast of Brazil, but migrate to Ascension every few

---

[1] R.C. Temple & L.M. Anstey (1936).

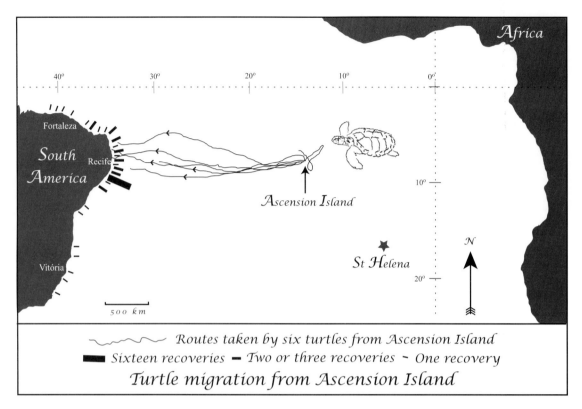

Routes taken by six turtles from Ascension Island
■ Sixteen recoveries ▬ Two or three recoveries ⌒ One recovery
Turtle migration from Ascension Island

Figure 25
Adapted from J.A. Mortimer
& A. Carr (1987), *Copeia*,
and P. Luschi et al. (1998),
Proc. R. Soc. Lond. B.

years to lay their eggs on the beaches. A key question was posed by the late Archie Carr, a well-known American herpetologist: How did such a remarkable pattern of breeding migration evolve, given the great distance between Ascension and South America, and the problem of finding Ascension in such an expanse of ocean?

The work of Carr and his colleagues on the Ascension turtles spanned a quarter of a century, starting in 1958 and culminating in the intensive study by Jeanne Mortimer; the visiting scientists had much help from people on the island, especially the farm manager Peter Critchley. The main task was to put numbered metal tags on adult female turtles when they came ashore on Ascension to lay their eggs, and then to search the beaches for marked animals returning in the same season and in subsequent years; by the end of this work, 3384 females had been tagged. The results confirmed Peter Mundy's deduction, showing that females nested up to five times within a single season, with the most frequent intervals being 13-14 days.[2] Between nestings in a given season, the females remain close to shore.

In due course, more exciting results began to trickle in, as tagged turtles were found further afield, and by 1987, 66 recoveries had been made, all of them on the coast of Brazil and mainly close to Recife, which is due west of Ascension. Scattered recoveries extended southwards to 24°S beyond Vitória, and along the north coast to 41°W beyond Fortaleza, but there were none north of the equator.

These results – based on recoveries of tagged turtles – were published in 1987, but in 1997 a team of Italian and British scientists applying modern telemetry techniques

---

[2] J.A. Mortimer & A. Carr (1987).

managed to track individual turtles when they left Ascension Island after egg-laying.[3] Satellite transmitters were attached to six females while nesting on Long Beach, Ascension, and their positions were plotted over the next three to seven weeks (Figure 25). One turtle was evidently confused and wandered in various directions from Ascension, but the other five swam westwards, and were last recorded close to the Brazilian coast; unfortunately, it was not possible to chart their movements during the time before their next trip back to Ascension, since the transmitters soon failed.

This pattern must be viewed in the context of the currents in the area (see Figure 3 in Chapter 1). The South Equatorial Current flows westwards past Ascension and on towards Brazil. As it approaches the continent the current splits, the northern part flowing parallel with the north coast of South America as the Guyana Current and the southern part turning south to form the Brazil Current. There is now some evidence from the satellite tracking that the adult turtles adjust their course as they travel west, so as to make a landfall on the coast of Brazil close to Recife and due west of Ascension.

In the southern winter the South Equatorial Current flows past Ascension at about half to one kilometre per hour. It seems to decrease in speed further to the west, but may accelerate again as it approaches the South American continent. Recoveries of drift bottles suggest that floating objects starting at Ascension would travel west at a speed of roughly 30 km per day (but varying with the season) and would reach the longitude of South America in roughly 2-3 months.[4] However, the statellite data show that the turtles travel much faster than the current, maintaining an average speed of about 2.5 km per hour. Indeed, the confused turtle which can have had no overall help from the current, nevertheless managed to travel on average more than 2 km per hour. The fastest documented migration involved a female released with a transmitter on Ascension on 12th May 1997, which was off Recife, Brazil, 35 days later. It had travelled just over 2 300 km, giving an average speed of more than two and three-quarter km per hour.

In Brazil, the adult turtles live in shallow water, feeding on algae growing on the sea bottom. Intriguingly, in the northern part of their Brazilian feeding range, the Ascension breeders are intermingled with turtles that breed in Surinam, further to the northwest along the South American coast. In spite of this, none of the turtles tagged on Ascension were found nesting either in Surinam or in any other rookery.

At intervals, the Ascension turtles return to the island. By 1987, 69 turtles had been found back on Ascension two or more years after being tagged while nesting, presumably having made round trips to Brazil in the meantime. Nearly always, the females returned to the same beach. Much the commonest intervals were three or four years, with a few turtles reappearing after only two years but none after only a single year. Carr assumed that when the Ascension turtles in Brazil are ready to breed again, they get back to the island by travelling north or south along the Brazilian coast to the neighbourhood of Recife, and then swimming due east.

Carr and his team were not successful in the more difficult task of charting the movements of the hatchling turtles after they scuttled down the beaches of Ascension and plunged into the sea. It proved impossible to tag them in such a way that the tags survived into adulthood, so Carr could not prove that the young – on reaching maturity – returned to breed on the island where they themselves were born. It seems

[3] P. Luschi et al. (1998).

[4] C.W. Brown (1990).

certain that this is what normally happens, but the mechanisms by which the turtles achieve it are still unclear.

Some young turtles may even start their first trip by moving eastwards. Although the South Equatorial Current flows steadily westwards at the surface from about May onwards, the Countercurrent flows eastwards past Ascension below the surface, and in the southern summer the eastward movement may affect the surface waters. Since turtle nesting starts in December-January and incubation takes just over two months, the earliest hatchlings may sometimes find themselves in eastward-flowing surface waters.

However, most young turtles leaving Ascension probably drift westwards. They presumably swim less strongly than the adults and may drift almost passively with the current, in much the same way that larval eels hatched in the Sargasso Sea drift to Europe in the Gulf Stream. In the case of the hatchling turtles from Ascension, however, the immediate destination is not known. Many years ago scientists on a research ship released hundreds of drift bottles (containing a return address) in the middle of the tropical Atlantic. The recoveries suggested that turtles drifting passively from Ascension should pass to the north of Brazil and eventually reach the Caribbean. In a later study, however, buoys released south of 8°S (the latitude of Ascension) entered the Brazil Current, which flows southwestwards down the coast of South America.[5]

The question of where young sea turtles in general live during the many years before they reach maturity has long been a puzzle to turtle biologists. Unexpectedly, we found ourselves marginally involved in the solution to this problem. Back in the 1960s, when working in the equatorial Pacific, we had promoted the idea that seabirds and other animals in unproductive oceans were feeding on the concentrations of marine life where two water masses converge at an oceanic 'front'. It recently became clear that the young of some species of turtles were doing just this.[6]

Whereas upwelling or divergence plays a crucial role in bringing nutrients to the surface and increasing the fertility of the sea, convergence involves sinking water, either where two currents come together, or in local rips, or in small-scale circulation cells caused by the wind. Convergence has the effect of concentrating at the surface any objects that resist sinking, including driftwood and floating weed like *Sargassum*, but also plankton or larger animals and even terrestrial insects that have come down in the sea during aerial dispersal.[7] Many of these objects form potential food, and in the 1980s, when Archie Carr laboriously collected records of young turtles at sea, he found that many were associated with weed at convergent 'driftlines' where the turtles were evidently feeding.[8]

Experienced seamen could have told scientists about this phenomenon centuries ago. Indeed, even the land-based Samuel Taylor Coleridge in the *Ancient Mariner*, may have been unwittingly passing on observations of turtles in an oceanic front, when he wrote:

---

[5] G. Reverdin & M.J. McPhaden (1986).

[6] W.H. Hammer (1988).

[7] J.I. Richardson & R. McGillivary (1991).

[8] A. Carr (1987) found that oceanographers were also becoming interested in fronts, and quoted observations on one of the space-shuttle *Challenger* missions showing that the oceans of the world teem with fronts of all dimensions and configurations. It also turns out that many fronts occur at the edges of rotating oceanic features termed 'mesoscale eddies', which are up to a few hundred kilometres across and may last for several years. These eddies are usually budded off from major currents such as the Gulf Stream, and their discovery has forced rethinking of the normal stereotype of monolithic, smoothly-flowing ocean currents.

"Water, water, everywhere,
And all the boards did shrink;
Water, water, everywhere,
Nor any drop to drink.
The very deep did rot: O Christ !
That ever this should be !
Yea, slimy things did crawl with legs
Upon the slimy sea."

Carr's information on young turtles at sea related mainly to loggerheads (genus *Caretta*) in the Caribbean and North Atlantic. He concluded that these young turtles had a prolonged 'pelagic phase'[9], and that they might be making a complete circuit in the North Atlantic Gyre (the clockwise surface circulation that includes the Gulf Stream); similar migrations of loggerheads have recently been suggested in the Pacific and Indian Oceans.

If the hatchling Green Turtles of Ascension drift westwards with the South Equatorial Current, they might eventually reach the Caribbean. It is possible that they do this, and then have a prolonged pelagic phase in the Caribbean or even in the North Atlantic Gyre. However, there are few records of young Green Turtles from the latter area, and it would be worth investigating another hypothesis, that the young turtles from Ascension spend this period in eddies and fronts associated with the great anticlockwise gyre in the South Atlantic (Figure 3).

As already mentioned, drift bottles released just south of the latitude of Ascension enter the branch of the South Equatorial Current that turns southwards as it approaches South America and forms the Brazil Current, the descending western limb of the South Atlantic circulation. If the same thing happened to young turtles from Ascension, they could spend several years making one or more leisurely circuits of the central South Atlantic, living as carnivores feeding on the animals of the 'pleuston', including floating molluscs, jellyfish and goose barnacles growing on flotsam.

Some of the North Atlantic records of young turtles are from the stomachs of dolphins, and the vast majority must succumb to predation of one sort or another. However, they probably obtain some protection by sheltering in weed or underneath driftwood or other objects concentrated at the fronts. A few of the Ascension hatchlings do survive the various dangers and grow to a size large enough to give them protection against the more numerous predators of inshore waters. If our idea is right they then migrate westwards out of the main oceanic circulation to start the herbivorous stage of their life cycle on the Brazilian coast. Here, they reach maturity while grazing on algae along with the adults that have returned from breeding migrations to Ascension.

The Ascension turtle population has interested evolutionists as well as ecologists. In 1974 Carr and his colleague Coleman put forward an ingenious idea to explain the breeding migration of the Ascension turtles from Brazil to the island, making use of the theory of plate tectonics that had recently revolutionized geological science. By then it was known that the South Atlantic was formed by the splitting apart of West Africa and South America. Carr & Coleman postulated that the ancestral turtles – about 80 million years ago – started nesting on islands formed by volcanic activity around the line of separation of the continents, which was to become the Mid-Atlantic Ridge. Since West Africa and South America had only recently moved

---

[9] Pelagic animals are those that live on or near the surface of the open sea.

221

apart, these offshore breeding islands would still have been close to the feeding grounds along the South American coast.

Carr & Coleman suggested that although no single island still exists from that time (islands tend to be transformed into submerged seamounts as they get older and move further from the ridge) there might always have been one or more islands in the area of the ridge on which turtles could breed. With the steady widening of the Atlantic the distance between the continental feeding grounds and islands near the ridge became steadily greater. Each year the spreading axis at the ridge is about 2 cm further from South America as a result of the creation of new sea floor, so the turtles have to migrate slightly further in each generation. The required direction of migration, however, would have remained roughly the same, so that navigational abilities evolved early in the process would merely be honed to maximum efficiency by natural selection during the long history of the population.

Attractive though it was, this hypothesis was soon challenged by another evolutionist, Stephen Jay Gould. He argued that if the ancestors of the modern Ascension Island turtle population had become separated so long ago from their relatives breeding in other places, they would by now have evolved differences from them. Since consistent external differences were not apparent, Gould promoted the alternative idea that the Ascension Island turtle population might have its origin in a recent colonisation.

The two ideas subsequently became testable using new techniques of molecular biology. These involved analysis of differences in the DNA molecules present in the mitochondria of each cell, in which evolutionary change is relatively rapid. In 1987 the American scientist John Avise and his co-workers analyzed green turtle DNA samples from four rookeries – Hawai'i in the Pacific, Hutchinson Island off Florida, Aves Island off Venezuela and Ascension Island in the Atlantic.[10] The results were clear cut. The Pacific samples showed a number of differences from the three Atlantic ones. The samples from the latter were distinguishable from each other but the degree of difference between Ascension and the other sites was much less than would have been expected if the population had been evolving separately for 80 million years or so, as suggested by Carr & Coleman.

Avise and his colleagues pointed out that over evolutionary time, suitable beaches (and indeed islands) arise and disappear, so that no population is likely to represent an ancient independent lineage. Since Ascension is little more than a million years old, the Carr-Coleman hypothesis would anyhow have required the original mid-Atlantic turtle population – if it was to survive as an independent unit – to shift several times from one disappearing island to a younger one nearer the ridge. The DNA study does not support this idea, but implies that the Green Turtles of Ascension have relatively recent common ancestry with other Atlantic populations; similarity is particularly marked with a West African population on the coast of Guinea-Bissau.[11]

Avise and his team appeared unaware that St Helena also is – or at least has been – a breeding site for Green Turtles. Since St Helena is a much older island, it is possible that the Ascension population was founded by lost individuals that had been aiming at St Helena, at a time when more sandy beaches were available there and a substantial population was present. Positive proof of this idea would be impossible to get, but evidence against it would be provided if DNA from one of the few turtles that

---

[10] B.W. Bowen, A.B. Meylan & J.C. Avise (1989).

[11] S.E. Encalada et al. (1996).

still appear off St Helena turned out to be very distinct from that of the Ascension animals.

This discussion, of course, leaves unanswered the question of how migrating sea turtles find their way. Complete answers are not yet available, but recent research demonstrates that they are capable of using an extraordinary array of navigational cues, differing according to the demands of each stage of the life cycle.[12]

Hatchling turtles need to move offshore, and have been shown to be sensitive both to the tendency for natural light to be brightest in the direction of the sea, and for waves to approach beaches from almost directly offshore. Hatchlings use these two types of cues successively while crawling on the beach and after entering the sea. Experiments have now shown, however, that during these initial movements the young turtles acquire a magnetic preference that enables them to continue swimming out to sea even further out where the waves are often not oriented shorewards.

During their life as juveniles, Loggerhead Turtles and probably also Green Turtles spend years in the major oceanic gyres, as discussed above. It has now been demonstrated that young Loggerheads are sensitive to the magnetic inclination angle and to variations in the intensity of the earth's magnetic field, both of which vary in a predictable way across the surface of the earth. It is thus possible that young sea turtles may use these magnetic cues to remain within the appropriate current systems.

Sensitivity to magnetism may also help adult Green Turtles from Ascension facing an even more severe challenge. Many times during their lives, they need to find their tiny natal island after setting out from the coast of Brazil, more than 2000 km away. Their evident success in this, coupled with recent experimental evidence involving artificial displacements, seems to imply a capacity to determine position relative to a goal, which is a much more complex task than simply orienting in a given compass direction. Evidence that birds possessed an ability of this kind provided the focus for extensive and often controversial research some decades ago.

In relation to the Ascension turtles, a recent hypothesis of magnetic navigation depends on the fact that in the relevant oceanic region, the lines of equal inclination angle and the lines of equal magnetic field intensity intersect almost at right angles, forming a sort of grid in which a pair of values specifies a unique position. Given the demonstrated ability of sea turtles to detect these magnetic forces, it seems plausible that the Ascension adults might use them to home to the general vicinity of the island. At this stage, another set of cues may become available.

It was long ago suggested that the Ascension turtles might return to the island by means of sensitivity to an odour plume, in a manner analogous to salmon homing to their natal streams.[13] Chemical substances from the island would tend to drift westwards with the surface current, so that adult turtles approaching from the west might encounter the plume and recognize the chemical signal in the water as the one they had experienced when they left Ascension as hatchlings. If they remained within the plume while travelling generally east, they would eventually reach the island. Such a mechanism would not work in turtle populations where adults do not approach the breeding sites up-current. It is possible, however, that the Ascension Green Turtles may use chemical cues in the final approach to Ascension, having travelled to the general area using magnetic cues.

---

[12] K.J. Lohmann et al. (1997).

[13] D.W. Owens et al. (1986).

Further advances in understanding of the life cycle and migrations of the Ascension Green Turtles seem likely to come mainly from additional satellite tracking, using both adults and young. We also feel, however, that observations by yachtsmen could help. In particular, there is the exciting chance of finding out whether young Green Turtles are living in the central South Atlantic during their pelagic phase.

Seabird biology

Ascension Island has played a significant role in the development of understanding of tropical seabirds. The island got off to a good start, since it is the type locality for four species of seabirds: the Red-billed Tropicbird, Ascension Frigatebird, Masked Booby and White Tern were formally described and named on the basis of specimens from Ascension. Indeed, the first two were named in 1758 by Carl Linnaeus, the founder of the modern system of biological classification.

Two hundred years later, in the late 1950s, the science of ornithology had still only recently emerged from the era in which the primary objective was cataloguing and classification of the birds of the world.[14] It was well known that most birds in strongly seasonal high latitude regions have fixed and well synchronised breeding seasons in the early summer, when their food supply is greatest. But what about birds in areas where seasonal changes are slight? Would they breed all year round, and would individuals breed more than once in the year? In the 1950s the scanty evidence was equivocal and more data were clearly needed.

The ecologist Eric Duffey suggested that Ascension Island was a place where the breeding cycles of an entire community of seabirds living in a relatively seasonless environment could be studied in detail. Duffey was aware that the American ornithologist J.P. Chapin, who had been on Ascension during the second world war, had later published an article on *"The calendar of Wideawake fair"* showing that the Wideawakes started laying on average every 9.6 months, and thus in a different month in each year. This intriguing and almost unique situation, on a British island that had populations of several other little known seabird species, offered an obvious opportunity for studies that would break new ground. Consequently the British Ornithologists' Union decided to celebrate its centenary by sending an expedition to Ascension. Philip was a member of the expedition, which is described in the box overleaf.

Studies of reproductive cycles – in the 1950s and earlier – had shown that most birds, when they finish breeding, immediately start a complete moult, replacing all their feathers. After this, the birds remain in a reproductively quiescent stage until the start of the next breeding season. Many of them also migrate into lower latitudes for the winter, or even cross the equator so that they experience more or less perpetual summer.

During the BOU expedition we were able to show that in the absence of strong seasonal constraints, the seabirds of Ascension exhibited an extraordinary variety of breeding cycles. Some species laid at less than annual intervals (and thus in different

---

[14] Intensive life-history studies of birds, based on the relatively new technique of ringing (banding), had been pioneered in Britain by David Lack with his *"Life of the Robin"*. Lack had later become Director of the Edward Grey Institute of Field Ornithology in Oxford (always referred to as the EGI), from which he published a stream of stimulating books and papers about bird ecology. *"The Ibis"*, journal of the British Ornithologists' Union (BOU), was at that time edited from the EGI by the redoubtable Reg Moreau. He had transformed it from being largely a passive receiver of reports on specimens shot in the outposts of empire, into a rigorous scientific journal in which the editor wielded a formidable red pencil with such humour and good nature that hardly anyone took offence. It was natural, therefore, that when the BOU decided to include in its centenary celebrations an expedition to study breeding seasons of tropical birds, the EGI should be the base.

The British Ornithologists' Union Centenary Expedition 1957-59

When Philip – then a final year undergraduate in the Zoology Department at Oxford – was recruited to join the BOU expedition, the basic brief was simple. We were to document the breeding cycles of all the Ascension seabirds and to find out, for each species, how the cycles of the individual birds fitted into the pattern shown by the population as a whole.

To study breeding cycles, it was obviously necessary to spend at least a year on the island. At the time, Ascension was occupied only by Cable & Wireless and Pan American (under contract to the U.S. Air Force). Cable & Wireless ran a farm on Green Mountain which provided some fresh food, but received all their other supplies on the Union Castle liners that called once a month in each direction, on their way between South Africa and Britain. The expedition therefore needed to be relatively self-sufficient, and we went with prefabricated huts, a Land Rover, a seaworthy boat and almost all our stores for 18 months.

The expedition was led by Bernard Stonehouse, who already had extensive experience in the Antarctic; his confident and steady hand was crucial in assuring success. Bernard's wife Sally came as organiser of the domestic side of the expedition and increasingly participated in the biological work. Douglas Dorward came as deputy leader, so that with Philip there were four permanent members of the party, all from the Edward Grey Institute of Field Ornithology in Oxford. We were joined for a few months by Mike Cullen, a member of Niko Tinbergen's animal behaviour group at Oxford, who had a special interest in terns, and by Eric Duffey, who came to make a general ecological survey of the island. Later we were reinforced by Dick Allan, a Scot who was doing doctoral work at the University of Florida, who came mainly to study the introduced landbirds but also worked on the petrels.

A base camp was established at the foot of South Gannet Hill close to the track down to Mars Bay; the site is now almost unmarked. With the help of Cable & Wireless a buoy was put down in North East Bay, from which we operated the expedition boat *Ibis*, an ex ship's lifeboat on which we mounted a Seagull outboard motor at each side of the pointed stern. This enabled us to maroon members of the expedition, two at a time, on Boatswainbird Island, where they could work for up to a week before being collected or replaced.

The expedition was on Ascension from September 1957 to April 1959. A general account of it was written by Bernard Stonehouse in a book called *Wideawake Island*, which is now hard to find, while the scientific results were published in two special issues of *Ibis* (Vol. 103b, Nos. 2 & 3) in 1962 and 1963. Between us we studied the Masked and Brown Boobies, Red-billed and White-tailed Tropic Birds, Ascension Frigatebird, Sooty Tern, Black and Brown Noddies, White Tern and the Madeiran Storm-petrel.

months each year), while in others some laying occurred in all months but with distinct annual peaks; yet others showed fairly conventional annual breeding.

For most species we were able to follow the activities of individual birds. We ringed large numbers, and well over a thousand of these were recovered and examined again either once or several times. For many of these birds we knew when their eggs were laid and how successful they were in rearing chicks. We also punched tiny holes in the main wing and tail feathers so that on a later occasion we could tell which ones had been renewed, and Philip developed a way of analysing the progress of moult, using numerical scores.[15] The system was later adopted by the British Trust for Ornithology and became standard in studies of moult. Much to our surprise, this obscure achievement earned us warm hospitality in Cape Town, *en route* to St Helena nearly forty years later!

The information that we gathered on moult of the seabirds turned out to be important, as we gradually realized that breeding and moult of the flight feathers hardly ever occurred at the same time; this is probably because replacement of feathers both increases nutritional requirements and decreases flight efficiency. The fact that the two activities were mutually exclusive seemed to imply that the time required for breeding and the subsequent moult might determine the minimum interval between successive breeding attempts.

Bernard Stonehouse showed, for instance, that White-tailed Tropicbirds could complete their whole cycle of breeding and moult in about 38 weeks; failure in breeding led to a quicker return. Furthermore, individuals could be found breeding at all times of year. This population thus appeared to have adopted a system in which individuals occupied all their time in either breeding or replacing their worn plumage, coming and going in their own time (though normally meeting up again for breeding with the same mates).

Wideawakes, unlike the tropicbirds, are colonial and breed fairly synchronously in large fairs in the southwest of the island. On average, breeding starts every 9.6 months (38 weeks) and the birds are absent between breeding periods. In this species – mainly because of the enormous population – Philip was only able to follow a few marked individuals through two breeding periods. It appeared, however, that if a bird was successful in rearing a chick in one breeding period it was barely able to finish its moult and get back in time to breed again in the next period; unsuccessful birds, however, were back in good time for the next breeding period.[16]

Most of the other seabirds of Ascension showed basically annual breeding. This was clearest in the Madeiran Storm-petrel, in which breeding was well synchronised, with peak laying in November. In the White Tern the laying season lasted from October to May but with a peak in January. In the Ascension Frigatebird the spread was even greater, with some laying in almost all months but a peak in September. The Masked Booby showed a similar pattern to the frigatebird, but the breeding cycles of the Brown Booby were more interesting and were fully investigated a few years later by Ken Simmons (see below).

It was obvious that we could only understand why the different seabirds showed different patterns of breeding if we could find out about variations in their food supply. We were frustrated by not being able to do this. Few of the species foraged within sight of the island and some of them seemed to be going very far afield, even when breeding. The main clue to this came from our measurements of the length of the incubation

---

[15] N.P. Ashmole (1962).

[16] N.P. Ashmole (1963a) There was scrappy evidence that on a few islands in the Pacific, Sooty Terns had breeding seasons every six months. This intriguing contrast with the Ascension situation led us to arrange to work on Christmas Island a few years later. It turned out that in this population unsuccessful breeders started moult but then halted it and returned for another breeding attempt after six months; successful parents took things in more leisurely fashion, completing a moult and returning after a year (N.P. Ashmole 1965).

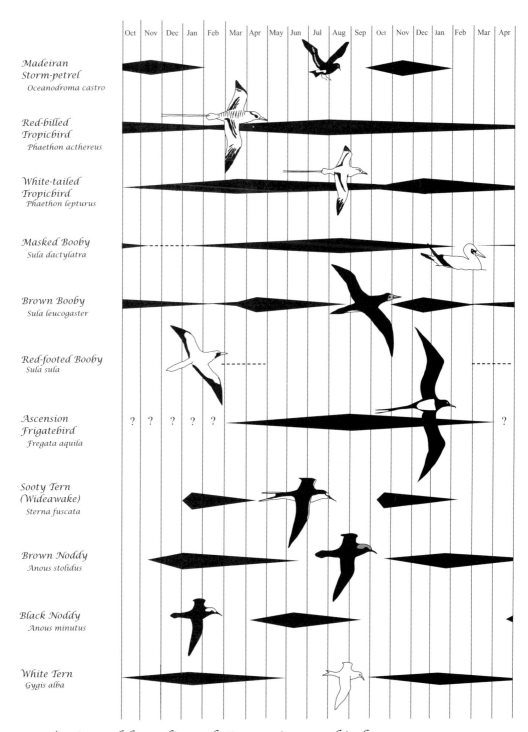

Timing of breeding of Ascension seabirds, 1957 - 1959

Figure 26   Data mainly from B. Stonehouse (1960); drawings of birds based on G.E. Watson (1963).

227

shifts: in all these seabirds both parents play a full role in incubation and rearing of the chick, and we recorded the time spent on the egg by one member of the pair while the other went off to forage.

Some of the shifts were startlingly long. In Wideawakes on Ascension, for instance, the normal shifts averaged more than five days.[17] We knew that in Florida the shifts in the same species typically lasted only one to two days. This difference implied that the Ascension birds were going further afield, and indeed was so long as to suggest that even after reaching the feeding zone they had to spend much time searching for patchy food sources. Shifts were also long in some of the other species, but relatively short in others, such as the inshore feeding Brown Boobies which usually changed over twice a day.

Unlike the rich waters of the continental shelves, the tropical ocean around Ascension is a desert in which a cap of warm and impoverished water at least 50 m deep floats stably on the cooler, denser water below, which contains almost all the nutrients. In such an environment it is clear that food for seabirds will be generally scarce. Most tropical seabirds are dependent on schools of predatory fish such as tuna to make their prey available by driving small squid and fish to the surface and putting flying-fish to flight.

In order to take advantage of the opportunities, the birds must search for actively feeding tuna schools, which are typically widely dispersed over the ocean but are much more numerous in areas where enrichment of the surface waters improves the food supply. As mentioned in Chapter 10, there is an area 2-4° south of the equator, where upwelling of nutrient-rich water leads to increased marine fertility. Fisheries data show that catches of tuna (especially Yellowfin) are enormously higher there than in the area around Ascension (which is at 8°S).[18]

Recently, marine ornithologist Bill Bourne and other members of the Royal Naval Bird-Watching Society have made observations from ships travelling past Ascension and have shown that seabird densities are more than 100 times higher within five degrees of the equator to the north of Ascension than they are to the south of the island.[19] It is likely, therefore, that the seabirds which breed on Ascension and have long incubation shifts are feeding around the tuna schools in the enriched area closer to the equator, more than 400 km to the north of the island.

It seems, however, that the food supply of the Ascension seabirds fluctuates in an unpredictable way, posing problems to the birds of a type that are rare in more seasonal temperate latitudes (at least in the absence of human overfishing). Early in the BOU expedition we observed a moderately successful Wideawake breeding period, but this was followed by a disastrous one nine months later in which hardly any chicks were raised; they stood around on the fairs for weeks on end, waiting for their parents to return with food, but the visits were too infrequent and eventually almost all the chicks died.

A few months earlier – at a time when the Wideawakes were absent – we had found the same thing happening among the Black Noddies on Boatswainbird Island. They had laid eggs and hatched chicks as expected, but only the very first ones were full

---

[17] N. P. Ashmole (1963a). Although Wideawakes can fast for many days, they do need water, and we were intrigued to see incubating birds leave their eggs on the baking hot fairs for a few minutes while they made short trips down to the sea; there they dipped to the surface to drink sea-water and sometimes also splashed their bellies into the sea. It was only at about this time that ornithologists elsewhere discovered the salt glands of seabirds. These are glands above the eyes capable of extracting excess salt from the blood and discharging concentrated brine from the nostrils; without them, it would be impossible for seabirds to balance their water and salt budgets.

[18] J. Scullion (1990).

[19] W.R.P. Bourne & W.F. Curtis (1985).

grown when an apparent famine developed. Philip watched as the parents of the others returned to their ledges night after night, after apparently unsuccessful fishing trips. In spite of obvious efforts, they were almost or entirely unable to regurgitate food, even when pestered by the desperately hungry chick. Although no adults seemed to die, the ground below the ledges gradually became littered with corpses of partly grown young (Plate 20). During the same period the Brown Boobies were also suffering severely from food shortage and the Masked Boobies to a lesser extent. The tropicbirds, however, did not seem to be affected.[20]

One general idea resulting from the BOU expedition related to the very low reproductive rate of tropical oceanic birds, and arose from our observations of starving chicks. We became aware of the tenuous nature of the food supply of the Ascension birds. None of the species normally raised more than one chick in a single breeding period, but even with a single chick, the adults were sometimes unable to collect enough food to ensure its survival.

Philip suggested that the low reproductive rate was caused by a combination of factors.[21] First, the general scarcity of food in tropical oceans. Second, the lack of seasonality, so that there is no regular time of year at which food becomes much more abundant. And third, the fact that while breeding, the adults are concentrated on randomly placed islands and have to commute long distances to and from their feeding grounds (while moulting, in contrast, many of them are able to roam the oceans, staying close to the richest food sources).

The life of adult oceanic birds – especially in the tropics – is relatively safe and results in long lifespans. Because of this, Philip suggested, numbers would tend to build up and result in competition among individuals for the scarce available food, especially around the breeding colonies. This would make it hard to provision chicks, and could have led to the evolution of a clutch of only one egg, because individuals that tried to raise several young might actually fail to raise any.

The Masked and Brown Boobies on Ascension were clearly relevant here. They were notable in that they laid two eggs, breaking the general rule of single-egg clutches. However, they never seemed to raise more than one chick. Douglas Dorward was able to throw some light on this curious situation. He noted that the two eggs in a clutch were laid about five days apart, but incubation started with the laying of the first egg. The result was that the first chick was several days old when its sibling hatched. Within a few days, the second chick almost invariably died. Douglas investigated the situation by switching chicks between nests so that the two chicks were more similar in size. Even so, the smaller one was doomed, although it appeared that feeding two small chicks was normally not a problem for the adults.

Douglas concluded that the larger chick physically bullied the smaller one, and that the parents failed to intervene, with the result that the smaller chick died. He suggested that

---

[20] At the time we had no information about changes in the oceanographic conditions around Ascension that might be causing the birds to have difficulty feeding. Some years later, however, we were studying the guano birds on the coast of Peru and became aware of the catastrophic effects on their populations of the worldwide oceanographic disturbances called El Niño (or ENSO) events. What we saw on Ascension in 1958-59 was related to a 1957 El Niño event in the Pacific. The next such event, in 1963, had drastic effects on the Brown Boobies, but there were no ornithological observations on Ascension during the similar events that led to massive rainfall in 1974 and in 1984-85. The latter event, however, was studied intensively by oceanographers and climatologists (S.G.H. Philander 1986). In the years strongly influenced by El Niño, upwelling in the feeding areas north of Ascension may fail altogether, and the abnormally warm water at the surface may offer hardly any prey for the seabirds.

[21] N.P. Ashmole (1963d).

an innate tendency to bully a smaller sibling could favour the survivor by eliminating potential competition for food at a later stage in development, when demands on the parents would be higher. Furthermore, if food was not normally sufficient to raise two healthy chicks the parents would be wasting effort by feeding the smaller chick.

Why, then, should these boobies lay two eggs? In the booby and gannet family (Sulidae) the eggs are relatively small and the incubation period long. It is therefore reasonable to suppose that the laying of the second egg could still be favoured by natural selection as an insurance against the loss of an egg during incubation and the consequent waste of time – if only one was laid – in having to start the breeding attempt over again.[22]

In the last few decades the new science of behavioural ecology has analyzed the way in which natural selection can operate among related individuals. This work by Douglas Dorward was one of the earliest serious attempts to interpret aspects of breeding behaviour within this theoretical framework.

The work of the BOU expedition on the Ascension seabirds was soon complemented by that of Ken Simmons, an ornithologist with special interest in bird behaviour. He was schoolmaster on the island from 1962 to 1964 and has been visiting the island to continue his work on the Brown Boobies at intervals ever since. Simmons made his observations at the stacks near Comfortless Cove, where he was able to keep regular watch on the birds over many months. One of Simmons' important contributions was his demonstration of the direct influence of unpredictable fluctuations in the local food supply on the breeding activity of the Brown Boobies.[23]

In the almost non-seasonal environment of Ascension there was evidently no overwhelming reason favouring breeding by Brown Boobies at a particular season in each year. Dorward's work had suggested that individuals of this species had a basic eight-month breeding periodicity on Ascension. Simmons showed, however, that this cycle was modified by the availability of food. Brown Boobies are inshore feeders, and breeding could be triggered opportunistically, or the laying period prolonged, when there was an influx into coastal waters of one of the boobies' main prey fish, the Steenbrass or Bigeye Scad, *Selar crumenophthalmus*. When such an influx was especially prolonged (as in 1961-62) Brown Booby breeding became continuous.

Conversely, the boobies stopped breeding when feeding conditions deteriorated. During the El Niño event of 1963, the birds in the colonies studied by Simmons stopped egg-laying from 7 February to 15 July, and the males lost the breeding colour of their bills and feet. During the same period the adults made unusually long hunting trips out to sea, and the period of dependence of fledged young was prolonged.

When the food supply improved, the response of the boobies was immediate. Males began collecting nest material, copulations occurred and the moult was halted at whatever stage it had reached, thus allowing all available energy to be channelled into breeding activity. Simmons agreed with Dorward on the 'insurance' role of the second egg and pointed out other adaptations to the unpredictable food supply. For instance, there was a tendency for females to lay new clutches repeatedly to replace failed ones, so long as feeding conditions remained favourable.

Furthermore, on the relatively rare occasions when a pair of Brown Boobies managed to rear a chick to fledging, they continued to feed it for many weeks. One

---

[22] D.F. Dorward (1962). Intriguingly, the Red-footed Booby – another tropical species – lays only a single egg. However, members of this species build a substantial nest of twigs, so that the risk of egg loss is probably lower than in the Brown and Masked Boobies, which lay their eggs on the ground with only a feeble attempt at a nest.

[23] K.E.L Simmons (1970).

juvenile was seen to beg and be fed 51 weeks after fledging. For this long-lived species with low breeding success, such behaviour makes sense in evolutionary terms. In a stable population, each pair would raise on average only two chicks to adulthood in the course of their life together, which might last for several decades. Continued feeding of the occasional offspring that survives as far as fledging, thus helping it to achieve the difficult transition to independence, will be favoured by natural selection even if it delays the start of the next breeding attempt.

Breeding cycles of the Ascension seabirds proved to be as interesting as the organisers of the BOU expedition had originally hoped. Further major studies of seabird ecology on the island will probably be undertaken only when a decision has finally been taken to eliminate the predatory feral cats and rats that infest the mainland of Ascension Island, and so initate a process of recovery in the seabird community. At that time, the eyes of ornithologists around the world will be focused on Ascension.

If, for the first time for two centuries, the main island is available as a safe breeding site for seabirds, re-establishment of colonies will surely ensue, and populations of several species are likely to increase substantially. Gradually, it may become apparent what numbers of seabirds can make a living in the seas around Ascension under present conditions. It may turn out that one anthropogenic factor will prevent some of the species from regaining the great abundance noted by the early human visitors. This factor is commercial fishing.

Norman Ratcliffe has recently emphasized the danger to frigatebirds and boobies (perhaps especially Brown Boobies) of becoming ensnared and eventually drowning as a result of attempting to take bait from fishermen's hooks. In relation to small-scale sport fishing around Ascension this may be negligible, but in recent years a Japanese longline fishery for tuna and swordfish has been operating within 200 nautical miles of Ascension. The hundreds of thousands of hooks set by the longlining fleet could pose a serious threat to seabirds.[24]

Intensive commercial fishing also poses a threat through its tendency to 'overfish' stocks. A large proportion of the world's fish stocks are already overfished, and there is little sign of effective regulation of fisheries being internationally enforced. If numbers of surface-feeding tuna (especially Yellowfin) are significantly reduced, so is the availability of food for seabirds such as Sooty Terns that depend on tuna and other predatory fish to scare smaller fish and squid to the surface. In the long run, therefore, the numbers of seabirds on Ascension after elimination of the feral cats and rats is likely to depend on the extent to which the international community is able to maintain tuna stocks, and to reduce seabird deaths during fishing operations.

The search for subfossil bird bones

During the British Ornithologists' Union expedition Philip systematically searched for bird remains in guano deposits on the main island, gradually building up a collection of subfossil bones that provided tangible evidence of the presence of large colonies of several species of seabirds on the lowlands of Ascension in the past.

In September 1958 members of the BOU expedition were taken by some American 'spelunkers' (caving enthusiasts) to visit a 'fumarole' or spatter cone which had been pointed out to them by a young Cable & Wireless engineer, John Packer; they had explored the cave and found that it contained bird bones, which they knew would

[24] N. Ratcliffe (1999).

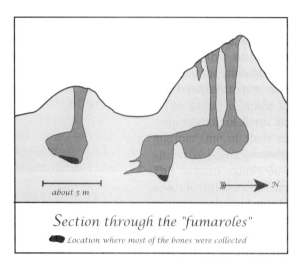

Section through the "fumaroles"

about 5 m

◣ *Location where most of the bones were collected*

Figure 27
Adapted from S.L.Olson
(1973), *Smithsonian
Contributions to Zoology*

interest us (Plate 12). When we got down into the bottle-shaped cave we found the floor carpeted with bones. Most were of seabirds, but among those collected was the skull of a small rail. A leg bone from old guano deposits in the Mars Bay lava flow also turned out to belong to a rail.[25] These finds were particularly exciting because of the account by Peter Mundy of a flightless bird that he found alive on the island in 1656 (see Chapter 11) which ornithologists had assumed was a rail that had later become extinct. Here was concrete evidence of Mundy's rail.

The story was developed by Storrs Olson of the Smithsonian Institution, who worked on Ascension in 1970 and 1971. He collected intensively in the two 'fumaroles' near Sisters, obtaining bones of more than 50 individuals of the extinct rail, which he formally described and named as *Atlantisia elpenor*.

Olson's other finds included remains of two landbirds not previously recorded from the island. In the smaller of the two fumaroles he found the ends of a leg bone of a larger species of rail, which he provisionally identified as the Lesser Gallinule *Porphyrula alleni*, an African species which is well known as a wanderer and reaches St Helena from time to time. The single specimen contrasts with the large number of bones of the Ascension Rail and suggests that the Lesser Gallinule did not establish itself on Ascension.

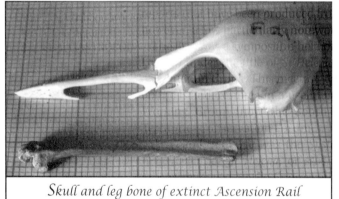

Skull and leg bone of extinct Ascension Rail

Figure 28
From N.P. Ashmole
(1963c), *Ibis.*

Olson's more important find was of bones of a single night heron in the genus *Nycticorax*. Olson thought that this also might be a vagrant, but we found remains of at least three more individuals in a different cave (Chapel Grotto) in 1995, making this possibility less plausible. Study of the bones shows that the birds were smaller than members of any African populations; the conclusion is that this night heron was resident on Ascension and represents a new but extinct species.[26]

One more seabird was added to the list of species known from the main island when Olson found remains of an individual of Audubon's Shearwater in a cave at the back of Clarkes Beach (north of South West Bay). We recently found more bones in other caves, and a single live individual was caught during the BOU expedition (Plate 18). Evidently this species was originally part of the original seabird community of Ascension.

The various collections of subfossil bones, together with historical information, indicate that the lowlands of the main island of Ascension in the past were populated not only by the Wideawake but also by the Red-billed Tropicbird, three species of boobies, the Ascension Frigatebird, White Tern, Madeiran Storm-petrel and Audubon's Shearwater.

---

[25] N.P. Ashmole (1963b).

[26] With some colleagues we are formally describing it. Although night herons are typical of aquatic habitats they have established themselves on several other groups of islands, including the Falklands, Galápagos and the Mascarene Islands in the Indian Ocean. Night herons are generalized predators and the Ascension birds probably foraged around the coast and also in the seabird colonies, taking eggs and young birds, and possibly also insects.

Three more species, White-tailed Tropicbird and Brown and Black Noddies, have not been found as subfossils and may always have bred only near the coast.

Investigations in caves and guano deposits on Ascension may now have completed the list of seabirds and large landbirds previously breeding on Ascension. One or more small landbirds might have been able to establish themselves on the originally vegetated parts of Green Mountain. If so, they probably became extinct soon after rats arrived at the beginning of the eighteenth century, and the chances of finding fossil remains are slim.

Animals of clinker and caves: colonisation, ecology and evolution on a young volcanic island

Investigations of the invertebrate fauna of Ascension were slow to get going, partly because most people thought that the animals of the island – apart from the seabirds – were either a nuisance or simply uninteresting. In 1834 the blind traveller James Holman commented that:

"...the residents almost consider themselves as labouring under some of the plagues of Egypt in the swarms of flies by which they are annoyed.... Ants are beyond all number, mosquitoes plentiful as they are tormenting, scorpions, centipedes, large spiders and crickets, in ample quantity...."

In 1861 T.V. Wollaston – who was later to do classic zoological work on St Helena – studied a small collection of beetles from Ascension. He published a short note on these, commenting with words that we treated as a challenge when we began our work on the clinker and caves in 1990:

"I may add that they would be totally unworthy of notice if it were not as a voucher for the utter sterility of this miserable spot and to warn naturalists from ever attempting to go there again for the purpose of collecting."

In spite of Wollaston's injunction, some more entomological work was done on Ascension before our own visit. In 1892 the experienced naturalist F. Dahl visited the island with a German expedition and wrote the first account of the land fauna. Insects that he noted included an aphid and a lacewing which he found living on the endemic Ascension Spurge; as far as we know, neither of these was ever described. Since then, entomologists have failed to find any aphids on the spurge; we cannot tell if they were endemic, and the population may now be extinct. Lacewings were not seen again on the island for more than a century, but an African species was recently found south of Two Boats village, and may be the one seen by Dahl.[27]

In 1958 a systematic study of the terrestrial ecology of Ascension was carried out by Eric Duffey, an ecologist and arachnologist who came to the island as a member of the BOU expedition. Duffey searched for invertebrates in many different habitats, making particularly important discoveries on Boatswainbird Island, as discussed later. Thirty years later, Charles Kirke collected butterflies and moths using a light-trap. In the resulting review, Kirke, writing with Gaden Robinson of the Natural History Museum in London, concluded that the list included few – if any – endemics and comprised a mixture of natural immigrants and introduced species.

The general picture of the land fauna of Ascension which emerged from the accounts of the visiting entomologists was of an island in which almost the only animals of

[27] W. Röhricht (1998).

233

interest were the seabirds. The invertebrates were few in number and were mainly geographically widespread insects known to be easily transported by people from place to place; it seemed likely that many had arrived by accident with introduced plants.

Up to this time, however, very little attention had been paid to the barren areas which were the most characteristic habitats of Ascension in its pristine state. During the 1980s we worked on the Canary Islands and the Azores, investigating the way in which invertebrate animals colonise the hostile new habitats produced by erupting volcanoes. We found communities of scavengers and predators managing to eke out a living on jagged lava flows, cinder fields and in volcanic caves that on first sight appeared to be devoid of life.[28]

This experience led us to think that a similar study on Ascension would make an interesting comparison. It is a single island rather than an archipelago, and is both geologically young and very distant from the nearest land: this last characteristic makes Ascension as great a challenge to potential animal colonists as any place in the world.[29] Capitalizing on opportunities to visit the island in 1990 and 1995 for ornithological work, we were able at the same time to carry out systematic work on the animals of the caves and of the barren lava.

We visited most of the known caves and put traps and searched in those that seemed most interesting. We also managed to find one additional and relatively high cave near Spoon Crater. In selecting clinker areas for study, we searched for places as remote as possible from any vegetation. This was because our special interest was in the animals depending upon wind-blown detritus or vagrant insects for their food, rather than those utilizing plants; the latter had been looked at by other people and anyhow many of them would have been absent from the island in its pristine state. Some of the most interesting results came from a series of trapping stations on the jagged lava flow east of Mars Bay, running in from the coast at Shelly Beach towards South Gannet Hill; for comparison there was also a 'control' station on older lava with some plants. We did similar work in various other parts of the island, including some places where we could simultaneously sample on the surface and in the caves nearby.

At the end of our short but intensive periods of field work we felt that the project had gone well, but the significance of the results became apparent only gradually. It is notorious that an enormous proportion of the work of expeditions has to be done after the return, and this was no exception. After the sorting and preliminary examination of the specimens, almost all of them had to be sent to taxonomists who specialized on the various groups. Only in this way can species be securely identified and new ones properly described. Luckily we were already in contact with many of the relevant people, but we were nonetheless amazed to find, when we were ready to publish our

---

[28] For our previous expeditions we had collaborated with Spanish colleagues in developing a miniaturized trapping system using small plastic fizzy drink bottles baited with Danish Blue cheese, and pitfall traps made from small jars containing a cocktail of beer and various additives. In the Canary Islands this system has enabled us to detect the presence of scarce, tiny and nocturnal animals, living unnoticed in habitats that have been little disturbed by human activities (N.P. Ashmole et al. 1992). Similarly, on Capelinhos volcano in the Azores, we found a minute beetle – known from nowhere else in the world – living on the edge of a volcanic crater which had been formed in an eruption only 30 years previously, and which was rapidly crumbling back into the Atlantic Ocean (N.P. Ashmole et al. 1996). In work of this kind the animals caught are inevitably killed. We are not happy about this, but feel that it is probably justified on a small scale, since one cannot design a sensible conservation plan for an area until one knows what animals and plants are present there. When dealing with such small animals, preserved specimens are essential for identification or description of new species; photographs and descriptions of live animals simply will not do.

[29] Anak Krakatau and Surtsey, classic examples of volcanic islands that are gradually being colonised by plants and animals, have other islands nearby, whereas Ascension emerged from the sea more than 1000 kilometres from any other land.

work after several years of complex correspondence, that we had needed the help of some 60 specialists in 15 different countries – and we were dealing with an island with one of the least rich faunas in the world!

In spite of this low diversity, the results showed that the invertebrate fauna of Ascension was much more interesting than had appeared from the earlier studies. There was in fact an array of tiny animals – many of them endemic – living in the most barren places on the island: the lava flows, drifts of cinders and volcanic caves. We discovered three new animal genera – of spiders, mites and booklice – and about 14 new and apparently endemic species, more than doubling the number previously known from the island; six of the new species were found in caves. The known fauna is summarized in Table 12.

During our 1995 visit, Philip had the opportunity to make an overnight stay on Boatswainbird Island.[30] This was a chance to amplify the intriguing results of Eric Duffey's work there in 1958. During his ecological survey of Ascension, Duffey had found no less than three endemic species of pseudoscorpions. These are minute relatives of spiders and scorpions, distinguished from the former by the presence of a pair of (relatively) enormous pincers and from the latter by the absence of a stinging tail. Two of these species were found only on Boatswainbird Island.

The extraordinary aspect of Duffey's discovery was that one of the Boatswainbird species was the world's largest pseudoscorpion. It was duly named *Garypus titanius*, and has a body up to 15 mm long.[31] During our overnight visit in 1995 we went up to the summit plateau after dark, and were fascinated to see the giant pseudoscorpions searching for their insect prey on the surface of the guano. Elsewhere pseudoscorpions are mainly tiny and live in small spaces inaccessible to larger predators. We imagine that the evolution of such large size by this species is related to the low diversity of other predatory animals on Ascension before 1501. This has enabled the ancestors of the giant pseudoscorpion to occupy an ecological niche on Ascension which is barred to its relatives in continental areas where there are dangerous enemies.

In the past the giant pseudoscorpion probably also occupied the seabird colonies on the main island of Ascension, but it is likely to have been exterminated there by mice or the formidable centipede *Scolopendra morsitans*. By good fortune, neither of these introduced species seem to have got to Boatswainbird Island during the period of the guano workings. We suggest that the future of *Garypus titanius*, a remarkable endemic species with a total range of less than five hectares, depends on strict control of human access to Boatswainbird Island, so as to minimize the risk of introducing mice, centipedes or other alien predators.

Surprisingly, we also found another apparently new pseudoscorpion during the short visit to Boatswainbird Island in 1995, bringing the total there to three endemic species. Since we had also found a new species of this group in a cave on the mainland in 1990, Ascension as a whole now has the remarkable tally of five endemic species of pseudoscorpions.[32] There is probably nowhere else in the world where this group – not noted for its high diversity – has a higher number of described endemic species than any other invertebrate order. As Duffey pointed out, the ancestors of the Ascension

---

[30] Landing on Boatswainbird Island is normally prohibited. In 1995 Philip and our New Zealand colleagues Brian and Paul Bell obtained permission for an overnight visit as part of the feasibility study on the eradication of feral cats and rats from the whole of Ascension Island.

[31] M. Beier (1960).

[32] J. Mahnert (1993).

Giant Pseudoscorpion and a Smaller Relative
Scale bar shows units of 0.5 mm

Figure 29
From N.P. Ashmole &
M.J. Ashmole (1997),
J. Biogeography.

pseudoscorpions are likely to have reached the island by hitch-hiking, attached to the plumage of seabirds or even the legs of insects.

Other interesting discoveries during our work on the clinker of Ascension were of springtails (Collembola), minute flightless insects which feed on a wide range of organic material including pollen and fungi. We found at least three new species, which seem to be closely related to each other and may have evolved on the island from a single colonising ancestor. Now, however, they have distinct ecological niches. One species is deep blue and is abundant on the shore; a second is pale grey and occurs on all the barren lava flows; and a third is colourless and eyeless, and lives in subterranean spaces.[33]

A group of flightless crickets (Mogoplistinae) showed a rather similar picture, again involving three species. One lives on the shore, one on lava flows, and the third was found underground, both in caves and in the deep crevices of the 'Lava Lake' at the foot of Sisters Peak.

Another intriguing discovery was a minute, white and blind spider, almost invisible on filmy webs deep in Packer's Hole Cave. This endemic species was considered sufficiently distinct to form a new genus, but seems most closely related to a northern hemisphere group which are well known as aeronauts: they travel on a silken thread that acts as a parachute and can keep the spider aloft for many hours in the right weather conditions.[34]

The psocids (or booklice) are minute insects which are hard to collect by hand and had not been found previously on Ascension; however, they were well represented in our traps. The most interesting group have reduced eyes and seem to be adapted to subterranean life; they represent a distinctive new genus in a subfamily which in all other parts of the world is very uniform. Some psocids are so small that they can travel long distances by drifting passively in the air, even if they are wingless, and the Ascension populations of psocids were probably founded in this way.[35]

The same mode of travel may also have been used by the ancestors of a new genus of mites (Acari) which we found on barren lava and ash. Microscopic examination of these minute animals showed that they feed on pollen and perhaps also lichen.

For some other invertebrates of Ascension Island, sea travel is more likely. One example is a new soil centipede that we found near the coast where driftwood and other flotsam tend to accumulate. Possibly this centipede species arrived relatively recently and the population may still be confined to the coast in this area. The springtails and crickets mentioned earlier may also have arrived by this route long ago.

The woodlice are also relevant here. Before our work, woodlouse experts thought that all the species on Ascension were introduced. However, one discovered by Duffey (in the genus *Niambia*) had never been found elsewhere, although it had relatives in Africa. When we discovered a new and closely related species it became more plausible that an ancestor of both had reached the island long ago and evolved to give rise to the

---

[33] Kenneth Christiansen (1998), who studied the springtail specimens, has been particularly intrigued to find that in the cave species the modifications to the claws that form part of the adaptation to cave life have followed a different evolutionary pathway from those seen in members of the same group elsewhere. Ascension seems to have provided an opportunity for an independent evolutionary 'experiment', parallel to that going on in various continental cave systems.

[34] P. Merrett & N.P. Ashmole (1997).

[35] Some of the psocids were a considerable surprise to the specialist in Geneva who studied our specimens C. Lienhard (1996). Apart from the new genus, one group appeared to belong to a species that had just been described – on the basis of a single specimen – from the Yucatán Peninsula in Mexico, while another individual has its only known close relatives in Chile.

two modern species.[36] Colonisation was probably by sea, but this is more certain in the case of *Littorophiloscia tropicalis*, found at Shelly Beach. This woodlouse is not endemic, being widespread on tropical coasts, and there is little doubt that the founders of the population arrived long ago as passengers on driftwood.

Another woodlouse is more of a puzzle: this is *Elumoides coecus*, a blind, white species, new to science, which we found in Chapel Grotto and Command Hill Caves. It is a member of an obscure group and its only known relatives are in Cameroon and the Indo-Pacific region; it may or may not be endemic to Ascension and we have little idea how its ancestors arrived.

One striking result of this work was the demonstration that even in the most barren parts of the desert lowlands of Ascension there is a community of minute animals inhabiting the vast network of underground spaces that permeate the lava flows and also the drifts of cinders and scoria covering some parts of the island.[37] We were able to show this by using specially developed pipe traps, which were driven 1-2 metres into the clinker and cinders (Plate 12). These traps caught several species previously found in caves: a pseudoscorpion, a springtail and the cave-adapted psocid.[38]

When we returned to Britain after our 1990 visit we were already confident that we could show that Ascension had a significant fauna of endemic invertebrate animals, derived from colonists which had reached the island long ago by natural means and had become adapted to life on barren lava flows and in caves. However, in wondering about how the ancestors of these animals had reached the island, we gradually found ourselves investigating the biology of all the invertebrate species known from Ascension, especially their means of dispersal.

Eventually, we became convinced that a substantial number of the non-endemic species, previously assumed to have been introduced by people, were likely to be natural colonists of the island. The evidence was only circumstantial, and lay in the fact that a disproportionate number of the species concerned were either well known as aerial migrants (or closely related to migrant species), or were salt-tolerant species likely to able to travel by sea.

Many cases are detailed in Chapter 15, but the locusts provide a convenient example of aerial colonists. Both the Desert Locust and the Tropical Migratory Locust are well known as long distance travellers, a swarm of the former recently even having been recorded crossing the Atlantic from east to west. The original vegetation of Ascension would have provided suitable though sparse food for these generalized herbivores, and we believe that both species colonised the island naturally. An example of probable colonists by sea is provided by the shore flies (family Ephydridae), three species of which occur on the beaches of Ascension; they are widely distributed on oceanic islands and probably reached Ascension by rafting.

We have recently published a complete analysis of the Ascension fauna, in which we show that out of the roughly 317 species of land animals known from the island,

---

[36] S. Taiti & F. Ferrara (1991).

[37] N.P. Ashmole & M.J. Ashmole (2000). Although people naturally pay most attention to the underground spaces that are large enough for a caver to enter, these are of only marginal importance to subterranean animals. It is the network of narrow cracks and crevices that are the prime habitat. In these situations, where they experience equable temperature and high humidity, animals have evolved adaptations for permanently subterranean life.

[38] Using the same equipment on St Helena we had generally found only soil animals, apparently because the subterranean spaces on that older island had gradually become filled up with silt. We suspect that the spaces are also absent in those eastern parts of Ascension where the rocks are a friable, hydrothermally altered trachyte.

some 29 are endemic (including the Ascension Frigatebird and two extinct landbirds) and about another 60 (including turtles and seabirds) are probably indigenous. About 80 others are considered to be of doubtful status, with the probability of natural colonisation and introduction roughly equal; the remainder are almost certainly introduced (Table 12).

We like to think that the picture of the fauna of Ascension that has emerged from the recent work would persuade Wollaston to revise his opinion on the entomological interest of the island. Although Ascension undoubtedly has many introduced species, it also has a set of indigenous species adapted to life in the peculiar habitats that it provides, some of which have undergone evolutionary changes sufficient for them to be recognized as endemic species or even genera.

The new results also suggest that the fauna of Ascension can help to increase understanding of the origin and evolution of island faunas in general. In the past, evolutionists have paid most attention to archipelagos such as the Galápagos and Hawaiian Islands, or to single ancient islands such as New Caledonia, Madeira and St Helena. In contrast to these, Ascension provides an intriguing example of a remote island at an early stage in the evolution of its own special fauna. It shows, in particular, that invertebrate animals can colonise and evolve into endemic species on barren lava flows and cinders, and also in caves, at a stage in the geological history of the island when few plants are established and vegetation has a very restricted distribution.

In a certain sense, Ascension also provides a snapshot of an island which is analogous to St Helena at an early stage in its development. We suspect that while it was young and still volcanically active, St Helena had a fauna comparable with that on Ascension today. Later, as woody plants became established, evolutionary opportunities arose for different kinds of animals to make a living on the island. Beetles – hardly represented in the native fauna of Ascension – will have reached St Helena and diversified, forming new species and occupying a wide variety of ecological niches. Gradually, they became dominant, and as similar adaptive radiations took place in other groups – for instance of plant-eating bugs – the ecosystem became more and more different from that which we see on Ascension today.

It is now clear, however, that similar processes are already at work on Ascension, with speciation and ecological diversification occurring – for instance – in the springtails, crickets, booklice and pseudoscorpions. We need not regret the low diversity of the Ascension fauna, but can make use of the insights that it provides into the development of richer communities elsewhere.

238

Table 12.   Summary of land animals with wild populations established on Ascension Island, now or in 1501

Vagrants and non-breeding visitors (and their parasites) are omitted.
Full details of the land fauna were published by N.P. Ashmole & M.J. Ashmole (1997).

GROUP Scientific and English names	Total species	Endemic species	Indigenous species	Doubtful species	Introduced species
VERTEBRATES					
MAMMALIA (mammals)	6	0	0	0	6
REPTILIA: CHELONIA (turtles)	2	0	2	0	0
REPTILIA: SQUAMATA (lizards)	2	0	0	0	2
AMPHIBIA (amphibians)	1	0	0	0	1
AVES (birds)	17 + 2 ext.	1 + 2 ext.	11	0	5
INVERTEBRATES: not Arthropoda					
TURBELLARIA (free-living flatworms)	1	0	0	0	1
MOLLUSCA: GASTROPODA (snails & slugs)	10	0	1	3	6
ANNELIDA: OLIGOCHAETA (earthworms)	6	1?	0	0	5
ARTHROPODA: not Insecta					
SCORPIONES (scorpions)	2	0	0	0	2
PSEUDOSCORPIONES (pseudoscorpions)	5	5	0	0	0
ARANEAE (spiders)	43	4	3	23	13
ACARI (mites & ticks)	9	c.2	1	5	1
CRUSTACEA (crustaceans)	17	3	2	2	10
DIPLOPODA (millipedes)	3	0	0	0	3
CHILOPODA (centipedes)	7	1	0	2	4
ARTHROPODA: INSECTA (insects)					
COLLEMBOLA (springtails or collembolans)	12	3	2	5	2
THYSANURA (thysanurans)	3	0	0	0	3
ORTHOPTERA (grasshoppers & crickets)	9	c.3	4	1	1
DERMAPTERA (earwigs)	1	0	0	0	1
ISOPTERA (termites)	1	0	0	0	1
BLATTODEA (cockroaches)	5	0	0	1	4
EMBIOPTERA (web-spinners)	2	0	0	0	2
THYSANOPTERA (thrips)	1	0	1	0	0
HEMIPTERA: HETEROPTERA (bugs)	9	0	3	1	5
HEMIPTERA:HOMOPTERA (hoppers, aphids, scale insects)	10	0	2	2	6
PSOCOPTERA (psocids)	8	1	3	4	0
PHTHIRAPTERA (lice)	1	0	1	0	0
COLEOPTERA (beetles)	41	0	3	5	33
NEUROPTERA (lacewings)	1	0	0	1	0
HYMENOPTERA (parasitic wasps, ants, bees & wasps)	17	1	0	2	14
LEPIDOPTERA (butterflies & moths)	34	2	11	13	8
SIPHONAPTERA (fleas)	1	0	1	0	0
DIPTERA (flies)	28	0	11	9	8
TOTALS	**315 + 2 ext.**	**27 + 2 ext.**	**62**	**79**	**147**

Chapter 13

The major habitats on land today

The coast and coastal pools

The northeast and especially the south coast of Ascension are exposed to heavy wave action under the influence of the South East Trade Winds. The west coast is sheltered, but subject to the effects of oceanic rollers from the southwest or northwest, which occur without warning at any time of year and persist for a few days. These enormous waves tend to scour the shore, both directly and by rolling around loose rocks and sand. The submerged slope area surrounding the island is also strikingly barren, with only rock, sand and rubble.[1] This situation, together with the small tidal range, steeply shelving shores and simple geography, leads to Ascension lacking many of the habitats that are found in (or just below) the inter-tidal zone of many other tropical islands: there are no lagoons, estuaries, sea-grass beds, mangroves or coral reefs. The absence of reefs, together with the extreme isolation of the island, perhaps explains why only seventy-one species of fish have been recorded from around the shore, which is a very low number for a tropical island. Eleven of the fish are endemic, and a further twelve are known only from Ascension and St Helena.

Although the fish diversity is low, one species is extraordinarily abundant. This is the Blackfish *Melichthys niger*, which will be seen in large numbers around the pierhead at Georgetown by anyone arriving at the island by ship. The Blackfish is a widespread tropical species, but elsewhere it does not seem to play such a dominant ecological role. It is a member of the triggerfish family (Balistidae), which are mainly carnivores. Blackfish, however, are omnivores, eagerly taking scraps thrown from boats, but also grazing algae off the rocks; they also effectively clean weed from the hulls of ships anchored offshore.[2]

Since weed provides important shelter and resources for many kinds of fish, the low diversity of fish species as well the general barrenness of the underwater rock surfaces may be partly caused by the activities of the Blackfish. However, one could also speculate – in a somewhat circular argument – that the abundance of Blackfish at Ascension is a result of the low fish diversity: there may be few effective competitors in the alga-eating ecological niche.

The Blackfish doubtless also have a major influence on the marine invertebrate community. In particular, 'sessile' animals (those that remain fixed in one place on the rocks) must have difficulty in establishing themselves in areas grazed clean by Blackfish. Most of the rocky surfaces in shallow water are covered by a layer of

[1] R. Lubbock (1980).

[2] G.F. Simmons, leader of a biological collecting expedition from the Cleveland Museum in the 1920s, recounted how their vessel, the windjammer *Blossom*, reached Ascension encumbered by a heavy growth of weed, in spite of the fact that she was sheathed with copper to minimize 'fouling' by animals and plants. Within a short time the weed was removed and the copper gave the appearance of having been burnished by the Blackfish. The effect of the Blackfish on algal growth was also unintentionally demonstrated by Bernard Stonehouse in an experiment during the BOU expedition in the 1950s. He suspended glass slides in the sea at Comfortless Cove in an attempt to monitor seasonal changes. Slides protected from Blackfish by wire mesh grew a heavy, grass-like crop of weed in a matter of days, but unprotected slides bore little more than a faint green scum and clearly showed the tooth-marks of the Blackfish which had scraped them clean.

Anchialine shrimps in a cave by a coral pool

Figure 30
Diagram adapted from
L.G. Abele &
B.E. Felgenhauer (1985).
J.Crustacean Biology.

calcareous algae, which tend to cement together the rubble into a uniform surface that does not support a great diversity of animal life.

Nonetheless, recent studies have shown that there are far more species of invertebrates in shallow water at Ascension than had previously been recorded. For instance, workers from the Smithsonian Institution in Washington have increased the number of decapod crustaceans (the crabs, lobsters and shrimps) known from the island to 74 species, of which 14 are endemic. Another North American biologist has identified 27 species of marine amphipods around Ascension.[3]

Some of these fish and invertebrates can be found in the rock pools that are present in several accessible sites around the coast. One of the most impressive is a large circular pool, connected to the sea by an arch, at Deadman's Beach between North East Point and Hummock Point; beside it is a blowhole that can be spectacular in rough weather.

Just inland from Shelly Beach to the east of Mars Bay is a group of somewhat different pools which are of extraordinary interest to biologists (Plate 16). These represent an 'anchialine' habitat, a term referring to pools and water-filled crevices that have no surface connection with the sea but are salt or brackish and are influenced by the tides.[4] The pools at Shelly Beach are about 50-100 m inland but are evidently connected to the sea underground, since some of them vanish almost entirely at low tide; the water in them is probably filtered through the bank of shell sand on the beach before reaching the fissures in the lava. These tiny pools are the only known habitat for two particularly interesting species of shrimp, which are found nowhere else in the world; they also contain a number of other endemic animals, as well as clusters of the striking globular green alga *Valonia ventricosa* and an interesting coral in the genus *Favia*. The shrimps probably survive because no predatory fish have managed to get into this habitat.

The presence of shrimps in the pools was recorded by John Packer in the 1968 edition of his *Ascension Handbook*, but the first collections were apparently made in 1970 by Douglas S. Rogers, an employee of Pan American World Airways and at the time Curator of the Fort Hayes Museum of the Ascension Historical Society. The first species to be found was named *Typhlatya rogersi* in honour of Mr Rogers. This tiny shrimp is pale pinkish and semi-transparent, and is abundant in the pools. The remarkable fact about it is that its close relatives – the other members of the genus *Typhlatya* – live mainly in freshwater subterranean habitats, especially on islands in the Caribbean. The second species was collected by Mr Rogers later in the same year and named *Procaris ascensionis* (Figure 30). It was the first known member of a new family of shrimps, but related species have now been found in similar situations in Bermuda and Hawai'i. It is bright orange in colour and is larger but less common in the pools than *Typhlatya*, of which it is a predator (Plate 23).

[3] R.B. Manning & F.A. Chace, Jr. (1990) and C.K. Biernbaum (1996)

[4] F.A. Chace, Jr. & R.B. Manning (1972).

The origins of the Ascension populations of *Typhlatya* and *Procaris* are quite obscure. Our guess, however, is that both these shrimps will eventually be found in crevices on the slopes of the submarine part of the Ascension volcano, and that related populations will prove to occur on seamounts in the area and on the submarine slopes of other volcanic islands. These shrimps can be considered part of the fauna of the groundwater, which in this situation is almost pure seawater which has penetrated into the bedrock of Ascension from the coast. The late Jan Stock also searched for groundwater animals on Ascension and, with a colleague, described an endemic and blind isopod (a relative of the woodlice) found deep in the wet sand at a beach near Hummock Point.[5]

Larger animals can also be found on the sandy beaches of Ascension. Many of these beaches superficially resemble battlefields, with the entire surface covered with craters and the slope up from the sea scarred by what look like miniature tank tracks. These are, of course, made by Green Turtles, which have travelled from the other side of the Atlantic to lay their eggs in their traditional rookeries. The male and female turtles mate in the water just offshore, but only the female comes out on land. She lumbers up the beach at night during the laying season (mainly January-May), spends several hours digging a pit for the eggs above the high tide mark and then leaves them to be incubated by the warm sand.

Boatswainbird Island

Boatswainbird Island is one of the famous seabird islands of the world. However, it is invisible from most parts of the main island, so that many people see it only as they arrive or depart by plane or ship. The energetic can gain superb views of the islet from Weather Post, Powers Peak or Letterbox (Plate 10), and a boat trip around it is an unforgettable experience. Landing is now prohibited to safeguard the breeding birds.

Boatswainbird Island is precipitous, with more or less vertical cliffs interrupted by steep slopes and rock-strewn gullies. There is an undulating summit plateau, formed by a thin cap of basalt that has protected the underlying soft trachyte from weathering. At the southern extremity of the islet there is a natural arch and buttress on which the guano company constructed a concrete landing platform in the 1920s. It was on this that the members of the BOU expedition in 1957-59 constructed a hut, in which Philip and his colleagues lived for up to a week at a time while studying the seabirds (Plate 11). The guano company also cut a winding path for their workers up the eastern cliffs, which made access to the plateau relatively easy. During the 19th century visitors had climbed the steep southern slopes with the help of ropes and cables installed by the Royal Marines.

Boatswainbird Island lacks vegetation, but the animal communities are diverse and spectacular. Eight species of seabirds breed in large numbers, free from the menace of cats or rats. For almost all of these birds, the populations are remnants of much larger ones that previously had major breeding colonies on the main island of Ascension. Boatswainbird Island is effectively full of birds, with the different types of potential nesting sites divided among the species according to their particular adaptations.[6]

The summit plateau is occupied mainly by Ascension Frigatebirds and Masked Boobies (Plate 16). The frigatebirds nest mainly in dense groups on rough and sloping ground;

[5] R. Vonk & J.H. Stock (1991).

[6] Accounts of the various seabird species are in Chapter 15, and fuller information can be obtained from Ashmole et al. (1994).

243

scattered pairs also occupy slopes and ravines on the sides of the island. The Masked Boobies breed in closely packed colonies on the relatively flat areas.[7] Brown Boobies nest mainly on the steep slopes of the island, generally in small groups. Red-footed Boobies are present in only tiny numbers and breeding attempts are uncommon; the one nest found by the BOU party was on a narrow ledge in a steep cliff-top gully and was a substantial construction of twigs, collected on the main island (Plate 19). This breeding attempt was unsuccessful, but young have evidently been raised from time to time in recent years. The Red-billed and White-tailed Tropicbirds compete for nest cavities on the sides of the island, often under boulders or in narrow rock crevices.

The Madeiran Storm-petrels nest in tiny holes on the sides of the island, and sometimes also crevices at the back of cavities already occupied by tropicbirds. When Dick Allan was studying the petrels during the BOU expedition, he found that they readily occupied plywood nest-boxes, making it much easier to monitor the progress of breeding attempts. Once or twice during the expedition we heard calls of a shearwater at night, and in March 1959 an Audubon's Shearwater was caught by Dick Allan in a complex rock cavity at the edge of the summit plateau. As mentioned in Chapter 12, the fossil evidence indicates that a breeding population used to be present on Ascension, but it is not known whether breeding ever occurs now.

Black Noddies nest in large colonies on the cliffs of Boatswainbird Island. Many of the ledges that they occupy are really too small, or slope outwards, but the birds (especially males) spend much time collecting feathers in the weeks before breeding. Furthermore, the adults regularly defaecate while standing or squatting on the ledges and facing the cliff, so that the nests tend to become wider and safer by accumulation of guano on the outer rim.

When Philip was studying the Black Noddies in 1958-59 he was able to find a hundred or so accessible nests on small cliffs in various places towards the top of the island, at which breeding success and development of the chicks could be studied. For behavioural observations, however, Mike Cullen and he used a colony of about 200 pairs on an inland-facing cliff. These nests were not accessible, but using a series of black-and-white photographs, a panorama of the cliff was assembled and mounted on a board, and the nests were numbered on this. About 100 birds were caught with a long-handled net and individually marked with coloured plastic leg rings, so that their relationships and association with particular ledges could be monitored.

White Terns also nest abundantly on Boatswainbird Island.[8] They are adapted to nesting on ledges smaller than those used by the Black Noddies; the only requirement appears to be that the egg can be lodged on the rock surface. The adults use obvious caution when laying, settling on or leaving the egg, and successfully incubate on ledges that appear quite inadequate on first sight. The chicks have sharp claws which enable them to cling to the rock, and can hang upside down from a finger when newly hatched. Brown Noddies do not breed on Boatswainbird Island, but a few Wideawakes breed on the summit plateau, normally in places where upstanding rocks form a sheltered recess.

---

[7] For frigatebirds, exposure to the wind is crucial, since their legs are so short and weak that they can barely walk. Their bodies are light and wing area enormous, giving very low wing loading, so they can normally take off simply by facing into the wind and spreading their wings. However, a naturalist working for the US Fish & Wildlife Service once told Philip how he had visited one of the uninhabited western Hawaiian Islands and found a number of frigatebirds on their nests on low scrubby vegetation, all with their wings outstretched and facing the same way, and all dead. He surmised that there must have been a complete calm lasting several days, preventing the birds from launching themselves into the air and leading to their death – probably from dehydration.

[8] D.F. Dorward (1963).

Apart from seabirds, the main interest of Boatswainbird Island lies in its invertebrate animals. The saturation of almost the whole surface of the island with seabird guano provides a special habitat to which some arachnids, crickets and beetles are evidently well adapted. Another possibly indigenous species on the islet is the moth *Tinea subalbidella* which belong to the clothes-moth family and has a diet including feathers and dead insects.

The channel between Boatswainbird Island and the main island evidently formed long before the discovery of Ascension by people, so that Boatswainbird Island has been largely protected from the disturbance caused to the rest of Ascension throughout the period since 1501. Cats, rats, mice and centipedes seem not to have reached the islet, but there are introduced cockroaches and one species of ant. It is probably because of the relative absence of alien predators that Boatswainbird Island still has a population of the giant pseudoscorpion, as discussed in Chapter 12.

Stacks and coastal cliffs

In addition to Boatswainbird Island, some 14 stacks are sufficiently separated from the main island to provide seabirds with nesting places that are safe from cats; they are indicated on the main map. The stacks are now the main breeding sites of the Brown Noddy, the only seabird species that is not normally found on Boatswainbird Island. Most of the stacks are small and low, so the noddies often have their eggs washed away when the rollers are severe.[9]

The stacks are also important breeding sites for the Brown Booby. Unfortunately, the birds sometimes roost on the mainland nearby, and the bones and feathers that can be found littering the lava show that they are often taken by cats. Masked Boobies breed in very small numbers on White Rock and White Bluff in Cocoanut Bay and possibly a few of the other southern stacks (Plate 15). Individuals of this species that roost on the mainland are also vulnerable to cats, a fact brought home to Douglas Dorward and Philip when they disturbed a cat from beside a freshly killed adult near Cocoanut Bay in 1958. Red-footed Boobies can also occasionally be seen on the stacks. During our 1990 visit a few birds (including a juvenile) were present on a stack near English Bay, and a pair were seen copulating. The stacks may be as important as Boatswainbird Island in maintaining the tiny population of this species on Ascension.

A few of the other seabirds breed on the stacks in small numbers: Black Noddies have colonies on stacks in Cocoanut and Pillar Bays, and both Red-billed and White-tailed Tropicbirds also sometimes nest there; these birds, however, have larger populations on the mainland cliffs. The stacks may also have interesting invertebrate populations, but these have not yet been studied.

Some of the coastal cliffs of Ascension are also important habitats. Although the lava flows in the western part of the island generally slope gently down to the sea, the eastern high part is largely bounded by cliffs, and these are more than 100 m high in places. The ecological importance of the cliffs has increased in the past few centuries, since they offer a degree of protection for the seabirds from feral cats and rats.

Black Noddies are the most abundant seabirds on the mainland cliffs. They have their colonies principally on the cliffs facing Boatswainbird Island and on the south coast between Letterbox and Pillar Bay; the total population on the main island may exceed that on Boatswainbird Island. Brown Noddies are present in only small

---

[9] D.F. Dorward & N.P. Ashmole (1963).

numbers, mainly near South East Bay (Plate 16). White Terns also breed on the mainland cliffs, but mainly close to Boatswainbird Island.

Apart from these terns, the Brown Boobies nest in small numbers on the eastern cliffs, and both Red-billed and White-tailed Tropicbirds have nests scattered along the eastern and southern cliffs. The Ascension Frigatebird does not nest on the cliffs as far as we know, but there are persistent roosts, especially at Crater Cliff and a few other places in the area of Letterbox and South East Bay (Plate 16). Masked Boobies do not nest on the cliffs themselves, but occasionally attempt to nest just inland from them; almost always their young – if they even hatch – fall prey to feral cats (Plate 13).

The lava desert

Although many people may find the volcanic landscape of the lowlands forbidding on first sight, we would challenge anyone to be near Sisters Peak at sunset – avoiding the numerous aerials – and be unmoved by its austere beauty (Plate 9). Although the main desert areas are in the west of Ascension, there is a strip of similar basaltic terrain along the south coast. The Letterbox peninsula in the eastern extremity of the island is a somewhat different desert, based mainly on whitish trachytic rock but in some places with a conspicuous overlay of dark basaltic lava recalling chocolate icing.

When formed, lava and cinder habitats are totally barren, and in dry climates such as that of Ascension large areas may remain almost devoid of vegetation for thousands of years; eventually, however, they are colonised by plants, and this process is accelerated by the introduction of alien species adapted to similar climates elsewhere. Apart from this, the main agents of change are the occasional periods of intense rainfall. These cause erosion and leave shallow gullies, which are often floored with fine cinders that provide much more favourable seedbeds for plants than the surrounding rock.

Several indigenous plants can still be found in these gullies, for instance the sedge *Cyperus appendiculatus* and the grass *Aristida adscensionis* (Plate 28), along with the straggling Hogweed *Commicarpus helenae* (Plate 29). The last specimen of the extinct endemic shrub *Oldenlandia* (ex *Hedyotis*) *adscensionis* was apparently collected in 1899 from a plant in one of the gullies near Sisters.

Nowadays a variety of introduced plants spring up in the gullies after rain, but many of them later succumb to drought. Among the more noticeable species are the Yellow Thistle, Castor Oil and the leguminous shrub *Leucaena leucocephala*, recognizable by its spherical white flowers. Another widespread species, both in the gullies and elsewhere, is *Waltheria indica*, a spreading shrub with leaves reminiscent of alder and small yellow flowers in dense, hairy clusters (Plate 16).

Away from the gullies the endemic Ascension Spurge and indigenous Purslane are still present in scattered colonies. The spurge colony that is easiest to find is on the southwest face of South Gannet Hill; the plant has also colonised banks of cinders formed when the road was bulldozed up the hill, showing that it can thrive on steep and loose cindery slopes. Another attractive colony is in an open rocky area inland from Hummock Point (Plate 16). The spurge plants are attractive to insects, and among the ones we found on them are several probably indigenous species. These included flies belonging to two families known for efficient dispersal (Ephydridae and Chloropidae) and also the small heteropteran bug *Tropiconabis capsiformis*, a predator which has relatives on many oceanic islands.

After wet periods large parts of the lowland deserts are transformed by the growth of the grass *Enneapogon cenchroides*. For instance, in May 1984, two months after more than 300 mm (12 inches) of rain fell in the lowlands, the whole of the island appeared from a passing ship to be covered in hay. When we arrived in May 1995 the situation was similar, with pale gold sheets of grass in the more open areas of the lowlands. When such an episode is followed by a period of drought, the grasses and opportunistic alien herbs die back and much of the land again takes on the aspect of desert.

If one is on the island after a wet period, several kinds of insects can be found swarming around the grasses (Plate 23). Most conspicuous are the finger-sized Desert Locust and the somewhat smaller Tropical Migratory Locust, both of them notorious as pests on the African continent. Also common is the cricket *Gryllus bimaculatus*, which is shiny black with two creamy patches at the base of the wings. All these species are capable of long distance aerial migrations and probably reached Ascension naturally. Under the normal dry conditions both these and some smaller grass-feeding insects are inconspicuous, but even in barren areas a walker will sometimes disturb a locust which takes off and makes a long, wavering flight over the clinker, almost like a flying fish on land. After rains all these insects reproduce rapidly, and occasionally reach plague proportions.

The surface lava and cinders of this part of the island, and the caves and other subterranean spaces, form habitats for the indigenous insects and other invertebrate animals discussed in Chapter 12. These barren habitats are typical of young volcanic islands such as Ascension, but by the time an island is as old as St Helena they have almost entirely disappeared. None of these animals will be noticed by the casual observer, since they are mostly nocturnal. Furthermore, we found that they occurred mainly in the most barren and jagged areas where walking is extremely difficult. These include the lava flow east of Mars Bay, the black flow west of Sisters Peaks and a large area between the north side of Sisters and the coast near Porpoise Point. In dry seasons there is virtually no vegetation here, although the occasional rain permits the temporary growth of scattered grasses and other plants. There are animals, however, and turning over loose rocks – for instance in the area around the inland pools near Shelly Beach – may reveal a few endemic insects such as tiny springtails (Collembola) or even a soft-bodied mogoplistine cricket.

In the areas with more vegetation it is easy to find some of the invertebrates that are either certainly or possibly introduced. The first category includes the ubiquitous American cockroach *Periplaneta americana*, the large centipede *Scolopendra morsitans* (Plate 23) and the American wasp *Polistes fuscatus*. Similarly, the bristletails, which can often be seen for an instant when one turns over a rock, occur even in the most barren areas, but their apparent absence from Boatswainbird Island suggests that they have been introduced to Ascension since 1501.

Various kinds of spiders – some of them probably indigenous – can also be seen in the lowlands. Among bushes one is likely to come across orb-webs of *Araneus theisi*, one of only two spiders on Ascension that make this type of circular web, with an elegant spiral superimposed on a set of strong radial threads. Under rocky overhangs there is a chance of finding the tough, filmy web of the Brown Widow spider, which has a globular body and is variable in colour, but normally with an hour-glass shaped marking on the underside which is visible if the spider is hanging in its web; this species can inflict a poisonous (though not lethal) bite. Other less distinctive kinds of spiders are to be found mainly under loose rocks.

Introduced landbirds are fairly scarce in this area. Canaries and Waxbills can generally be seen around the houses, while the Mynas are more widely distributed and are often seen along the coast. In Georgetown there is, at the time of writing, a colony of about nine House Sparrows. The introduced gecko (Plate 17) and lizard also occur in these dry lowlands.

In the south of the island at Mars Bay and eastwards as far as South Red Crater are the Wideawake fairs. During the peak activity time these are truly impressive, with clouds of wheeling birds and an extraordinary clamour of the characteristic 'wide-a-wake' calls. The nests are barely perceptible scrapes in the ground, each with a single egg; they are closely spaced, with densities sometimes as high as five per square metre.

Careful visitors avoid walking into Wideawake colonies, since it is all too easy to step on an egg, and panicking birds can also cause losses. When hatching starts the danger is even greater, as the downy chicks can bolt away from the nest-scrapes, and are then pecked unmercifully by any adults that they pass. Probably this behaviour – surprising at first sight – has evolved so as to minimize the risk of accidentally adopting a 'foreign' chick and thus wasting effort in rearing an individual carrying the genes of another pair of adults.

As discussed in Chapter 12, Wideawakes in this relatively seasonless environment are not tied to a yearly cycle but return to the island to breed every 9.6 months. A visit to the island during breeding would enable a visitor to see the huge colony at Mars Bay, but a return at the same time in a later year might lead to disappointment because of the gradual progression of the breeding calendar.

Visiting a Wideawake fair, one can hardly fail to notice the corpses of adult terns scattered around, some fragmented and dry, others fresh and gory (Plate 15). These are the birds taken by the feral cats, voracious predators that are rarely seen but tend to collect around the fairs when the terns are present. At the start of the breeding period, when the Wideawakes first settle at night on the future nesting grounds, one can sometimes go out at night and catch in the beam of a torch a series of pairs of eyes of hungry cats, waiting for the first birds to settle. Birds that fall prey to cats on the first few nights are eaten almost totally, often with only wing bones, quills and perhaps a foot to tell the tale. Within a week of the first night landing, however, the cats are sated, taking only a few mouthfuls from the abdomen or breast. The Wideawake corpses are gradually consumed by dermestid beetles which are common under rocks in the fairs.

The middle levels

On the trip from Georgetown or the airfield towards Green Mountain, the sparse and often desiccated vegetation of the lowlands changes suddenly on the approach to Two Boats village or the Travellers Hill camp. This change occurs at a height of about 200 m, evidently due partly to the somewhat higher rainfall above this level. The geology is also different; climbing, one leaves behind most of the raw basalt lava and enters a region where much of the underlying rock is trachyte, although this is overlain in many areas by pyroclastic fragments.

This middle zone, extending from about 200 m to 600 m and comprising the foothills of the mountain, offers pleasant walks with magnificent views, but the vegetation is almost entirely unnatural; the original plants are extinct or scarce and species introduced during the last two centuries now dominate the landscape, as described in Chapter 11. In many areas the vegetation is still highly dynamic, as shown by comparison of some of our photographs taken in 1958 and in the 1990s (Plate 14).

On both the southwest and northeast flanks of the mountain there are areas of open ground, for instance between Grazing Valley and Middleton and between North East Cottage and Upper Valley Crater. The grassland is often dominated by Greasy Grass, a tropical African species with an aromatic and somewhat musty scent that is a memorable feature of midday walks in these areas. Another key species is Guava. A quick survey that we did in 1995 showed that it dominated the vegetation in large areas on the southern and western slopes of the mountain, for instance around Palmers, Castle Hill and the old NASA site by the Devil's Ashpit.

In many places, but perhaps especially in the grassland on the northeastern slopes, Bermuda Cedar is a dominant element in the vegetation. Its seeds are probably spread by the Mynas, and it might come to form a continuous belt of evergreen forest in the most humid, eastern part of the middle zone. Another tree that is becoming important is Casuarina, which has its main stronghold around Two Boats and near the road from there to North East Bay; it is spreading naturally, and may eventually make as great an impact on the landscape of the drier parts of the middle zone as Bermuda Cedar in the higher and moister parts. On the other side of the mountain, just east of Palmers, is a group of Norfolk Island Pines, which are now regenerating freely; smaller numbers of this fine tree can be seen at higher levels on the mountain.

The only native bird easily seen in the middle zone is the White Tern; it breeds in trees in Cricket Valley and on cliffs near Powers Peak and at Middleton. The Francolin can be seen or heard as low as the Devil's Riding School and as high as the Devil's Ashpit. Some introduced songbirds have their strongholds in this zone; Canaries are common, and Averdavats can be seen drinking in gardens at Two Boats village.

Few native invertebrates are conspicuous in the middle zone, although when a visiting entomologist ran a 'light trap' to attract nocturnal moths, he caught a fair number of species, including several that had not been found on the island previously. The moth family Noctuidae was particularly well represented – these strong-flying moths have probably colonised the island naturally.

Landcrabs – or at least their shells – can be found almost anywhere on Ascension, but are especially abundant at middle levels in the east of the island (Plate 23). Landcrabs are nocturnal animals, normally spending the day in burrows, but they can sometimes be found under bushes or in the open in daytime. Rats are also common in the middle zone and Lionel S. Bartlett, the Resident Magistrate from 1934 to 1936, commented in a manuscript in the Fort Hayes Museum that: "*In many cases, the crabs, which have extremely powerful claws, disposes of the rat by breaking its back*". However he then went on to give an eye-witness account of an encounter with a different outcome:

> "*A rat had apparently surprised a crab in the open, and the latter was, therefore, unable to adopt the usual tactics of defending its rear by backing against a rock or tree. Circling around the crab, and feinting attacks, the rat kept its victim very much on the move – a sudden rush, and an equally rapid retreat, resulted in damage to the crabs eyes, which are, of course, rather prominent, another dash, and one of the powerful nippers was snapped off. The fight was then hopeless from the point of view of the crab. The second claw was removed, and the disabled crab was at the mercy of the rat, who methodically gnawed through the hard shell of its disarmed opponent, and proceeded to make a meal of the soft interior.*"

There are also interactions between crabs and rabbits. A 19th century writer reported that the larger landcrabs: "*steal the young rabbits from their holes and devour them*". Another observer gave a first-hand account of an occasion when he was out hunting and a very young rabbit that fled from him and went down a hole, was promptly killed by the landcrab that was already in it.

Green Mountain

The upper part of Green Mountain, from about 600 m to the summit at 859 m, is a moist region where there is now luxuriant plant cover which in places amounts to a cloud-forest. Before the arrival of humans the vegetation here consisted largely of ferns, and although some of these survive, the dominant plants today are almost entirely introduced. We have spent little time here, since although it is attractive and pleasantly cool after the desert lowlands, it represents a wholly artificial ecosystem in which a host of alien plants are competing for space.

Right at the top of the mountain there is a dew pond (Plate 10), where imported *Xenopus* toads have survived for many years. The pond also has water lilies, and is surrounded by a dense grove of bamboo. There is much rain up here, and the path has been churned into a mud slide by people visiting the peak, especially during the annual race up Green Mountain. The ridge just below the bamboos provides magnificent panoramic views of the lower parts of the island, especially to the north.

Getting a feel for the vegetation at a slightly lower level is easy, since three paths have been cut into the steep sides of the mountain (Plate 14). Elliot's Path goes right round at a little over 700 m; it was cut in 1840 to link the mountain settlement with lookout posts to the east. Rupert's, built later, runs lower down on the north face of the mountain, giving access to pastures beyond North East Cottage; a branch continues round the east end of the mountain at about 550 m to a tank above Castle Hill and eventually connects with a track coming down Breakneck Valley. Cronk's Path, built in about 1920, leads from the gardens near the Red Lion to Northeast Cottage.

On a misty walk along Elliot's Path in 1995 we saw a rat eating the fruit of a screwpine, which was one of the earliest trees introduced to the island. Another tree doing well at this level is Cape Yew. Other similarities with the introduced flora of St Helena include the presence of several species of Buddleia and of the Cape Gooseberry. The genus *Kalanchoe*, a group of succulent plants related to houseleeks which occur only very locally on St Helena, includes one species that is widespread on the mountain on Ascension and another probably spreading at middle levels. Guava also occurs at this level, growing much taller than at lower altitudes.

Few traces of the original vegetation of the mountain survive. The only endemic flowering plant here is the tiny tussocky grass *Sporobolus caespitosus*, which can be found in a few places on the northern and eastern slopes where bare rock or cinders are exposed to strong winds or mist. Easier to find is the indigenous and perhaps endemic fern *Marattia purpurascens*, with fronds over a metre long, which occurs among the bamboos near the peak and also in a few places on the high eastern slopes. The stagmoss *Psilotum nudum* (Plate 32), which has bare, branching green stems with orange brown tips, occurs mainly in the east, around the transition between the middle zone and the high part of the mountain; it is probably indigenous to Ascension, and also occurs in the Cape Verde Islands. Several other indigenous species of ferns and mosses can be found on the mountain, but are not so easy to identify.

Chapter 14

Conservation and ecological restoration

Ascension has undergone extensive change in the last 50 years. Hills have been removed or decapitated, giant domes and radar dishes have sprouted on volcanic craters, forests of antennae have appeared on barren lava fields, geometric arrays of buildings have materialized in improbable places, and hundreds of acres of land have disappeared under tarmac. There has also been an accumulation of rusting steel scrap and other junk, in spite of the attempts of successive Administrators to ensure that organisations bringing equipment to the island also clear it up.

None of these human impacts, however, have been as far-reaching as biological ones that started 500 years ago and are still in progress. These have led to devastation of the native bird populations and elimination of almost all of the original vegetation. In spite of the scale of the irreparable damage already done, there are still good reasons for developing conservation and restoration initiatives on the island. This is mainly because Ascension is a unique seabird and turtle island. It lies right in the middle of the tropical South Atlantic and is the only speck of land where seabirds and turtles from a vast expanse of ocean can come to rest and breed. The introduction of alien mammals by humans has denied many species of seabirds access to their traditional nesting grounds, and has enormously reduced the size of their populations. Only removal of the predators holds the potential to remedy this situation.

Apart from the issues relating to the seabird populations, the main conservation priorities concern the volcanic landscapes, the native vegetation, the turtles and the invertebrate animals (marine conservation is a separate matter which we do not consider here). The volcanic landscapes are of special value because the youth of the island and the aridity of the lowlands have left spectacular geological features largely exposed to view. The vegetation of the mountain was never properly described and is now almost lost, but the Ascension Spurge, some endemic ferns and a few other species need more effective protection. The Green Turtle population is flourishing, but vigilance is needed. The interest of the native fauna lies mainly in the insects and other invertebrate animals of barren lava and cave habitats which demonstrate an early stage in the development of an island ecosystem; they are at risk mainly from ecological changes in the lowlands.

The main difficulty with conservation initiatives on Ascension lies in maintaining continuity of effort. The high staff turnover in all the organisations impedes the development of a conservation ethos; there is a general lack of awareness – both on Ascension and elsewhere – of the uniqueness of the island and the importance of caring for its native flora and fauna. In the same way, education in local environmental issues is sporadic, depending upon the teachers of the time.

Nonetheless, many individuals who live on Ascension for a period are keenly appreciative of the wildlife, and a few people have actively stimulated the interest of others. The Ascension Heritage Society (previously the Ascension Island Historical Society) has a small museum and has been the focus for interest in natural history.

Recently, a conservation management plan for the island has been prepared by A.R. Pickup for the Royal Society for the Protection of Birds, building on the suggestions made over many years. This is intended as a prelude to implementation of a coherent scheme for the ecological restoration of Ascension Island, based primarily on the elimination of feral cats and rats and control of the invasive Mexican Thorn.

Protection of volcanic landscapes

The need for policies to protect the outstanding geological features of Ascension Island has been recognised belatedly. Decades after analogous landscapes in other parts of the world had been protected as National Parks (for instance in the Galápagos and on Lanzarote) disfiguring development continued apace on Ascension, apparently without any serious attempt at environmental impact assessment; neither was there any attempt to control the importation or spread of alien plants. From the 1970s onwards, K.E.L. Simmons expressed concern about these issues in unpublished reports to the Royal Society. In a consultancy report in 1995 we suggested that since the geology of Ascension Island was of outstanding interest, its scoria cones and craters, lava flows and caves deserved preservation.[1]

The various threats to geological features were reviewed in the management plan for the island. They fall into two main groups. First, there is the physical damage caused by people, either in the course of construction, by tipping and littering, or as a result of recreational activities (including the formation of prominent paths up cinder cones). Now that attention is focused on these dangers, there is a chance that some preventive action can be taken.

The second group of threats relates to alteration of landscapes by expansion of alien vegetation, including the deliberate planting of trees and the donkey-mediated spread of Mexican Thorn. It is obviously impracticable to prevent the further spread of many kinds of introduced plants on Ascension. We suggest, however, that urgent action should be taken to keep Sisters Peak free of alien trees. This mountain is one of the youngest manifestations of volcanic activity on the island and the 300-metre high cone rising from the lava desert is of great visual importance in the landscape (Plate 9). There is a well-marked path up Sisters, but the cone is otherwise unmodified except for the invasion of introduced vegetation and in particular Casuarina, which we understand was intentionally planted. These trees are beginning to alter the spectacular skyline of Sisters and there is a strong case for their immediate removal.

The Mexican Thorn poses threats not only to the landscape but also to native plants and animals, so we consider its future here. A biological control expert, Simon Fowler, visited Ascension in 1996 and 1997 and wrote a report in 1998 on the status and potential control of the thorn. He concluded that the anticipated future spread of the plant was likely to have serious impacts on the nesting sites of the Green Turtles, on the nature reserves at Hummock Point and Mars Bay (the latter with a major Wideawake fair), and on the rare Ascension Spurge. Fowler also suggested that eradication of feral cats and rats, so as to allow re-establishment of seabird colonies on the main island, would become much more difficult as the spread of the thorn continued, and that in the long run it could make the sites of old seabird colonies unsuitable for future nesting.

Fowler advocated mechanical removal and the use of herbicides, but argued that in the long run biological control methods would have to form part of the programme required to control the plant. He arranged for two species of seed-feeding beetles to be introduced, and suggested that other control organisms could probably be found. It

---

[1] B.D Bell & P. Ashmole (1995).

seems clear to us, however, that the Mexican Thorn is unlikely to be brought under control while its seeds can be spread so easily by donkeys (and to some extent sheep).

In early 2000 the Administrator invited the public to express views on possible control or removal of the donkeys. We appreciate that these animals are valued by people as a traditional feature of Ascension. However, because of their effect as dispersers of the Mexican Thorn, and given the importance of the conservation issues discussed below, we believe that elimination of donkeys (and probably also sheep) or their permanent confinement within an enclosure is unavoidable. A similar conclusion might be reached on purely economic and amenity grounds, since the Mexican Thorn is already having a direct impact on the human community and the cost of mechanical or chemical control along roadsides and around settlements and beaches will inevitably be high.

Conservation of endemic plants
Apart from one (or perhaps two) grass species, the only surviving endemic flowering plant on Ascension is the Ascension Spurge, *Euphorbia origanoides*. The various historical accounts of its distribution suggest that the number of plants is much lower than in the past, although the reasons for this are not clear.[2] The introduction of the tree *Casuarina equisetifolia* brought with it the cottony-cushion scale *Icerya purchasi*, which promptly became a pest of the spurge. Biological control for this pest was introduced in 1976, but the results are unknown. Now there is the severe threat posed by the spread of Mexican Thorn, since this invasive plant thrives in the conditions preferred by the spurge.

Two nature reserves suggested in our 1995 report were established in 1997 (see endpaper map). They are intended to contribute to conservation of the spurge, as well as of other species. The Hummock Point Nature Reserve is in the northeast of the island, including the coast from Hummock Point to Spire Point and its hinterland. This is one of the least disturbed parts of the island, with magnificent cavernous lava flows, very few alien plants and an undisturbed – though recently declining – colony of the spurge. The Mars Bay Nature Reserve includes a major colony of the spurge on the slopes of South Gannet Hill (where it may be threatened by competition with several alien plants) and is also important for other aspects of conservation. Although the designation of these reserves has little immediate effect, it emphasizes the need for caution in considering future development in these sensitive parts the island.

There is also a case for special protection measures for some rare endemic ferns and a few other native plants on Green Mountain. It is clear that the existing Green Mountain (Natural Resources) Protection Ordinance of 1955 does not achieve the required effect.[3]

---

[2] Duffey listed nine stations for the spurge in 1958 and Cronk found 16 stations in 1976. Pickup (1998) recorded only a few current sites, but no-one has made a thorough search recently. Our observations in 1990 and 1995 suggest that some of the old colonies have disappeared but that others may exist unnoticed. The colony on Letterbox seems to have undergone a drastic decline, presumably from natural causes, but a colony close to the site of the modern BBC buildings at English Bay was probably eliminated by the disturbance caused during construction. We feel that environmental impact assessments should be made before new facilities are erected anywhere on the island, to avoid inadvertent damage to this species or to other indigenous plants or animals.

[3] The protected area is bounded by lines drawn between Two Boats, Weather Post, Castle Hill, South East Crater, Mountain Red Hill and Two Boats. It prohibits the lighting of fires in the open, interfering with water sources, and – except with written permission – the cutting, gathering or carrying away of any forest produce. The latter term is defined comprehensively, to include substances as diverse as honey, guano, rock, grass and trees. This ordinance may have served a useful purpose at a time when the island community depended on farm produce, but we find it hard to see any rationale for it under modern conditions. The rules tend to inhibit removal of invasive alien plants, and give no special protection to the surviving endemic species.

Conservation of invertebrates

Most of the endemic invertebrates on Ascension live in the barren parts of the island. These small creatures of the lava flows, cinder plains and underground cavities are adapted to these spartan conditions, and are unlikely to be able to compete with animals that colonise areas in the wake of spreading introduced vegetation or in association with buildings occupied by people. There is thus a case for actively restricting the spread of alien plants and minimizing the erection of buildings, especially in the most barren parts of the island that have escaped the effects of human activity in the past.

The two new nature reserves at Hummock Point and Mars Bay include large areas of barren lava (clinker) and provide some protection for the native land invertebrates. In addition the Mars Bay reserve includes the salt water pools near Shelly Beach which are the only known habitat of the two endemic shrimps, *Procaris ascensionis* and *Typhlatya rogersi*.

Another area important for endemic invertebrates is Boatswainbird Island, which is the only known habitat of the world's largest species of pseudoscorpion, *Garypus titanius*, and one other endemic pseudoscorpion (yet another species is probably also endemic). As explained in Chapter 12, it is important for the survival of these unique species that alien animals such as rats, mice, centipedes or additional species of ants are prevented from colonising Boatswainbird Island. We are particularly concerned at the danger posed by scientists working on the island – as Philip did in the 1950s – who might take equipment to Boatswainbird Island in boxes or bags in which small animals might have taken refuge. Rigorous scrutiny or fumigation of baggage should be a condition of any permit to work on the island.

Conservation of turtles

The turtles of Ascension and their eggs are now fully protected by law. Site development takes account of potential disruption to females and hatchlings by noise and lights, and guidelines minimise disturbance of nesting females by the steady influx of people keen to see egg-laying in progress. Furthermore, if feral cats can be eradicated (see below) the turtles will benefit by reduced predation on their young. Some years ago an experienced turtle biologist commented: *"Ever since the 1930's the protection afforded the green turtles of Ascension has been exemplary. The turtles and their eggs have been protected in a manner unparalleled at turtle nesting beaches anywhere else in the world."*

Nonetheless, the future of the Ascension turtles is not secure. A clear threat is from the Mexican Thorn, which is salt tolerant and in its original range flourishes on beaches; there is no doubt that it must be controlled if Green Turtles are to continue breeding with maximum success on Ascension.[4] The other new threat relates to potential development of tourism. Experience elsewhere has shown that the opening up of originally deserted beaches for tourism can have a catastrophic effect on the breeding of turtles. The undoubted success of conservation measures during the 20th century should not be allowed to instil overconfidence in our ability to protect the Green Turtles of Ascension in the context of the pressures of commercial tourism. If such development takes place, both direct disturbance and the mining of beaches for sand will present grave threats.

---

[4] The management plan prepared in 1998 listed six potential threats to the turtles by the Mexican Thorn: roots would prevent turtles from excavating nests; plants would form a barrier to the upper beach and reduce the area available for nests; turtles being forced to nest lower down would increase risks of inundation; plants roots could penetrate nest chambers; the plants would alter the moisture content of the sand; and shading would alter sand temperature, potentially affecting sex-determination of turtle embryos with the consequence of disrupted sex ratio.

Restoration of seabird populations and the eradication of feral cats and rats

Conservation issues on Ascension are dominated by the catastrophic decline of the seabird community during the last few centuries. As the paleontologist Storrs Olson pointed out in 1977:

> *"Ascension and St Helena constitute the only dry land in an area of 15,000,000 km² .... so their former significance as breeding sites for seabirds can hardly be overestimated. In the five centuries since the discovery of these islands, man and his introduced predators have reduced seabird populations that must once have numbered in the tens of millions almost to non-existence (except for the Sooty Terns of Ascension). Thus the composition of seabird populations over a vast extent of ocean was probably dramatically affected by relatively minor alterations on two very small specks of land. The vulnerability and fragility of seabird populations have rarely been more forcefully demonstrated."*

No blame need attach to Britain for the initial tragedy: animal communities on islands around the world have been unwittingly devastated by casual or accidental introduction of alien species. On Ascension the greatest damage was set in motion with the introduction of cats shortly after settlement in 1815, at a time when the repercussions of such acts were not understood.[5]

There have been frequent calls for more attention to seabird conservation issues on Ascension. However, it appears to be an inevitable consequence of frequent changes in administration and the transient human population of the island, that very little of lasting value has been done. In the past, there has been a tendency to react to calls for conservation by culling feral cats more intensively; as we go to press, this is happening yet again, with talk of recruiting more St Helenians to control cats. It cannot be overemphasized that the effect of such efforts is negligible over the long term, since intensive culling is never maintained for more than a few years at a time, and the cat population quickly recovers. Furthermore, since culling is inevitably concentrated near places occupied by humans or around Wideawake fairs, the other seabirds do not benefit. So long as there are any feral cats on the island, mortality of the Wideawakes will continue and the seabird species now confined to Boatswainbird Island or the stacks will be unable to re-establish themselves on the mainland in significant numbers.

As early as 1961 a campaign to eradicate feral cats was discussed by Ken Simmons, Douglas Dorward and Philip, and a formal proposal was presented to the authorities in 1962, but could not be implemented. In 1964 Eric Duffey – in his study of the ecology of Ascension Island – emphasized that *"Eradication of these animals* [cats] *is the most important wildlife conservation problem on the island."* In 1966 R.A. Davis, a pest control expert from the British Ministry of Agriculture, commented that the extensive cat predation on the Sooty Terns: *"is a factor that ought not to be tolerated any longer."*

Our 1990 visit to Ascension with Ken Simmons was suggested by the International Council for Bird Preservation (ICBP, now known as BirdLife International). The resulting review of the situation led to the ICBP World Conference passing a resolution in November 1990 which urged the UK government to eradicate the introduced cats and rats from Ascension Island.

A few years later the UK Foreign and Commonwealth Office (FCO) provided the main funding for a study to assess the feasibility of the eradication scheme; this was organised by the Royal Society for the Protection of Birds (RSPB) and was carried out

---

[5] Contrast this with the reprehensible introduction of pet cats to Marion Island in the Indian Ocean around 1949, leading to catastrophic mortality of seabirds which was halted only recently when the cats were eradicated at great expense by the South African government (M.N. Bester et al. 2000).

during our 1995 stay on Ascension, by the New Zealander Brian Bell – an expert on eradication programmes – and Philip as the ornithological consultant. The report concluded that eradication was feasible and should result – over a period of years – in a dramatic increase in the numbers of seabirds. Further studies have been carried out since then by RSPB, who are hopeful that a programme to eradicate feral cats and rats can be initated in the near future.[6] The UK government has agreed in principle to provide partial funding for the work, and the RSPB are investigating the potential for international support.

In the meantime, Boatswainbird Island and the larger stacks around the coast provide sites where seabirds can breed free of predation from feral cats and rats. However, virtually all attempts by seabirds other than Wideawakes to breed on the mainland are doomed to failure. Furthermore, individual birds – for instance young Brown Boobies and Ascension Frigatebirds – are heavily predated if they try to roost in sites on the mainland accessible to cats. Wideawakes have some breeding success because they arrive suddenly to breed in large numbers, thus tending to satiate the cats, but they suffer substantial losses. Only when the feral cats and rats are finally eradicated will seabirds be able to breed safely on the main island once again.

Several governments, including those of New Zealand and South Africa, have shown their commitment to the conservation of islands in their care, by putting substantial resources into the eradication of alien mammals that were causing devastation of the island ecosystems. The United Kingdom, which has already supported a feasibility study on the eradication of feral cats and rats from Ascension Island, now has the opportunity to raise its status in the eyes of conservationists worldwide, by driving forward this restoration initiative. A restored seabird community on Ascension Island and in the surrounding South Atlantic Ocean would provide a beacon of hope for people everywhere who care about the world environment, demonstrating that a modern western society can muster the determination, skills and resources to rectify fundamental but inadvertent mistakes made centuries ago.

---

[6] N. Ratcliffe (1999).

Part IV

Animals and plants of
St Helena and Ascension Island

This section of the book provides a systematic treatment of the animals and plants of St Helena and Ascension. This is not primarily an identification book, but where practicable we have included information that will help to identify plants and animals encountered on the islands.

Where English names are given, the first one mentioned is normally the name used on the islands. Following a convention used by many ornithologists and some botanists, we treat these as proper nouns and spell them with capitals if (but only if) they refer to particular species. Thus we would say Brown Booby and Black Cabbage, but flocks of boobies and woodland with cabbage trees (since there might be several species); we also abandon capitals in the case of domestic animals.

We also have to use many formal scientific names, both of species and the groups to which they belong. Each species of animal or plant has a 'binomial' scientific name, consisting of a generic name and a specific name (e.g. *Passer domesticus* for the House Sparrow). There is a well established convention that generic and specific names are written in italics to make them stand out from the general text. The generic name is always capitalised, but the specific name is not.

We have always been frustrated by publications that refer to plants and animals by name, without providing any indication of their relationships. The best way of indicating such relationships concisely is to arrange the species in the groups that taxonomists have established in their classification of living things. However, taxonomy is often complicated and opinions (and thus names) sometimes change, so we emphasize the most important and well established groups and names.

Conventions:

H	occurs on St Helena
A	occurs on Ascension
(H) or (A)	no longer present in a wild state on the island or (in the case of turtles or birds) does not breed on the island;
*	endemic species
**	endemic species in an endemic genus
†	extinct
?	Question marks, where used, are placed in front of the symbol they qualify.

258

Chapter 15   **Animals**

This chapter lists systematically nearly all groups of land animals occurring on the two islands. The animals are initially separated into a few major groups (vertebrates, invertebrates other than arthropods, arthropods other than insects, and finally the insects. Within these groups the treatment is generally at the level of order, and within the arthropods (the great majority of animals listed) the orders are arranged in the well established taxonomic sequence of Borror et al. (1981). Within orders, the families, genera and species are listed alphabetically.

In zoology the orders do not have entirely consistent endings, but readers will notice some pattern; for instance orders of birds usually end in -formes and orders of insects in -ptera (the latter referring to wings). Family names of animals always end in -idae (as in Carabidae for the ground beetle family). Where a family of animals does not have an established English name (as in many of the more obscure groups of insects), we prefer to use informal anglicised versions of the latinised family names (ending in '-ids', e.g. carabids) rather than 'made up' English group names that are hard to remember.

In the brief description of each family we normally mention the number of species on each island. If one of the islands is not mentioned, the family can be assumed to be unrepresented (or at least unrecorded) from it.

All endemic species are mentioned except in the case of a few families of beetles (Coleoptera) and a scattering of other groups where we have only mentioned the number of endemic species within each genus. We have also included those additional species that we consider to be probably indigenous (rather than introduced by humans) on either of the islands, as well as many that – though introduced – are conspicuous or of particular interest. A comprehensive list of the land animals known from Ascension is provided in our recent article, which includes the authorities for the scientific names.[1] For St Helena similar information for most groups is provided in the Belgians' reports;[2] however, some name changes have occurred since their publication.

---

[1] N.P. Ashmole and M.J. Ashmole. (1997).

[2] P. Basilewsky ed (1970, 1972, 1976, 1977).

259

MAMMALS

There have never been any native land mammals on either St Helena or Ascension. However, rats and mice have been accidentally introduced and cats and some other domestic animals have now established feral populations (living in a wild state). Beau Rowlands et al have recently provided full documentation of the history of the introduced mammals, so we give only the general picture here.

FELIDAE – cats

HA   Cat   *Felis catus*

H: At present there are some domestic cats on the island and also a feral population of unknown size. Although there is no record of the date of arrival of cats, they may have been introduced deliberately by the Portuguese to control rats. Anyhow it is clear that the feral population was established during the 16th century, becoming sufficiently numerous to be noted by travellers in 1599 and 1634. In 1715 Captain Daniel Beeckman wrote: *"vast numbers of cats, that went away from the houses, and became wild, living among the rocks, where they find good prog (sic), feeding on young partridges, so that they became as great a plague as the rats"*. A century and a half later Melliss commented: *"it assumes wild habits, existing abundantly on the rocky outskirts of the Island in holes and caves, where, amongst the eggs and young of partridges and other birds, it commits such havoc that sportsmen never lose an opportunity of killing it. Cats abound at a place called Cat Hole, where they live chiefly upon pigeons."* In 1757 it is recorded that soldiers were employed killing wild cats.

Cats were doubtless largely responsible for the demise of the seabird colonies which were on the main island of St Helena when it was discovered by people. Cats in the outlying parts of the island are now rarely seen by day, but they still prey on seabirds when these are unwise enough to settle on land. At Gill Point we have seen cat lairs with masses of seabird feathers and bones. When Storrs Olson looked at the contents of 150 cat scats (faeces), he found bird remains in 19 of them; in almost half of these the birds concerned could not be identified, but seven had White Tern remains, two had Myna remains and one had a bunch of Trophy Bird feathers.

A: Cats were introduced to Ascension in 1815 in the hope that they would control the rats. Around the settlements they seem to have been fairly effective in this, but they quickly spread over the island and the damage they inflicted on the seabird colonies was noted as early as 1823. We have little doubt that feral cats were primarily responsible for the elimination of most of the seabirds from the mainland of Ascension during the 19th century. The modern cat population can be considered in three categories: pets, strays or scavengers around settlements, and feral cats elsewhere in the island. It is the feral cats that have been a dominant factor determining the size and composition of the seabird communities on Ascension and hence throughout the huge expanse of the tropical Atlantic Ocean. The cats are mainly found along the coast among the beach huts, near the dump, periodically in association with the Wideawake fairs and also around seabird roosting areas such as the cliffs of Letterbox and near the stacks between Comfortless and English Bay. Our estimates of numbers in 1995 were 300 pet cats, 400 in the stray and scavenger category and 200-400 that have no association with humans. Everywhere we went on the island we saw evidence of cat predation on seabirds (Plate 15). Around the Wideawake fairs the litter of dead birds bears witness to the toll taken by the cats, and in many other places there are cat 'middens' containing masses of bones and feathers, especially of boobies and frigatebirds; remains of White Terns were especially noticeable at Letterbox. Seabirds that try to breed on accessible parts of the mainland almost always have their chicks killed and often are killed themselves. Cats also catch and eat young Green Turtles on the beaches as they hatch and scamper down towards the sea.

CANIDAE – dogs, wolves and foxes

H   Dog   *Canis familiaris*

There seem to be very few feral dogs on St Helena at present, although we have seen them in Prosperous Bay valley. In earlier centuries they were certainly common. In 1638 and 1656 Peter Mundy recorded: *"Dogges here in great store ... We saw (in Lemon Valley) a kennell of dogges off sundry sorts, aboutt 15 or 16, all white for oughtt wee could see, who, as soone as they had espied us, tooke right uppe against the steepy rocky hill. Some Dogges, att First lost or run away, have since encreased, and in tyme will Diminish the Cattle."* ... *"Neither did I, nor any of our company (for ought I could heare), see soe much as one goate: supposed to bee devoured by dogges, which have mightily encreased here."* We have not found records of the later history of this feral dog population, but we suspect that the settlers arriving in 1659 quickly killed most of the dogs for the sake of their grazing stock. There are no records of feral dogs on Ascension, although small numbers have been used on the farm and a few are now kept as pets.

EQUIDAE – horses, donkeys and zebras

HA   Donkey   *Equus asinus*

H: Although both Melliss and Jackson suggested that donkeys were left on the island at or near the time when it was discovered, we are not aware that any of the early travellers mentioned them. However, donkeys were evidently imported at about the time of human settlement. The Records for 1679 state: *"The Company our Masters have several asses on this their island some of which may be useful to those inhabitants that stand in need of them."*

In the succeeding centuries it seems likely that there were always substantial numbers of domestic donkeys on the island. We suspect that some of them roamed widely and did considerable damage to the native vegetation, although always subsidiary to the effect of the much more numerous goats. When the flax industry was established late in the 19th century donkeys were used to transport the flax to the mills. In the first decade of the 20th century an attempt was made to improve the local breed and in 1927 some of the Ascension Island donkeys were brought to St Helena. Donkeys are still used in a small way as beasts of burden by the Department of Agriculture and Forestry, and a few are kept privately. Efforts have been made recently to eliminate the feral population and these have been largely successful; in 1995, however, there were still a few individuals living wild, some of them in places where they could feed on surviving or reestablished endemic plants.

A: Donkeys were brought to the island shortly after 1815 and escaped from domestication in the 1830s; they live mainly in the dry parts of the island below 300 m. Numbers in the past are largely unknown. In 1927, after exporting about 30 to St Helena, there were thought to be still 40-50 at large. In 1936 the population was estimated as about 100 and in 1957 as somewhat higher. In 1994 we thought that there were about 100 and later in that year about 50 were put down by the local police. The donkeys are protected by an ordinance, but this allows for their numbers to be culled from time to time. Being generalized herbivores, donkeys have had and are still having a profound effect on the vegetation. Most importantly, they are largely responsible for the spread of the Mexican Thorn *Prosopis juliflora*. They feed on the pods and the seeds pass out in their droppings; young plants then grow up along the donkey trails. Donkeys may also do some damage to the Wideawakes if they wander on the fairs when the birds are breeding.

(H)   Horse   *Equus caballus*

There are no horses on St Helena at present. However, a feral population of horses became established on the island shortly before the East India Company settlers arrived in 1659. A few were apparently turned loose on the island by a passing ship in 1652; three years later two mares and the stallion were caught, but the stallion was set free to serve the two mares which could not be caught, and four horses were seen by Peter Mundy's party in 1656. However, the herd evidently did not survive for long after settlement, since in 1666 the French visitor de Rennefort was told that horses had been present, but that they had become so wild that when they were pursued to the ends of the island, they threw themselves off the rocks into the sea rather than be caught. We do not know how quickly the settlers acquired horses, but by 1757 the authorities limited horse ownership to a maximum of three even for the largest landholders, and ruled that: "*No horses at any time to graze on waste lands as they eat up and destroy the Herbage from the Black Cattle.*"

SUIDAE – pigs

(H)   Pig (hog, swine)   *Sus scrofa*

There are no feral pigs on the island today. They were introduced very early on and were mentioned as early as 1530 by travellers who welcomed the opportunity to obtain fresh meat. Numbers increased, as in the case of the goats, and they must have caused tremendous damage. Imagine a herd of wild pigs, which eat almost anything, wandering across a breeding colony of seabirds in the more accessible areas such as Prosperous Bay Plain, munching their way through eggs, chicks and even adult birds in their burrows. In 1588 Cavendish wrote: "*Here are in like manner great store of swine, which are very wild and fat and of great bigness; they keep all together upon the mountains, and will very seldom abide any man to come near them.*" In 1656 Mundy recorded "*Hogges there are many, having seene 25 or 30 in a heard together, little and greatt.*" The transition from an island with herds of wild swine to one in which swine were considered as private property evidently took place rapidly after settlement, since by 1679 the authorities were complaining that certain inhabitants were driving their swine on to: "*Tompstone* (sic) *wood, Manatee bay and parts adjacent*", areas that were reserved by the East India Company for grazing by its own animals.

BOVIDAE – cattle, antelopes, goats and sheep

(HA)   Cattle   *Bos taurus*

    H: We are not entirely convinced that cattle were introduced to St Helena by the Portuguese. Mundy in 1638 and Van Riebeeck in 1655 both mention 'cattle' but the word at that time was used in a very general sense to refer to livestock – in this case perhaps goats and pigs. However, by 1666 a visitor noted that the Governor had about 24 cows and many of the settlers doubtless also had some. From this time onwards many of the cattle belonging to the East India Company probably roamed freely on what are now the Crown Wastes, their numbers fluctuating drastically as a result of successions of dry or wet years. We therefore feel that cattle, along with goats and pigs, must be considered as a significant ecological factor on St Helena, implicated in the destruction of the native vegetation.

A: Cattle were kept on the mountain farm from the earliest years of the settlement, but with varying quality of husbandry; an 1821 report quoted by Hart-Davies mentions that there were eight or nine oxen wild on the mountain. Some decades later, cattle were sometimes kept near Georgetown, fodder being brought down from the mountain and manure returned there. Those on the mountain may have had some effect on the native vegetation.

(HA)   Goat   *Capra hircus*

H: At the time of writing it is thought that there are few – if any – feral goats on the island, and only small numbers are kept on smallholdings. Things were very different in the past. Goats were introduced by the Portuguese early in the history of St Helena, possibly in 1531. In the following centuries they were a welcome source of meat for the crews of passing ships. Since there were no predators and the native vegetation on the island had no chemical or physical protection against mammalian herbivores, the goats must have thought they were in paradise. With more than enough to eat, it is not hard to imagine how rapidly they must have multiplied. The later story of the goats, the settlers and the native vegetation has been told in Chapter 7.

A: There are no goats on Ascension now. They were introduced in the 16th or early 17th century to provide fresh meat for passing ships. Their effect on the native vegetation is discussed in Chapter 11. Throughout the 19th century there were around 600 goats on the island, but by 1922 numbers had been reduced to about 55, probably largely as a result of the hunting parties organised by Captain (later General) Morgan of the Royal Marines, who was in charge of the garrison from 1905 to 1908. It is thought that the last few were killed by servicemen in 1944.

(H)A   Sheep   *Ovis aries*

H: Some sheep were left on the island in 1617 but it is not clear whether they survived; they may well have suffered both competition from the already established goats and predation by the feral dogs. Peter Mundy did not mention sheep on any of his visits and many early reports refer to 'cattle' which may or may not have included sheep. However, after 1659 the settlers had sheep and by 1728 these were sufficiently numerous to be mentioned several times in the records as causing damage – along with goats – to young trees. In 1757 an agreement was reached by which proprietors kept no more than three sheep for every three acres of land which they owned; it was calculated that this would reduce the number of sheep on the island by about 400. There are still about 800 domestic sheep, but no feral ones, on the island.

A: A few hundred sheep were kept on the island in the 19th century, evidently ranging widely; their descendants still roam the island today. In 1995 we thought there might be as many as 1200-1500, but numbers are hard to estimate because the animals are in small scattered flocks. Some culling has recently taken place.

LEPORIDAE – rabbits and hares

HA   Rabbit   *Oryctolagus cuniculus*

H: Rabbits were apparently introduced by the early Portuguese explorers, but are said to have been exterminated by the feral cats before the end of the 16th century. A further introduction took place around 1770, and by 1805 they were evidently sufficiently widespread to be hunted. The St Helena records for that year state: "It is ordered that hereafter Rabbits are to be considered the property of those persons on whose land they may be seen and that a penalty of £5 stirling will attach to any person convicted of shooting, firing at, or hunting down with dogs any rabbit or rabbits without permission." By 1838 rabbits were considered game and subject to similar laws as Partridge and Pheasant. Loveridge established that the feral rabbits on St Helena belong to the subspecies *Oryctolagus cuniculus huxleyi*, which is slightly smaller than the north European form; *huxleyi* is the Mediterranean subspecies and has also been introduced to the Azores, Madeira and the Salvage Islands. Rabbits are now found almost everywhere on the island, even in the most improbable places with very little vegetation. We suspect that they seriously affect the distribution of certain endemic plants, perhaps especially Salad Plant. Melliss recorded that they were either grey or black and Loveridge noted that there were still some black or partially black rabbits a century later. They breed at any time of the year and have litters of two of three young.

A: Hart-Davis suggested that rabbits were introduced to Ascension by Colonel Nicholls in the 1820s; they were certainly present by 1833. They had become a considerable pest by 1874, damaging pasture and young trees, but a few years later they were struck by an epidemic which apparently also affected the rats. Although the population recovered, it then declined again early in this century, possibly as a result of ferreting; by 1936 there were not many left. Rabbits are now widespread – mainly between 200 and 600 m – but they are not very commonly seen by day.

MURIDAE – rats and mice

HA   Tree Rat (Black, Ship, House or Roof Rat) Plate 17   *Rattus rattus*

H   Brown Rat (Norway, Sewer, Common, Wharf or Ground Rat)   *Rattus norvegicus*

H: Two species of rats, *Rattus rattus* and *Rattus norvegicus*, are present on St Helena. Both species have several common names and we shall refer to them respectively as Tree Rat and Brown Rat. The Tree Rat probably established itself shortly after discovery of the island, since Portuguese ships made regular visits in the 16th century. Rats were recorded as present on the island in 1599, and although early records do not distinguish between the species, studies of the way they spread around the world with humans indicate that the Tree Rat was the species present on ships in the early 16th century; it would have reached St Helena first, followed by the Brown Rat in the 18th century.[3]

Loveridge concluded that the Brown Rats on the island belonged to the subspecies *Rattus norvegicus norvegicus*, and that the Tree Rats were *Rattus rattus frugivorus* which he called the Cream-bellied Tree Rat.[4] The two species can be hard to distinguish and characters used

---

[3] I.A.E. Atkinson (1985).

[4] Rowlands (1998: 60) is incorrect in stating that "*The present populations are sufficiently distinct to warrant subspecific status – Cream-bellied Tree Rat R. r. frugivorus*". The subspecies *frugivorus* occurs in the Mediterranean region and was originally described from Sicily; the St Helena population was probably founded by members of this subspecies from the Iberian peninsula, but it does not constitute a distinctive island subspecies.

elsewhere tend to break down on St Helena. Droppings can usually be separated, those of the Tree Rat being spindle-shaped and of the Brown Rat capsule-shaped. Perhaps most useful is the analysis by Loveridge, a professional taxonomist with long experience on the island. He concluded that tail length was the best character and provided the following key:

Length from snout to vent much shorter than the length of tail from vent to tip; throat, chest and belly normally pure white or cream, occasionally bluish grey.
Tree Rat, Rattus rattus frugivorus

Length from snout to vent equal to or exceeding the length of tail from vent to tip; throat, chest and belly <u>usually</u> a grizzled grey
Brown Rat, Rattus norvegicus norvegicus

However, Loveridge also commented:

"My own view, based on what occurred at Varneys, is that under certain circumstances interbreeding takes place with the norvegicus tending to displace the frugivorus." [5]

Rats evidently became an intractable problem soon after settlement of the island in 1659, and the concern of the authorities is reflected in the St Helena Records over more than two centuries.[6] Melliss quoted the following extract from a report written by Napoleon's surgeon in 1819:

"The rats are so numerous at Longwood, and so fearless, that they often assemble, even in the daytime, in flocks to feed when the offal of the kitchen is thrown out, and have not unaptly been compared to broods of young chickens collected about the parent hen. The floors of Longwood were so perforated with their holes as to resemble a sieve. Over these the servants had nailed pieces of tin, to keep them out. Napoleon's dining-room was particularly infested with them; and it is a fact that one of these noxious animals sprung out of his hat when he was going to put it on one day after dinner. The devastations committed by them were almost incredible, and latterly rat-hunting became a favourite sport at Longwood. The chase was performed in the following manner:- A little before dark the holes were uncovered, and entrance afforded to the game. Soon after, five or six of the

---

[5] Loveridge records that in 1957 the then Superintendent of Agriculture considered that the Brown Rat had been eradicated as a result of their poisoning campaign. However, this was a vain hope; although Loveridge did not catch any Brown Rats in his garden at Varneys during the following ten years, he started getting them in his traps occasionally during 1968. He says: *"In 1969 their numbers waned at Varneys and thereafter I got the impression of a noticeable reduction in tail length among our frugivorus, which also appeared to display a tendency towards norvegicus in the matter of colouration."*

[6] Entries that we have noted include the following:
1684: *"You must be careful and diligent in destroying Rats for which purpose we shall send 20lb of impalpable powdered glass."*
1700: *"We have also heard that in the year 1700 the rats were grown so exceedingly numerous that after they had destroyed everything ... they at last fell upon one another and devoured themselves and the island at that time was quite clear of them but the shipping soon after furnished the place with more."*
1709: *"The account is very surprising to us to suffer the letters Consultation books, Register of Wills, etc, to be so much destroyed and damaged by Ratts, Moths, and Wett or any of them to be missing."*
1715: *"Soldiers pouches often destroyed by Ratts who have sometimes eat great holes in them while the soldiers who wore them were asleep."*
1732: *"Send us some Beehive Wired Trapps with holes in the tops and sides for the ratts to get in, with which we hope to thin if not quite destroy them, these traps being much more useful than steel or any other sort of trappes."*
1756: *"Our reason for acquainting you last year of the rats and mice barking the young trees in the Longwood was only because we looked upon it as something extraordinary. We wish we could find out a method of destroying them, but this we look upon to be next to an impossibility."*
1768: *"Rats and mice increase considerably. Reward for destruction a half penny each Rat, a farthing each Mouse."*
1902: According to Philip Gosse, Governor Sterndale: *"...an authority on the small mammals in India, offered a reward of one penny for every dead rat, and then twopence, and at last, as they became yet more scarce, a reward of threepence a head; a wise measure, as it turned out, for the rat population became greatly reduced and the island was never before so free from these vermin."*

servants rushed in, with lights, sticks, and followed by dogs, covered the holes as fast as possible and attacked the rats, who, when driven to desperation, made a vigorous defence, assailed the dogs, and sometimes even the men, by running up their legs and biting them. Sixteen were killed in this manner in less than half an hour in one of the rooms!"

In 1965 R.A. Davis of the British Ministry of Agriculture, who was on St Helena to advise on rodent control, carried out an extensive trapping survey. He found some ecological separation between the two species of rats. In Jamestown the Brown Rat inhabited sewers, cellars and other spaces below floor level, whereas the roof spaces and tall warehouses contained the lighter and more agile Tree Rat. In the yam guts the Brown Rat had burrows in the banks of the watercourses and the rubbish tips, while the Tree Rat was found in trees and shrubs. However, Davis found both species among farm buildings, in the flax, in *Lantana* scrub and in waste land close to the shore. In the 1990s poisoning campaigns keep rats under control in the towns, although they are still found in the countryside and also on the coast, where they benefit from fishermen's discarded catch. Both species are omnivorous, eating plants, fruits, invertebrates, young birds and offal; Tree Rats are particularly fond of vegetables, and ripening bananas are often badly damaged. Some nests of Tree Rats examined by Loveridge were placed about 12 feet up in Port Jackson Willows; they were about the size of a rugby football and composed of woven green leaves.

Rats pose a significant public health problem on St Helena because they are carriers of leptospirosis (Weil's disease), known locally as rat fever, which is sometimes fatal in humans. The disease is caused by a spirochaete (spiral-shaped) bacterium which is harboured by rats and excreted in their urine. The main danger is to people habitually working in damp conditions, especially in guts; walking barefoot in such places is very unwise. The disease has an incubation period of one to three weeks, and then causes an acute illness with fever, chills, an intense throbbing headache, severe muscle aches, eye inflammation and a skin rash. The kidneys are affected in most cases and liver damage can also occur. Prompt use of antibiotics is essential.

A: The only species of rat on Ascension Island is *Rattus rattus*, which was introduced accidentally, probably about 1700 (see Chapter 11). The rat population was studied by R.A Davis in 1965, and by Brian and Paul Bell in 1995 during the feasibility study for eradication of rats and feral cats from the island. Three distinct colour morphs or varieties are present, but there is no evidence that they are geographically or ecologically separated on the island.

There is little information on fluctuations in the rat population, but high numbers are probably associated with years of high rainfall; this was certainly the case in 1927, a wet year in which an unprecedented plague of rats and mice was recorded. On the whole, rats are kept in check around the settlements. Away from buildings they are commonest on the mountain, presumably because of the availability of cover, moisture and food, and are less common at middle levels and rare in the desert lowlands. In May 1995, however, rats were trapped close to sea level at the edge of the Mars Bay lava flow, where they probably scavenge around the Wideawake fair; this was a wet season with a good growth of grass, and almost all the females were pregnant. On the mountain Davis found that this rat species sometimes burrowed in earth, which it apparently does not do either in Britain or St Helena where *R. norvegicus* is also present. Rats compete for food with landcrabs and there are accounts of fights with either the rat or the crab winning. The rat-borne disease Leptospirosis is not known to be present on Ascension.

HA   House Mouse   *Mus musculus*

H: The first written mention that we have found of mice on St Helena dates from 1599. It is likely, however, that they got ashore from ships visiting earlier in the 16th century. The race concerned (*Mus musculus brevirostris*) is native to the Iberian peninsula, so Portuguese ships were probably responsible. Mice are now very common and can be found virtually everywhere on the island, including almost vertical sea cliffs. The colour varies considerably, from pale brown to deep grey and in some cases almost black.7 They are often active in the daytime and show remarkably little fear of people.8 Mice on St Helena are omnivorous and the remains of their meals can be found under stones, in crevices and among the dead leaves at the base of plants. These often consist of the husks of seeds, flowers and invertebrate remains, and until fairly recently sometimes included elytra (wing cases) of the Giant Ground Beetle; it may be that smaller beetles can retreat into cracks too small for mice to follow, whilst a giant beetle would have had more difficulty.

A: Mice are common, occur in all parts of the island and are often active by day, as on St Helena. They vary considerably in size and colour, being black, grey, sandy and reddish brown: it seems probable that mice from different regions have come ashore from time to time and that the variation in the present population is partly due to this. Plagues of mice are sometimes noticed in the months following heavy rains; the rains result in a flush of grass on otherwise barren parts of the island, and the mice flourish on the grass seeds. In times of drought, the population falls.

MARINE MAMMALS

Marine mammals are largely outside the scope of this book. Alasdair Edwards has written an excellent account of whales and dolphins and the history of the whaling industry on St Helena, and John Packer mentions a few species of dolphins that occur off Ascension. The possible occurrence of seals on St Helena is discussed in Chapter 5.

REPLILES⁹

CHELONIIDAE – sea turtles
In this family of sea turtles the carapace is made up of large bones and covered by horny plates. At least two species occur in the waters around St Helena and Ascension.

(H)A   Green Turtle Plate 17   *Chelonia mydas*

The Green Turtle can grow to a carapace length of 140 cm. The carapace has five large plates down the middle but only four (the costal plates) on each side. The plates

---

7 While we were on the island a South African visitor reported seeing in Lemon Valley a large mouse with a stripe down either side, resembling the South African Striped Mouse; this record clearly requires confirmation.

8 One may speculate that both these characteristics result from the absence of predators: there are no birds of prey or weasels and the feral cats are largely nocturnal; however, Loveridge recorded mice being caught by Mynas and harassed by poultry.

9 In addition to the wild reptiles listed in this section, several kinds of land tortoises have been brought to St Helena in the past. The female that was on the island at the time of Napoleon's imprisonment had been imported in about 1766, probably from Mauritius, but subsequently died. The ones now kept at Plantation are Aldabran Giant Tortoises. Jonathan, the old male, was imported in 1882, when he may have been about 50 years of age. The oldest female (Myrtle) was imported from the Seychelles in 1972 at the age of 25. There are also four younger individuals brought in at various times. The tortoises have not bred successfully on St Helena.

do not overlap and the hind margins of those in the middle row are almost straight. On the head, the Green Turtle has only one pair of prefrontal scales between the eyes, while the Hawksbill has two pairs.

Ascension Island is the type locality for the species *Chelonia mydas*: the specimen on which Linnaeus based his description in 1778 came from the island. The species is widespread, however, occurring in the Caribbean, on the coast of West Africa and throughout the tropical oceans, although some rookeries (for instance in Bermuda and Grand Cayman) have been wiped out by humans. In earlier chapters we have treated the history of human interaction with the turtles of St Helena and Ascension, and discussed the remarkable life history and migrations of the Ascension population.

People on land, however, will see only a few episodes in this life history. The turtles mate after arrival offshore at the end of their journey from South America; it seems likely that there is a mating associated with each of the several clutches of eggs laid by a female in a given season. Copulation is said to be prolonged over several days. In some kinds of animals, prolonged copulation has been shown to be an adaptation by which a male increases the chance that the whole of the current batch of eggs is fertilized by his sperm, rather than by those of another male mating subsequently; probably this is true also of Green Turtles.

When ready to lay, the female comes on shore at night on a sandy beach and digs a pit above the high tide mark. At first she uses all four flippers to get rid of the dry sand, throwing it violently away and gradually forming a wide depression averaging 33 cm deep. When she gets down to damp sand she changes the action, delicately using her hind flippers as scoops, so as to form a cylindrical egg chamber averaging 59 cm deep. She lays a clutch of glistening white, leathery-shelled eggs, occupying nearly half of the egg chamber; next she fills in the pit, and scatters so much dry sand around that it is impossible to see where the eggs were placed. With the operation completed, she returns to the sea. Laying is almost always between 9 pm and 5 am, and the most popular time is around midnight.

The eggs are about 46 mm in diameter and the average clutch is close to 120 eggs, though varying to some extent with the size of the female and within the season; females generally lay three or four clutches in a given year (typically at intervals of 13-14 days), but tend to lay fewer eggs in later clutches. Incubation in the damp sand, warmed by the sun, lasts for just over 60 days. When the young turtles hatch, they work their way up to the surface and finally emerge and scuttle straight down to the sea (Plate 17). Usually they do this at night, thus avoiding being caught by frigatebirds which eagerly take stragglers that emerge in daylight. However, we are told by Brendan Godley that on Ascension some are eaten by the nocturnal landcrabs. The numerous tracks of feral cats on the sandy beaches also suggest that nowadays, a good many young turtles are eaten by these alien predators before they reach the sea (Plate 15).

H: The status of Green Turtles on St Helena has been discussed in Chapter 5. Successful breeding probably does not now occur, but turtles still visit the island in small numbers between about December and June.

A: Research on migration of the Ascension turtles carried out from the late 1950s into the 1980s has been discussed in Chapter 12. During that period nesting activities were also studied, and it was estimated that the number of clutches laid was around 8-11000 and 5-7000 respectively in the seasons 1976/77 and 1977/78. Using a similar technique, Brendan Godley, Annette Broderick and Graeme Hays estimated that in the 1998/99 season about 13900 clutches were laid. Since the 1970s data show large variation in nesting activity between seasons, comparison between the two periods must be done with caution. However, it seems likely that the number of turtles nesting at Ascension has roughly doubled in the past two decades. Calculation of the overall size of the population is subject to large potential errors, but a rough estimate is possible. The earlier work indicated that individual females typically laid 3-4 clutches per season, leading the researchers to suggest that the number of laying females was around 2000-3600 and 1300-2400 in the two seasons. Since their tagging data indicated that female turtles returned to breed at intervals of 3-4 years, we deduce that the overall number of females breeding at Ascension at that time was of the order of 8000. At the present time it seems likely to be around 16000. If the sex ratio is around 1:1 (a big if) the total population of Green Turtles now breeding at Ascension may be over 30,000.

The peak nesting season in 1999 was in March, with 95% of nesting activity occurring between 4th January and 18th May. The major nesting sites are South West Bay, Long Beach, North East Bay and Hannay Beach. In the seasons 1976-77 and 1977-78 these four sites together accounted for 60% of all nesting activity; the rest was spread around 28 other beaches on the western and northeastern coasts of the island. The research team now working on the island have shown that the use of a variety of beaches for nesting has great significance.[10] In marine turtles the sex of offspring is influenced primarily by the incubation temperature, females being produced when the nest is warmer and males when it is cooler. The 'pivotal temperature' at which 50% females and 50% males are produced is about 29°C. It has been shown that at Ascension differences in nest temperature are mainly determined by the 'albedo' of the beach, light coloured beaches (composed almost entirely of shell sand) being markedly cooler than darker ones (which have a greater proportion of volcanic sand particles). For instance, during the nesting season Long Beach typically has sand temperatures at nest depth of 27 to 29.5°C, while at North East Bay the range is 30 to 31.5°C. The effect of this is presumably to produce mainly males at Long Beach and mainly females at North East Bay.

HA   Hawksbill   *Eretmochelys imbricata*

This turtle is found in all the tropical oceans and can grow to 90 cm carapace length. The large horny plates on the carapace are arranged in the same way as in the Green Turtle, but they are distinctly overlapping and those in the middle row are pointed behind. However, these features are less clear in old adults, which can be recognized by the two pairs of scales on the snout between the eyes (Green Turtles have one pair). The bill is distinctly pointed, as the name implies

H: Melliss said that the Hawksbill was occasionally caught on the leeward coast, and this is still true today. Loveridge liberated one caught by a fisherman with carapace about 40 cm long; some years later he was given a carapace 44 cm long, which presumably could have been from the same individual. We were given a photograph of an individual captured recently, which appears to have carapace length about 60 cm. There seems to be no evidence that the Hawksbill breeds on St Helena..

A: Hawksbills are occasionally seen around the coasts, and Packer considers that they breed on the island in small numbers.

---

[10] G.C. Hays et al. (1999).

GEKKONIDAE – geckos

H   Java Gecko Plate 17   *Hemidactylus frenatus*

This gecko is the only land reptile living wild on the island. It is a native of Java but has also reached Madagascar, Mauritius and South Africa; the date of its arrival at St Helena is unknown. It grows to 11 cm long, with the tail – when intact – sometimes contributing more than half of the length. The male is grey above with paler blotches, and generally whitish below, but with the belly lemon yellow. The female is grey to brown, with dark and pale markings, and the young tend to be pinkish.

Melliss recorded the gecko as plentiful about the neighbourhood of Jamestown. Loveridge noted that they were particularly abundant beneath irregular blocks of lava on the floor of Ruperts Valley, and once found one on sand still damp from the receding tide, under a boulder at West Rocks. Intriguingly, the Belgians – whose expeditions were in 1965-67 – commented that the geckos never came into houses but lived under stones in the open. Loveridge tried unsuccessfully to introduce them to the garden of Varneys at 530m, but his wife saw one being carried off by a Myna and the others soon disappeared. However, one came of its own accord to Varneys in 1974; we had them at Little Varneys in 1995 and they are now established in other houses nearby. We suspect that the apparent upward spread of the species, and its colonisation of houses, is associated with the installation of mains electricity: geckos can now often be seen in the evening, catching insects attracted to lights. The hard-shelled, pill-like eggs are commonly found in pairs beneath stones; they range in size from as little as 4 x 5 mm (rare) up to 8 x 9.5 mm. Loveridge recorded them from sea-level up to about 300 m. He also occasionally noticed eggs with a pin-sized hole in the shell and the contents removed, but had no explanation for this.

A   Coconut-palm Gecko Plate 17   *Hemidactylus mercatorius*

This species was on Ascension by 1959, when specimens were sent to Arthur Loveridge to identify (they were his speciality). It comes originally from Madagascar and many islands off the East African coast. It occurs in east, south and southwest Africa, and also in West Africa where its distribution is spotty, apparently due to introduction at ports. It was probably imported accidentally though it might conceivably have reached Ascension naturally by rafting. It is now found in many buildings.

IGUANIDAE – iguanids

A   Lizard   *Liolaemus wiegmanni*

This small pale-coloured lizard is a native of South America. It was present by the early 1940s;[11] we do not know how or when it arrived, but it was undoubtedly brought by humans. It is common in the desert and semi-desert parts of the island.

AMPHIBIANS

RANIDAE – true frogs

H   Grass Frog Plate 17   *Rana grayi*

This is a South African species which was introduced shortly before 1883 by Miss Phoebe Moss of the Briars – apparently for ducks to feed on. The head and body are up to at least

---

[11] A. Loveridge (1959).

52 mm long. The skin on the back is smooth or warty. A pale fawn band (variable in width) runs from the snout along the spine for the full length of the body, bordered by darker areas; elsewhere, there are various dark bars and blotches on a fawn ground.

Frogs now occur wherever there is fresh water, from the high central ridge down to sea level. The call is a sharp, repetitive, resonant "plink", rather like water drops falling into a metal tank. It can be heard in damp places, day or night, wet or dry weather, probably all the year round, and often forms a chorus. The female attaches her eggs in small groups to water plants or the undersides of submerged stones. Loveridge recorded tadpoles in May, July, August, November and January. The frogs feed on insects, and have themselves been observed to be eaten by Mynas; we imagine that Moorhens also eat them.

PIPIDAE – clawed toads

A   African Clawed Toad   *Xenopus laevis*
This toad became established in the dewpond on Green Mountain and in some water tanks. It is clearly introduced and was possibly brought in during the Second World War. We have never noticed it but presume that it is still present.

FRESHWATER FISH

There are no indigenous freshwater fish on either island. However, there have been occasional attempts to introduce them to St Helena. In 1973 a small shipment of *Tilapia mossambica* (family Cichlidae) was brought in to put into the small dam at Broad Bottom.[12] We do not know whether they survived, but there are at least two reports of 'sleepers', which might refer to *Tilapia*. One of these was in the *St Helena News* for 4th August 1995 and recorded a fish found in a pool below the Agricultural Station at Sandy bay: *"The fish is about 20 centimetres in length and about five centimetres wide, being brown in colour with black stripes on both sides."* We were also told of 'guppies' being in some of the streams.

BIRDS

When we started writing this book we decided that we would always use the St Helena names for plants and animals. We had been in the company of people on St Helena for long enough to talk of the 'Sea Bird' (White Tern), 'Trophy Bird' (Redbilled Tropicbird), 'Cardinal' (Madagascar Fody) etc. However, when we came to writing about the Ascension birds we became more aware how confusing these names could be for visitors. With apologies to our St Helena friends we therefore give priority – for widespread species – to English names that are in general use elsewhere, although people from outside clearly have no right to decide what a bird is called in a local community. We follow the sequence for birds adopted by Beau Rowlands and his colleagues in their recently published book.

---

[12] F.J. Simmonds (1973).

This is primarily a list of breeding birds (including extinct ones). However a few non-breeding but more or less regular visitors are included. Tables 5B and 11A in Chapters 5 and 11 provide summary information for St Helena and Ascension respectively.

In addition to the birds included here, a large number of seabirds have been recorded near the islands and some landbirds have been found on shore. Most of the latter are evidently vagrants which have arrived by accident, either under their own power or after hitch-hiking on ships; they are unlikely to survive. A few other birds, however, probably reach St Helena and Ascension fairly regularly; all these, unsurprisingly, are well known wandering species. On both islands they include Sanderling *Calidris alba* (Plate 21), Turnstone *Arenaria interpres* (mainly Ascension), swifts *Apus* species and Swallow *Hirundo rustica*; on St Helena the records also include Grey Heron *Ardea cinerea*, Night Heron *Nycticorax nycticorax*, and unidentified birds of prey; and on Ascension they include Bar-tailed Godwit *Limosa lapponica*, Whimbrel *Numenius phaeopus* and also House Martin *Delichon urbica*.[13]

PROCELLARIIDAE – petrels and shearwaters

?H   Bulwer's Petrel   *Bulweria bulwerii*
This medium-sized petrel (length 26 cm, wingspan 67 cm) is entirely sooty brown with a paler diagonal wing bar visible at close range. It is long-winged and has a long pointed tail. The flight is erratic and twisting close to the waves with only short glides. Bulwer's Petrel has colonies on several archipelagos in the North Atlantic but is not known to breed south of the Equator in the Atlantic, although it is sometimes observed at sea much further south. However, the species has recently been found breeding south of the equator in the Indian Ocean (Round Island, Mauritius) so the fresh remains of this species found recently on St Helena (see Chapter 5) could possibly have belonged to members of a small breeding colony.

*†H   St Helena Bulweria   *Bulweria bifax*
Fossil bones of this extinct small gadfly petrel were found by Norman Kerr and then by Douglas Dorward and Philip at Sugar Loaf; in Olson's large collection it was one of the most numerous species at that site and also occurred at Sandy Bay. Olson placed it in the genus *Bulweria* but accepted that it was also similar to *Pterodroma*; hence the name *bifax*, meaning two-faced.

*†H   St Helena Petrel Plate 18   *Pterodroma rupinarum*
This extinct medium-sized gadfly petrel was first noted by Bill Bourne, who found a skull in the British Museum collected by Lieut. Turton in the 19th century. It proved to be abundant in the fossil deposits and was evidently a prominent member of the seabird community for several million years prior to 1502. Storrs Olson, who named the species, concluded that it is related to the *Pterodroma rostrata* group, previously known only from the Indian Ocean and Pacific. These birds have a strongly down-angled bill which distinguishes them from other members of the genus.

(H)   Murphy's Petrel ?   *Pterodroma ultima*
The mystery bird seen several times during the mid 1980s on St Helena (see Chapter 5) probably belonged to this species.

---

[13] Detailed accounts of all published records of bird visitors to St Helena and the surrounding seas can be found in B.W. Rowlands *et al.* (1998). Ascension records are in W.R.P. Bourne & K.E.L. Simmons (1998).

(HA)   Audubon's Shearwater Plate 18   *Puffinus lherminieri*
This small shearwater (length 30 cm, wingspan 69 cm) is blackish above and largely white below. The flight is a characteristic flutter followed by a short glide. The species is widespread in the warm parts of the Indian and Pacific Oceans but does not now breed in significant numbers in the Atlantic south of the equator.

  H: Audubon's Shearwater is represented at almost all the fossil sites but is more abundant in the recent ones; it was clearly a major component of the seabird community at the time of the island's discovery.

  A: On Ascension subfossil bones of this species have been found in two caves. Shearwater calls were heard by Douglas Dorward and Philip in 1958 and an adult was found in a hole on Boatswainbird Island in March 1959. However, although the species was evidently a member of the seabird community in the past, breeding in recent times has not been demonstrated.

*†H   St Helena Shearwater   *Puffinus pacificoides*
Bones of this large extinct shearwater were found at Sugar Loaf by Norman Kerr and then by Douglas Dorward and Philip; they were recognized as being related to the Wedge-tailed Shearwater *Puffinus pacificus*, a species characteristic of the tropical Indian and Pacific Oceans but conspicuous by its absence from the Atlantic. However, some of the bones differ slightly from those of *P. pacificus*, and Olson later named the St Helena species as *P. pacificoides*. Intriguingly, it has been found only in the oldest deposits, suggesting that it died out long before the discovery of the island by people.

(H)   Sooty Shearwater   *Puffinus griseus*
Two bones apparently belonging to this large shearwater were found by Olson in the oldest fossil deposits at Sugar Loaf. This is a subantarctic species and it is hard to imagine that there was ever a breeding colony on St Helena.

OCEANITIDAE (= Hydrobatidae) – storm-petrels

HA   Madeiran Storm-petrel (Pickering, Tuna Bird) Plate 18   *Oceanodroma castro*
This is a medium-sized storm-petrel, 20 cm long and with wingspan 43 cm. The wings are broad and the tail fairly long with a shallow fork. It is blackish brown all over except for a narrow, even band of bright white across the rump and a rather indistinct diagonal pale band on the wings; the legs are short and black. The flight has been compared with that of a House Martin; at sea it is buoyant and zigzagging, with alternating flapping flight and low glides like a small shearwater; around colonies it is more erratic. The call (used at the breeding colonies) has been described as a soft, squeaky note exactly like that of a finger rubbed hard on a windowpane. This petrel breeds on tropical and sub-tropical Atlantic Islands. It is hard to distinguish from Leach's Storm-petrel, which spends the northern winter in the tropical Atlantic.

  The Madeiran Storm-petrel nests in holes and crevices, and readily accepts nestboxes. At St Helena a nest was once found in an old cannon, and on George Island Beau Rowlands found eggs in a prominent open cave laid alongside large stones, in small holes and under overhangs. This ability to breed in the absence of soft soil for burrowing has allowed small populations of the species to survive on offshore rocky islets in several parts of the Atlantic (including St Helena and Ascension) after exclusion from the main islands by the arrival of mammalian predators. The single egg is white with fine, pale red spots at the large end, and averages 32 x 24 mm (Ascension, 44 eggs). Incubation lasts c.39 days and the nestling period is c.64 days

273

at Ascension. The birds are absent from the islands for much of the year; when breeding, they arrive at the colonies only around dusk. These storm-petrels feed on a variety of small animals which they take from the surface, both close to land and far out to sea.

H: St Helena is the southernmost breeding station of this species, and it is now almost certainly less common than in the past. It is known to nest on George, Shore and Egg Islands and probably does so on Speery Island and other islets. Abundant feathers and bones of this petrel can be found at Gill Point, implying that breeding attempts still take place in this area; the birds are doubtless killed by feral cats (and perhaps rats).

A: About 3,000 birds nest on Boatswainbird Island, where their biology was studied by Richard Allan on the British Ornithologists' Union Centenary Expedition in the 1950s. In 1971 Ken Simmons heard and recorded the burrow-call of the species in a barren lava area near Comfortless Cove, so occasional nesting attempts may still occur on the main island. Breeding is annual, with peak laying in November.

(H)   White-faced Storm-petrel   *Pelagodroma marina*
This species was abundant on St Helena in the past, but as a burrow nester on the main island which is almost helpless on land, it was doomed when rats arrived. It is 20 cm in length, with a wingspan of 42 cm and the longest and strongest legs of any storm-petrel: the long leg bones (tibia and tarsus) together measure more than half the length of the whole body. The upperparts are brownish grey with a pale diagonal bar across the wing and pale grey rump; the underparts are white and there is also white over the eye and around the base of the bill.

P. marina is a species of the subtropical and temperate oceans that still breeds in the Cape Verde Islands and the Tristan group. Subfossil bones of the species are abundant in most of the fossil deposits on the island, dating from the oldest period through to the most recent. This storm-petrel was evidently one of the most characteristic members of the St Helena avifauna and it may well be that even now, individuals visit the island from time to time.

PHAETHONTIDAE – tropicbirds

HA   Red-billed Tropicbird (Trophy Bird) Plate 18   *Phaethon aethereus*
This is a chunky, powerful bird, 48 cm long (about 100 cm including the central tail feathers) and with wingspan 105 cm. It is white with black near the wing tips, fine dark grey barring all over the back and two long, white, trailing tail feathers; the bill is long, strong and bright red (yellowish in juveniles) and the legs are yellowish. The range of the Red-billed Tropicbird includes the warm parts of the eastern Pacific, Caribbean, Atlantic and northern Indian Ocean; in other parts of the tropical oceans it is replaced by its close relative the Red-tailed Tropicbird *P. rubricauda*. At sea the flight is strong and direct, with rapid wing beats resembling a pigeon, but when seen from land the birds are generally making repeated hesitant approaches to nest sites; one can sometimes watch courtship flights where several birds alternate rapid flapping and dramatic glides, accompanied by chuckles and screams (these apparently gave rise to the name boatswainbird, referring to the boatswain's whistle). Like all tropicbirds, this species feeds on fish and squid by hovering and then plunging vertically into the sea, usually far from land. The nests are in holes and crevices, and fighting for these – sometimes to the death – is common in places where they are in short supply. The single egg is fawn to rich purple brown and averages 65 x 45 mm (Ascension, 245 eggs); incubation lasts about 43 days. Both parents incubate, sometimes taking shifts of several days. The birds spend the non-breeding season far out to sea, undergoing a complete moult before returning to land.

274

H: On St Helena there are probably a few hundred breeding birds. Nests are often in loose groups, on mainland cliffs (from close to sea level to 200 m above it) and also on the offshore islets. The laying season on St Helena is thought to be from July to January.

A: The breeding population is about 1,100 birds, mainly on Boatswainbird Island but with a substantial number on the adjacent mainland cliffs. Some laying occurs in all months, but there is an apparently annual schedule with peak laying around August.

A   White-tailed Tropicbird (Yellow-billed Tropicbird) Plate 18   *Phaethon lepturus*
This species is distinctly smaller than the Red-billed Tropicbird (length 39 cm, or 76 cm including central tail feathers). A mostly white bird with long white tail streamers, black near the wing tips and a strong black diagonal bar near the base of each wing. The bill and feet are yellowish. The range of this species includes tropical and subtropical Atlantic, Pacific and Indian Oceans.

On Ascension there is a breeding population of about 2,200 birds, mainly on Boatswainbird Island but also along the south coast of the main island and with a few pairs on stacks. Laying occurs in all months, but with peaks at different times in different years and individuals breeding at less than annual intervals. The birds leave the island between breeding periods. The egg varies in colour from pale fawn to rich purple brown, and averages 54 x 38 mm (Ascension, 811 eggs); incubation lasts about 41 days.

SULIDAE – gannets and boobies

HA   Masked Booby (White Booby, Gannet) Plate 19   *Sula dactylatra*
This is large and powerful seabird, 86 cm long and with wingspan 152 cm. It is white, with the wing tips, trailing edge of the wings and tail black; there is a blue-grey patch around the eye and the bill and feet are yellow or greenish. Juveniles can be confused with Brown Boobies since they have dark grey-brown heads and upperparts; the best distinction is the white upper breast and white collar. The female has a loud honking call but the male only a wheezy whistle. Masked Boobies fly with rapid and steady wing beats alternating with glides and often travel in small parties. They hunt by plunging from high up, catching mainly flying-fish. They tend to forage far from land and often float on the water. The Masked Booby is a species of warm tropical waters around the world. It prefers to breed on relatively flat ground. On Ascension the two whitish, thick-shelled eggs average 64 x 44 mm (12 eggs measured) and are laid about five days apart; the second chick soon dies (see Chapter 12); fledging takes about 17 weeks.

H: The fossil record shows that there were colonies of this bird on the mainland in relatively recent times; it is now confined to offshore islets. St Helena seems to be a marginal breeding station, with feeding conditions and thus breeding success varying from year to year. Observers in the 1950s failed to see any Masked Boobies on Shore and George Island. The first record of breeding in recent times was in 1968 (see Chapter 5) and in the 1990s about 200 adults seemed to be resident on Shore and George Island. Laying is usually in summer, and regular observations of the colony on Shore Island would be of great interest; ideally there should be a census (including counts of young) from Gill Point in about December and April each year, preferably with an overnight stay. Beau Rowlands has implied (on the basis of leg colour) that the St Helena population may be composed partly of members of the Indian Ocean race (with grey legs and feet) and partly of the Atlantic race (with orange-yellow legs). We are intrigued by this idea, although caution is required since the colour of soft parts in boobies changes to some extent according to reproductive condition.

A: Ascension has a population of about 9,000 birds, but there may be only about 3,000 breeding adults. Breeding is mostly on the more level parts of the top of Boatswainbird Island, but with small colonies on stacks along the south coast of the main island and perhaps a few pairs breeding on cliffs. There are still frequent attempts at breeding inland at the eastern end of the island. The population may now be limited by breeding space free of cat predation. In the middle of this century laying was mainly in May to August, but recent records suggest that it now occurs rather later in the year. The birds are resident, at least as adults, and return to the island at night.

HA   Brown Booby (Duck) Plate 19   *Sula leucogaster*

The Brown Booby is smaller than the last species (length 69 cm, wingspan 141 cm) with brown upperparts and breast but the rest of the underparts white. The bill and feet are yellowish or greenish. The Brown Booby occurs in inshore tropical waters around the world. Adults are securely distinguished from the other two Atlantic Ocean boobies (and also from gannets) by the sharp boundary between brown and white on the lower breast; young birds have partially brown underparts and could be confused with the young of the Masked or Red-footed Boobies. Brown Boobies fly with steady wing beats, alternating with glides. They typically feed in groups, mainly close to the shore. The prey is fish and squid, caught by plunging – often at a low angle – from close to the surface of the water. Roosting and breeding is typically on ledges, often fairly close to the water, but in many respects the breeding biology of the Brown Booby is similar to that of the last species. On Ascension two eggs are normally laid; they average 59 x 40 mm (130 eggs) and the incubation period is 43-47 days; only one chick is raised, fledging between 15 and 17 weeks old.

H: On St Helena the population is small and poorly documented, but four females were collected by the *Blossom* expedition in 1925 and a few pairs now breed on Shore Island (one chick present in February in both 1989 and 1995) and probably on George and Egg Islands. This species is not represented in the fossil deposits, perhaps because of its tendency to nest in steep places and ledges on cliffs. Individuals are probably present on offshore islets throughout the year.

A: There is a population of about 2,000 birds, mainly on the steep higher slopes of Boatswainbird Island and the broader ledges lower down. Other birds breed on inaccessible cliffs at the eastern end of the main island and on most of the coastal stacks. Work by Ken Simmons on the behaviour of Brown Boobies on the stacks has been described in Chapter 12. Breeding is non-seasonal and is highly responsive to fluctuations in the local food supply. Adults at least remain based on the island even when not breeding.

(H)A   Red-footed Booby Plate 19   *Sula sula*

This is the third species of widespread tropical booby; it is about the same size (length 74 cm, wingspan 150 cm) as the Brown Booby, with red feet and pale blue bill. There are several colour variations (phases or morphs). In the South Atlantic adults are distinguished from both Brown and Masked Boobies by the white tail; the wing tips and trailing edges of the wings are black and the rest of the plumage is either creamy white or pale brown. Juveniles are wholly grey brown, with yellowish grey legs. Throughout its range, except on Ascension and Trindade, the Red-footed Booby is a tree-nesting species; this habit is reflected in the shortness of its legs compared with those of the other boobies. It also lays only a single egg; it is bluish with a chalky covering and is variable in shape but averages 63 x 41 mm (38 eggs from various places).

276

H: Only a few fossil bones of this species have been found, all of them at Prosperous Bay. Two white phase birds were collected on Shore or George Island in 1925 by the *Blossom* expedition, and another was seen on Shore Island by Douglas Dorward and Philip in May 1959; there are a few subsequent records but no evidence of breeding.

A: The subfossil bone record indicates that this species was abundant in the past, breeding on ledges on the roughest lava. The 18th century visitor Osbeck left an excellent description of the white phase of the Red-footed Booby as one of the species he found breeding on the lowland plains. The current population is only about 30 birds, spread between Boatswainbird Island and various stacks. A pair had a large twig nest and a downy chick on a ledge on Boatswainbird Island in May 1958, but the chick subsequently disappeared. Several sightings of juveniles and subadults during the last few decades indicate successful breeding in very small numbers.[14]

FREGATIDAE – frigatebirds

*A   Ascension Frigatebird (Frigatebird) Plates 13, 16, 19 and 20   *Fregata aquila*
This is only a medium-sized frigatebird, but the body length is 91 cm and the wingspan 198 cm (well over six feet). The plumage is basically black, but some adults have white bellies (see figure) and juveniles have white heads and bellies. The bill is horn coloured and very long (around 9.5 cm) and with a right-angled hook at the tip, making a perfect grapnel for picking objects off the sea surface or catching flying-fish in the air. The adult male has an inflatable scarlet throat pouch and black feet, while the female lacks the throat pouch and has reddish feet and pale blue skin around the eye. The nest is a small scrape with a collection of pebbles, bones and feathers. A single white egg is laid; it is thin-shelled (probably reflecting tree-nesting ancestry of the group) and is easily broken; the eggs average 68 x 47 mm (96 measured eggs). Incubation is shared and lasts for roughly 44 days. Chicks begin to fly in their sixth or seventh month, but are fed by their parents for a further three or four months.

This endemic seabird was evidently abundant on the main island of Ascension in the past but now breeds only on Boatswainbird Island, with a population of less than 10,000 birds and possibly closer to 5,000. There are traditional mainland roost sites on cliffs on Letterbox, Crater Cliff and west of Crystal Bay. Frigatebirds are especially conspicuous over the Wideawake Fairs, where some individuals prey on young chicks, and over the beaches when young turtles are hatching. Laying can occur in any month, but there seems usually to be a peak around October. Birds are present in the colonies all year round, but individuals sometimes range 1000 km or more from the island. Ascension Frigatebirds catch much of their own food, although they sometimes pursue other birds and force them to regurgitate fish or squid. They cannot rest on the water without becoming waterlogged, and their tiny legs and feet make them almost unable to walk, so they have to nest and roost in places where they can catch the wind at take-off.

(H)   Great Frigatebird   *Fregata minor*
Storrs Olson discovered some bones of this widespread large frigatebird among more numerous remains of the Lesser Frigatebird in the Prosperous Bay deposits; he also found one bone in the most recent deposits at Sugar Loaf. It therefore appears that in the past a large and a small frigatebird coexisted on St Helena, as the same two species do on

---

[14] K.E.L. Simmons (1990).

some other islands, including – at least in the past – Trindade at a similar latitude in the western South Atlantic. The frigatebirds that survived into the early 19th century (see Chapter 5) were most likely this species. A high point of the south-west coast is labelled 'Man-of-war Roost' on early maps and in 1995 Philip visited this site with George Benjamin. They collected a white powder from among the rocks at the cliff-top which proved to have a high phosphate content, indicating that it contained old guano. Probably frigatebirds roosted rather than bred here, as the Ascension Frigatebirds still do on the mainland cliffs of that island; individuals on St Helena may have survived for a century or more, before dying of old age or being caught by the feral cats that prevented them from breeding.

(H)   Lesser Frigatebird   *Fregata ariel*
The Lesser Frigatebird is widespread in tropical oceans, but until the discovery of the bones on St Helena its distribution had an obvious gap in the eastern South Atlantic. There were evidently substantial colonies of the Lesser Frigatebird on St Helena at the time of its discovery by people, although the large number of bones of this species in the deposits at Prosperous Bay, compared with the small number of the Great Frigatebird, may be misleading. On Christmas Island in the Pacific we have noticed the contrast between the dense colony of the Lesser Frigatebird and the more dispersed breeding of the Great Frigatebird; on St Helena the latter species may have had colonies in exposed sites where onshore winds would assist take-off, but where preservation of bones is unlikely. As discussed in Chapter 5, the fact that frigatebird bones occurred only in the most recent deposits on St Helena probably reflects improving conditions for tropical seabirds after the end of the last ice age.

ARDEIDAE – herons

(HA)   Cattle Egret (Cattle Bird)   *Bubulcus ibis*
This is a small, relatively stocky white heron with yellowish bill and dark greenish legs; in the breeding season it has buff plumes on the head and elsewhere, and the legs are reddish. This heron has extended its world range dramatically during the last century or so; it is a well known wanderer which has become an almost regular visitor to both islands during the last fifty years. It often feeds among cattle, eating the insects that are disturbed as the animal moves along.

*†A   Ascension Night Heron   *Nycticorax* species
This endemic but extinct species of night heron was clearly related to the widespread Black-crowned Night Heron *N. nycticorax*, but was distinctly smaller. The first specimen was found by Storrs Olson in the smaller of the two spatter cones north of Sisters Peak and the second by us in Chapel Grotto Cave. Olson, though noting that his specimen was extremely small for *N. nycticorax*, was naturally reluctant to assume that a resident population was living in such unlikely heron habitat. The finding of a second specimen has convinced us that a night heron had reached the island and evolved small size, while retaining full powers of flight. Night herons are well known as wanderers and prey on a wide variety of vertebrate and invertebrate animals; we imagine that the Ascension species hunted around the shore but also scavenged in the bird colonies. It probably became extinct after the introduction of rats around 1700, or perhaps even in the 19th century.

278

PHASIANIDAE – pheasants and partridges

H   Chukar Partridge (Partridge)   *Alectoris chukar*
A colourful bird about 33 cm long, with red legs and bill, a white throat with a black border, and flanks with conspicuous black, white and chestnut bars. This is a shy bird which feeds on the ground, usually in groups. The birds are often first noticed by hearing the call – a resonant "chuck chuck" – from prominent rocks; when disturbed they take off noisily and glide away across the valley. The species was introduced by the Portuguese, perhaps from southern Persia around 1531; by the end of the 16th century it was abundant and tame.

   The Partridge is now widely distributed in the arid parts of the island, in rocky places with little vegetation. Rowlands suggests that the population is numbered in the hundreds; abundance seems to vary considerably from year to year. The nests are on the ground, sometimes on ledges or under Samphire bushes, and consist of a shallow scrape, sometimes lined with grass or leaves. Clutch size on St Helena is unrecorded, but is probably between six and twelve. The eggs are cream or buff with red or brown speckles, and average 39 x 30 mm. They are incubated by the female for just over three weeks and the chicks can fly at little more than one week old. The Partridge has been hunted throughout the history of St Helena and has become very shy.

H   Ring-necked Pheasant (Pheasant)   *Phasianus colchicus*
This is a large gamebird (53-89 cm long) with striking differences between the sexes. The plumage of the male is copper-coloured with black barring; the head and neck are metallic green, with the face red; the tail is very long. Females and young are brown and short-tailed. The voice is a loud, hard "korr-kok". The Pheasant flies mainly when disturbed, and only short distances; it feeds entirely on the ground. The nest is a shallow, barely lined scrape on the ground. The eggs are usually pale olive; in Europe they average 46 x 36 mm, and up to 12 eggs are lain. Clutch size does not seem to have been recorded in St Helena, but a brood of eight young chicks was seen by Loveridge. Incubation lasts 23-27 days and the chicks can fly within two weeks. The laying season is extended but perhaps mainly in early summer.

   The Pheasant was introduced by the Portuguese in the 16th century, probably around 1531, and quickly became abundant. It may have declined as the growing of grain was abandoned, but is still frequently seen in gardens, agricultural areas and in woodlands. Some hunting still occurs, but probably less than in the past.

A   Red-necked Francolin (Francolin)   *Francolinus afer*
The Francolin is a partridge-sized gamebird (35 cm long). The general colour of the upperparts is brown, with a white stripe above the eye and white cheeks; the underparts are pale with broad black streaks. The bill, throat and skin around the eye are red, as are the legs and feet. The immature is duller, with the bill brown. These birds fly rarely and only short distances. They feed on vegetable material and invertebrate animals. The nest is a hollow in the ground and 3-9 eggs are laid. Incubation is 23 days and the young can fly at ten days. The Francolin is not abundant on Ascension and is apparently confined to well vegetated areas, especially near Palmers. It was probably introduced in 1851. Mike Blair pointed out that the only subspecies with the plumage characteristics shown by the Ascension birds is the one from the borders of Angola and Namibia (*Francolinus afer afer*).

RALLIDAE – rails

*†A   Ascension Rail   *Atlantisia elpenor*
The Ascension Rail is an extinct flightless species seen by Peter Mundy in 1656 and
rediscovered as a subfossil three centuries later; Mundy's description is given in Chapter 5
(Figure 23). The second (specific) name of this bird refers to Elpenor, one of Odysseus'
crew members, who, while stranded on Circe's island, fell to his death from the roof of
her palace and descended straight to Hades: it reflects the fate of the Ascension Rails
trapped in the fumaroles and other caves. The first (generic) name depends on Olson's
conclusion that this species was closely related to *Atlantisia rogersi*, the diminutive
flightless rail still living on Inaccessible Island in the Tristan group.[15] *A. elpenor* was a
lightly built rail which Mundy compared in size to a Starling *Sturnus vulgaris*. It had a
medium-length bill, strong legs and much reduced wings. A number of specimens have
been found in caves and elsewhere on Ascension, implying that it was fairly numerous,
as Mundy's account also implies. It doubtless made its living partly by scavenging in the
vast seabird colonies of the pristine island, where beetles, flies and their larvae would
have been abundant.

*†H   St Helena Rail   *Atlantisia podarces*
This extinct large rail was discovered in 1959 by Douglas Dorward and Philip in the
deposits at Prosperous Bay and was described by Alexander Wetmore (see Chapter 5).
Storrs Olson showed that it was also present at Dry Gut and Sandy Bay and in the
oldest deposits at Sugar Loaf, implying that its ancestors reached the island millions of
years ago. The St Helena Rail was one of the largest known rails and notable for its
strong legs and feet with particularly long and sharp claws. The wings were somewhat
reduced, and Olson concluded that this rail was flightless but that it might have used
its short wings and long claws for fluttering up the steep sides of the rocky ravines of
St Helena. The large number of fossils found implies that it was common on the island.
Like most members of the family it was doubtless an omnivore, eating plant material
and invertebrate animals, and also scavenging around the seabird colonies.

*†H   St Helena Crake   *Porzana astrictocarpus*
Bones of this small flightless rail were first found by Olson, in the Prosperous Bay, Dry
Gut and Sandy Bay deposits. This is a short-billed crake considerably smaller than the
Ascension Rail. Its bones are slightly commoner in Olson's collections than those of
the large rail, and the two species collectively must have formed the core of the
vertebrate community at ground level in the pristine St Helena. It seems likely that
both of them fed extensively on the endemic snails which were so diverse and
abundant on the island in the past but which vanished along with their predators after
discovery of the island. Olson argues convincingly that the St Helena Crake could have
evolved from Baillon's Crake *Porzana pusilla*, a widely distributed migratory species
whose range includes Angola. Intriguingly, *P. pusilla* may also have given rise to
another flightless island species on the other side of the globe, *P. palmeri* of Laysan
Island in the Hawaiian chain, which became extinct only half a century ago.

---

[15] However, Bourne has pointed out that the Inaccessible Rail sometimes has distinctive spots like those of the South
American Spot-winged Crake *Porzana spiloptera*, suggesting that its ancestors may have reached Inaccessible from the west
and raising doubts as to whether it deserves to be placed in a distinct genus. Olson also placed the St Helena Rail (originally
described as *Aphanocrex podarces*) in the genus *Atlantisia*, which was established for the Inaccessible Rail. Since the St Helena
and Ascension Rails probably (though by no means certainly) reached their respective islands from Africa to the east, we
now feel that there is a case for renewing the search for their relatives using techniques of molecular biology, and perhaps
for abandoning the genus *Atlantisia*.

(HA)   Lesser Gallinule (Allen's Gallinule)   *Porphyrula alleni*

American Purple Gallinule   *Porphyrula martinica*

These two species, respectively inhabiting Africa and South and Central America, are closely related and could even be considered as geographical races within a single species. Both are great wanderers and the American form has frequently been found in South Africa, presumably blown across the Atlantic in the westerlies. Both have been found more than once on St Helena and on Ascension. There have been suspicions of breeding by the Lesser Gallinule near the Briars on St Helena. In a cave on Ascension Olson found a subfossil leg bone possibly of the Lesser Gallinule, but it is extremely unlikely that there was ever an established population on that island. Members of the genus *Porphyrula* are adapted to life walking on floating vegetation and in general do not make successful colonists of oceanic islands.

These are moorhen-like birds with purple and green plumage (the Moorhen lacks the purple tinge). They are generally similar, and because of the great interest of their trans-oceanic flights it is important for anyone finding a bird of this type to take careful note of the distinguishing features. The Lesser Gallinule is the smaller species, with wing length (the outermost section of the wing, measured with the wing folded) about 140 mm; the lower leg bone (tarsus) is shorter than the middle toe without the claw; the bill is wholly red and the legs and feet are also red. The American Purple Gallinule is larger, with wing length in the range 177-190 mm; the tarsus is not shorter than the middle toe without the claw; the bill is red, but broadly tipped with yellow or light green, and the legs and feet are yellowish. Immature birds have less bright bill, legs and plumage, and for these size may be the most reliable distinguishing character. However, the Moorhen has wing length intermediate between the two and may have a bill pattern like the American Purple Gallinule, so care is needed.

H(A)   Moorhen (Water Bird, Water Duck, Water Hen, Water Fowl) Plate 21

Gallinula chloropus

This bird is 32 cm long; it appears black from a distance, though it is actually dull olive brown above and sooty grey below. The underside of the tail shows bold white edges and there are also conspicuous white feathers on the flanks. The bill is red with a yellow tip, and there is a red shield above its base; the legs are greenish-yellow. Young birds are dull grey brown, and the base of the bill and shield are greenish brown. The call is a loud croak. The Moorhen is normally quite secretive, searching for insect and plant food on the ground or in shallow water, and is rarely seen flying. It is, however, capable of crossing vast areas of ocean, has colonised or been recorded as a visitor to many oceanic islands and has a worldwide distribution. It builds a nest near or on the ground near water, with a variable number of eggs. These are dark buff to whitish, spotted or freckled with red brown or slate; in South Africa they average 42 x 31 mm. Incubation takes about three weeks and the chicks can fly at about seven weeks old.

H: The Moorhen is presumably indigenous, colonists arriving from Africa. However, the island population is not endemic (i.e. is not distinct from the African birds) and no fossil bones have been found, suggesting that the species may have repeatedly colonized the island and then become extinct. Alternatively, a small population in the limited areas of suitable habitat may have been supplemented relatively frequently by more vagrants from Africa, thus maintaining a genetic link with the continent and preventing the island population from evolving into a distinct endemic form. Since Moorhens depend on standing water or very damp vegetation, it is possible that human occupation of St

Helena has benefitted them; the large population of introduced frogs undoubtedly makes feeding easier than it might have been in the past. The species now occurs in many damp places on the island. The laying season is probably in midsummer.

A: The Moorhen does not breed on Ascension, which is much too dry for them, but Philip well remembers an exhausted individual walking into the expedition camp on Ascension Island in 1958 at breakfast time and eating Rice Krispies out of his hand; other vagrant individuals have been seen on the island from time to time.

CHARADRIIDAE – plovers and turnstones

*H   Wirebird (sometimes referred to elsewhere as 'St Helena Plover')   Plate 21

Charadrius sanctaehelenae

The Wirebird is the last surviving endemic bird on St Helena. A few fossil bones of the species have been found in the most recent and middle period deposits, implying that it has been evolving on the island for at least several thousand years. Although it is closely related to Kittlitz's Plover *Charadrius pecuarius* of southern Africa, there are interesting differences. The Wirebird is substantially larger (length 19 cm) and has longer legs and bill, more rounded wings and relatively smaller flight muscles. The latter features are often found among birds on oceanic islands and sometimes culminate in the loss of flying ability. The Wirebird, however, is a capable flyer over the short distances required for life on St Helena. This flying ability may have been crucial in enabling the Wirebird to survive in the presence of feral cats.

Wirebirds (especially males) defend territories throughout the year, though most aggressively in the breeding season, which is mainly in the period October to March. The nest is an unlined shallow depression on the ground. Two eggs are normally laid and are grey to green with darker blotches; they average 34 x 25 mm (72 eggs). Incubation is about 28 days and the young can fly at four to five weeks. The incubating bird, when disturbed, will often partly cover the eggs with loose material before leaving the nest. If a person approaches the nest the bird will sometimes use a 'distraction' display, with trailing wing and spread tail, and may even collapse on the ground in a rumpled mass of feathers.

The Wirebird received remarkably little scientific attention until recently. Loveridge made a series of detailed behavioural observations, but it is only with the systematic work by Neil McCulloch in 1988-89 and in the last few years that a full picture of the biology of this intriguing species has emerged. McCulloch spent most of his time censusing the population and assessing its future prospects. He estimated that there were rather less than 500 individuals, with highest densities on relatively dry, flat pastures; the best areas were Bottomwoods, Longwood Golf Course and Farm, and Deadwood Plain. The birds also occupy semi-desert areas and frequently visit places with caked mud along streams, for instance below Gregory's Battery near Turks Cap Ridge and in Fishers Valley; they also bathe and drink at the pools near Cooks Bridge. However, the future of the Wirebird is now inevitably linked to the maintenance of pasture land, since about four-fifths of the population live in this habitat.

The Wirebird feeds on surface living invertebrates, mainly beetles, caterpillars, crickets and grasshoppers. The most important single prey at present is the tenebrionid beetle *Gonocephalum simplex*, which is among the most abundant species on the island. It is notable that this group of beetles is very abundant in open country in southern Africa, so the ancestors of the Wirebird evidently found familiar prey available to them when they reached St Helena

Many people have wondered about the habitat of the Wirebird on St Helena at the time when a large proportion of its current range was covered with trees. McCulloch pointed out that as a bird of open country it may have actually benefitted from deforestation. Quentin Cronk suggested that it might have lived in the dry gumwood woodland, which lacked undergrowth, but this is a type of habitat not used by any other plover. It seems more likely that during periods of high sea level like the present, the Wirebird was largely confined to the semi-desert area of Prosperous Bay Plain (where it still occurs in significant numbers) and to a few smaller level areas where there were only scattered bushes.

During periods of lowered sea level, however, the Wirebird would have had a much larger population, since it would also have occupied the broad apron of flat sandy land around the fringes of the island (see box in Chapter 6). It is easy to imagine a group of exhausted and hungry vagrant sand-plovers from open, dry areas in Africa settling down in such a habitat to feed on tenebrionid beetles and the endemic snails. We suspect that these plovers established themselves on the island at such a time, and were then able to maintain at least a small population on and around Prosperous Bay Plain during the interglacial periods when the apron was inundated by the sea.

STERCORARIIDAE – skuas

(HA)   Arctic Skua (Cape Hen)   *Stercorarius parasiticus*

Pomarine Skua (Cape Hen)   *Stercorarius pomarinus*
The smaller skuas (jaegers in American usage) are hawk-like seabirds about as large as a middle-sized gull, with long wings and powerful flight; they are either all dark or dark with pale underparts, and show a white flash at the base of the outer flight feathers. They are pirates and can be seen chasing other seabirds, especially terns, trying to make them drop or disgorge their food so that they can grab it. These skuas breed at high latitudes in the northern summer and spend the northern winter much further south, some of them apparently congregating around colonies of resident tropical seabirds.

H: These are the only non-breeding seabirds that are regularly and easily seen from the shore of the island. They are present from September to March, especially in Jamestown Bay and Ruperts Bay. The best observations were made by Dr Trevor Trueman in summer 1987/88. He found a large group (maximum 135 birds) on most evenings from December to early March, but much smaller numbers on 28th March. The Pomarine Skua is more thickset and powerful than the Arctic Skua, but separation of the two species is often not possible and both are often present.

A: Less information is available than on St Helena, but both species have been recorded and may be present regularly in winter.

LARIDAE – gulls

(H)   Kelp Gull ?   *Larus dominicanus*
Two bones of gulls have now been found on St Helena, both in Dry Gut. As explained in Chapter 5, the most likely species is *L. dominicanus*. We cannot be sure that this species was breeding on St Helena, but it seems certain that individuals were present and scavenging around the seabird colonies, like those watched by R.C. Murphy on Lobos de Tierra off the coast of Peru.

STERNIDAE – terns

HA   Sooty Tern (Wideawake, Egg Bird) Plates 12, 13, 15 and 20   *Sterna fuscata*
The Wideawake is a fairly large tern (length 44 cm, wingspan 90 cm) which is easily distinguished from noddies, being black above and white below and with a long, forked tail that is conspicuous in flight. Juveniles are sooty black with pale speckling. The most distinctive call can be rendered "wide-awake, wide-awake". The flight is graceful, buoyant and strong with steady wing beats, though the birds occasionally soar high in the air at sea and have a spectacular gliding courtship flight. Wideawakes forage mainly far from land, and can travel hundreds of kilometres from the colony even when breeding. They feed on fish and squid by snatching them as they break the surface when chased by tuna and other predatory fish. This is probably the most numerous tropical seabird, breeding in huge colonies on islands surrounded by seas at a temperature of 23°C or higher.

    The nest of the Wideawake is a slight scrape in the ground and there is a single egg; on Ascension it averages 52 x 36 mm (mean of 635 eggs).[16] Incubation is shared – as in all tropical seabirds – and averages 29 days; the fledging period varies between just over five and nine weeks according to the rate at which food is brought to the young. This species is famous for having a less than annual breeding cycle in some parts of the world. The birds leave their colonies when breeding is finished and apparently fly continuously until the next breeding season. Their plumage is not waterproof, and they soon become helpless if forced to swim. We interpret this not as a failure of evolutionary adaptation, but as an indication that for a fairly small seabird associated with large predatory fish, staying in the air is the safest policy!

    H: Breeding colonies were present on the mainland until quite recently. Ernest Roberts told us how he used to go fishing and collecting eggs at Castle Rock, climbing down to near sea level and then up again to reach the place where the Wideawakes were nesting. His father had said that around 1900 there were more Wideawakes and they used to breed on Castle Rock Plain (which he called Castle Rock Flat). The other traditional Wideawake nesting area on the main island is around Gill Point. Alex Knipe told us how as a young lad he used to go and collect eggs from the 'bird ground', evidently at Gill Point, where there were clouds of Wideawakes; his wife recalled that the eggs were excellent for 'caking'. This was apparently around the 1940s, matching with the records of J.P. Chapin (quoted by Rowlands) who was told of 300-400 birds breeding at Gill Point in 1948. However Raymond Leo of Levelwood saw an active colony there as recently as about 1985; he took us to Gill Point to show us the many Wideawake feathers, bones and eggshells that are still in holes and crevices there, along with many remains of Madeiran Storm-petrels. Breeding now occurs only on offshore islets, and even there numbers have apparently decreased during the last half century. Estimates made in 1948 and 1952 were of around 2,000 birds, with substantial colonies on Speery, George and Shore Islands. Recent estimates are much lower and in 1994-95 we saw very few birds, although about five were apparently incubating on Shore Island on 23rd April 1995. The laying season seems to be highly variable: mainly in early summer, but with eggs recorded in many different months.

---

[16] The eggs are very large and at an average weight of 35 grams are almost one fifth of the weight of the female, which is close to the maximum for a flying bird. They have pale ground colour and dark spots, but the details are extremely variable. Tests that Philip did in 1959 indicated that the adults used the particular colour pattern of their egg as one of the clues by which they recognised their own nest, but surrounding landmarks were also important. After hatching it is clear that the Wideawakes use calls for recognition, and when the chicks are older one can sometimes see and listen to prolonged duets as an adult returning from sea establishes contact with its chick, which may have wandered some distance from the nest. Chicks which try to cheat by begging from recently returned adults who are not their parents are fiercely driven away.

A: These terns nest in large colonies or Wideawake Fairs on the mainland, with a few pairs on Boatswainbird Island. The breeding schedule is non-annual, laying starting about every 9.6 months. All birds leave the island when the last chicks fledge (or are eaten by cats) at the end of the breeding period and do not settle again for 2-3 months. There is then a 'night club' period lasting 2-3 months before laying starts, during which many adults settle on favoured areas at night. During this period (as well as while breeding) they suffer severe predation from feral cats.

In 1958 Philip guessed that there were 750,000 breeding birds; recently several more systematic surveys have been carried out. In 1990 we worked with members of the Army Bird Watching Society to make an estimate of the overall numbers of pairs. We counted eggs in 234 circular 'quadrats' of 10 square metres spaced along transects through the different colonies (which had widely varying egg densities) and the army team made surveys and calculated the area of the colonies. Our initial estimate of the number of pairs breeding was 175,000, but a better statistical analysis of the data gave a figure of 189,000 plus or minus 19,200. In 1997 another census was carried out by N. Ratcliffe and F.A. Roberts of the Royal Society for the Protection of Birds, using improved methods. It provided an estimate in that breeding period of 150,500 plus or minus 7,100 pairs, which is significantly lower than the revised 1990 figure. However, 1997 was an El Niño year which may have disrupted the food supply and led to some birds deferring breeding. The data do not yet show whether the total population of Wideawakes based on Ascension is stable or declining, but repetition of the censuses over the next few decades should provide the answer. Total numbers (including immature birds that do not yet breed) are now probably well under half a million.

HA Brown Noddy (Black Bird, Egg Bird) Plate 21   *Anous stolidus*
This tern is about the same size as the Wideawake (length 42 cm, wingspan 83 cm) but is coffee brown all over, the underwing paler with dark margins; the head is also pale, grading almost to white on the forehead; the bill and legs are black. The tail is long and somewhat wedge shaped, with a slight notch at the end. The birds are generally silent, but when disturbed they use a grating call (like the "caw" of a Rook, but deeper) and often fly aggressively at intruders. Their flight is swift and strong, but somewhat erratic; they do not soar like Wideawakes. When fishing, Brown Noddies generally fly between two and three metres above the water and swoop to the surface, occasionally splashing, to catch small fish and squid driven to the surface by predatory fish. Both this species and the Black Noddy often use their fully webbed feet to keep themselves up off the surface while feeding. Brown Noddies can often be seen feeding close to the shore, and unlike the Wideawake, they probably do not travel far from their colonies when breeding.

The Brown Noddy occurs throughout the tropical oceans. It is a colonial breeder and in some parts of its range it lays on open ground, or builds substantial nests in trees. On St Helena and Ascension, however, it normally uses rock crevices or ledges, usually in gently sloping areas, with pebbles as the only nest material. Unlike the next species, the Brown Noddy never has guano in the nest. A single egg is laid and on Ascension is 53 x 36 mm (mean of 113 eggs); it is fawn or stone-coloured with reddish or purple flecks and smears. Incubation is shared and lasts roughly 32-35 days. Chicks at many breeding stations show polymorphism in down colour, with different frequencies in different places. During the British Ornithologists' Union expedition to Ascension, Douglas Dorward and Philip recorded 48 chicks as being dirty white, eight as brownish black (with or without a white crown) and one as intermediate. The chicks run from their nests when threatened, unlike the cliff-nesting Black Noddy. Neither the Brown nor Black Noddy is represented in the fossil record on St Helena or Ascension, presumably because both species nest on cliffs or rocky places close to the shore.

H: The Brown Noddy is still fairly common, although it has been subject to heavy egg collection and numbers may have declined substantially. Laying is usually around midsummer but with much variation. In 1988 the breeding population was estimated by Trevor Trueman at 1400 individuals, with about 300 pairs on Speery Island, 100 on George and Shore Islands and about 300 pairs at other sites including Egg and Peaked Islands and Lighter Rock; some birds may breed at the foot of cliffs of the main island. On 6th February 1992 Rowlands found 75 nests, with eggs, under the Hood on George Island. On 8th February 1995 we visited Egg Island and found around 100 young chicks and less than 100 eggs; some pairs seemed not to have laid yet.

A: There is a population of around 1000 individuals, roughly equally divided between stacks and mainland cliffs, mainly in the easternmost part of the island; this species does not breed on Boatswainbird Island. Birds are present on the island at all times of the year. Breeding on some of the stacks near Georgetown was investigated by Philip and his colleagues on the BOU expedition in the 1950s and by Ken Simmons in the 1960s. Unlike most other birds here and elsewhere, the Brown Noddies of Ascension can often be found breeding and moulting flight feathers at the same time. Probably this is because breeding is opportunistic, commencing whenever a good supply of food becomes available close to the island. Furthermore, eggs and chicks are often lost during periods with oceanic rollers that wash over the stacks, increasing the apparent irregularity of breeding. It is therefore not yet clear whether there is a basic annual cycle.

HA   Black Noddy (Noddy Bird, Egg Bird) Plate 21   *Anous minutus*
The Black Noddy is darker brown than the Brown Noddy, smaller (length 37 cm, wingspan 69 cm) and dark under the wings, with the tail not conspicuously wedge shaped. The bill is finer than in the Brown Noddy and the white on the head extends from the forehead down the back of the neck giving a white-capped effect. The colouration of the young, from the moment of hatching, resembles that of the adults (an unusual situation in birds). A variety of grating calls is used, most noticeably when the colony is disturbed or when a bird arrives to join its mate. The flight, method of feeding and food are similar to those of the Brown Noddy, although smaller prey are taken; foraging takes place mainly close to the shore.

The Black Noddy and a closely related species in the Indo-Pacific area are the most abundant small terns of tropical oceans. Black Noddies never breed on open ground; in some areas they build nests in bushes or trees, but on St Helena and Ascension they always use ledges on cliffs; nests are made of feathers and plant material plus accumulations of guano, so that breeding sites are always conspicuous. There is often fighting for ledges, and the birds use a rich array of displays during aggressive encounters as well as between the members of a pair. The single egg is pale to deep fawn brown with reddish brown or grey flecks; it averages 48 x 32 mm (Ascension, 9 eggs). Incubation is shared and lasts about 35 days, and the development of the chick varies a good deal according to the food supply. Adaptations to cliff nesting include crouching rather than leaving the nest when threatened. The birds frequent their colonies throughout the year.

H: The Black Noddy is now the most abundant seabird of St Helena. Careful estimates by Beau Rowlands on 2nd February 1989 and 28th January 1992 indicated a breeding population of around 7,600 individuals. The largest colonies are on Egg and Peaked Islands and associated mainland cliffs, Speery and Shore Islands, with small colonies elsewhere. Laying seems to be mainly in November and December, but with considerable variation.

A: There is a total population of around 20,000 individuals, making the Black Noddy the second most numerous seabird, though far behind the Wideawake. Nests are restricted to cliffs; the breeding cycle is variable, but there may usually be a peak in laying around June-July.

HA   White Tern (Fairy Tern, White Bird, Sea Bird) Plate 21   *Gygis alba*
The White Tern is a small (length 30 cm, wingspan 78 cm) all-white tern with black around the eye and a black bill. It is heavier than the Black Noddy and with greater wingspan; the tail has a shallow fork. The voice consists of a series of grunts and squeaks. The flight is buoyant and graceful at sea, but light and fluttering when near the nest; the birds often seem very inquisitive and this sometimes leads to their capture by feral cats. The White Tern resembles the Wideawake in its unwebbed feet which are not used when fishing; the legs are very short, however, unlike those of the ground-nesting Wideawake. The diet includes a wide variety of fish and squid; crustaceans are also taken. Although the birds sometimes feed by day, they also capture deep-sea fish that migrate to the surface at night. These are probably caught at dawn and dusk, when the white colour and translucent wings of the terns make them almost invisible when viewed against the sky.

The White Tern occurs in tropical oceans round the world. It is not a strongly colonial species, nesting dispersed or in loose groups on cliffs or in trees. In fact 'nest' is a misnomer, since the female lays her single egg on a branch or tiny ledge, selecting a place where there is a slight dip to keep it in place. There is no truth in the idea that the egg is glued down, but adults are very careful when settling on or leaving the egg, and the chick has sharp hooked claws and clings tightly as soon as it is hatched. Even so, chicks sometimes fall off and may then be abandoned. The egg is blunt and almost elliptical, pale buff with dark straggling lines and speckling; it averages 44 x 33 mm (Ascension, 203 eggs). Incubation is by both sexes and lasts about 36 days. The rate of growth – and age at first flying – is evidently highly variable depending on the food supply. At the St Helena nests noted by Loveridge the chick stayed in the 'nest' for 42-50 days, but on Ascension in 1958 Douglas Dorward knew of five chicks that began to fly when 60-75 days, and three of these were still being fed by their parents at 84, 90 and 95 days.

H: Storrs Olson found that the fossil bones of this species are distinctly smaller than those from Ascension and elsewhere in the Atlantic and suggested that the St Helena population should perhaps be treated as an endemic subspecies. Numbers are very hard to judge. The maximum estimate for the coastal cliffs and Jamestown area is 480 pairs in November 1952; more recent estimates are closer to 100 pairs. However, an unknown number breed inland in various parts of the island, often in Thorn trees. The total population (including immature birds) is likely to be less than 2,000 individuals. There are few data on the laying season and birds can be seen all the year round, but of 21 breeding attempts at Jamestown recorded by Loveridge, 14 eggs were laid in the period June-August and four in October-November.

A: The best estimate of the breeding population is about 5,300 birds, mainly concentrated on Boatswainbird Island, but with small numbers on inland cliffs and in a few places also in trees. White Terns can be seen at any time of the year, but individuals leave the island after breeding and young birds may spend some years away from the colony; if so, the total population may be at least 6,000. There is an approximately annual breeding schedule, with the peak of laying around January and February.

COLUMBIDAE – pigeons and doves

H   Feral Pigeon (Rock Dove, Pigeon)   *Columba livia*

The pigeons of St Helena are generally similar to other feral derivatives of the Eurasian Rock Dove stock. They are about 33 cm long, basically grey in colour, usually with some purple around the head, and with black barring on the wings and tail. However, the plumage is extremely variable, with many individuals very dark. The voice is a gentle and mellow "coo-roo-coo". The flight is fast and direct.

The history of pigeons and doves on St Helena is obscured by confusion in the records with the White Tern, as mentioned in Chapter 5. It is likely that the feral pigeon was established on the island in the 16th or early 17th century. There were probably also later importations, and the local population may have been reinforced after the end of the First World War by the release of military carrier pigeons which had been kept on the island for use in emergency. Individuals have also made their own way to the island: we were told of the finding of a pigeon ringed in Windhoek (Namibia). Pigeons are now common and widespread in the lower and central parts of the island, roosting and nesting especially on rocky ledges beside waterfalls; cliffs near the Heart Shape Waterfall and Cat Hole have long been favoured sites. There are other colonies around the waterfall near Turks Cap Ridge and on cliffs in Jamestown, Prosperous Bay Valley and in many other parts of the island, as well as around the coasts. The nest is a loose accumulation of twigs. Two white eggs are laid at any time of year. In South Africa the eggs average 38 x 29 mm, incubation lasts for 17-18 days and the nestling period is 28-35 days. On St Helena pigeons feed mainly in agricultural areas at middle levels on the island, but we have seen one eagerly eating the tiny fruit of Saltbush near the road above Jamestown. Flocks of up to 200 have been seen in the Longwood area and Rowlands estimated the total population as at least 1000.

*†H   St Helena Dove   *Dysmoropelia dekarchiskos*

The terrestrial dove (or pigeon: there is no basic distinction) is one of the most notable of the extinct birds of St Helena, and Storrs Olson honoured it by giving it a specific name meaning 'little corporal', a nickname often applied to Napoleon. The St Helena Dove was much larger than its distant relatives in the genus *Streptopelia*, and had heavy legs and reduced wings; it was probably flightless. Intriguingly, fossils of this bird have been found only at Sugar Loaf in the oldest deposits; in view of the intense collecting that has been done at more recent sites, it seems likely that it became extinct in the distant past. Large doves are normally fruit eaters and some eat fruits of palms, so it is tempting to speculate that the dove became extinct at the same time as the palms that are known to have flourished on the island some eight million years ago (see Chapter 4). Nonetheless, a niggling doubt lingers from the passing comment by Melliss: *"it is said that" ..."a larger Ground Dove"* exists in the island.

H   Peaceful Dove (Dove)   *Geopelia striata*

This is a small (length 24 cm) ground-dove with crown and back scaly brown, face bluish grey and buff on the breast. In flight the tail appears rather long and tapering, and the white outer feathers are conspicuous when the tail is spread before landing. The bill is grey and the legs pinkish. The Peaceful Dove is of Malaysian origin but was introduced to Mauritius in about 1750 and may have been brought from there to St Helena later in the 18th century. The species is now abundant around the settlements and throughout much of the island, though not on the central ridge or in the drier parts of the Crown Wastes. It feeds on the ground, usually in groups, and can often be seen by the roadsides. The nest of twigs is in low trees and two white eggs are laid; they average 21 x 17 mm. The laying season is extended and may be year-round. Incubation lasts for 13-14 days and the nestling period about 16 days.

CUCULIDAE – cuckoos

*†H   St Helena Cuckoo   *Nannococcyx psix*
A single broken wing bone found by John Bailey at Prosperous Bay was identified by Olson as belonging to a cuckoo, but differing in its small size and other characters from most kinds of cuckoos. It may, however, be derived from the small forest cuckoos of the genus *Chrysococcyx*, which occur in West Africa. As discussed in Chapter 5, these are brood parasites and the host on St Helena is unknown.

UPUPIDAE – hoopoes

*†H   St Helena Hoopoe   *Upupa antaios*
Bones of this bird, which is related to the widespread old world Hoopoe *Upupa epops*, were first found in deposits of the middle period in Dry Gut and then in recent ones at Prosperous Bay; in 1995 we found several more bones on Prosperous Bay Plain (see Chapter 5). The St Helena Hoopoe had much reduced powers of flight. Storrs Olson, in an elegant analysis, estimated that its wing area was only two thirds that of its continental relative, but its body weight was about twice as great, giving a high wing loading. Hoopoes are birds of grassland or open forest, and Olson suggested that the presence of a hoopoe on St Helena was: *"another argument against the island's having been entirely covered with heavy forest in pre-European times."* We feel that the St Helena Hoopoe would not only have utilized open arid areas around the coasts and at Prosperous Bay Plain, but probably also foraged for insects around seabird colonies and on the ground in the dry gumwood woodland described in Chapter 4, which then occupied about a quarter of the area of the island.

STURNIDAE – starlings and mynas

HA   Indian Myna (Miner Bird) Plate 22   *Acridotheres tristis*
The Myna is a large (26 cm long) dark coloured starling with yellow legs, a yellow bill and a yellow patch behind the eye. The head is blackish with a green gloss, grading into chestnut brown on the back and lower breast. There is white under the tail and on the edge of the wing. In flight the white tips of the tail feathers and white patches on the wings are conspicuous. The birds are very noisy, with an extremely varied repertoire of repeated short calls and the ability to make a great variety of whistles and calls, sometimes mimicking local noises. The nest is an untidy accumulation of any available materials. The eggs are uniform pale greenish blue and in South Africa average 29 x 22 mm; on St Helena they may be a little smaller. Incubation lasts for 17-18 days and the nestling period is 22-24 days. This is a native of Afghanistan, across to India and southeast Asia, but it has been introduced to many islands and other places.

H: Two species of myna have been brought to St Helena, causing some confusion in the records. The Hill Myna *Gracula religiosa* was introduced in 1829 but did not spread beyond Jamestown and became extinct some time after 1875. Five individuals of the Indian Myna were released at the Briars in 1885 by Phoebe M. Moss. This species has been very successful and is now found in every part of the island, though it is scarce in the driest areas. It is omnivorous and we have even seen it feeding on nectar in blossoms of the Thorn Tree. It eats all kinds of fruit and is a considerable pest to fruit growers; it is also implicated in the spread of the invasive shrub Wild Currant, since it is fond of the fruit and regurgitates the seeds. It also takes invertebrates, frogs and eggs and young of other birds, probably including the Wirebird. Mynas roost in trees in noisy flocks. At dusk on 7th March 1995 we counted 646 (plus or minus a few) going to the roost in Jamestown over a period of 70 minutes. The Myna breeds in a variety of sites including tree-holes, rock cavities, old buildings and flax plants. The clutch on St Helena is 2-4 eggs and laying is at all times of year, but especially November to May. Humans are sometime mobbed near the nest and may even be struck. The birds also have prolonged and intense territorial fights.

A: The Myna was apparently introduced to Ascension from Mauritius in 1879. It is common over most of the island and especially around settlements.

PASSERIDAE – sparrows

A   House Sparrow (Sparrow)   *Passer domesticus*
This species is 14.5 cm long and has a strong stubby bill. The male has a chestnut back, grey crown, black bib and white throat patch; the female and young are dull, streaked brown. A small group of House Sparrows was brought to Ascension in 1986 and has established a breeding colony in Georgetown. Numbers have increased very little and the birds are normally seen within about 50 metres of where they were originally introduced.

PLOCEIDAE – weavers

H   Madagascar Fody (Cardinal, Robin, Red Bird) Plate 22   *Foudia madagascariensis*
This weaver bird is 13 cm long. The male in breeding plumage, from about August to April, has bright scarlet head and breast and scarlet-orange rump. Occasionally males are seen with orange-yellow replacing the red areas of the plumage; one such bird seen by Loveridge had the cap of the head green. In winter the males lose their bright colours and become secretive, preferring dense vegetation; they then resemble the sparrow-like females, which are buff brown with a dark eyestripe, yellowish rump and tawny and striated sides. Distinguishing brown Cardinals from female Canaries requires care, and the similarity has led to persistent confusion about the shape of the nests of the two species. Canaries have cup-shaped open nests. The nests of Cardinals are built by the male and are domed and 10-13 cm across by about 16 cm high, with the entrance at the side, usually facing away from the prevailing wind; they are placed in dense bushes or trees. One to three (three probably normal) light blue eggs are laid, and there is sometimes a second clutch; the eggs are roughly 18 x 14 mm. Incubation and the nestling period are both about two weeks; Loveridge recorded a case in which the third (last) fledgling left the nest four weeks to the day after the first egg had been laid. The laying season is October to March or even later. While breeding the male is

aggressive to both his own and other species. We sometimes heard an elementary song consisting of several churling calls all on the same note, rather like a squeaking door, and also a cricket-like "tick tick tick".

This species is endemic to Madagascar and has been introduced to Mauritius and other Indian Ocean islands. It was probably brought to St Helena towards the end of the 18th century. The Cardinal is now fairly common throughout the high parts of the island and in valleys with vegetation. The birds are strongly territorial in flax and woodland, but feed in flocks in grassland; we have seen a field flash red with them on Longwood Plain. They take nectar from flowers and feed and perch on flax inflorescences, but also take insects and seeds.

H   Java Sparrow (Sparrow)   *Padda oryzivora*

This dramatically coloured seed-eating bird is the size of a House Sparrow (15 cm long) with a massive bill that continues the line of the crown, giving it a bull-headed appearance. Both sexes have delicate pale grey upperparts, black head and tail, white cheeks and lilac breast; the bill and legs are red. This species originates from Java and Bali, and was established on the island by 1776. Numbers seem to have fluctuated considerably in the past, probably because of agricultural changes coupled with trapping of birds for sale to passing ships. As early as 1796 the Records imply that the population was under threat from exploitation: *"Proposed that no person whatever be suffered to destroy or catch Java Sparrows for the term of one year from the date hereof, under penalty, if a child of a whipping, if a grown person of being fined by the Governor and Council."*

Java Sparrows are now fairly common, but with a patchy distribution. They are usually seen in pairs or small flocks in inhabited or agricultural areas. Loveridge recorded that in about 1960 many died after eating treated (poisoned) imported grain that had been spilt in the lighters during unloading. There was also an incident of poisoning of Java Sparrows and Doves and Fodies at the start of a rat-eradication campaign in 1969. There is a large communal roost in the gardens in Jamestown, where we counted 2,859 (approximately!) arriving at dusk on 21st March 1995, over a period of one and three-quarter hours. Breeding occurs throughout the year and is not colonial. The domed nests are placed in buildings or trees or cavities in cliffs. The white eggs are roughly 20 x 14 mm, with a clutch of up to eight elsewhere; on St Helena Loveridge recorded a brood of five young. Incubation is 13-14 days and the nestling period nearly four weeks.

HA   Common Waxbill (Amadavat, Averdavat) Plate 22   *Estrilda astrild*

A small (13 cm long) finch in which both sexes have brownish, finely barred plumage, long black tail, red bill and eyestripe and a small rosy patch on the belly. The call is a nasal "cher cher cher" and there is a "ping ping" flight note. There is also a song comprising a few twittering notes followed by a more strident note on a slightly lower pitch. The nest is roughly spherical, about 18 cm in diameter and built of grass and feathers, with an almost closed tubular entrance at the side near the top. Eggs are white and roughly 14 x 11 mm; in South Africa the clutch is 4-6. Incubation is 11-12 days and the nestling period 17-21 days. On St Helena nests are placed in high trees, cliffs, caves, overhangs and low bushes, and even in rock crevices on the coastal islands; they are loosely constructed and are often dislodged in strong winds. On Ascension nests are often practically on the ground in cactus and even in crevices in the lava. The Amadavat is a native of southern Africa but has been introduced to many places.

H: The Amadavat was abundant by 1776 and was probably introduced a decade or so earlier. From this time until the 1930s the birds were caught and traded in substantial numbers with ships calling at the island. It is common over much of the island, including the neighbourhood of houses. Numbers may fluctuate considerably from year to year. It feeds mainly on grass seeds and can be seen in large flocks on Deadwood Plain when seeds are ripening; Loveridge reported a pair apparently feeding on aphids on a rose bush. Breeding occurs year round.

A: Introduced, Packer says in 1860. It is now common, especially in the lower part of the island.

FRINGILLIDAE – finches

HA Yellow Canary (Canary, Yellow Bird) Plate 22   *Serinus flaventris*
This is a small (12 cm long) greenish or yellowish finch with more or less streaking. Typical males are yellow below and greenish with some brown streaking above; they have a bright yellow stripe round the forehead and back over the eye, fading out on the nape; the crown and a stripe through the eye are green but there is a yellow patch below the eye and below this a strong black moustachial stripe. Females are drab, streaky, greenish grey, with dull greenish yellow on the rump; the greenish tinge separates them from brown Cardinals. The flight is rapid and buoyant. The song is a long flowing warbling without definite phrasing. The Yellow Canary is native to the western half of southern Africa.

H: The identity of the canary on St Helena has been the subject of considerable confusion. However, we agree with Rowlands that canaries were probably brought in around 1776 and that the established population is now basically of *Serinus flaviventris* stock. However, there may have been hybridisation with other species brought in at various times and the modern population is conspicuously variable. Canaries were fairly common in the early 19th century and were sold to people on visiting ships until the 1930s. They are now very common, but published records indicate that numbers have fluctuated. The main habitat is in scrub or open areas with some trees. The food is mainly seeds, but fruit is also taken and we saw them hawking insects. The nest is usually at a height of less than two metres in bushes such as Furze, Wild Coffee and Samphire, but sometimes higher up in larger trees (including pines) or on the ground. The nest is an open cup, constructed of fine twigs, rootlets, leaves and grass and lined with feathers, thistle down or wool. The clutch on St Helena seems to be usually 3-4 eggs, which are faintly bluish white, sparsely speckled with minute brown dots around the larger end; they measure about 18 x 13 mm. Breeding seems to occur at all times of year, but probably mainly in summer.

A: On Ascension the Canary is fairly common, especially on the lower parts of Green Mountain. There is some confusion about the date of its introduction. Eric Duffey, in his 1964 account of the ecology of the island, said that Canaries were reported as common in 1878. Yet Lionel S. Bartlett, who was Resident Magistrate from 1934 to 1936, made a comment which seems to imply that they were not present before the 1930s; he wrote: *"During the last two years, we have received from St Helena .... over thirty canaries, which appear to be on the increase."*

INVERTEBRATES – animals without backbones

TURBELLARIA – free-living flatworms

Turbellarians are flattened, worm-like, unsegmented animals, usually less than 25 mm long. They generally live at the bottom of the sea or in freshwater, but a few occur on land. About six species have been found on St Helena, of which one represents an apparently endemic genus and two others are endemic species; there is one species on Ascension.

MACROSTOMIDAE – macrostomids

*H   *Macrostomum parmum*. This is a minute flatworm, little more than 1 mm long, with a broad, shield-like body, strongly convex in the centre; it is almost transparent and has two tiny dark eyes, very close together and about 15% of the body length from the front end. Several individuals were found by the Belgians in freshwater at Sandy Bay. No close relatives of *M. parmum* are known from Africa.

PROCERODIDAE – procerodids

The procerodids are members of a group known as triclads, which includes marine, freshwater and terrestrial subgroups. Intriguingly, the procerodids belong in the marine subgroup ('Maricola'), yet those on St Helena occur in freshwater. The implication is that their ancestors are marine forms and that they may have relatives still living in salt water around the island.

*H   *Dinizia sanctaehelenae*. A slender, whitish flatworm up to 3.25 mm long by 0.75 mm wide. It has two minute dark eyes which are about 14% of the length of the body from the front end, level with a slight constriction that marks the separation of the 'head' from the rest of the body; they are more widely spaced that in *Macrostomum*, the distance between them being about the same as that from each of them to the edge of the body. The Belgians found this species at Sandy Bay and at Rose Hill. Another member of the genus is found in Brazil.

**H   *Tryssosoma jennyae*. This species is a pale streaky brown; it grows to the same length as *Dinizia* but is broader (maximum 3.25 x 1.5 mm) and with the two eyes closer to the front end (around 5% of the body length). *T. jennyae* is the only known member of an endemic genus; its distant relatives are found in the southern hemisphere. The Belgians collected this species in freshwater seepage pools; the precise locality is not recorded, but the pools are probably connected to groundwater systems and the main population may be subterranean.

Tryssosoma jennyae
3 mm   MRAC

BIPALIIDAE and RHYNCHODEMIDAE – bipaliids and rhynchodemids

Bipaliids and rhynchodemids are terrestrial flatworms ('Terricola') living in moist places on land. One bipaliid and two rhynchodemids have been found on St Helena by the Belgians and one rhynchodemid is known from Ascension; none have been securely identified and it is not clear whether any of them are endemic.

H   *Bipalium ?kewense*. Several specimens were obtained by the Belgians, but we have little information about them. *B. kewense* is now widely distributed but may originate from islands in the Pacific. It was originally described from Kew Gardens, and is likely to have reached St Helena with plants imported from there. It is a large flatworm with five distinctive longitudinal stripes.

A   *Microplana* species. This rhynchodemid was recorded by Duffey, but we have no details.

H   *Rhynchodemus* species A. Only a single specimen of this flatworm has been found and we do not know where on the island. It is pale grey and 9 by 0.7 mm, with the front seventh of the body much narrower than the rest. The two eyes are about 4% of body length from the front end.

H   *Rhynchodemus* species B. This flatworm is only tentatively placed in the genus *Rhynchodemus*. As in the last species, only a single specimen has been found and the collecting locality is not recorded. This is a much larger but very slender flatworm, 25 mm by 1 mm; it has two eyes, very close to the front end of the body, which is 'truncated' (ending abruptly, as if cut off).

NEMERTINA – ribbon worms or nematines

The ribbon worms are flattened and unsegmented worms which are often extremely long; unlike flatworms (Turbellaria) they have an alimentary canal opening separately at a mouth and an anus. Most species are marine, but freshwater species are known from all continents. A single species has been found on St Helena.

TETRASTEMMIDAE – tetrastemmids

H   *Prostoma eilhardi*. A single specimen of this freshwater ribbon worm was collected by the Belgians at Sandy Bay, in company with the flatworm *Dinizia*. It was creamy white in colour, 8 mm long by 0.4 mm wide, and with six eyes. This species has been found in many parts of the world including Africa and South America; its occurrence on St Helena seems extraordinary and we have no idea how the species is dispersed.

NEMATODA – nematode worms

All of the free-living nematode worms collected by the Belgians on St Helena were subsequently mislaid; it seems likely that they were mainly species introduced with soil associated with imported plants. One parasitic nematode found infesting the introduced frog *Rana grayi* proved to be new to science and was given the misleading name *Amphibiophilus sanctaehelenae*: it was presumably introduced to the island from South Africa along with the frogs.

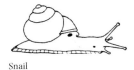

Snail

MOLLUSCA: GASTROPODA – snails and slugs

Snails are soft-bodied animals with a shell into which they can withdraw, thus protecting themselves against enemies or dry conditions. They have no legs, but move along using a muscular 'foot' which they extrude from the shell. In the evolution of slugs the shell has been lost or reduced and covered by a layer of muscle.

The land snails do not – on first sight – seem likely animals to make transoceanic journeys, but tiny snails have reached oceanic islands all over the world; it seems that they usually 'hitchhike', being carried accidentally by birds. Subsequently, they may evolve larger size.[17] Island snails are hard to classify and it is difficult to be sure how many of the described species represent biologically meaningful units, especially when they are extinct and only the shells can be studied; the precise number of genera and species is thus subject to argument. It is obvious, however, that the snails of Ascension and St Helena provide a fascinating contrast. Ten species are known from Ascension, but none are endemic and it is doubtful whether any are indigenous. St Helena used to have a spectacular snail fauna comprising some 20 endemic species and about 5 endemic genera. Introductions, mainly with plants imported from Europe, swelled the list to 35-40 species, but sadly, all but one or two of the endemic species are probably now extinct. A close look at the St Helena fauna suggests that the island was colonised naturally by only about six kinds of snails. In two of these stocks (Charopidae and Subulinidae) a substantial group of closely related species evolved on the island.

The first systematic account of the land snails of St Helena was by G.B. Sowerby, based on a collection obtained by Darwin during his visit in 1836. In 1875-76 T.V. Wollaston made a collection and published a full account. However, another major collection was made in the 1880s by Captain W.H. Turton of the Royal Engineers; it was studied by Edgar A. Smith, who published his results in 1892. When the Belgians went to the island in the 1960s they found that the deposit in which Turton had found most of his fossils had entirely disappeared; it was a stratum of greyish-brown friable earth about 3-4 feet thick, which was covered by a depth of some 5-6 feet of dark brown or black mould, and occurred at an altitude of 1400 to 1700 feet (c.400-500 m) on the ridge between Sugar Loaf and Flagstaff. In 1502 and earlier these deposits presumably formed the soil under the dry gumwood forests. We mention below all the snail families represented on the islands, but give details only of the endemic species and a few other snails of special interest.

ARIONIDAE – roundback slugs

These slugs are thought to be descended from snails similar to the Charopidae. Two species of roundback slugs have been found on St Helena. Both are clearly introduced and neither is common.

BRADYBAENIDAE

A single introduced species has been recorded on Ascension.

---

[17] J. Vagvolgyi (1975).

295

CHAROPIDAE (or ENDODONTIDAE) – charopids

These are some of the most interesting snails on St Helena, showing an impressive adaptive radiation which is mirrored on some of the high volcanic islands in the Pacific. All of the St Helena species may have arisen from one ancient colonisation from Africa, and possibly even from a single pregnant individual. The classification of these snails is controversial and the reports of the Belgian expeditions include two incompatible accounts of them, but a reasonable compromise is to consider that there are seven species in three endemic genera. Of this spectacular radiation, six species are almost certainly extinct, although their shells can be found in deposits in various parts of the island; the seventh – Helenoconcha relicta – was still alive on the central ridge when the Belgian expeditions came. As the sole possibly surviving member of an endemic genus and a member of a particularly interesting family, the finding of this species and preservation of its habitat must be one of the most important conservation priorities on St Helena.

   All of the charopids have flattened shells, the breadth measured across the whorls being much greater than the height measured from the spire to the lowest part of the aperture. Most of the species have alternating pale and dark bands across the whorls, which are laid down successively as the snail grows, giving a finely patterned appearance.

Helenoconcha relicta
3 mm   MRAC

**H   *Helenoconcha* has five species: *H. polyodon*, *H. pseustes*, *H. minutissima*, *H. leptalea* and *H. relicta*.[18] These are (or were) tiny snails, mostly much less than 5 mm across, with prominent radial ribs; the aperture of the shell is obstructed by six or more projections.

   It must be admitted that the only possible survivor of the genus, *Helenoconcha relicta*, is not an impressive animal. It is less than 3.5 mm across and almost disc-shaped, with a very low spire giving a height to breadth ratio of about 1:1.7. The whole shell has a series of finely spaced prominent ridges across the whorls giving a radial pattern; on the underside these are reminiscent of the spokes of a bicycle wheel (see picture). *H. relicta* is closely related to *H. minutissima*, known from subfossils at Sugar Loaf. It was discovered by the Belgians in 1967; they found it on Cabbage Tree Road and perhaps other places nearby. It was evidently fairly abundant, since in about four visits they collected nearly five hundred individuals, and it seems likely that it still survives.

**†H   *Helenodiscus bilamellata*. This species has sometimes been included in *Helenoconcha*, but differs in its large size (c.12 mm), the almost unobstructed aperture (there are only two thread-like ridges) and less prominent radial ribbing; the shell is almost flat above and there are radial streaks tinged with red. Fossils have been found in several places in the northwest of the island.

**†H   *Pseudohelenoconcha spurca*. This species entirely lacks obstructions to the aperture and the shell surface is smooth, with radial growth wrinkles; the shell breadth is 4-5 mm and the spire is low.

CHONDRINIDAE

A   *Granopupa granum*. This minute species may possibly have reached Ascension naturally on birds or by drifting in air currents.

---

[18] We are unclear about the status of one other form, *H. sexdentata*.

COCHLICOPIDAE – agate snails

The agate snails are small and have elongate shells with a long spire but a blunt apex. A single introduced European species is now abundant in the lower parts of St Helena.

ELLOBIIDAE – hollow-shelled snails

These snails have almost cylindrical shells with a blunt apex; the internal walls of the whorls are dissolved to make more room as the animal grows. A tiny member of this family seems to have been introduced recently to St Helena.

FERRUSACIIDAE – spire snails

A small family of tiny snails, though they are related to the world's largest snail, Achatina. The shell is thin and translucent and forms a narrow cylinder or blunt-ended spire. The single species present on St Helena was probably introduced from Britain.

HELICIDAE – typical snails

The family Helicidae contains more species than any other molluscan family. They are varied in shape but generally have a more or less globular shell with a medium-sized spire and a large aperture. A single species is present on St Helena.

H   *Helix aspersa*. A common European edible snail, now well established on St Helena; it can be a significant pest. It grows to 35 mm in both height and breadth and is light brown with up to five very broken dark brown bands. It can be found living in clumps of Creeper, for instance on Horse Point.

HELICODISCIDAE

A   *Helicodiscus singleyanus*. A poorly understood species with patchy distribution on both sides of the Atlantic; it is conceivably indigenous on Ascension.

LIMACIDAE – keelback slugs

These slugs have a small, concealed shell on their backs which betrays their relationship with snails. One common British species has been introduced to St Helena; there are old records of another, but the identification is suspect.

PUPILLIDAE – pupillids (sometimes included in Vertiginidae)

These are elongate and almost cylindrical snails with rounded whorls and a blunt apex. At least one natural colonisation of St Helena has occurred, giving rise to an endemic but extinct species; another species has uncertain status and a third is probably introduced; it is also present on Ascension.

H   *Gastrocopta* species. The Belgians found many dead individuals of an unidentified species near the Baptist Chapel in Sandy Bay. They are 2.5 mm long by 1 mm wide, rather cylindrical and usually with three teeth in the aperture. The genus is widely distributed, but the St Helena specimens seem not to belong to any European or African species, so it is possible that they represent an endemic species; living specimens are clearly needed to sort the matter out.

HA   *Lauria cylindracea.* This species is common on cultivated land on St Helena, and an unidentified species of *Lauria* is present on Ascension; it is doubtful whether either species is indigenous.

*†H   *Pupa obliquicostulata* (*P. obliquicostata* of the Belgians). Fossils of this minute species were found by Captain Turton in a quarry on Sugarloaf. It is 2 mm long by 0.75 wide and according to the original description it has no teeth in the aperture. The relationships of this species are not clear and it may belong in a different genus.

SUBULINIDAE – subulinids

The subulinids – like the charopids – have undergone a major adaptive radiation on St Helena. An evidently ancient colonisation, probably originating in Africa, was followed by speciation and the evolution of an array of eight species of varied size and shape, which are placed in a single endemic genus; all are now probably extinct. St Helena also has another unidentified species which may prove to be endemic, as well as one introduced species. On Ascension there are two or perhaps three introduced species.

**†H   *Chilonopsis* species. The recognised members of this endemic genus are: *Chilonopsis blofeldi, C. exulatus, C. helena, C. melanioides, C. nonpareil* (plus a subspecies), *C. subtruncatus, C. subplicatus* and *C. turtoni.* These snails contrast with the St Helena charopids in their general form: they are much taller than broad, with a strong spire, and when full grown have six and a half to nine whorls; the aperture is typically much less wide than high. Some of the extinct species were large, robust snails with a strong conical spire: the largest *C. nonpareil* were 50 by 32 mm (length to breadth ratio 1.6:1) and with the aperture up to half the height of the shell; other individuals placed in the same species were much slimmer, with the ratio as high as 2.2:1. Other species were even more elongate and with the aperture relatively smaller. Most of the robust forms were found fossilized on the Sugar Loaf ridge, although we have found some in Dry Gut; it seems likely that they were typical of the areas with dry gumwood forest in the north of the island. The egg capsules have a calcareous shell and fossilized ones associated with *C. nonpareil* measure up to 6.5 by 6 mm. The more elongate and smaller species of *Chilonopsis* probably lived in the humid forests of the central ridge. Two of these species (*C. melanioides* and *C. turtoni*) were still alive close to the end of the 19th century. A serious search for surviving groups of these two species seems a high priority.

    The last living specimen precisely recorded was of *C. melanioides*, apparently taken by Mr P. Whitehead in moss and grass on Cabbage Tree Road. This snail grew to 23 mm by 8 mm and is extremely pointed, with a height to breadth ratio of about 2.9:1 (ie about three times as high as it is broad). There are 8 to 9 whorls, separated by a very deep wavy suture. The shell is dark reddish brown, flecked with irregular longitudinal brownish yellow streaks. This species lived in humid places on the northern slopes of the ridge of the Peaks. *C. turtoni* is larger (up to 17 mm long by 7.5 mm breadth) and very sharply pointed but rather less elongate, with a height to breadth ratio of 2.3:1. The shell is extremely thin and fragile, glossy, and with irregular longitudinal creamy stripes. *C. turtoni* used to occur on High Peak.

Chilonopsis subplicatus
15 mm   MRAC

Chilonopsis nonpareil
50 mm   MRAC

SUCCINEIDAE – amber snails

This is an extremely widespread family, typical of damp places. The front pair of tentacles are much reduced but the hind ones are cylindrical and swollen at the base. The shell is very thin and its shape is notoriously variable within species, so that in continental areas identification usually requires dissection. A single distinctive endemic species is present on St Helena.

Succinea sanctaehelenae
Blushing Snail
12 mm   MRAC

H   *Succinea sanctaehelenae*, Blushing Snail. Plate 22. This snail gives the impression of being too big for its shell. There are only a few whorls and they increase rapidly in size, so that the spire is short but pointed and the aperture is very large (up to three quarters of the total length). The snails grow to a maximum of only 12 mm long by 9 mm wide. The shell is glossy and the colour varies from pale amber to golden brown; the blushing effect is caused by light striking through the translucent body and shell. Populations in different parts of St Helena are very different in shell shape and colour, varying from swollen animals with enormous apertures on the humid central ridge to more compressed types from dry areas such as Horse Point Plain. In the 19th century many of these variants were considered to be separate species, but they prove to have consistent internal anatomy, so they are all considered as one species; modern evolutionary studies on the various populations are now under way. The Blushing Snail has no close relatives in Africa or elsewhere and is evidently derived from an ancient colonisation, probably by means of eggs or young individuals carried accidentally by aquatic birds such as Moorhens.

Unlike most of the other endemic snails, this species has survived the drastic ecological changes on the island and is abundant in many habitats at middle and high levels. On the central ridge it may even have benefitted from the extinction of some of its endemic competitors, although in drier areas it has presumably suffered from the reduction of vegetation.

VALLONIIDAE – grass snails

These are small squat snails with the breadth sometimes more than twice as great as the height and the aperture large. One species is known from each island.

H   *Vallonia excentrica*. This minute species is found in many parts of the island. It has been assumed to be introduced, but it occurs on other Atlantic islands and careful excavation of old deposits might indicate natural colonisation.

A   *Vallonia pulchella*. A minute species capable of self-fertilisation which occurs in northwest Africa and various Atlantic islands. It is probably indigenous on Ascension.

VERTIGINIDAE – whorl snails (sometimes includes Pupillidae)

The whorl snails have cylindrical, dumpy or globular shells with a fairly prominent spire; they are generally very small and the front tentacles are absent. The aperture is often guarded by a palisade of teeth. At least one stock of whorl snails has colonised St Helena naturally, giving rise to an endemic but extinct genus; a second extinct species may or may not represent a separate colonisation. In addition to the endemic species, both islands have a single species of introduced whorl snail, *Vertigo pygmaea*.

**†H *Campolaemus perexilis* (ex *Tomigerus perexilis*) A probably extinct species which is so distinct that it is considered as forming an endemic genus. It is possible, however, that

299

Campolaemus perexilis
1.5 mm   MRAC

Campolaemus evolved on St Helena from a colonising stock of the genus *Nesopupa*. *C. perexilis* is a minute, whitish or reddish brown, stumpy, conical snail with the aperture so broad that the maximum width is as great as the length of the shell (1.5 mm by 1.5 mm); the upper margin of the aperture is constricted to form a small hole. Both left hand and right hand spiral shells exist. Fossils have been found along Side Path and on the ridge of Sugar Loaf.

*†H   *Nesopupa turtoni* (ex *Pupa turtoni*). An extinct endemic species which is similar to a species of *Nesopupa* from Fernando Noronha island, off Brazil. It is 3 mm long and 1 mm wide, with a squarish aperture in which there are six conspicuous teeth.

ZONITIDAE – glass snails

These snails have smooth, thin shells which are either flattened or moderately conical. One introduced species is present on both islands and St Helena has two additional species.

ANNELIDA: OLIGOCHAETA – earthworms

Earthworms are cylindrical, soft-bodied, segmented animals. They move by means of circular and longitudinal muscles in the body wall which produce waves of alternate elongations and bulgings, together with small bristles on the underside of each segment which give the worm purchase on a rough surface. Earthworms die if exposed for long to the sun, and do not easily disperse except through the soil. In his account of the Belgians' collection from St Helena, G.E. Gates, a North American earthworm specialist, stated that: *"The only agent known to carry earthworms across oceans is man."* The logical conclusion is that the earthworm faunas of St Helena and Ascension are entirely introduced, and thus of relatively little interest. Accordingly, we do not list all the families formally, but summarise the information here. However, some caution is necessary, since Gates admitted that St Helena was the first oceanic island on which the earthworm fauna had been studied. As we shall see, one record from Ascension presents a serious challenge to his position.

On St Helena earthworms make up an important part of the fauna of the agricultural zone, and 21 species have been reliably recorded. The families represented, with the number of species in parenthesis, are: Acanthodrilidae (1), Eudrilidae (1), Glossoscolecidae (1), Lumbricidae (10), Megascolecidae (6), Ocnerodrilidae (1), Octochaetidae (1). Only in the last family does the possibility of an endemic species arise. Gates identified an octochaetid as belonging to the genus *Dichogaster*, and implied that it was different from any known species; he concluded, however, that it: *"is unlikely to be endemic and probably was brought, also by man, from Africa (if not from central America)."*

Gates mentioned a prediction that species in which there was a possibility of parthenogenesis (reproduction by a single individual without mating) might be expected to establish new populations more readily than those in which two parents were needed. On St Helena, however, nine out of the 21 species required two parents for reproduction, indicating that this characteristic does not prevent colonisation aided by humans. Only a small amount of earth on the roots of an imported plant may be sufficient to conceal worms or their cocoons, and many species can survive adverse conditions in an inactive state known as diapause.

The only other earthworm on St Helena worthy of comment is the eudrilid *Eudrilus eugeniae*, a species first described on the basis of specimens collected on St Helena by the ship's surgeon of the frigate *Eugenia* during her short visit to the island in the 1860s. It is not endemic to the island and was probably introduced from Africa or somewhere further east. It is now widespread in warm areas and has even been bred for use by anglers, but ironically, it may be extinct on St Helena.

Ascension, so far as is known, has many fewer introduced earthworms than St Helena. The total number of recorded species is six, in the following families: Lumbricidae (2), Megascolecidae (3) and Ocnerodrilidae (1).[19] The last of these, however, represents a most extraordinary record. Two juvenile worms were collected by John Packer on Green Mountain in 1962 and studied by Gates. He found that they had unusual calciferous glands: *"No other ocnerodrile is known to have glands of the kind indicated above. Although reference to any known genus is impossible, the worms obviously were ocnerodrile."* We feel that we must for the moment treat these Ascension specimens as representing an endemic genus. The question is whether they were brought in with plants from some area in Africa or South America where the earthworms are little known, or whether they arrived naturally long ago (perhaps as egg cocoons in mud on the feet of waterbirds) and evolved their unusual characters on the island.

ARTHROPODA – arthropods

The arthropods are an enormously varied and successful group. Apart from the vertebrates – which are generally larger and more conspicuous – the arthropods make up the vast majority of the animals that we notice in our daily lives. They are easily distinguished from other groups by having at least six pairs of legs or similar appendages. Their bodies are made up of a series of segments, but in some groups (e.g. spiders) this segmentation is partly obscured. Arthropods have a hard external skeleton made of chitin (which superficially resembles a synthetic plastic); this has to be shed and renewed periodically as the animal grows. We shall be considering several large groups of arthropods: the arachnids (including the spiders), the crustaceans (including the woodlice), the millipedes and centipedes, and the insects.

ARACHNIDA – scorpions, pseudoscorpions, spiders and mites

The arachnids normally have four pairs of legs, which makes them easy to distinguish from insects which have only three pairs (but some immature mites also have only three). In front of the legs arachnids also have a pair of chelicerae (fangs) and a pair of pedipalps (often referred to as palps) which may take the form of large pincers, be modified to help in reproduction (in male spiders) or may look rather like a small extra pair of legs.

---

[19] An oligochaete worm has been found in the gill chambers of the Landcrab *Gecarcinus lagostoma* on the Brazilian island of Trindade: it would be very interesting to know whether this worm is also present in the Landcrabs on Ascension.

SCORPIONES – scorpions

Buthidae – a scorpion
60 mm

Scorpions have a large pair of pincers which are held in front of the head; these are modifications of the pedipalps characteristic of arachnids in general. The hind end of the body is elongate and bent upwards and forwards, and carries a conspicuous sting. Most scorpions prefer dry, warm places; they hide during the day and come out to feed on insects and spiders at night. Two species have been found on Ascension and one of these also on St Helena; they must have been brought to the islands accidentally by people. Scorpions sting in self-defence, but the sting of these island species is not dangerous, though it is painful.

BUTHIDAE

A   *Buthus hottentota*. We were given a specimen found in Georgetown. The species is native to West Africa and it is not yet clear whether it is established on Ascension.

HA   *Isometrus maculatus*, Spotted Isometrus. This species, which is widespread in the tropics, is pale yellowish brown patterned with black and can reach 7 cm in length. It has a very patchy distribution on both islands; on St Helena localities include Broad Gut, Horse Point and Prosperous Bay Plain.

PSEUDOSCORPIONES – pseudoscorpions

Cheliferidae
– a pseudoscorpion
4 mm

Most pseudoscorpions are minute (but see below). They resemble scorpions in having large pincers (palps) which they hold out in front as they walk, but are easily distinguished as they lack the stinging tail. They can walk backwards and forwards equally well. Pseudoscorpions are well known for hitchhiking (technically known as phoresy), dispersing by attaching themselves to various insects and birds; any of the species (or their ancestors) could have reached the islands in this way. However, live pseudoscorpions have also been found on flotsam, so it is possible that some species (for instance Paraliochthonius and Garypus) reached the islands by sea.

On St Helena there are eight species in four families; they include five endemic species and three endemic genera. At least three groups of pseudoscorpions must have reached the island naturally.

On Ascension pseudoscorpions have the highest percentage of endemism of any group, with five species (probably all endemic) in four families and five genera, implying that five different types reached the island naturally and evolved differences from their mainland counterparts.[20] None of the genera are endemic to Ascension, but none are known to be represented on St Helena; this may be because hardly anyone has looked for invertebrates in the seabird colonies on the latter island.

CHEIRIDIIDAE

*A   *Apocheiridium cavicola*. We found a male of this species in the semi-dark Ravine Cave in 1990, a female in a pipe trap in a completely barren ridge of loose clinker beside Lower

[20] M. Beier (1961), V. Mahnert (1993).

Valley Crater in 1995. The intriguing implication is that this animal is capable of living underground even in arid volcanic areas without vegetation. *A. cavicola* is adapted to subterranean life; most of its relatives live under the bark of trees, but a cave-dwelling species was recently found in Texas.

*A   *Neocheiridium species*. Our 1995 collection on Boatswainbird Island included a single minute specimen which seems to be of an undescribed endemic species.

CHELIFERIDAE

*A   *Allowithius ascensionis*. This species was found by Duffey on the coast opposite Boatswainbird Island.

**H   *Scotowithius helenae*. A new genus was created for this species, which is about 3 mm long and dark chocolate-brown. The Belgians found it at Teutonic Hall and in Fishers Valley.

**H   *Sphallowithius excelsus*. This and the next species form another endemic genus. *S. excelsus* is apparently restricted to Prosperous Bay Plain, where it is abundant. It can be distinguished from *Hemisolinus helenae* (see below), which is also found there, by its larger size (up to 4 mm), dark chocolate-brown colour and by the pincers: in *S. excelsus* the hand (the final segment of the pincers, bearing the claw) is relatively long and slender (especially in the male) and has long bristles only on and around the claw itself.

**H   *Sphallowithius inhonestus*. This second member of an endemic genus is smaller than *S. excelsus* but with more sturdy pincers. Only one male and one female have been found, between Luffkins and Peak Gut.

*A   *Stenowithius duffeyi*. Figure 29. Another species found only on Boatswainbird Island, where it is common.

H   *Withius subruber*. This species has been distributed widely by humans in warm regions. On St Helena it has been found only on Peak Hill and in Friars Valley.

CHTHONIIDAE

H   *Chthonius ischnocheles*. This European species is now widely distributed in the interior of St Helena.

*H   *Paraliochthonius helenae*. This species is known from only one male and one female, found at Mt. Eternity and Oakbank. It has seashore-inhabiting relatives on North Atlantic islands, and its ancestors may well have reached St Helena by rafting.

GARYPIDAE

*A   *Garypus titanius*, Giant Pseudoscorpion. Plate 22 and Figure 29. A species found only in the seabird colony on Boatswainbird Islet. *H. titanius* is the largest known pseudoscorpion and is apparently confined to this 5 ha island. In 1995 individuals were found hunting at night in the open on the guano surface (see Chapter 12). Species of *Garypus* are typically found under rocks on the seashore, so it seems likely that the ancestors of *G. titanius* reached Ascension by rafting on driftwood.

NEOBISIIDAE

H   *Roncus lubricus.* This European species is now well distributed in the interior of St Helena.

OLPIIDAE

**H   *Hemisolinus helenae.* This species is so distinct that a new genus was created for it. It is one of the many invertebrates found only on Prosperous Bay Plain. It is tiny (about 2 mm long) and reddish olive-brown. Its pincers have a more stubby hand than in most pseudoscorpions and there are relatively long bristles on all parts of the pincers (cf. *Sphallowithius excelsus* which occurs in the same area).

ARANEAE – spiders

The bodies of spiders are divided into two sections, joined by a narrow stalk, the pedicel. The front section is called the cephalothorax and is covered by a hard shell or carapace; it carries four pairs of legs and in front of these a pair of more or less leg-like palps and a pair of chelicerae with their associated poison glands. The hind body section is called the abdomen and is soft, permitting expansion. The length of spiders is measured from the front of the cephalothorax to the hind end of the abdomen (ie excluding the legs).

An outstanding feature of the biology of spiders is their ability to produce silken threads from spinners near the end of the abdomen. The silk has many uses: it helps spiders to capture their prey (in different ways in the various groups), helps them to move about, to make homes for themselves and to protect their eggs. Many spiders also use silk to undertake 'ballooning' flights suspended from a thread, and these species have high dispersal ability; it thus seems likely that spiders were well represented in the prehistoric fauna of both St Helena and Ascension. It is not easy, however, to distinguish indigenous from introduced species, since many spiders have been carried around the warm regions of the world by humans: these are mainly species found in or on buildings.

On St Helena about 100 species of spiders have so far been recorded in 29 families; of these, 45-46 species and 12-13 genera are endemic. On Ascension 43 species have been found (in 17 families); four species are thought to be endemic and one is placed in an endemic genus. As in other groups, we do not list separately all the widespread introduced species, being especially selective in families with many species that are not easy to distinguish.

AGELENIDAE – funnel-web spiders

Agelenids are long-legged, dark-coloured, fast-moving spiders in which the anterior part of the carapace is parallel-sided and cut off square in front (cf filistatids, below). They make untidy webs that lead to a funnel in which the spider lurks, in crevices or under rocks; the web is often built up over the surface of the rock and gets encrusted with dust. Two species are recorded from St Helena and one from Ascension.

Tegenaria sp.
10 mm

HA   *Tegenaria domestica.* This spider has travelled around the world with humans. On St Helena it is found only in dry areas. On Ascension it was recorded at the end of the 19th century in holes in the rocks at around 500 m on Green Mountain.

H *Tegenaria pagana*. This is a northern hemisphere species, which on St Helena is found in damp areas at middle and high levels; it is frequent in flax plantations.

ARANEIDAE – orb-web spiders

Araneids are one of the few groups of spiders that build beautiful orb-webs to catch their prey. The webs are usually more or less vertical and can be seen stretching between branches of trees and shrubs. The spiders themselves are mostly broad-bodied, with globular abdomens. Three species are known from St Helena; only one has been recorded from Ascension.

H *Araneus rufipalpis*. Members of this genus have a broad, somewhat humped abdomen and build medium-sized orb-webs. The spiders hang upside-down on the web during the night and normally hide nearby during the day; if disturbed, they often drop on a thread. *A. rufipalpis* is yellowish-brown and has been found on scrubby vegetation in James Valley and Fishers Valley; it is widespread and common in Africa.

A *Araneus theisi*. This is the only orb-web spider on Ascension. It is a widespread tropical species which could have reached the island either naturally or by ship.

H *Argiope trifasciata*. Plate 22. A large and conspicuous spider with a silver-grey carapace, black and silver abdomen and long, banded legs. It spins a large web, in which the female hangs upside-down with two pairs of legs pointing forwards and two backwards. It is more or less colonial, occurring in warm, sheltered places at medium altitudes, and usually in scrubby vegetation such as prickly pear. This is probably the spider noted by early visitors to the island; it is widespread in warm regions of the world.

H *Gasteracantha sanguinolenta*, Kite Spider. This species is unmistakeable, having a hard, flattened abdomen, much wider than long and with conspicuous spiny projections. On St Helena it was first found by Arthur Loveridge at Sandy Bay; we also noted it at Flagstaff. *G. sanguinolenta* is widespread in sub-Saharan Africa.

CLUBIONIDAE – sac spiders[21]

Clubionids are nocturnal and ground-living spiders. They roam free, move very fast and are aggressive hunters. Most species live by day in silken sacks, for instance between blades of grass or under stones. Only one St Helena species is now retained in this family. It is in the endemic genus *Bucliona*, which is related to *Clubiona* as the anagram name implies. Two spiders probably belonging in this family have been found on Ascension, but they have not been identified.

**H *Bucliona dubia*. This spider is up to 8 mm long, with chestnut brown carapace and whitish abdomen. It occurs in many parts of the island from 100 m up to about 650 m. The Belgians commented on the possibility that this species is not really endemic, but an introduced species (implicitly from Africa); however, we shall be very surprised if this turns out to be the case.

Argiope sp.
15 mm

Bucliona dubia
8 mm

[21] Several genera placed in the Clubionidae by the Belgians have now been transferred to other families: *Xeropigo* is now in the Corinnidae, while *Helebiona* and *Tecution* are now in the Miturgidae.

305

Xeropigo tridentiger
12 mm   MRAC

CORINNIDAE – corinnids[22]

St Helena has one species of corinnid in an endemic genus. One species from Ascension has not yet been studied in detail.

**H *Xeropigo tridentiger* (ex *Corinna tridentigera*). This is a brown spider up to 16 mm long, with spiny legs. Dark marks radiate from the centre of the carapace, which is much narrower in the front around the eyes. The chelicerae are large but the fangs relatively small and pointing inwards, in contrast to *Tecution* (see Miturgidae). *X. tridentiger* is normally found under stones, where one can also see the disc-shaped silky egg sacs. The species occurs at low to middle levels in dry parts of the northern half of St Helena.

DICTYNIDAE – hackled-web spiders

Dictynids are small spiders, sometimes covered in white hairs. They make irregular, lacy webs, often forming a net over the ends of branches or twigs. St Helena has two species of dictynids, considered as an endemic genus which has possible relatives in desert areas in northeast Africa.

**H *Helenactyna crucifera*. The two members of this genus are both found in dry areas in the north of the island. *H. crucifera* is a brown spider with black markings, up to 4 mm long. It has been found in Ruperts Valley and near Deadwood Plain.

**H *Helenactyna vicina*. This species is similar to the last but only just over 2 mm long. It has been found only on Prosperous Bay Plain.

DYSDERIDAE – dysderids

Dysderids are nocturnal, free-running solitary spiders, often spending the day under stones. They eat woodlice, which are not taken by most other spiders (but see Miturgidae). One species is present on both islands; it is almost certainly introduced.

Dysdera crocota
eating woodlouse
12 mm

HA *Dysdera crocota* (sometimes spelt *crocata*). This spider is up to 15 mm long, with long and divergent chelicerae. *D. crocota* is readily distinguished from the species of *Tecution* (Miturgidae) – which also have reddish coloration and large fangs – by the six eyes in a tight group (*Tecution* have eight widely spaced eyes). *D. crocota* has the carapace bright reddish-brown, the legs red and the abdomen pale cream. This is one of the most successful introduced spiders on St Helena, found in all habitats. The Belgians commented that its arrival probably had a serious effect on the endemic invertebrates that also live under stones.

FILISTATIDAE – filistatids

Filistatids are long-legged brown spiders that live in tubular retreats. They have eight tightly-grouped eyes near the front of the top of the carapace. A single species has been found once on St Helena, but it may not be established.

(H) *Pritha condita*. Melliss found a single specimen, but the species has not been seen since. *P. condita* is otherwise known only from the island of San Miguel in the Azores.

---

[22] This group was previously included as a subfamily within the Clubionidae.

GNAPHOSIDAE – mouse spiders[23]

Gnaphosids are free-living, dull-coloured, nocturnal hunting spiders that retreat into silken nests under stones by day. The abdomen is covered in fine hairs reminiscent of mouse fur, which may glisten with metallic brightness. The front (outermost) spinnerets are long and cylindrical and are used to lay down bands of silk which immobilize the prey.

Five species of gnaphosid have been found on St Helena, including three or four endemic species and two endemic genera; at least two separate colonisations must have been involved. Ascension seems to have six species; several of these cannot yet be fully identified, but probably include members of the genera *Drassodes* and *Nodocion*. This is one of the few groups of invertebrates in which diversity is apparently higher on Ascension than St Helena; more work on the offshore islets of St Helena might alter this picture.

**H   *Benoitodes caheni* (ex *Actaeodes caheni*).[24] Plate 22. The two members of this genus have the carapace oval but squared off in front; the abdomen is rather long. *B. caheni* is up to 12 mm long, with the carapace and legs rusty brown and the abdomen mouse-grey. The Belgians found it to be common on Prosperous Bay Plain but it was absent elsewhere.

**H   *Benoitodes sanctaehelenae*. This species is up to 8.5 mm long and paler in colour than *B. caheni*; the outer spinnerets are extremely long. *B. sanctaehelenae* occurs in damp places at middle and high levels on the island.

**HA   *Pterochroa funerea*. This spider is up to 12 mm long and brown, with black radiating marks on the carapace. The eight eyes are in two rows, both curved backwards: the central pair in the second row are not circular. On St Helena the species is known only from one male found by Melliss and a female found by the Belgians just south of Flagstaff. *P. funerea* has also been recorded from Ascension, but seems likely to have been introduced to that island from St Helena.

A   *Trachyzelotes jaxartensis*. This species occurs in both lava and cave sites on Ascension and may be indigenous.

HA   *Urozelotes rusticus* (ex *Zelotes rusticus*). This is a dull brown spider with a faint orange wedge-shaped mark on the front part of the abdomen. It has been taken to many parts of the world by humans and in the past its identity has been obscured by many different scientific names.

A   *Zelotes inauratus*. This species was found near South Gannet Hill. Like *T. jaxartensis* (above) it is native to the Mediterranean region and may perhaps have reached Ascension naturally.

?*H   *Zelotes errans*. This spider is about 7.5 mm long and rusty red in colour, with some black marks. Although it is known only from St Helena, where two females have been found in Fishers Valley, it may not be really endemic: the Belgians suspected that it might have been introduced.

---

[23] The Gnaphosidae were called Drassidae by the Belgians and many earlier writers.

[24] The endemic genus *Benoitodes* was previously called *Actaeodes*, but this had to be changed because the latter name was found to be already in use for another group.

LINYPHIIDAE (including Erigoninae) – sheetweb weavers and dwarf or money spiders

These are small or very small spiders which build sheet-like webs, usually close to the ground; some make a dome over the sheet. The linyphiids are highly diverse and successful in the north temperate zone but relatively scarce in the tropics. On St Helena nine species are known, three of them endemic. Ascension has three species, one of which constitutes an endemic genus; the other two have not been fully identified.

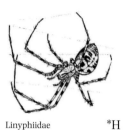

Linyphiidae
3 mm

*H   *Bathyphantes gracilipes.* This species has been found only on High Peak, in one case on the trunk of a dead Tree Fern.

*H   *Bathyphantes helenae.* This is a species of the high part of the island and is only recorded on the high central ridge.

**A   *Catonetria caeca.* We found this spider in a cave in 1990 and again in 1995. It is minute, blind and white and probably now incapable of living outside caves, but its ancestors doubtless reached Ascension by ballooning.

*H   *Lepthyphantes albimaculatus.*[25] Melliss discovered this species in 1873 but it has never been recorded since.

LOXOSCELIDAE – brown spiders[26]

Loxoscelids have six eyes in well separated groups of two. They are bristly, free-living spiders with drab colouration, living under stones or in crevices; some species come into houses. They weave a sheet of sticky silk in which they entangle insects, but also tend to roam at night. Their bite is very poisonous, and the wound often ulcerates, becomes infected and leaves disfiguring scars. Two species have been recorded from St Helena and one of these also from Ascension.

HA   *Loxosceles rufescens.* On St Helena this species has been found only on Prosperous Bay Plain. On Ascension we found it in Georgetown. Elsewhere it occurs in the Mediterranean region but also on many oceanic islands.

H   *Loxosceles distincta.* This species is widely distributed in the dry parts of St Helena, from sea level to about 300 m; it occurs not only under rocks but also in the litter around clumps of flax.

LYCOSIDAE – wolf spiders

The lycosids are free-running, ground-living spiders that hunt their prey by day, often in sunlight. They have four tiny eyes just above the chelicerae, two large ones above, and two smaller ones further back on the sides of the head (salticids, another group with two large forward-facing eyes, lack the four tiny ones below). Lycosids often disperse by ballooning – letting out a silken thread which gets caught in the wind – and they have successfully colonised many oceanic islands.

Lycosids are not easy to identify and the boundaries between the genera are often obscure. St Helena has seven species, all of them endemic. The species were placed by the Belgians in five genera, two of them endemic, but we suspect that they may be

---

[25] The generic name is spelt *Leptyphantes* by the Belgians and some other taxonomists.

[26] The loxoscelids were included by the Belgians in the family Scytodidae.

derived from only two or three colonisations. Only one species has been found on Ascension.

**H   *Dolocosa dolosa.* This is a large species, about 18 mm long, with a relatively low, broad carapace; the width of the head is at least three quarters of the widest part of the carapace (cf. the next two species). The carapace is red-brown with a yellowish oval patch towards the front; the abdomen is yellowish brown. The first specimen was a female collected by Melliss; the Belgians found two more females on Horse Point Plain.

*H   *Hogna nefasta.* This spider is similar in size and general colour pattern to *Dolocosa* but has three or four pale patches on each side of the carapace. The head is also distinctly higher and narrower; its width is only two thirds of the widest part of the carapace. Females and juveniles have been found on Prosperous Bay Plain and Horse Point Plain, but the male is unknown.

*H   *Isohogna cinica.* This species is about the same length as the two previous species, but the width of the head is only just over half that of the widest part of the carapace. *I. cinica* has been recorded from two very different localities – Bryan's Rock at Horse Point and at High Peak.

*H   *Lycosa elysae.* This species and *L. ringens* are the small wolf spiders of the island, but it is not clear that populations of either of them survive. *L. elysae*, which is around 6 mm long, is known only from a single male found by the Belgians on Prosperous Bay Plain.

*H   *Lycosa ringens.* This species is about 5 mm long and is similar to *P. elysae*. It is known only from a single male found by the Belgians in Fishers Valley.

**H   *Lynxosa inexorabilis.* This and the next species are both chestnut brown with a broad pale stripe down the centre of the carapace and abdomen; they also have pale patches along the sides of the carapace, and legs 'annulated' with yellowish and brown (these are absent or much less marked in *Dolocosa*, *Hogna* and *Isohogna*). In *L. inexorabilis* the pale stripe in the rear part of the carapace is roughly parallel-sided and the spider is about 10 mm long. This species is found in a variety of habitats at middle and high levels.

**H   *Lynxosa ligata.* This species has the pale median stripe forming a roughly star-shaped mark in the rear part of the carapace; the spider is somewhat smaller than the previous species. *L. ligata* is found in the middle and high parts of the island, overlapping substantially with the previous species, but is particularly associated with the Peaks.

Lynxosa ligata
9 mm

A   *Pardosa inopina.* This small wolf spider is widespread in Africa and probably colonised Ascension naturally.

MIMETIDAE – cannibal spiders

Mimetids are often found in debris and on vegetation. When hunting they lurk in the webs of other spiders where they mimic the vibrations of a captured insect, and then kill and eat the owner spider when it comes to investigate. A single species has been found on St Helena.

H   *Ero aphana.* This spider is less than 3 mm long and has curved spines on the front legs. The Belgians found it in several places on the central ridge above 500 m. *E. aphana* is widespread in the Old World.

309

MITURGIDAE – miturgids

This family now includes some genera previously placed in Clubionidae. The miturgids are generally short-legged, robust hunting spiders. Two endemic genera on St Helena are now considered as members of the family: *Helebiona*, which is a very distinctive form, and *Tecution* with three species that evidently originated on the island from a single colonising stock. It is worth remembering that these species are closely related to the genus *Cheiracanthium*, which in other places are quite common in houses and bite if provoked; one species of *Cheiracanthium* is thought to be responsible for 90% of spider bites in southern Africa. The bite is painless and the only initial sign is two separated puncture marks; later it becomes inflamed and swollen and is sometimes accompanied by a temperature and headache; it is slow to heal but not fatal. This suggests that one should try to avoid handling any of the St Helena species in this family.

The species of *Tecution* are perhaps the most impressive endemic predatory invertebrates of St Helena. Their chelicerae are enormous, with the basal part much enlarged and the long fang (unguis) articulated so that it moves forward and back as in the mygalomorph spiders rather than towards the mid-line as in almost all other groups. The Belgians twice found *Tecution* species feeding on the endemic woodlouse *Littorophiloscia alticola*, and it seems likely that the enlarged chelicerae have evolved as an adaptation for dealing with this type of prey; in other parts of the world the specialist woodlouse predators are members of the family Dysderidae.

**H   *Helebiona wilma*. This is a small spider (5 mm long) with conspicuously high carapace and abdomen and vertically oriented chelicerae. The carapace is pale brown and the abdomen mottled grey. Only three specimens of *H. wilma* were found by the Belgians, on Prosperous Bay Plain; however, we found several juveniles that may belong to this species on Gumwoods at Peak Dale.

**H   *Tecution helenicola*. The members of this genus have the sides of the carapace almost parallel, with the eye region hardly narrower than the part further back (cf. *Xeropigo* in Corinnidae). *T. helenicola* is up to 9 mm long, similar in colour to *T. mellissi* but with chelicerae relatively shorter. Only a single male and a dozen juveniles have been found, all of them on the Peaks.

Tecution mellissi
10 mm

**H   *Tecution mellissi*. This spider is pale red with whitish abdomen, and is up to 11 mm long. This is the most formidable of the three Tecution species: the basal part of the chelicerae is almost as long as the carapace and the fang is long and stout, closing onto massive teeth. Melliss collected a male at the Hermitage and the Belgians found a male in rotten trunks of cabbage trees on the central ridge. We found a female which probably belongs to this species on Gumwoods at Peak Dale.

**H   *Tecution planum*. This spider is up to 8.5 mm long and yellowish white in colour, with the tips of the chelicerae black. It has been found near Diana's Peak, High Peak, Peak Dale and Teutonic Hall. It seems to be associated especially with the Tree Fern.

NESTICIDAE – scaffold-web spiders

Nesticids are small spiders similar to theridiids, with the first pair of legs longer than the others. They make a fine web in dark damp places. There is one endemic species on St Helena.

*H   *Nesticus helenensis.* This tiny yellow-brown spider has been found in a few places in the north of the island below 300 m.

OECOBIIDAE – oecobiids

Oecobiids are very small, squat spiders with a broad carapace and eight eyes closely grouped on top of it. They are ground-living, web-building and feed largely on ants. They build a small, flat, star-shaped web in crevices, but sometimes wander. Three species in the genus Oecobius have been recorded from St Helena and one of these also from Ascension; they may well have arrived with humans.

OONOPIDAE – oonopids

Oonopids are minute spiders, up to 3 mm long; some have hard orange plates or 'scuta' (singular scutum) on the abdomen, above and below. They are nocturnal and ground-living and typically move in a slow, steady fashion, but when necessary they can dart backwards or forwards at lightning speed. Endemic species of oonopids are present on Hawai'i and many other islands, suggesting great powers of dispersal. There are five species on St Helena, two of which are endemic; Ascension has one endemic and three unidentified species probably in the genera *Gamasomorpha*, *Oonops* and *Orchestina*.

*H   *Gamasomorpha atlantica.* This species is pale red and up to 1.5 mm long; the carapace is almost parallel-sided and the abdomen almost circular; there are no spines on the legs. *G. atlantica* has been found in several places at low and middle levels in the dry parts of the island. It has relatives in tropical Africa but is not closely related to *G. insularis*.

H   *Gamasomorpha insularis.* This spider is 2.5 mm long, with the carapace strongly narrowed in front. There is a scutum covering the upper surface of the abdomen and both this and the carapace are coarsely granulated; there are no spines on the legs. *G. insularis* is found near the coast north of Jamestown and in the area of Prosperous Bay Plain. Elsewhere, it occurs on islands in the Gulf of Guinea and the Indian Ocean.

H   *Heteroonops spinimanus.* A single female of this American species was found by the Belgians in Fishers Valley. It is 2.4 mm long, with spiny legs and a scutum on the upper surface of the abdomen.

H   *Ischnothyreus peltifer.* This species is only 1.5 mm long and has the carapace in the form of an irregular hexagon, narrowest in front; there are large spines on the front two pairs of legs. *I. peltifer* has been found in several places at low and middle levels, including Peak Dale. The species is widespread in the tropics.

*H   *Oonops erinaceus.* This spider is 1.8 mm long and entirely yellowish white apart from some black around the six eyes, which are in three pairs in a compact group. The legs are spiny and there are no scuta on the abdomen. This species is known only from a female found by the Belgians on Flagstaff and a juvenile from Prosperous Bay Plain; we collected a small juvenile – perhaps of the same species – underground near Prince Andrew School. *O. erinaceus* appears to be an ancient relict, apparently related to species on the mountains of central Africa.

*A   *Opopaea euphorbicola.* This is one of the few endemic spiders of Ascension; it has close relatives on the African continent and on North Atlantic islands. *O. euphorbicola* is about 1.5 mm long and uniform pale orange. The carapace narrows smoothly forwards to the eye region and the abdomen is covered above and below by rigid plates (scuta). *O. euphorbicola* occurs in the desert areas of the island.

OXYOPIDAE – lynx spiders

Lynx spiders do not make a web, but live mainly on plants, stalking their prey like cats and finishing the hunt with a jump. They have a high carapace, abdomen pointed behind and very long spiny legs. A single species is recorded from St Helena.

H   *Peucetia fasciiventris.* This spider has been found only in warm and sheltered parts of the island, in James Valley and Sandy Bay. The species is widespread in southern Africa, but the first specimens were found on St Helena by Melliss, so for a time it was considered endemic to the island.

PHOLCIDAE – daddy-long-legs spiders

Pholcids are delicate spiders with extremely long legs. They hang upside down on loose three-dimensional criss-cross webs in holes and damp places. Three species have been found on St Helena but there is no evidence that any are indigenous. Six species have been found on Ascension, but the four that are fully identified are widespread and unlikely to be indigenous. The larger number of species on Ascension probably reflects the adaptation of pholcids to barren lava habitats with many underground spaces. One species found in a cave on Ascension may be adapted to cave life and even be endemic, but the specimen is in poor condition.

PRODIDOMIDAE – prodidomids

This is a small family of little known spiders sometimes included in the Gnaphosidae. They are small, hairy spiders with extremely long spinnerets and long, widespread chelicerae. They seem to be well adapted to desert, coastal areas and we suspect that they may be capable of dispersal by rafting. On St Helena there is one endemic species in the genus *Zimirina*. Ascension has two apparently endemic species in the genus *Prodidomus*, and on the Mars Bay lava flow we found immature spiders that seem to belong to *Zimirina* and to a related genus, *Zimiris*.

*A   *Prodidomus clarki.* This species was discovered by Eric Duffey during his ecological survey of Ascension in 1958.

*A   *Prodidomus duffeyi.* This species was also found by Eric Duffey.

*H   *Zimirina relegata.* This is a small (3 mm), pale, hairy spider with eight eyes closely grouped in the form of a horseshoe, open above.[27] *Z. relegata* has been found near the coast at Ruperts and in Broad Gut, and also on Prosperous Bay Plain.

SALTICIDAE – jumping spiders

The jumping spiders are extremely diverse in warm parts of the world. They have eight eyes, but two of these are enormous and face forwards, so that the spider's gaze can be

---

[27] The diagram in the Belgians' account is upside down.

disconcertingly anthropomorphic. Salticids have excellent vision and are active during the day, often in sunshine. Hunting is by means of long pauses, quick darts and dramatic leaps. Many species have bright colour patterns and metallic glints. Salticids are evidently excellent natural dispersers. They have been collected at high altitudes in the air and were well represented among early colonists of Krakatau, and in the endemic fauna of other islands; however, some species also seem to have been carried around the world on ships.

Of the ten species recorded from St Helena seven are endemic and for four of these – which evidently evolved on the island from a single colonising stock – the Belgians created the endemic genus *Paraheliophanus*; however, this is closely related to the genus *Icius* and may eventually be suppressed. Two other endemic species in the genus *Pellenes* doubtless also evolved on the island. Four species of salticids have been recorded from Ascension; these are all widespread and three of them also occur on St Helena.[28]

Menemerus bivittatus
7 mm

HA   *Menemerus bivittatus.* This species is up to 10 mm long and was noted by Melliss as the Black and White Money Spider common in houses on the island. It is usually associated with humans and now occurs throughout the tropics.

?*H   *Myrmarachne isolatus.* Species of *Myrmarachne* are all mimics of ants, with which they live. The occurrence of an apparently endemic species on St Helena is a puzzle, since all the ant species on the island are probably introduced. *M. isolatus* is generally reddish black and is elongated, with a narrow 'waist' and long chelicerae. Only seven individuals have been found, by beating bushes in Friars Valley at about 200 m.

**H   *Paraheliophanus jeanae.* Members of this genus are up to 7 mm long, with square-fronted, almost rectangular carapace and particularly large central eyes. *P. jeanae* has been found in several dry places at middle levels, including the Gumwoods at Peak Dale.

**H   *Paraheliophanus napoleon.* This species is known only from a male found at Great Stone Top. It is distinctly smaller than the other species in the genus (less than 3.5 mm long).

**H   *Paraheliophanus sanctaehelenae.* This species occurs in humid places above about 500 m, including the central ridge.

**H   *Paraheliophanus subinstructus.* This species occurs in similar places to *P. sanctaehelenae* and seems to be particularly associated with organic debris of Tree Ferns and cabbage trees.

*H   *Pellenes inexultus.* The two endemic species of *Pellenes* are blackish spiders with the hindmost eyes almost half way back along the carapace, which is more strongly narrowed behind than in *Paraheliophanus*. *P. inexultus* has been found at Horse Point Plain, Peak Dale and a few other mid-level sites on the island.

*H   *Pellenes perexcultus.* This species has been found only on Prosperous Bay Plain, Ruperts Valley and the desert zone close to the sea near Sandy Bay.

A   *Plexippus paykulli.* This species is larger than the other salticids on Ascension. The male is up to 9 mm long and has a striking pattern of black and white bands running the length of the body; the female is somewhat larger and lacks the clear striped pattern. *P. paykulli* has been found both on the main island and on Boatswainbird Island. The species is widespread in the tropics.

---

[28] The Belgians provided a key to the St Helena salticids, but identification of these spiders is not easy and requires measurements of the eye arrangements and various structures best seen with a microscope: we have therefore not attempted to distinguish all the species.

SCYTODIDAE – spitting spiders

These nocturnal spiders have long delicate legs and a high rounded thorax which slopes down in the front; under the dome is a pair of large glands from which the spiders can squirt fine strings of a sticky secretion to immobilize their prey. There may be three species in the genus *Scytodes* (*S. velutina*, *S. fuscata* and *S. similis*) on St Helena and one (so far unidentified) on Ascension; none of them are endemic.

SEGESTRIIDAE – six-eyed tunnel spiders

These spiders, formerly included in Dysderidae, live in a tube of tough white silk and emerge to grab passing prey. They are unusual in holding three pairs of legs pointing forward and only one backwards. There is one species on St Helena, which is probably introduced.

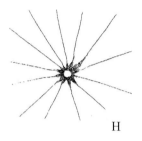

Segestriidae web on rock face
7 mm

H   *Segestria florentina*. This impressive blackish brown spider can grow to 22 mm long; it is often found in holes in walls. The female is the larger and has green iridescence on the chelicerae; she is very aggressive.

SELENOPIDAE – selenopid crab spiders

Selenopids are fairly large, with extremely flattened bodies, and spread their legs out in a crab-like fashion; they have eight eyes, six in the front row and two at the sides behind. One species occurs on both islands.

HA   *Anyphops stauntoni*. This very distinctive spider – known locally as 'flat spider' or 'crab spider' – lives mainly under stones. The Belgians suggested that it was introduced to St Helena shortly before 1940. It is now abundant and can be found from near the coast up to the summit of the central ridge.

SYMPHYTOGNATHIDAE – midget spiders

These are minute spiders that make sheet webs in damp places such as leaf litter and moss. The endemic species discovered on St Helena by the Belgians is evidently part of the ancient fauna of the island.

*H   *Mysmena isolata*. This spider is less than 2 mm long and blackish with white markings on the underside of the abdomen, which is held tilted up at right-angles to the carapace so that the markings face backwards. Three females were found on Mt Actaeon at about 800 m.

TETRABLEMMIDAE – tetrablemmids

This is a small family of minute spiders with only four eyes in a tight group. One endemic species has been found on St Helena.

*H   *Tetrablemma helenensis*. This spider is only 1.1 mm long and has a hard plate or 'scutum' covering most of the upper surface of the abdomen. Only a single female has been found, under Samphire in Ruperts Valley.

TETRAGNATHIDAE – tetragnathids

Tetragnathids make orb-webs similar to those of araneids but with less dense spiral threads and a hole at the centre. There are five species on St Helena, four of which are endemic; two of these are placed in an endemic genus. There is only one tetragnathid on Ascension.

A   *Dyschiriognatha argyrostilba.* This species probably reached Ascension naturally, as it is the African representative of a widespread genus with oceanic distribution. It is intriguing that on St Helena there is an endemic species (*D. atlantica*) which could be derived from the same stock.

*H   *Dyschiriognatha atlantica.* Only a single specimen of this species is known; it is a male found by the Belgians at Sandy Bay Beach.

*H   *Leucauge digna.* This is a brown, yellow and silver spider, less than 10 mm long and with very spiny legs. It spins a large and more or less horizontal orb-web, sometimes suspended in gaps between trees up to 40 feet across and high above the ground; the spider is often concealed in foliage at the outer end of one of the support strands. *L. digna* is a very distinctive member of its genus, probably related to west African species. It is the most abundant of the endemic spiders of St Helena, being found at all levels but especially on the central ridge; it thrives in the changed vegetation developed during human occupation of the island.

Leucauge digna
8 mm

**H   *Napometa sanctaehelenae.* This and the following species are the only members of a new endemic genus established by the Belgians, but placed by them in the family Araneidae. *N. sanctaehelenae* is yellow with black marks and up to 6 mm long. It is common in the high, humid parts of the island.

**H   *Napometa trifididens.* This spider has similar coloration to the previous species but with a very clear, Y-shaped, yellow pattern on the cephalothorax. It has not been seen since the 19th century, when it was found on the central ridge at about 800 m.

H   *Tetragnatha nitens,* Long-jawed Water Spider. This species has very long legs, a long, slender body and elongated jaws, features which distinguish it readily from spiders in the family Araneidae mentioned above. *T. nitens* has silver and gold markings on the abdomen. Its web is usually near water, and the spider hangs on it with two pairs of legs stretched forwards. The species is widespread in the tropics and could represent the stock from which the genus *Napometa* evolved after an ancient colonisation.

THERIDIIDAE – comb-footed spiders

This large family includes spiders of many different shapes, but some have a conspicuously globular abdomen; a number of species are poisonous. Theridiids are good natural dispersers and have endemic and non-endemic forms on many islands, but some are associated with dwellings and likely to be dispersed with human belongings. This is the most diverse spider family on St Helena, with 20 species, five of them endemic and one of these in an endemic genus; four species are known from Ascension. Only the endemic species and a few others are listed here.

Argyrodes mellissi
Golden Sail Spider
7 mm   MRAC

*H   *Argyrodes mellissii,* Golden Sail Spider. This striking species is recognizable by the pale yellow colour, extremely long legs and the abdomen, which is triangular (like a sail) in profile and extends upwards in a long point. Members of the genus *Argyrodes* normally live in the webs of other spiders, but it is not certain that this is true of *A. mellissi,* which has been collected by beating the trunks of Tree Ferns. It has been recorded only from the high central ridge.

A   *Latrodectus geometricus*, Brown Widow. The widows are large (up to 16 mm long) poisonous spiders; they have a globular abdomen with red markings. Female widows are sedentary and may bite if molested; males wander but do not bite. These spiders make tough, tangled webs and the spherical white egg sacs hang in the web. The rather similar spiders in the genus *Steatoda* are also represented on both islands; they do not have red markings and are not considered poisonous. The Brown Widow is brown to black with a red mark on the underside of the abdomen; it is found in dry rocky places. The bite of this spider is poisonous, although not as bad as that of the next species.

H   *Latrodectus tredecimguttatus*, Black Widow. This is a black and red Mediterranean species which seems to be rare on St Helena, having been definitely recorded only a few times; the Belgians found it by beating bushes, but it is likely also to occur under loose objects. Its bite is very poisonous but rarely fatal.

*H   *Theridion sciaphilum*. This spider is about 3 mm long and pale yellowish with black markings. It has been found in high parts of the island above 500 m, mainly on the central ridge. Several non-endemic species of the genus *Theridion*[29] are also found on both islands.

*H   *Theridion solium*. This species is known only from a single male found at Oakbank.

*H   *Theridula huberti*. Females of this species have been found only on the central ridge and High Peak; the male is unknown.

**H   *Zercidium helenense*. The Belgians created a new genus for this species, but admitted that it was close to the genus *Coleosoma*. The species has been found only on ferns and in the associated litter, both on the central ridge and at High Peak.

THOMISIDAE – small crab spiders

The thomisids are very crab-like, with broad, flattened bodies. They lurk on flowers and catch insects visiting them for nectar or pollen; some of them can take on the colour of the flower in which they sit. There are three species on St Helena, two of them endemic and one of these currently placed in an endemic genus.

**H   *Bonapruncinia sanctaehelenae*. This spider is known only from two juvenile females found by the Belgians on Prosperous Bay Plain. Although related to the genus *Runcinia* (see below) they are sufficiently distinctive that a new species and genus has been established for them. The mottled coloration, matching the stony background, will make it very difficult to find the adults needed to confirm the validity of the new genus. As in *Runcinia grammica* the front two pairs of legs are large and spiny, the abdomen is oval and there is a prominent shelf extending above the lateral eyes.

Philodromus signatus. Members of this genus differ from the other thomisids on St Helena in having the front two pairs of legs not much larger than the last two. The front of the carapace is rounded (without a shelf near the eyes) and there is a broad

Philodromus signatus
6 mm

---

[29] This generic name is sometimes spelt *Theridium*.

316

yellowish band along the centre of the carapace. *P. signatus* has been found in several habitats, from about 100 m in Banks Valley up to the central ridge at about 750 m.

H   *Runcinia grammica*. In this species the front two pairs of legs have strong spines and are much larger than the others; they are held out in front, so that the spider becomes almost invisible on a stem. It has been found at middle and high levels on the island. Elsewhere, it is found in southern Europe and North Africa.

ULOBORIDAE – uloborids

Uloborids make a type of orb-web but are not closely related to the araneids. The web is usually horizontal and the spiral threads are not sticky but are made of fuzzy silk which entangles the prey; there is often a white band of silk across the web on both sides of the hub, which camouflages the spider in the centre. There are two species on St Helena.

H   *Uloborus walckenaerius*. This spider is about 5 mm long, hairy, and with broad dark and light stripes along the length of the body. *O. walckenaerius* is common at low and medium altitudes on St Helena, but only in wet places. The species is widely distributed in the Old World.

H   *Zosis geniculata*. This is a small, mottled, light-coloured spider with banded black and white legs. The web is about 25 cm across and the egg sacs are light purple and seven-sided. On St Helena *Z. geniculata* is scarce and occurs mainly around buildings; it is widespread in the tropics elsewhere.

ACARI – mites and ticks

The Acari (or Acarina) are tiny arthropods, either parasitic or free-living, easily separated from spiders by the lack of a major constriction or 'waist' part way along the body. They differ from insects in the absence of external segmentation of the abdomen and by the presence of four rather than three pairs of legs (although some immature mites have only three pairs); furthermore, no mites have wings, although they are often found drifting high in the air.

The group names used in classification of mites are extremely confusing and the animals themselves are small and hard to identify precisely; furthermore, not all groups were studied by the Belgians on St Helena, and little work has been done on the mites of Ascension. We treat the mites very briefly, and do not mention all the families or the species; we use three main groups. The group names in block capitals are the ones most frequently used.

Parasitiformes: MESOSTIGMATA

*H   Mesostigmata are represented by nine families on St Helena. Six endemic species of free-living mesostigmatids have been described, in five families. There are also 12 non-endemic species, of which 10 are free-living, one is found on *Rattus rattus* and one on Mynas.

317

Parasitiformes: IXODIDA (or Ixodides) – ticks

HA   Two species of widespread ticks occur on St Helena. The Blue Tick of Africa *Boophilus decoloratus* infests cattle and other animals; the Red Tick *Rhipicephalus evertsi* – also from Africa – occurs on cattle and affected goats at the time of the Belgians' visits; a member of the latter genus has also been found on Ascension. In addition, a member of the family Argasidae was found in a Wideawake fair and presumably parasitizes that species.

Sarcoptiformes: ORIBATIDA (or CRYPTOSTIGMATA) – oribatids

HA   On St Helena the Belgians recorded 48 species in 22 families, of which 27 were described as new to science. It seems certain that most of the latter are genuine endemics; many of them were found in endemic vegetation on the central ridge. Five genera account for 19 out of the 27 apparently endemic species, suggesting that speciation of these mites has been proceeding on the island. The groups concerned are *Scheloribates* (10 endemic species, one of which may justify a new genus), *Carabodes* (five endemic species), *Galumna* (two endemic species) and *Oppia* (two endemic species). Non-endemic species were considered to be introduced, and comprise 19 European and two African species. On Ascension we collected four species of oribatids, three of which have not been identified or described. The fourth, however, represents an endemic genus and species.

**A   *Cordylobates fragilis*. This species, which represents a new genus which has been tentatively placed in the family Ceratozetidae, was collected at several barren lava sites where there was hardly any vegetation. The guts of some of the specimens contained pollen and probably lichen.

Sarcoptiformes: ANALGOIDEA – feather mites

H   Analgidae. One new species from a Myna was subsequently found on Myna specimens from elsewhere in the Paris Museum.

H   Avenzoariidae. These mites live between the barbs on the inside face of the flight feathers of birds. One species was found on two specimens of Arctic Skuas. A second species, previously known from two species of African plovers of the genus *Charadrius*, was found on the Wirebird. A third species, previously known from Mynas *Acridotheres tristis* in Indochina, was found on the Myna on St Helena.

H   Proctophyllodidae. These mites live on the surface of the flight feathers of birds. One species was found on an Arctic Skua and another on a Myna.

H   Syringobiinae. These extraordinary mites live inside the shafts of the flight feathers (quills) of seabirds and shorebirds. A single specimen was found on an Arctic Skua.

Trombidiformes: TARSONEMINI

H   Pygmephoridae. Several mites belonging to a non-endemic species were found as parasites on a chloropid fly.

318

Trombidiformes: PROSTIGMATA

Sphaerolophus sanctaehelenae
2 mm   MRAC

*H   Anystidae. These are free-living predatory mites. There are three non-endemic species and also a radiation of the genus *Chaussieria*, with four endemic species.

*HA   Bdellidae, snout mites. These are fast moving predators of small arthropods and their eggs. On St Helena there are two endemic species and one non-endemic. On Ascension we found two species, but they have not been identified fully.

*H   Erythraeidae. These are terrestrial mites whose larvae are parasitic on insects and arachnids, while the adults are predators. Three apparently endemic species, in the genera *Sphaerolophus* and *Balaustium*, have been described by the Belgians, but they caution that the species may turn up in adjacent continents.

*A   Eupodidae. Mites collected by us on the South Gannet lava flow are being described as a new endemic species; it probably belongs in the Eupodidae. This mite is a plant feeder.

H   Tetranychidae, spider mites. These are red, yellowish or greenish and have soft, pear-shaped bodies 0.2-0.8 mm in length. They pierce the surface of leaves, causing brown spots and sometimes shrivelling of the leaf. On St Helena they are common but sporadic pests, damaging a variety of vegetable crops including tomatoes and French beans, fruits such as strawberries and also many ornamental flowers. We are not aware of records from Ascension but these mites are likely to be present.

CRUSTACEA – crustaceans

The crustaceans, which form part of the vast assemblage of arthropods, are the most conspicuous and diverse invertebrate animals of aquatic environments, just as their cousins the insects and arachnids are the dominant invertebrates on land. Crustaceans have two pairs of antennae near the front end, and generally have two distinct divisions in the body, the cephalothorax and abdomen. Most species are marine, including the familiar crabs, lobsters and shrimps, but here we deal only with those that come on to land or into freshwater. The groups concerned are copepods, ostracods, tanaid shrimps, amphipods, isopods (woodlice) and decapods (including the Landcrab of Ascension).

COPEPODA – copepods

Copepods are tiny (<5 mm long) marine and freshwater animals that normally live dispersed in the water as plankton, although some are parasitic on other animals. The front end of the body is covered by a broad carapace, but the abdomen is much narrower and ends in twin appendages. St Helena has four species of freshwater copepods, in three families; all of the species are widely distributed elsewhere and it is possible that they have reached the island naturally on the legs of aquatic birds. They have been found in small pools near the sources of a few streams, and doubtless also occur in the 'groundwater' flowing beneath the surface.

OSTRACODA – ostracods or mussel shrimps

Ostracods are tiny marine or fresh water crustaceans with a bivalved carapace; when this is closed, they look like minute mussels or clams. The Belgians recorded two species from freshwater streams on St Helena; both are endemic, and are also discussed in Chapter 6.

CYPRIDIDAE – cyprids

*H   *Herpetocypris helenae.* This species is up to 2 mm long and greenish in colour; it has been found only twice, from the spring near Napoleon's grave in 1903 and on the central ridge in 1966.

CYTHERIDAE – cytherids

*H   *Xestoleberis potamophila.* This species is less than 0.4 mm long and is brownish in colour: it has been found in seepage pools at high and middle levels and is much more abundant than the previous species.

TANAIDACEA – tanaid shrimps

TANAIDAE – tanaids

Tanais stanfordi
6 mm   MRAC

H   *Tanais stanfordi.* This minute (c.6mm) shrimp has been discussed in Chapter 6; on St Helena it occurs in Lemon Tree Gut and on the central ridge.

AMPHIPODA – amphipods

The amphipods are easily recognizable by being flattened from side to side but also flexed downwards into a strong bow shape, so that they typically rest on their sides; in this they contrast with their relatives the woodlice (see below). Amphipods are mainly aquatic, but some live in damp places on land; these ones are usually known as landhoppers, for reasons that become obvious when one turns over a rock under which a group of them are sheltering. Three species are present on St Helena: one is endemic, one is found only on St Helena and Ascension, and the third is widespread and occurs on both islands. Ascension has another widespread species, again making a total of three.

TALITRIDAE – talitrids

*H   *Platorchestia ashmoleorum.* This is a pale-coloured amphipod endemic to St Helena, discovered in 1995. The new species is more aquatic than the other talitrids on the islands and we found it in a muddy, brackish pool at the back of the beach at Potato Bay. Our Dutch colleagues, however, who were systematically searching for animals in

320

Top left Tree Rat *Rattus rattus* **HA** on agave

Above Java Gecko *Hemidactylus frenatus* **H**

Right, top to bottom:
Dead Green Turtle *Chelonia mydas* (**H**) **A**

Hatchling Green Turtles approach the sea (**H**) **A**

Coconut-palm Gecko *Hemidactylus mercatorius* **A**

Grass Frog *Rana grayi* **H**

PLATE 17
ANIMALS OF THE ISLANDS

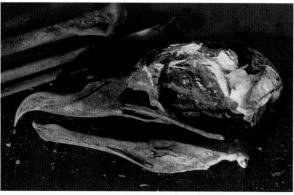

Fossil skull of extinct St Helena Petrel *Pterodroma rupinarum* *†H

Audubon's Shearwater *Puffinus lherminieri* (**HA**)

Madeiran Storm-petrel
(H: Pickering)
Oceanodroma castro **HA**,
with Masked Booby
Sula dactylatra

White-tailed Tropicbird *Phaethon lepturus* **A**

Fossil egg from St Helena, probably of Audubon's
Shearwater *Puffinus lherminieri* (**HA**)

Red-billed Tropicbird (H: Trophy Bird) *Phaethon aethereus* **HA**

PLATE 18
BIRDS OF THE ISLANDS

Masked Booby *Sula dactylatra* in flight **HA**

Masked Boobies arriving at colony on Boatswainbird island

Brown Booby (H: Duck) *Sula leucogaster* in flight **HA**

Red-footed Booby *Sula sula* brown phase on nest in 1958 (**H**)**A**

Red-footed Booby *Sula sula* white phase (**H**)**A**

Juvenile Ascension Frigatebird *Fregata aquila* *****A**

PLATE 19

BIRDS OF THE ISLANDS

Ascension
Frigatebird
Fregata aquila ***A**

Sooty Tern (Wideawake) *Sterna fuscata* **HA**

Brown Noddy (H: Black Bird) *Anous stolidus* **HA**

Black Noddy (H: Noddy Bird) *Anous minutus* **HA**

Dead Black Noddies on Boatswainbird Island

PLATE 20
BIRDS OF THE ISLANDS

Pair of White Terns
(H: Seabird)
Gygis alba **HA**

Wirebird *Charadrius sanctaehelenae* ***H**

Sanderling *Calidris alba*
on the beach at
Ascension

White Tern *Gygis alba* and
chick on Thorn *Erythrina caffra*
on St Helena

Wirebird nest with eggs ***H**

Moorhen(H: Waterbird) *Gallinula chloropus*, which breeds
on St Helena but is only a vagrant to Ascension **H(A)**

PLATE 21
BIRDS OF THE ISLANDS

Indian Myna (H: Miner Bird)
Acridotheres tristis **HA**

Yellow Canary (H: Canary)
Serinus flaviventris **HA**

Common Waxbill (H: Amadavat, Averdavat)
Estrilda astrild **HA**

Madagascar Fody (H: Cardinal) *Foudia madagascariensis* **H**

Giant pseudoscorpion *Garypus titanius*, found only on
Boatswainbird Island *****A**

Orb-web spider *Argiope trifasciata* **H**

Endemic mouse spider *Benoitodes*
species (family Gnaphosidae) ****H**

Blushing Snail *Succinea sanctaehelenae* *****H**

PLATE 22

ANIMALS OF THE ISLANDS

Left, top to bottom;
Endemic shrimp *Procaris ascensionis* ***A**

A centipede *Scolopendra morsitans* **HA**

Endemic bush cricket *Phaneracra bartletti* ****H**

Right, top to bottom;
Landcrab *Gecarcinus lagostoma* **A**

A migratory cricket *Gryllus bimaculatus* **HA**

Endemic cricket *Gryllus abnormis* ***H**

Tropical Migratory Locust *Locusta migratoria migratorioides* **A**

PLATE 23
ANIMALS OF THE ISLANDS

Top left African Monarch *Danaus chrysippus* **H(A)** on Blue Weed *Ageratum conyzoides*

Centre left Deaths-head Hawkmoth *Acherontia atropos* **H(A)** on honeycomb

Bottom left Painted Lady *Vanessa cardui* **H(A)** on White Flower *Eupatorium pallidum* **H**

Top right African Monarch caterpillar on Silk Cotton *Asclepias rotundifolius* **H**

Above left Diadem butterfly *Hypolimnas misippus* male **HA**

Above right Tubes made from faecal pellets by a moth of the genus *Opogona* (family Tineidae) on She Cabbage *Lachanodes arborea* **H**

Below Long-tailed Blue *Lampides boeticus* **HA** on Wild Currant *Lantana camara* **HA**

PLATE 24
BUTTERFLIES AND MOTHS OF THE ISLANDS

the groundwater of the island, found it in several wet, gravelly places near the sea in Sandy Bay and also in the Run in Jamestown; the late Professor Stock generously named the species after us. Its ancestors probably reached St Helena on driftwood.

A   *Platorchestia platensis.* This species, incorrectly recorded from St Helena by the Belgians, does occur on Ascension. It is widespread on warm islands and coasts elsewhere in the Atlantic, but the Ascension animals are somewhat different and occur at high altitude, suggesting the possibility that the stock reached the island naturally a long time ago.

HA   *Talitroides alluaudi.* This is a dark-coloured landhopper similar to the next species, which has been found in Fishers Valley on St Helena and on Green Mountain on Ascension. It is a 'tramp' species which has been carried to many parts of the world by humans; it was evidently introduced to both islands along with plants.

?*HA   *Talitriator insularis.* On St Helena we saw this species below the Heart Shape Waterfall, but it had previously been recorded at much higher levels on the island where damp habitats are more common. It was probably *T. insularis* which was noted in the 19th century by Melliss, who referred to: *"These little black, hopping creatures..."* On Ascension *T. insularis* is widespread on Green Mountain and has been found as low as Dampier's Spring. It has its closest relatives in South Africa, and is probably a St Helena endemic accidentally introduced to Ascension; a less likely possibility is that it is a South African species which has been overlooked there but introduced to both St Helena and Ascension.

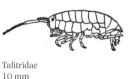

Talitridae
10 mm

ISOPODA – woodlice and their relatives

Most isopods are aquatic but the woodlice can live in moist places on land. They are flattened but also somewhat domed animals, with two pairs of antennae (although only one pair is conspicuous) and seven pairs of legs. Viewed from above they are typically oval and are thus easily distinguished from millipedes (see below) which have more legs and are much more elongate. Unlike the amphipods, woodlice do not hop, but walk relatively slowly; some of them can roll up into an armoured ball. We make no attempt to describe the different families or the individual species, since most woodlice are hard to identify unless one is a specialist. However, we discuss the endemic or probably indigenous species and list all the others, since the treatment of woodlice by the Belgians is seriously out of date.

St Helena has a rich woodlouse fauna of 20 species, but no more than 3-6 are endemic. One or two of the others are salt-tolerant and may be indigenous, but the rest are of little interest, having been introduced with plants, mainly from Europe.

The Ascension woodlice are also intriguing. Until recently, only nine species were known from the island and all were considered to be certainly introduced by man. Our collections in 1990, however, together with new information on African woodlice, changed the picture considerably (see Chapter 12).

ARMADILLIDAE – armadillids

A   *Cubaris murina.* This species has been found in Wideawake colonies and in the very barren lava of Lava Lake (which has traces of old guano). It is a widespread tropical species and we suspect that it may have reached the island naturally with seabirds.

?*H   *Pseudodiploexochus insularis.* This and the next two species, placed by the Belgians in the genus *Reductioniscus*, are now in *Pseudodiploexochus*. *P. insularis* was described on the basis of a single individual collected by C.R. Wallace at High Peak in June 1959. Study of more specimens is needed to confirm that it is really a new and endemic species.

?*H   *Pseudodiploexochus leleupi.* This tiny (3 mm) species was found by the Belgians only on the central ridge. It may be endemic, but there is a suspicion that it may actually be the same as *P. tabularis* (see below).

?*H   *Pseudodiploexochus mellissi.* As in the case of *P. insularis*, this species is based on a single individual collected by Wallace at High Peak; the same caution must be applied.

HA   *Pseudodiploexochus tabularis.* This species, collected by us on St Helena and by Duffey on Ascension, is also known from South Africa and may have been introduced to both islands.

*H   *Pseudolaureola atlantica.* This is now the correct scientific name for the endemic Spiky Yellow Woodlouse, previously known as *Laureola atlantica*, which is featured on the poster 'Invertebrate Wonders of St Helena'. It has recently been recognized as being related to species in Madagascar, the Comoro Islands and Western Australia.[30] Both we and the Belgians found it only on High Peak, but it may also be present elsewhere on the central ridge. It often climbs on endemic plants, and has been found on Dogwood, Black Scale Fern and Tree Ferns. The Spiky Yellow Woodlouse is well named, being bright yellow with black patches, and covered with conspicuous spines; it grows up to 10 mm long.

Pseudolaureola atlantica
10 mm   MRAC

A   *Venezillo parvus* (ex *Sphaerillo parvus*) was found on Ascension by Eric Duffey. It occurs in many islands in the Indian Ocean and was probably introduced to Ascension with plants.

ARMADILLIDIIDAE – armadillidiids

HA   *Armadillidium vulgare* is now widespread on both islands. It is native to western Europe and the Mediterranean but is now almost cosmopolitan. It is a large woodlouse (up to 18 mm) and is capable of rolling up into a tight ball, giving rise to the common name pill-bug.

CYCLISTICIDAE – cyclisticids

H   *Cyclisticus convexus.* Only one individual has been found on St Helena, in Lemon Tree Gut; it is European in origin.

EUBELIDAE – eubelids

*A   *Elumoides coecus.* This puzzling cave species was discovered by us in 1990. It is a member of a poorly known family almost entirely confined to tropical Africa. *E. coecus* differs from the other two member of the genus in being eyeless and in other ways. It is small (up to 3 mm long), colourless and able to roll up into a ball; it seems to occur only in caves low down on the island. *E. coecus* is apparently endemic, but it is not clear how its ancestors reached the island.

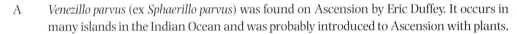

[30] D.H. Kwon et al. (1992).

JANIRIDAE – janirids

*H   *Iais aquilei*. Figure 18. This is a remarkable aquatic isopod, endemic to St Helena. It was found by the Belgians in freshwater pools at The Briars and in Lemon Tree Gut, and is discussed in Chapter 6.

ONISCIDAE – oniscids

H   *Oniscus asellus* is a large species (up to 16 mm by 8 mm) and is usually brownish black. It is found at all levels on St Helena, and is especially fond of rotting wood. *O. asellus* is widespread in Europe and is clearly introduced.

PHILOSCIIDAE – philosciids

H   *Halophiloscia couchii*. We found this species at Potato Bay; it has not previously been found on the island, but is almost certainly indigenous. The species is salt-tolerant, occurring on coasts of Europe, Africa and many Atlantic islands, including the Cape Verdes, and probably arrived on driftwood.

HA   *Atlantoscia floridana*. This is the species recorded from St Helena as *Chaetophiloscia paulensis* (where it has been found in several parts of the uplands) and from Ascension as *Atlantoscia alceui*. It also occurs in Florida and South America, and was probably introduced to both islands.

*H   *Littorophiloscia alticola*. This species was discovered in 1959 by C.R. Wallace, who beat it from fern fronds on Diana's Peak. The Belgians found it on the Peaks but also at Sandy Bay beach. It is the largest member of its group (up to 8 mm long) and is so distinctive that it was previously placed a new genus, *Helenoscia*. However, relatives have now been recognised in tropical Africa and in warm regions throughout the world, but always on coasts.[31] The salt-tolerant ancestor of the St Helena species doubtless arrived on driftwood at a time when there were few – if any – other kinds of woodlice on the island. It provides an example of a phenomenon familiar to island biologists and usually termed ecological release. A species reaching an island or other area where it has few relatives, expands its 'ecological niche' to fill a range of habitats that would be occupied in more richly populated continental areas by its related competitors. Although *Littorophiloscia alticola* has recently been found only on the coast and on the Peaks, it was probably widely distributed in moist places at intermediate levels before the destruction of the native vegetation and the introduction of many alien species.

HA   *Littorophiloscia tropicalis*. On St Helena this species has been found only in Jamestown, and was recorded under the name *Alloniscus compar*. On Ascension we found it in 1990, on and near the shore at Shelly Beach. *L. tropicalis* is a salt-tolerant species now recognized as occurring on coasts in many parts of the tropics; it probably colonised Ascension by dispersal on driftwood, and may possibly also be indigenous on St Helena.

Littorophiloscia alticola
10 mm   MRAC

---

[31] S. Taiti & F. Ferrara (1986).

PLATYARTHRIDAE – platyarthrids

H   *Niambia capensis.* This species has been found only near Lot's Wife and in Friars Valley. The species also occurs in southwest Africa; it has probably been introduced to St Helena, though natural immigration is possible.

*A   *Niambia duffeyi.* Eric Duffey found two males of this species and and we found two females, on lava at Letterbox and inland from Shelly Beach. This species and the next, which are apparently endemic to Ascension, probably originated from a single colonising stock that reached the island from South Africa. The stock evidently split (speciated) after colonising the island, since the two species on the island share characteristics of the head that distinguish them from their relatives.

*A   *Niambia longiantennata.* This species, found by us in 1990, proves to be the most numerous woodlouse on unvegetated lava flows both near the coast and some distance inland; it also occurs in Packer's Hole cave.

H   *Trichorhina tomentosa.* This species was collected by the Belgians in several places. It originates from the New World tropics and is evidently introduced to St Helena. Its ability to reproduce asexually means that a single female can found a new population.

PORCELLIONIDAE – porcellionids

A   *Agnara madagascariensis* was found by us in Command Hill Cave and in one place on lava with a good deal of vegetation. It is also known from West Africa and the Indian Ocean, and is probably introduced.

H   *Leptotrichus panzeri.* A single individual has been found at the Briars. The species also occurs in the Mediterranean region and on various Atlantic islands including the Cape Verdes.

H   *Porcellio laevis* is widespread on St Helena; it may originate from North Africa and now has almost worldwide distribution; it is clearly introduced.

H   *Porcellio lamellatus* has been found at Prosperous Bay, Bryan's Rock and Sandy Bay beach. This is a salt-tolerant species which also occurs on the Cape Verde Islands, and may be indigenous.

HA   *Porcellio pruinosus* (ex *Metoponorthus pruinosus*). On Ascension *P. pruinosus* seems to be absent from recent lava. Both this and the next species originate from the Mediterranean and are clearly introduced.

HA   *Porcellio scaber.* On Ascension this species seems to be absent from recent lava.

TRACHELIPIDAE – trachelipids

A   *Pagana dimorpha,* found in several localities by Duffey, is native to islands of the western the Indian Ocean. It is evidently introduced.

TRICHONISCIDAE – trichoniscids

H   *Haplophthalmus danicus* has been found at only a few places on St Helena. Both this and the next species originated in Europe but are now more widespread; they are evidently introduced to St Helena.

H   *Trichoniscus pusillus* is found at middle and high levels on the island.

DECAPODA – crabs, lobsters and shrimps

In all decapods, the whole of the cephalothorax is covered by a hard carapace. There are five pairs of leglike appendages, and the front pair usually bear large claws. There is a single terrestrial decapod on Ascension.

GECARCINIDAE – landcrabs

A

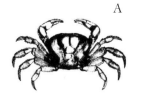

Gecarcinus lagostoma
250 mm

Gecarcinus lagostoma, Landcrab. This large terrestrial crab was the dominant terrestrial omnivore on Ascension at the time of its discovery by people. Young crabs were doubtless eaten by the endemic night heron and by frigatebirds, but adults had little to fear. The landcrabs doubtless had significant effects on the native vegetation, and may have determined which species of seabirds could breed on the main island of Ascension.

As in other crabs, the abdomen of the Ascension landcrab is much reduced and curled under the thorax. The body is broad and somewhat flattenned and the animal can – when necessary – run quickly in any direction; normally, however, the movements are slow and deliberate. The landcrab grows to a carapace length of 8 cm and a legspan around 25 cm. Two colour phases are present: smaller individuals are normally red or purple and tend to have the shell granulated around the front; the largest individuals are generally yellow or orange and the shell is smoother. On Ascension landcrabs are mainly nocturnal, living in burrows in pyroclastic deposits, but in high moist areas east of the mountain they can often be found in dark places under bushes during daytime. They are partial to the fruit of tungies (prickly pear) and probably consume much vegetable matter. However, they also eat a wide variety of animals when they can catch them; there is a record of one killing a young rabbit and they occasionally win a fight with a rat. In the past, eggs and young of seabirds probably suffered a good deal. At present the landcrabs do little harm to the Wideawakes, perhaps because the fairs are in low-lying arid areas unsuitable for the crabs; but we have found one Wideawake egg apparently crushed by a landcrab.

Storrs Olson has suggested plausibly that successful breeding of petrels that nest in the open or in burrows in soft ground may be impossible on islands with numerous landcrabs.[32] Petrel chicks are left alone by the parents while still young, and are almost helpless; they would be easy prey for landcrabs. The contrast between the undisturbed seabird community of St Helena, with large numbers of petrels, and that on Ascension, where only the crevice-nesting Madeiran Storm-petrel was abundant, may be due as much to the respective absence and presence of landcrabs on the two islands, as to differences in the surrounding seas.

Although landcrabs spend almost the whole of their life on land, they have to release their larvae into seawater. However, the larvae metamorphose into tiny crabs which then quickly become terrestrial. On Ascension, they then face the daunting task of climbing through the desert lowlands to the moister uplands where they can find food

[32] S.L. Olson (1981).

325

and avoid dessication. Many populations of land crabs show annual spawning migrations of the adults to the sea, but it appears that on Ascension the cycle is less regular. A 19th century record indicated seaward migration in February and March, and in late March 1963 John Packer noted thousands of tiny crabs invading Georgetown on their way inland. Young crabs were still present near the settlement in May 1963, when Arthur Loveridge collected juveniles with carapace length 3.5 mm. It seems significant that 1963 was an El Niño year, with substantial rain in some parts of the lowlands in January and quite exceptional falls in March. Spawning landcrabs were also seen on beaches by residents in late January 1987.

It is likely that on Ascension seaward spawning migration by the adults occurs mainly in years with high autumn rainfall, and that the tiny offspring survive only in the rare years – normally associated with El Niño – when cloudy and damp conditions persist for several months. The achievements of the young are impressive: we found a crab only 12 mm long near a cave north of Sisters Peak in 1990, which had already climbed some 185 m from sea level.

Gecarcinus lagostoma also occurs on Fernando de Noronha, Atol das Rocas and Trindade, all down-current from Ascension and conceivably colonised from it. A closely related species occurs in West Africa and other species in the Caribbean and Indo-Pacific. Assuming that landcrab larvae can drift in ocean currents, a possible scenario for the origin of the South Atlantic island populations would be colonisation of Ascension from the western coasts of Africa, and of the Brazilian islands from Ascension. St Helena, though further north than Trindade, is surrounded by much cooler water flowing from the south; it may never have been reached by landcrab larvae.

DIPLOPODA – millipedes

Millipedes have large numbers of similar segments, leading to an elongate and cylindrical or flattened body shape. They have up to 200 legs, with two pairs on nearly every segment: this is the primary distinction between them and the centipedes (see below). Millipedes feed on various kinds of plant material and prefer moist places. Fifteen species are known from St Helena and two from Ascension. There are no endemics, and all species seem to have been introduced, probably mainly with plants.

POLYXENIDA (or PENICILLATA)

This obscure order of minute (less than 3 mm long) animals is represented by three species on St Helena, all found by the Belgians in the central part of the island. Curiously, all are known from islands in the Indian Ocean but not from Africa.

POLYZONIIDA

A single specimen belonging to this little known order was found by the Belgians on St Helena.

SPIROSTREPTIDA

A single species belonging to this order was found by the Belgians in Lemon Tree Gut on St Helena; it is widely distributed on islands in the Southern Hemisphere.

JULIDA

Julidae

This order includes the best known millipedes. They are cylindrical animals usually with 40 or more body segments. On St Helena the family Blaniulidae is represented by three species.[33] They are easily recognized by the red spot on each side of each segment; these are formed by the glands which produce a foul-smelling secretion as a defence against predators. Blaniulids are common in soils in many parts of St Helena and can cause considerable damage to root crops. The large family Julidae is represented by four species on St Helena and two unidentified ones on Ascension.

POLYDESMIDA – flat-backed millipedes

Members of this order are easily recognized by the flattened body, the skeletal plates on the back being extended like 'wings' close to the ground; there are 18-22 body segments. Confusion with centipedes is possible, but in these the back plates are slightly convex and there are only half as many legs. Three species (in two families) have been found on St Helena and one of these also occurs on Ascension.

CHILOPODA – centipedes

These are carnivorous, land-dwelling animals ranging in length from 1 cm to 30 cm. In contrast to millipedes, there is only one pair of legs per segment, but the number of pairs varies from 15 to 177. Centipedes have antennae and the first pair of legs are modified into poison fangs. They are nocturnal and feed on other invertebrates. Centipedes are classified in four orders.

GEOPHILOMORPHA – soil centipedes

Members of this order are slender, eyeless centipedes, mostly less than 5 cm long and with 31 to 177 pairs of legs. They go deep into the soil and feed on insect larvae and worms. Four species have been recorded from St Helena; three of them are probably introduced but one is endemic. On Ascension there are three species, one endemic, one possibly indigenous (see below) and one probably introduced. We omit most of the introduced species.

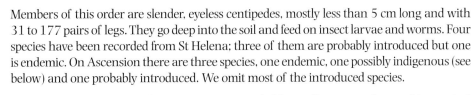

Geophilomorpha
c. 40 mm

A

Mecistocephalus insularis. This species was recorded by Duffey; it is widespread in tropical Africa and on a number of islands, including Sao Thome and Fernando Poo (Bioko) in the Gulf of Guinea. It may have reached Ascension naturally, or in soil with introduced plants.

---

[33] This includes *Choneiulus palmatus*, not previously recorded from the island but found by us in several small caves on and near the central ridge.

*A   *Tuoba ashmoleorum.* This new species is 39 mm long and has 57 pairs of legs.[34] We found a single specimen near the shore at Shelly Beach, a remote area little affected by human activities on the island, but one where flotsam accumulates. Members of the genus *Tuoba* are often found on beaches and have a special claw spine which is thought to serve as a hold-fast adaptation for clinging; this would also be useful during transportation, and we suspect that *T. ashmoleorum* or its ancestors reached Ascension on driftwood.

*H   *Tuoba benoiti.* This is the correct name for the species previously recorded as *Nesogeophilus benoiti.* It has been found only on Prosperous Bay Plain at 900 ft. It is about 35 mm long and has 63 pairs of legs. As with the last species, its ancestors probably arrived on driftwood.

SCOLOPENDROMORPHA – scolopendromorphs

Scolopendra sp.
c. 60 mm

These centipedes have 21 or 23 pairs of legs. Many are brightly coloured. They can both bite with their poison fangs and pinch with their last pair of legs. The largest species have been seen feeding on toads and lizards. Some species dig burrows, and females characteristically coil around the eggs and young to protect them. Each of the islands has three species, one of those on St Helena being endemic. All species are listed below.

*H   *Cryptops basilewskyi.* Members of this genus are eyeless animals, generally pale orange in colour. *C. basilewskyi* has been found only at Bryan's Rock and seems to be a surviving member of the fauna of the gumwood forest. Ancestors of this species presumably reached St Helena in driftwood.

HA   *Cryptops hortensis.* This is a northern species evidently introduced to both islands. It is found in damp places and is widespread on St Helena; on Ascension it seems to occur mainly on the mountain.

A   *Cryptops* species. We obtained a single specimen of a second species of *Cryptops* on barren lava at Command Hill. It is damaged, but appears similar but not identical to some South African species. It may prove to be endemic, although introduction on a ship from southern Africa is also possible.

HA   *Scolopendra morsitans.* Plate 23. This large centipede (body commonly up to 6 cm long) is quite common in dry parts of both islands, where it can often be found hiding under stones during the day. It can inflict a painful bite if disturbed. This is a large predatory invertebrate, and we suspect that it is at least partly responsible for the decline of the St Helena giant earwig and also the giant ground beetle and probably several other relatively defenceless endemic invertebrates. We assume that the species has been introduced to both islands by ships from southern Africa, although natural colonisation by rafting is conceivable. A second species of *Scolopendra, S. valida,* was mentioned by Melliss, but this was probably a misidentification.

LITHOBIOMORPA – stone centipedes

These centipedes are all less than 5.5 cm long and have 15 pairs of legs. When disturbed they throw out droplets of sticky material to deter enemies. Four species

---

[34] J.G.E. Lewis (1995).

have been recorded from St Helena (one apparently endemic) and one from Ascension; all are listed below.

HA   *Lithobius forficatus*. This species is doubtless introduced. It is widespread in the higher parts of St Helena. Confirmation is needed that this is the species present on Ascension.

H   *Lithobius melanops*. Found by the Belgians only in Fishers Valley.

?*H   *Lamyctes leleupi*. This species has only been recorded from the High Central Ridge. Confirmation is needed that this is an endemic species, as there is a possibility of confusion with *L. castanea* from South Africa.

H   *Lithobius aeruginosus* (ex *Monotarsobius aeruginosus*). A damaged individual collected by the Belgians on Mt. Eternity was provisionally identified as this European species; it may prove to be the same as two specimens which we collected in small caves at High Peak and Coles Rock.

SCUTIGEROMORPHA

These centipedes run extraordinarily fast. They have 15 pairs of very long legs, of which the last pair look very similar to the antennae, so that the eyes are the best way of distinguishing the front end. A single species occurs on St Helena.

H   *Scutigera coleoptrata*. This Mediterranean species has been found in several dry parts of the island.

SYMPHYLA – symphylans

These are small, slender and whitish animals with 10-12 pairs of legs. They live in damp situations, sometimes underground, and are not often noticed. Three species have been recorded from St Helena: one in the family Scolopendrillidae and two in the Scutigerillidae. All are widespread species and have doubtless been introduced with plants.

INSECTA (or Hexapoda) – insects

Insects differ from other arthropods in having only three pairs of legs (spiders and their relatives have four pairs, crustaceans, millipedes and centipedes many more); most adult insects also have one or two pairs of wings. There are three fairly distinct body regions, referred to as head, thorax and abdomen; the head normally has one pair of antennae and a pair of compound eyes, and there may also be one or more ocelli (simple eyes); the thorax bears the legs and wings; the abdomen bears no legs but may have appendages at the tip, and in some larvae it has several pairs of leg-like appendages. A few groups of insects are primitively wingless (i.e. have never evolved wings) while some species in many other groups are secondarily wingless. Winged insects fall into two major groups according to their style of development. In the first, which includes dragonflies, crickets, bugs and others, the young stage (known as a nymph) becomes more and more like the adult at each of a series of moults of the exoskeleton; the wings develop externally, becoming larger after each moult, but not functional until after the last. In the second group, including the beetles, butterflies, flies and wasps, the young (known as a larva) changes rather little as it grows, but there is a quiescent or pupal stage before the last moult which allows major reorganisation of the body including internal development of the wings; the perfect adult then emerges from the pupa.

COLLEMBOLA – springtails

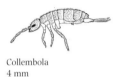

Collembola
4 mm

Springtails are minute wingless insects, mostly 5 mm or less in length and with short antennae. The abdomen has six or fewer segments and does not have cerci (feelers) at the rear end. There is, however, usually a forked structure (the furcula) attached to the underside of the abdomen and carried tucked under it with the fork facing forwards; it enables the springtail to jump upwards when the fork is suddenly released. Springtails live mainly in soil or decaying matter on the ground. There are two major groups (suborders): the Arthropleona (elongate-bodied springtails) and the Symphypleona (globular springtails); since these are easy to distinguish but the families are difficult, we use only this division and do not treat the families separately. On St Helena 21 species of collembolans have been recorded; most of these are known from elsewhere and several are cosmopolitan. Six species, however, have not been fully identified. Further study of these and of additional specimens from the desert areas might show that some endemic species are present. On Ascension 12 species have been found, of which three are endemic and three others (which have not yet been fully studied) are probably indigenous and perhaps even endemic. We list only the more interesting species.

HA   ARTHREOPLONA – elongate-bodied springtails

In this group the body is elongate and the abdomen (the part behind the last pair of legs) has six fairly clear segments. On St Helena 19 species have been found, five of them not yet identified. Ascension has 10 species, at least three of them endemic.

*A   *Pseudosinella* species (family Entomobryidae). The members of this genus are of particular interest on Ascension. The trapping that we did in 1990 and 1995 showed that there were three species, with distinct habitats. *Pseudosinella lava* is a subterranean species and is white and eyeless: it dominated the samples that we took with traps in caves and in pipes driven into the clinker. *P. ashmolae* is dominant on the inland barren lava flows: it is pale grey and has 12 ocelli (simple eyes). *P. miratio* is abundant near the shore: it is dark blue and also has 12 ocelli. The species have been described and named by Dr Kenneth Christiansen, who suggests that they have evolved on the island from a single stock, to form three endemic species.

A   *Seira* species (family Entomobryidae). A probably introduced species of *Seira* occurs on vegetated lava flows, but in the dark zone of Packer's Hole cave we found a single individual of a clearly distinct species which may turn out to be endemic.

330

SYMPHYPLEONA – globular springtails

In these springtails the body is globular, with the segments of the abdomen largely fused and indistinct. On St Helena there is one cosmopolitan species and another which has not been fully identified. On Ascension there are two species, listed below.

A   *Denisiella* species (family Sminthurididae). We found a few individuals belong to this genus in a remote site encrusted with old guano; the species is likely to be indigenous.

A   *Sphaeridia* species (family Sminthurididae). This genus was also represented in lava with old guano and is probably indigenous.

DIPLURA – diplurans

Diplurans are delicate, small, wingless insects with elongate, pale, clearly segmented bodies. They have long 'beaded' antennae and also a pair of filaments (cerci) at the hind end of the abdomen which are rather similar to the antennae; they also differ from collembolans in the lack of a forked jumping organ underneath the abdomen. St Helena has four species of diplurans. All are in the family Campodeidae and all are also known from Britain; they were probably introduced to St Helena with potted plants. No diplurans have been found on Ascension Island.

THYSANURA – bristletails

The thysanurans have smooth, tapering bodies with a pair of long antennae and three long, slender filaments at the hind end of the abdomen (cf. diplurans, which have only two); they often rest under rocks, but can move with great speed if disturbed.

NICOLETIIDAE – nicoletiids

A single species in this family has been found on St Helena; it was originally described from Sumatra and is clearly introduced.

LEPISMATIDAE – lepismatids

Four species of lepismatids have been found on St Helena; three of these have been widely distributed by humans and are clearly introduced. The fourth was discovered by the Belgians and has not been found elsewhere; the Belgians noted that its closest relatives occur in southern Africa and suggested that it would eventually also be found there, but we consider it to be endemic to St Helena. Three species occur on Ascension and one of them is widespread on barren lava, but they appear to be absent from Boatswainbird Island; this strongly suggests that the species have been introduced to Ascension recently, since Boatswainbird Island would have been connected to the main island during the last ice age.

Ctenolepisma sp.
7 mm

*H   *Ctenolepisma sanctaehelenae.* This species grows to 13 mm long and is whitish with a violet tinge. It was discovered by the Belgians and collected mainly on Prosperous Bay Plain, but also on Longwood Plain and at Sandy Bay beach. *C. sanctaehelenae* is not easy to distinguish from its introduced relatives on the island, but the presence of violet patches in various parts of the body indicate this species.

ODONATA – dragonflies

Odonata
50 mm

The dragonflies are strong fliers, with two pairs of long gauzy wings, a long narrow abdomen, huge eyes and legs set well forward and adapted to catch the smaller insects on which they feed. The nymphs (larvae) live in freshwater and are also voracious predators.

LIBELLULIDAE – darters

The darters are medium to large, robust dragonflies with the abdomen somewhat flattened. St Helena used to have an endemic species of darter, but it is probably now extinct. Another species, well known as a migrant, has been seen on both St Helena and Ascension.

HA   *Pantala flavescens.* This dragonfly is about 5 cm long and with wingspan about 8.5 cm. It is best recognised by the conspicuously tapered yellowish-orange abdomen and by its flight: it is a 'flier', typically spending most of its time flying to and fro several metres above the ground, often gliding in warm weather. *P. flavescens* has been collected on both islands, but on Ascension it seems to be only a vagrant. On St Helena an adult was captured in February 1990 in the earth dam at Harpers, and around the same time some dragonfly larvae were found in a cattle trough. It is thus possible that a small breeding population of this species is established.

*?†H   *Sympetrum dilatatum*, St Helena Dragonfly. This species is (or was) about 4.5 cm long and has a wingspan of around 7.5 cm. The abdomen is not tapered towards the tip and is red or pale brown, with blackish brown markings; the front of the head is greenish. Members of this genus typically perch low down, making only brief investigatory flights. This dragonfly was evidently well established on St Helena in the past. In 1875 Melliss' only comment was: *"The common large red-bodied Dragon-fly, which is abundant all over the Island."* Dragonflies were still well remembered by older people (under the name of 'horse-flies') when Arthur Loveridge enquired about them in about 1960. By that date, however, they had become very scarce. Loveridge saw and attempted to catch a dragonfly which he evidently considered to be this species on 5th January 1963, and a female was later captured by eight-year old S.D. Peters while it was eating a bee on a yam flower at Green Hill. This was on 13th October 1963, and is the last occurrence of the species that we are aware of; the specimen was preserved in the National Museum of Southern Rhodesia (now Zimbabwe) in Bulawayo.[35] It seems possible that the main reason for the decline of *S. dilatatum* was the introduction in about 1880 of the African Grass Frog, which is now ubiquitous in freshwater habitats and would probably eat the larvae. It has also been suggested that pollution from flax mills could have had an effect.

---

[35] E. Pinhey (1964).

ORTHOPTERA – grasshoppers and crickets

These are medium to large insects with a heavy, blunt head and usually enlarged hind legs modified for jumping. They are among the noisiest of insects, but in spite of the loudness of their chirps they are not always easy to locate, and some species blend well with their background. Some have no wings, whilst others have two pairs which they hold folded on their backs when they are not flying. The group includes some notorious migrant pests and several species have reached the islands naturally. Since there are relatively few species we list all of them.

TETTIGONIIDAE – bush crickets

Members of this family have long hairlike antennae. They also have a laterally flattened blade-like ovipositor, and four segments in the tarsus (foot). St Helena has one endemic genus (with two species) and one other species which is also found on Ascension.

**H   *Phaneracra bartletti*. Plate 23. This and the next species are members of an endemic genus with no close relatives; evidently this is an ancient colonising stock. *P. bartletti* has forewings less than 11 mm long. It has been found in several places on the central ridge, including High Peak; we found it on She Cabbages at Osbornes.

**H   *Phaneracra uvarovi*. This species has the forewings rather longer (>11 mm) than in *P. bartletti* and has a differently shaped ovipositor. It has been found near Cabbage Tree Road and at Teutonic Hall. It is not yet clear whether the two species ever occur together.

HA   *Ruspolia differens* (ex *Homorocoryphus nitidulus vicinus*). This is a very large green grasshopper, which on St Helena is found mainly in agricultural land and gardens. It is probably indigenous on both islands, since it is capable of long-distance migrations: individuals have landed on ships more than 1200 km from the African mainland.

GRYLLIDAE – crickets

Members of this family also have long tapering antennae, but have only three segments in the tarsus and the ovipositor is cylindrical rather than flattened; the outer edges of the front wings bend sharply down round the sides of the body. There are six species on St Helena, of which at least one is endemic. Ascension has five species, of which three are probably endemic (a record of a sixth, *Trigonidium (Metioche) fuscicornis*, requires confirmation).

H   *Acheta domesticus*. This is a cosmopolitan introduced species which Melliss noted as living in houses; it has not been recorded recently.

HA   *Gryllodes sigillatus*. This is a brown, stripey cricket about 17 mm long; the female is wingless. The species is widespread in warm regions of the world and is doubtless introduced to both islands. On St Helena Melliss says that it is known as the Ground Hopper; it seems to occur mainly in Jamestown and Rupert's Valley. On Ascension we found it to be widely distributed, but usually in places with some vegetation.

*H   *Gryllus abnormis*. Plate 23. Until recently this species was mistaken for an immature stage of *G. bimaculatus* (see below). The Belgians recorded it from Deadwood Plain,

Gryllus abnormis
20 mm   MRAC

Horsepoint Plain and Flagstaff, but we found it indoors at Little Varneys. It is similar to *G. bimaculatus* but lacks the pale spots and has very short wings; it is unable to fly.

HA   *Gryllus bimaculatus*. Plate 23. This is a large (up to 25 mm long) shiny black cricket with two pale contrasting spots at the base of the wings. It has been recorded at low and middle levels on St Helena and in lowland places on Ascension where there is some grass. The species is widespread in tropical and subtropical countries of the Old World, and there are records of swarms undertaking long distance overseas dispersal flights. Crickets from one such swarm once landed on a ship more than 900 km off the coast of West Africa.[36] We therefore consider that it has colonised both islands naturally.

?*HA   Mogoplistine crickets. These 'scaly crickets' are inconspicuous members of the island faunas, but by putting traps underground and on barren lava flows we have found one probably endemic species on St Helena and three on Ascension. Specialists in the group are rare and we have not yet been able to get these species studied and named.

H   *Myrmecophilus sanctaehelenae*. This is a tiny brown cricket that lives in ants' nests. It was described as a new species by the Belgians although they noted that it was extremely similar to the European species *M. acervorum* and considered that it was probably introduced from Europe with its ant host (*Pheidole*). It has been found at Holdfast Tom, Friars Valley and Peak Hill.

ACRIDIDAE – grasshoppers and locusts

In this group the antennae are much shorter than the body, the tarsus is three-segmented and the ovipositor is short. St Helena has two species in the subfamily Truxalinae which are among the most interesting endemic insects of the island. They have no close relatives, but other members of the subfamily are associated with the grasslands that developed in Africa in the Pliocene. The St Helena species are currently treated as being in separate endemic genera, *Primnia* and *Tinaria*, but it seems likely that both are derived from a single stock that colonised St Helena several million years ago. The colonists may have arrived by air, but the modern species both have reduced wings. The only other acridids on the islands are two species of locusts on Ascension, one of which has also been found on St Helena.

A   *Locusta migratoria migratorioides*, Tropical Migratory Locust. Plate 23. This relatively small grey locust has a wide distribution that includes Africa and many remote islands in the Indian and Pacific oceans. It has a distinct small form (c. 35-50 mm) on Ascension but this can hybridise with the west African form. As its name implies this locust is a well known migrant and is likely to have reached Ascension from southwestern Africa, or perhaps from West Africa in disturbed weather conditions. It requires grasses or sedges to complete its life cycle: both these plant groups were present in the prehistoric vegetation on Ascension and grasses are now more widespread there; the locust becomes abundant after rains.

**H   *Primnia sanctaehelenae*. Both this species and *Tinaria* are variable in colour and size, so that care is required in distinguishing them. *Primnia* seems always to be brown, while *Tinaria* is often brown but sometimes olive green or dark grey. The size range is similar

[36] D.R. Wragge (1972).

334

(about 10-20 mm, with females always larger) but *Primnia* is stouter, with more robust hind legs. The best way to separate them may be the shape of the hind margin of the back plate, which comes to a sharp point around (90 degrees) in *Primnia* but is much more rounded in *Tinaria*; however, the very young stages are not separable in this way. The species can also be distinguished by measuring the width of the back plate at the base of the wings (the broadest point) and dividing it by the total length of the body (ignoring the legs); this ratio is around 0.22 in *Primnia* and 0.16 in *Tinaria*. *Primnia* seems to be typical of the north of the island in relatively barren and dry areas up to about 500 m, including Prosperous Bay Plain.

(H)A *Schistocerca gregaria*, Desert Locust. This is a large (c. 60-70 mm) brown-grey locust with brown blotches on wings. Adults can be distinguished from those of *Locusta* by their larger size; both adults and the smaller hoppers of *Schistocerca* also have a boss or projection exactly between the bases of the front legs, which is lacking in *Locusta*. The Desert Locust is widespread throughout Africa and Asia. It is a well known migrant and huge numbers sometimes fly continuously for several days (flights of 5,000 km have been recorded); this is the species referred to in the Bible as one of the plagues of Egypt. Only one specimen has been recorded from St Helena but we suspect that the species does reach the island from time to time. On Ascension the species seems to be established and it can become numerous when there is a good crop of grass after exceptional rains.

Schistocerca gregaria
65 mm

**H *Tinaria calcarata*. This species is described along with its close relative *Primnia* (above). It seems to be typical of the central part of the island at high levels, including the Peaks, but has been found as low as 300 m on Prosperous Bay Plain and also at Varneys. It seems likely that before the natural vegetation of the island was devastated by humans, *Tinaria* and *Primnia* occupied more distinct ecological zones.

DERMAPTERA – earwigs

Earwigs are elongate brownish insects. Wings are present in some species, the leathery front ones (elytra) reaching only a short way down the body and the membranous hind ones being concealed at rest. At the hind end of the body is a pair of stout pincers; these distinguish earwigs from staphylinid beetles, which have similar elytra and are much the same shape. Earwigs are nocturnal and generally spend the day in dark, narrow crevices. They are fairly omnivorous, feeding on plant or animal material, and some species are predatory. The female earwig cares for her eggs and young in a way that is very unusual among insects. Four kinds of earwigs (one endemic) have been recorded from St Helena and one has been found on Ascension.

LABIDURIDAE – striped earwigs
Earwigs in this family have wings (or at least elytra) and usually have longitudinal dark stripes on their backs.

*?†H *Labidura herculeana*, St Helena Giant Earwig. This is a striking shiny black earwig with reddish legs; the elytra are short and the hind wings absent. The animals lived in deep burrows, appearing on the surface only at night after rains. *L. herculeana* is the world's

335

Labidura herculeana
50 mm   MRAC

largest earwig, with body length in some males over 50 mm plus forceps up to 34 mm. The remains of the largest known specimen – a male – were found by Douglas Dorward and Philip in 1959 when excavating fossil bird bones; in 1995 we found the forceps of a female during our similar work on Prosperous Bay Plain.

The Giant Earwig has not been seen alive since the 1960s and is possibly extinct. However, it has entered into the folklore of St Helena and many people feel intuitively that it is still living out there somewhere. In 1966/67 the Belgians found it to be reasonably common, though with distribution limited to a small area including Horse Point. The fact that they collected 40 individuals may have contributed to its disappearance. However, more fundamental is the destruction of the Gumwood forest in which the species evidently lived. Furthermore, if you walk over the northeastern plains and look under stones, you will soon encounter the introduced centipede *Scolopendra morsitans*. Although the earwig may have been the dominant invertebrate predator in the forest before 1502, we think that in conflicts between it and the centipede, the latter would have won. Mice are also common in these areas and may well eat earwigs.

H   *Labidura riparia*. This species is cosmopolitan and is probably introduced to the island. It is blackish or dark reddish-brown, with the legs and the edges of the back plate yellowish. Body length is 14-18 mm and forceps 4-5 mm. This species is primarily predaceous. It occurs in several places on St Helena including Deadwood and Plantation, but the Belgians did not find it in the same area as the giant species.

CARCINOPHORIDAE

Almost all members of this family lack both the membranous wings and elytra. The forceps of the male are asymmetrical, with the right branch shorter and more strongly hooked than the left.

H   *Anisolabis maritima*, Seaside Earwig. This is a shiny black earwig with yellow legs; it is about 20 mm long including the forceps. The head widens slightly just behind the eyes (cf. the next species). On St Helena *A. maritima* has been found on sea-washed rocks at Sandy Bay. The species is predaceous and has almost worldwide distribution; it may well have reached the island naturally on driftwood.

HA   *Euborellia annulipes*. This species is like a smaller version of the last. It is black and shiny, with yellow legs; its total length is up to 15 mm. It can be distinguished from young individuals of the previous species by the shape of the head, which narrows immediately behind the eyes. This is the commonest earwig on St Helena and is found all over the island but especially in the north. It is present on Ascension but has not established itself on the barren lava flows. *E. annulipes* is a cosmopolitan species and is regularly reported as a traveller on ships, so it probably reached the islands in this way.

ISOPTERA – termites or white ants

Termites are colonial insects and most species feed on wood. Some termites have their colonies underground or in wood whilst others build spectacular adobe towers above ground. Termites have distinct castes of individuals which play different roles in the colony. Each colony is headed by a king and a queen, which are much bigger than the workers or soldiers. The workers all have their special duties in the colony, such as tending the eggs that the queen lays, finding food or building the nest. Unlike many insects, adult termites are soft bodied, only their heads being hard and chitinous. Termites are notoriously destructive, and ironically, they have even eaten some of the volumes of the East India Company Records to which we wanted to refer. Two species are known from St Helena and one of these also occurs on Ascension.

KALOTERMITIDAE

Kalotermitidae nymph
3 mm

HA   *Cryptotermes brevis*, Dry-wood Termite. This species lacks a worker caste and the soldiers use their short, hollowed out, armoured heads to block the entrances to the colony. The termites remain inside the wood that they are consuming and do not maintain a base underground (cf. the next species). An authoritative book on termites states: "*It is never found in nature living in logs etc, but is entirely a house termite, damaging the woodwork of buildings and furniture.*" One wonders how it evolved! *C. brevis* was first recorded on St Helena in 1928. It is a pest in construction timber and furniture throughout the island. It also occurs in Georgetown on Ascension.

RHINOTERMITIDAE

H   *Heterotermes perfidus*, Damp-wood Termite. This is the species (previosuly misidentified as *H. platycephalus*) that has caused so much damage on the island. The workers are about 8 mm long and dirty white in colour; soldiers are easily distinguished from those of the Dry-wood Termite by their elongate, parallel-sided heads bearing enormous and almost straight red brown mandibles. These termites nest underground and rarely come into the open except when the males and females (which have two similar pairs of wings) emerge for a courtship flight; to reach a piece of wood or other edible object not resting on the ground they construct a tunnel of mud about 3 mm in diameter across the open space.

Damage to buildings was first noted in 1846, although Melliss noted that: "*It was known that they were eating books, furniture, papers and clothes, with occasionally a beam or two in the houses, but no one entertained the idea that in an additional five or six years their houses would be in ruins ...*" In 1863 "*Fearful ravages*" were noted and in 1869 specimens were exhibited to the Entomological Society of London. In 1875 Melliss gave a detailed account, indicating the extraordinary scale of the destruction caused. We quote only the first few lines: "*It was a melancholy sight five years ago to see the town, which had hitherto not been without its claims for admiration, devastated as by an earthquake, or, as a visitor remarked, a state of seige – the chief church in ruins, public buildings in a deplorable state of dilapidation, private houses tottering and falling, with great timber props, butting out into the streets and roadways, meeting the eye at every turn ...*"

Experiments organised by the Governor of the time showed that creosote provided some protection against the termites and that a few kinds of wood were naturally resistant. Reconstruction of Jamestown was carried out mainly using teak, and subsequently iroko has been widely used. Damage to buildings continued, but in 1960, a century after the first signs of termite attack were noted, C.R. Wallace was able to say that the situation in respect of termites was gradually improving as more appropriate building practices became prevalent. However, the contents of buildings are still in continual danger of attack.

Since its introduction the Damp-wood Termite has spread widely in the island and causes damage to some kinds of forest trees, especially acacias but also Norfolk Island Pine and oaks. In some cases the termites eat out the heartwood of living trees without giving any external signs of their presence; infested trees may then be blown down in gales. It is not clear that the endemic trees have suffered much: they were probably already scarce in the Jamestown area by the time the termite arrived and we have not heard of them being attacked where they survive. The termites have caused some horticultural damage, attacking the trunks of pawpaws and the stems of broad beans at the base.

The Belgians commented that: *"The species found on St. Helena appears to be endemic"*, presumably because it had not been found anywhere else. However, it was assumed in the nineteenth century that it had been introduced in 1840 in timber from a captured slave ship. Although the details may not be correct, we think that introduction is much more probable than natural arrival of this termite stock. Although the relevant group is found in many parts of the tropics, the only African representative is restricted to Ethiopia and Sudan, with the group entirely absent from western Africa. In 1875 Melliss noted explicitly that the termite was not present away from Jamestown, strongly supporting the idea that it reached the island with humans. In view of the nature of the slave trade it is likely that it came from tropical America.

BLATTODEA – cockroaches

Cockroaches are medium or large, flattened, fast-running insects, typically brown, grey or blackish in colour. The first pair of wings are broad and leathery and are held flat over the back, where they overlap; the second pair are membranous and are the ones used mainly for flight (which occurs infrequently). The legs are long and have strong spines. A pair of long, thin antennae are held out in front of the animal and there is also a pair of short tail feelers called cerci. On first sight cockroaches might be confused with beetles, but these do not have cerci and their wing coverings (elytra) alway meet in the mid-line on the back and never overlap. Some heteropteran bugs have wings that are held flat and overlap, but only near the tips; the bugs also have sucking beaks, which cockroaches never have. The most familiar cockroaches lay eggs in a curious leathery purse-like container, but some are live-bearing and show maternal care. Cockroaches are not adapted for long-distance flight and do not normally reach islands without the aid of man. However, several species are frequently transported by ships and a few of them live in buildings, where their omnivorous habits make them a pest. Nine species in four families have been found on St Helena and five species in five families on Ascension; only three species occur on both islands. All of them are doubtless introduced.

EUTHYRRHAPHIDAE

HA   *Euthyrrhapha pacifica.* A tiny (4 mm) black cockroach with yellow markings including a round spot on each of the front wings. Both sexes are winged. This species is usually found under stones; it originates from Africa but is now found throughout the tropics.

H   *Tivia oniscoides.* The male of this species is undescribed but is likely to be winged; the dull brown female is wingless and 7-8 mm long; the antennae are longer than the body, but the cerci on the tip of the abdomen are very short. The species is widely distributed but apparently scarce on St Helena; it seems to originate from East Africa but now also occurs in the Cape Verde archipelago.

BLABERIDAE

H   *Calolampra signatura.* A grey cockroach with a black stripe between the eyes; the body is about 16 mm long and the wings 22 mm. This species was common in Jamestown in the late 19th century but has not been found recently. It originated in Australasia and was evidently brought to St Helena by ship; it also occurs in Haiti, which it probably reached from St Helena, transported with freed slaves.

PYCNOSCELIDAE

HA   *Pycnoscelus surinamensis.* A very shiny, dark brown, medium-sized species (20-23 mm long). This species has oriental origins; some populations include both sexes, but the form on St Helena consists entirely of females, which are capable of reproducing without the intervention of a male. It is found out of doors under stones at low and middle levels.

OXYHALOIDAE

HA   *Leucophaea maderae.* A large (40 mm) cockroach, grey or brown in colour, which is common in houses in the lower parts of St Helena; it probably originates from West Africa. There is only an old record from Ascension.

H   *Nauphoeta cinerea.* A medium-sized light brown species which is now found in the open in many parts of the island. However, it was not recorded by Melliss in 1875, so it is presumably a relatively recent arrival; it is widely distributed in the tropics.

BLATTIDAE

A   *Periplaneta americana.* A large (30 mm) red-brown species that is now widely distributed around the world. On Ascension it is abundant in houses but we have also found it both above and below ground in remote lava flows, including some near Letterbox.

H   *Periplaneta australasiae.* In spite of its name, this species probably originates from tropical Africa. It is red-brown and about 25 mm in length. Melliss recorded it as the common red cockroach of the island, especially in houses but also out of doors; the Belgians recorded it from Horse Point Plain.

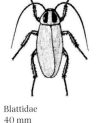

Blattidae
40 mm

BLATELLIDAE

H   *Afrobalta decellei.* This is a small (11 mm) yellow brown species in which both sexes have wings, also about 11 mm long. A single male was found by the Belgians in Friars Valley. This species was previously known only from the Ivory Coast in West Africa, and it seems likely that it reached St Helena on a slave ship.

?(H) *Blatella germanica.* This is a slender, light brown cockroach 10-13 mm long. There is some doubt as to whether it is now present on the island, as the Belgians failed to find it. Melliss commented that it occurred on the low land, but was rare.

A *Ischnoptera* sp. Found only once on Ascension.

EMBIOPTERA – web-spinners

These are small to medium sized insects with soft brownish bodies. Their unique feature is a pair of silk glands near the tips of the front legs, enabling them to build silk-lined webs and tunnels under stones in which they live in colonies: the female lays her eggs and defends them and the young when they hatch. Embioptera feed on a variety of dead and live plant material. The females always lack wings, but some males in some species have two pairs of similar wings. Embioptera can be distinguished from earwigs by their lack of pincers at the tip of the abdomen, and from termites by the elongate, parallel-sided abdomen and swollen segments near the tip of the front legs and at the base of the hind ones. One species is now present on St Helena and both it and a second species have been found on Ascension; they are all introduced.

OLIGOTOMIDAE
This family was originally restricted to Asia and Australia, but several species have become widely distributed by commerce.

A *Oligotoma* cf. *ceylonica.* This species was recorded from Ascension by Eric Duffey.

HA *Oligotoma saundersii.* On St Helena this species has been found only in Ruperts Valley, suggesting that it reached the island with a slave ship. On Ascension it occurs under bushes and trees (including *Prosopis*) in dry parts of the island; it is sometimes extremely abundant.

THYSANOPTERA – thrips

These are minute, dark, slender insects, usually with two pairs of feathery wings. They are most commonly found on flowers. They suck plant juices and some species eat dead plants; some are serious pests of cultivated plants. On St Helena 10 species have been recorded, of which two are endemic (one at the generic level); only one species has been recorded on Ascension.

*H *Diceratothrips meridionalis* (family Phlaeothripidae). An endemic species found in Fishers Valley but also on the high central ridge.

HA *Haplothrips gowdeyi* (family Phlaeothripidae). This species has been found in several places on St Helena; we caught one specimen on Ascension. *H. gowdeyi* is now almost cosmopolitan in warm regions, and since it is a well known migrant in the upper air it may have reached both islands naturally.

Thysanoptera
1.5 mm

**H   *Helenothrips tinctus* (family Thripidae). This species, the sole member of a new endemic genus, was found by the Belgians at Teutonic Hall and Plantation House; it was abundant at both sites.

H   *Thrips tabaci* (family Thripidae). This is the onion thrips, a cosmopolitan species that can be a significant pest; on St Helena it has been found on cabbages but is particularly damaging to onions.

HEMIPTERA – bugs, hoppers, aphids, scale insects

This is the fifth largest order of insects, with well over 50,000 species throughout the world. All hemipterans have a long beak (the rostrum) for piercing and sucking, which is held pointing backwards under the body when not in use. Most species have large eyes and four wings, but in some the wings are reduced or absent. Most hemipterans feed on plants and many are serious pests on crops. Immature stages usually resemble small adults.

The hemipterans fall into two main groups, which are sometimes considered as separate orders but which we treat as the suborders Homoptera and Heteroptera within a single Order Hemiptera. Confusingly, many American entomologists use the word Hemiptera to refer only to the Heteroptera (often termed "true bugs") and consider the Homoptera as a separate order.

HEMIPTERA: HETEROPTERA – heteropterans or true bugs

In the Heteroptera the front wings are in two parts, a leathery section at the base called the corium and a membranous one at the tip, with a sharp division between the two sections. The wings at rest are held flat over the body and there is a conspicuous triangular back plate (scutellum) with a point extending backwards between the base of the wings. The beak in the Heteroptera arises from the front of the head. The Heteroptera include many groups which are excellent dispersers; presumably because of this the suborder is diverse on St Helena with 20 endemic species and a number of endemic genera. Only one group (the Miridae) has undergone an adaptive radiation on the island, with a number of species dependent on different endemic plants. On Ascension nine species have been recorded and three are probably indigenous.

ANTHOCORIDAE – minute pirate bugs

These are small, somewhat flattened, stumpy bugs, often blackish with pale markings. The beak has only three segments and the antennae have four. The wings of anthocorids have a cuneus in the wings (see under Miridae). They are predaceous and some of them feed on blood, including that of humans. Five species are known from St Helena, of which two are endemic.

*H   *Cardiastethus bicolor.* This species is about 2 mm long and has shiny blackish head and shoulders and light brown hind part of the body; the wings are variable in length. It occurs at middle levels in the east and northeast parts of the island, including Horse Point Plain.

Lasiochilus contortus
3 mm   MRAC

H   *Cardiastethus exiguus.* This species is 1.5-2 mm long; the colour is variable, but generally rather uniform dull russet brown. *C. exiguus* is widely distributed in warm parts of the Old World.

*H   *Lasiochilus contortus.* This is a dull brown or sometimes russet-brown bristly insect, roughly 3 mm long and oval in shape. The wings are usually very short (about one third of the total length) but long-winged specimens have occasionally been found. *L. contortus* is restricted to the central ridge where it has been found in the dead and decomposing trunks of cabbage trees.

H   *Lyctocoris campestris.* A brown insect, 3-4 mm long. *L. campestris* has wide distribution elsewhere and is found at middle levels on the island. The wings of St Helena specimens seem to be somewhat shorter than in other parts of the world, suggesting that the species may have reached the island naturally.

H   *Orius thripoborus.* This species is about 2 mm long, with shiny blackish head and shoulders and yellowish wings with dark brown tips. It is now widely distributed at middle levels, but is probably introduced from South Africa.

BERYTIDAE – stilt bugs

These are elongate, slender bugs with very long legs and antennae. They are usually brownish and slow-moving and feed on plants. Two endemic species have been recorded on St Helena, one of them in an endemic genus.

Metacanthus concolor
5 mm   MRAC

*H   *Metacanthus concolor.* This species has large wings when it is adult and a strong vertical spine on the central back plate (scutellum). The antennae have the final segment swollen and dark-coloured with a striking white tip. *M. concolor* was originally described on the basis of a single specimen found in 1878; the Belgians failed to find it and considered it extinct, but we found several of the insects in 1995 feeding on Scrubwood at Flagstaff, Ruperts Hill, Powell Valley and Joan Hill. The species has fairly close relatives in the Cape Verde Islands and in Africa, and is evidently derived from a fairly recent colonisation.

**H   *Plyapomus longus.* This species – discovered by the Belgians – is one of the most interesting insects of St Helena. It has no obvious relatives in Africa and evidently represents an ancient colonisation of the island. Its ancestors may have arrived by air but it now has only minute vestiges of wings. *P. longus* is the largest known member of the family Berytidae (body 12-16 mm long). It is easily distinguished from *Metacanthus concolor*, which is only 5 mm long. *P. longus* has been found only on the high central ridge at around 800 m elevation. It has been collected from Tree Ferns but it is not clear if this is the main food plant.

CIMICIDAE – bed bugs

These are flat, oval wingless bugs about 6 mm long, which suck blood from mammals and birds.

HA   *Cimex lectularius*, the Common Bedbug. This species has travelled around the world with humans.

342

CYDNIDAE – burrower bugs

These are small black or reddish brown bugs with very spiny legs. They are usually found under stones or around the roots of plants on which they feed. A single species is present on St Helena.

H   *Aethus pallidipennis*. This species is widely distributed in Africa and is probably introduced.

LYGAEIDAE – seed bugs or ground bugs

Lygaeidae
6 mm

This large family consists mainly of oval, flattened, tough insects; they are usually brownish but often have red markings. Lygaeids can be distinguished from mirids by the presence of ocelli (minute simple eyes on the top of the head between the main compound eyes) and the lack of the cuneus which is conspicuous in the wings of mirids. Some lygaeids (especially in the genus *Nysius*) are well known as long distance migrants and are effective natural colonists, with endemic species on many oceanic islands; in the Hawaiian archipelago, for instance, there is a major adaptive radiation of Lygaeidae with more than 90 species.[37] On St Helena there are probably three species, including two in the genus *Nysius*: one of these is endemic while the other is widespread and has also been found on Ascension.

HA   *Nysius ericae*. Members of the genus *Nysius* have strong 'punctuations' on the head and thorax. *N. ericae* is between 3 and 5 mm long – smaller than adults of the next species – and its colour is a mixture of black and yellowish brown. On St Helena it is found mainly at lower and middle levels; it seems to be especially associated with Samphire but also occurs on Scrubwood and other plants. *N. ericae* is widely distributed in warm regions and has been been recorded on flotsam; it has probably reached both islands naturally, perhaps several times.

*H   *Nysius sanctaehelenae*. This very distinctive species can be separated from *N. ericae* most simply by its larger size: when adult it is more than 5 mm long; it is russet-brown, yellow-brown or blackish in colour. *N. sanctaehelenae* occurs at middle to high levels; it was probably originally associated with the Gumwood forests and still occurs at Peak Dale, but it has also been found on Scrubwood.

MIRIDAE – plant bugs

This is much the largest family of Heteroptera, with especially high diversity in the tropics. Mirids are generally rather small and delicate, and are often brightly coloured. They lack ocelli and both the beak and antennae have four segments. A useful distinction from most other heteropteran families is that in the front wings the leathery basal section has a separate roughly triangular piece (the cuneus) where it joins the membranous section (see also Anthocoridae). Mirids are mostly plant feeders. On St Helena there are 14 species of Miridae. Four of these are in the subfamily Mirinae (genera *Trigonotylus*, *Creontiades* and *Lygus*) and have a relatively narrow and elongate head region; one species (*Lygus mutabilis*) is endemic and the other three widely distributed. The subfamily Phylinae, which is characterised by a relatively broad head, giving the front of the body

---

[37] F.G. Howarth & W.P. Mull (1992).

a blunt-ended appearance, includes one widespread species (*Tytthus parviceps*) and nine or ten endemic species. They are diverse in their general characteristics and have been placed in eight endemic genera, but with one exception (*Insulopus*) the genitalia are very similar. This strongly suggests that the species have evolved by adaptive radiation from one or two ancient colonisations; they now seem to be adapted to different endemic plants. We think that eventually these species will be grouped in only one or two endemic genera, reflecting their evolutionary history. Some of the species are fairly easy to recognize and the Belgians provide a key; all the species are mentioned below. Ascension Island has at least two mirids but neither of them has been fully identified.

Agrametra aethiops
3.5 mm

**H   *Agrametra aethiops*. This species is about 3.5 mm long and the front part of the body is pitted and entirely brown black. This species is evidently adapted to life in the gumwood forests, and is still present at Peak Dale.

H   *Creontiades pallidus*. This species is 6-7 mm long and is yellowish or greenish in colour, with red or brown markings. On St Helena *C. pallidus* occurs mainly below 300 m freeding on a variety of plants including Samphire. It tolerates dry conditions and is found around the Mediterranean, in Africa and on a number of oceanic islands including the Cape Verdes; it may well be a natural colonist of St Helena.

**H   *Helenocoris horridus*. This species is 2.4-4.5 mm long, elongate in shape, covered with long hairs and with antennae about as long as the body. The most distinctive feature is that the wings lack the membranous tip section and appear cut off short (in all the other species except *Oligobiella* there is a membrane and the wings reach nearly to the end of the abdomen). *H. horridus* lives on Tree Ferns and other ferns, and has been found only on the central ridge, including High Peak.

**H   *Hirtopsallus suedae*. This genus is considered to be related to the large and widely distributed genus *Psallus*. It is 2-2.5 mm long and is whitish and brownish with darker brown markings. It has been found in several parts of the island but always on Samphire.

**H   *Insulopus asteri*. This is a fairly uniform yellowish brown insect about 2.5 mm long. It has been found only on Scrubwood in various localities.

**H   *Lopsallus flavosparsus*. This species is known only from a single female found by Wollaston at Thompsons Wood, probably on Gumwood. The Belgians failed to find it and suggested that it was already extinct. It is 3.0 mm long and generally yellowish white, with orange brown markings.

*H   *Lygus mutabilis*. This species, which is in the subgenus *Orthops*, is yellowish brown and usually 4-5 mm long. Its original plant hosts may have been the Jellicos and perhaps the Black Cabbage, but it is now sometimes found on introduced species.

H   *Lygus pallidulus*. This species, which is in the subgenus *Taylorilygus*, is 4-6 mm long and yellowish or greenish in colour. On St Helena it occurs at middle to high levels. Elsewhere, it is widespread in warm regions and prefers dry conditions.

A   Mirinae unidentified. At least one species in the subfamily Mirinae has recently been collected on Ascension by Simon Fowler and by us.

**H   *Naresthus hebes*. This genus is close to *Neisopsallus* but the antennae are even shorter. *N. hebes* is only about 2.5 mm long and is entirely dirty yellow, with red eyes. The species is known from only four specimens, found at High Peak and in the upper part

344

of Fishers Valley; one individual was found on Whitewood and the species is probably adapted to one or more of the cabbage trees.

**H   *Neisopsallus lutosus.* Members of this genus have relatively short antennae and are marbled with brown and red-brown markings on a creamy ground colour. *N. lutosus* is 3.5-4 mm long and has been found at Peak Dale and Longwood; it is clearly an insect of the Gumwood.

**H   *Neisopsallus vinaceus.* This species is very similar to the last but somewhat smaller (2.9-3.6 mm). It has been found only on the central ridge and is associated with the Tree Fern.

?**H   *Neisopsallus* new species? A single male mirid found by us on St Helena Tea on the Turks Cap ridge has been examined by W.R. Dolling who considers that it may represent a new species of *Neisopsallus.*

**H   *Oligobiella fuliginea.* This is the smallest of the St Helena Miridae and one of the smallest known members of the family, being only 1-1.5 mm long and much broader and less elongate than normal mirids. The front wings are like the elytra of a beetle, entirely lacking the membranous tip section that is characteristic of the Heteroptera as a whole. *Oligobiella* is brownish black with alternating dark and pale bands on the antennae. Only a few individuals have been found, all on the central ridge.

A   *Rhinocloa* species. A species of this genus (which is in the subfamily Phylinae) was found by Simon Fowler in 1996/97 to be causing considerable (desirable) damage to the invasive Mexican Thorn.

H   *Trigonotylus dohertyi.* This species is 4-5 mm long and greenish. On St Helena it has been found at low and medium levels and probably feeds on grasses, sedges or rushes. It is widespread in the tropics.

H   *Tytthus parviceps.* This bug is only 2-3 mm and is brown with a pale yellow patch beside each eye. It feeds on eggs of Homoptera and has been used in biological control; on St Helena its main prey are members of the genus *Sogatella* (family Delphacidae). *T. parviceps* is widespread elsewhere.

NABIDAE – damsel bugs

These are medium-sized, slender bugs with oval abdomen, elongate heads and prominent eyes; winged members of the family can be recognized by the pattern of small cells around the edge of the membranous part of the front wings. Nabids are predaceous, eating other insects such as aphids and caterpillars. They are well known aerial dispersers. St Helena has three species, two of which are in separate endemic genera; the third species is widespread and is also known from Ascension.

Nabidae
8 mm

**H   *Kerzhneria hirsuta.* This species was found by the Belgians in 1967, along Cabbage Tree Road and at High Peak. *Kerzhneria* is among the most significant endemic insects of St Helena; it represents an ancient relict stock which evidently colonised the island independently from *Vernonia* (see below). It is much smaller and less elongate than the latter, 4.3-5.0 mm long and with an oval abdomen; the wings are minute and the colour is pale brownish yellow.

HA   *Tropiconabis capsiformis* (ex *Nabis capsiformis*). This species is rather uniform yellowish brown, 6.5-8 mm long and with a noticeably elongated head. On St Helena the

Belgians found it in several places at middle levels; it is a predator on caterpillars and is thus considered beneficial. *T. capsiformis* is a cosmopolitan insect which has colonised many oceanic islands including the Tristan group. The wings of St Helena specimens are somewhat shorter than those from mainland Africa; we consider the species native to both islands.

Vernonia wollastoniana
10 mm

**H   *Vernonia wollastoniana*. This rare and distinctive insect is 10-13 mm long, with minute wings and extremely long antennae and legs. It is an ancient relict species, with no obvious links to the modern African fauna. *Vernonia* is known from a handful of specimens and has been recorded only on the high central ridge in cabbage tree woodland. There is no certainty that it still survives, but the best hope for the species lies in active conservation measures in the Diana's Peak area.

PENTATOMIDAE – stink bugs

This is a large and diverse family of bugs characterised by their five-segmented antennae (most heteropterans have four segments). They are generally broad and shield-shaped and often brightly coloured; they give off a nasty small when disturbed. Most species are plant-feeders but some are predatory. Two species are known from St Helena, one of them endemic. Ascension now has two species but both are probably introduced.

Pentatomidae
13 mm

*H   *Macrorhaphis wollastoni*. This species is known only from a single specimen found by Wollaston at West Lodge; it may now be extinct. It is 13 mm long, red-brown and with strong punctuations on the head and back. The main back plate (pronotum) has sharp triangular extensions at each side. *M. wollastoni* has close relatives in Africa and on a number of Atlantic and Indian Ocean islands.

A   *Mecidea longula*. This species, which is unusually elongate for a pentatomid (presumably as an adaptation to its grass-feeding habits), has been discovered on Ascension only recently. It comes from the American tropics and may have been introduced when construction workers from the Caribbean were employed on the island.

H   *Nezara viridula*, Green Shield Bug. This is a large bug, 13-18 mm long and up to 9.5 mm broad. It feeds on a wide variety of plants and can become a pest on legumes, tomatoes and other crops. It has been found in several parts of St Helena. *N. viridula* is a widespread species of warm regions.

A   *Thyanta* species (or a member of a related genus). This species was recently collected on Mexican Thorn.

REDUVIIDAE – assassin bugs and thread-legged bugs

These are blackish or brownish predaceous bugs which feed on other insects. The beak is short, with only three segments and is strong enough to penetrate human skin. Three species have been recorded from St Helena and one constitutes an endemic genus.

H   *Amphilobus venator*. A single larva, probably of this widespread Old World species, was found in Ruperts Valley by the Belgians.

H   *Empicoris rubromaculatus*. This insect has very long legs and antennae and looks rather like a mosquito. It is a cosmopolitan species found on St Helena at middle levels.

346

**H   *Napoleon vinctus.* This species represents a highly distinct endemic genus, probably derived from an ancient colonisation by members of the cosmopolitan genus *Oncocephalus. N. vinctus* is a heavily built, reddish brown, wingless bug 11-13.5 mm long; the femur (innermost long segment) of the front legs is massively swollen. The species is known from only from a handful of specimens found by the Belgians on the central ridge, including High Peak.

RHOPALIDAE – scentless plant bugs

This is a small family of bugs in which the front wings are often largely membranous; they feed on seeds.

A   *Liorhyssus hyalinus.* This is a cosmopolitan species known as a migrant and it is surprising that it has not been found on St Helena. On Ascension it is found on the endemic spurge and we consider it as indigenous.

SALDIDAE – shore bugs

The shore bugs are small, oval and flattened, with four-segmented antennae and a three-segmented beak; they are predators and scavengers, typically found on the ground in waterside habitats. A single species in an endemic genus is known from St Helena: it evidently represents an ancient colonisation and its presence is not surprising since members of the family occur on coasts – and sometimes inland – on many oceanic islands.

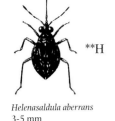

Helenasaldula aberrans
3-5 mm

**H   *Helenasaldula aberrans.* This is a flightless species which lacks the membranous part of the forewings. It is 3-5 mm long with a narrow head, and is shiny black with pale markings. It has been found only on the central ridge, in 1878 and 1967: curiously, the two sets of specimens are somewhat different.

TINGIDAE – lace bugs

Lace bugs are small, flattened, broad-bodied insects. Adults have the upper surface of the body and wings sculptured into an elaborate lace-like pattern; young stages are usually spiny. Tingids are all herbivorous. One species has been introduced to both islands.

HA   *Teleonemia scrupulosa,* Lantana Bug. This species was introduced to St Helena in 1971-72 for the biological control of the poisonous weed *Lantana camara,* and was later taken from there to Ascension.

VELIIDAE – watercrickets or small water striders

These are dark coloured insects which spend most of their time skating on the surface of freshwater pools or small streams. The genus *Microvelia* has colonised many oceanic islands and produced a number of endemic species. One species is known from St Helena.

H   *Microvelia gracillima.* This is a tiny (2 mm) brownish to blackish insect. The taxonomy of this genus is complex, but it appears that the species present on St Helena is widespread in sub-Saharan Africa and occurs also on islands in the North Atlantic and Indian Ocean. On the continent most individuals are winged but on islands a wingless form is often more common; on St Helena only the wingless form has been

347

found. The species was collected by the first of the Belgian expeditions, in 1965, from both Fishers Valley and Pleasant Valley near Silver Hill. The Belgians considered that the species might have been accidentally introduced to St Helena in recent years; however, the species might have been overlooked in the past, and natural colonisation by rafting is conceivable.

HEMIPTERA: HOMOPTERA – hoppers, aphids, scale insects

Adult Homoptera usually have four wings; both pairs are uniform in texture (unlike Heteroptera) and at rest are held roof-like over the body. The sucking beak arises far back on the head. This group includes many of the principal pests of crop plants all over the world. It is well represented on St Helena, but many of the species have been accidentally introduced along with plants or fruit and vegetables. Ascension has at least ten species, of which two are probably indigenous.

ALEYRODIDAE – whiteflies

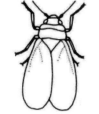

Aleyrodidae
2 mm

Whiteflies are minute insects which look like tiny moths, but with the wings covered with a waxy powder. Immature stages look like scale insects (see below). There are some whiteflies on St Helena, including one or more species of *Aleurocanthus* which occasionally reach plague proportions on green beans and other vegetables, and a citrus whitefly which is probably either *Dialeurodes citri* or *Aleurothixus floccosus*. Other species may well be present.

APHIDIDAE – aphids

Aphids are small, soft-bodied insects, often seen in large numbers sucking sap from stems or leaves. Many are severe pests on crops, causing damage by feeding but also by transmitting plant viruses. Many species excrete a sticky substance called honeydew, which can make a plant and the surface beneath it sticky. Many aphids are economic pests on St Helena, where 17 species have been recorded, none of them endemic. The aphids feed on the endemic as well as introduced plants, but it seems likely that all are introduced. The most serious pest aphid on St Helena is the Cabbage Aphid *Brevicoryne brassicae*; these insects are grey and are locally called 'lice'. As well as damaging cabbages they are particularly harmful to cauliflowers in early stages of growth. The Belgians suggested that additional widespread aphid species might be present on the island, especially on grasses. For Ascension the only record of aphids is from 1892, of an unnamed species found on the endemic *Euphorbia origanoides*; it has not been found in recent years, despite careful search.

Brevicoryne brassicae
2 mm

CICADELLIDAE – leafhoppers

Leafhoppers are best distinguished from planthoppers (see below) by their antennae: in the leafhoppers these arise on the front of the head between the eyes. These are small insects (mostly less than 10 mm) which are often colourfully patterned; they are characteristically wedge-shaped, with very broad heads.

On St Helena this family has undergone one of the most substantial of all the cases of adaptive radiation on the island. The most recent classification, by Mick Webb of the Natural History Museum, disagrees with some conclusions of the Belgians and places 12 of the 13 endemic species in eight endemic genera. This demonstrates the divergent evolution that has adapted the insects to different ecological niches on endemic plants. However, the island species may be derived from only a few ancient colonising stocks and future taxonomic revision using molecular data may reflect this more clearly. Apart from this radiation, we found one additional species which seems to be endemic and is perhaps a new group. On Ascension two species of cicadellids have been recorded, at least one of which probably arrived naturally. All the species are listed below.

Argaterma alticola
4 mm

**H   *Argaterma alticola*. The genus *Argaterma*, along with *Sanctahelenia*, '*Atlantisia*', *Nyhimbricus* and an undescribed genus, are place in the tribe Macrostelini of the subfamily Deltocephalinae; Webb comments that the male genitalia of these genera are extremely similar, so it seems possible that they are derived from a single colonisation. The species of *Argaterma* are stumpy, robust hoppers up to 5 mm long. *A. alticola* can be distinguished from the next species by its shiny blackish brown 'face'. It has been found only on the high central ridge above 700 m.

**H   *Argaterma multisignata*. This species has a yellowish brown 'face'. It is found on Tree Ferns on the central ridge above 700 m.

**H   '*Atlantisia*' *leleupi*. The generic name *Atlantisia* is technically invalid for these insects, since it was given to a bird – the flightless rail of Inaccessible Island – long ago. Anyhow, '*A.*' *leleupi* is closely related to the members of the genus *Sanctahelenia* (below), being distinguished mainly by more prominent eyes, which have the effect of making the head wider than the thorax immediately behind it. The Belgians found this species on the northwest face of Flagstaff. We found it in the same area but also in several other places: Ruperts Hill, Powell Valley, Rock Mount and Joan Hill. In all these localities it was collected off Scrubwood, and it is evidently one of the most important endemic insects associated with this species.

A   *Balclutha saltuella*. This tiny green homopteran can reach plague proportions in grasslands. A swarm was reported in Georgetown in May 1976 and it was suggested that since conditions on the island were unsuitable for the species the insects must have arrived by air from Africa. However, John Packer recently sent us specimens of the "tiny pale green grass fly" which he collected in 1963 after a period with heavy rains. These have now been identified as *Balclutha*, demonstrating that the species was on the island long before the supposed mass arrival in 1976. We suspect that the species survives in small numbers through the periods of low rainfall, but undergoes population explosions whenever exceptional rains lead to a substantial growth of grass. It seems very likely, however, that the species did originally reach the island by air from Africa, and that similar arrivals gave rise to the endemic cicadellid species on St Helena.

?**H   '*Chlorita*' *edithae*. This species, discovered by the Wollastons but not found by the Belgians, is now considered to be a member of an undescribed genus in the subfamily Typhlocybinae. It is whitish yellow and 3 mm long, and was found at Cason's, High Peak and Diana's Peak.

A   *Exitianus* species. We found a single specimen belonging to this genus in grass near Mars Bay in 1995.

349

Nehela vulturina
7 mm

**H   *Nehela vulturina.* This and the two species of *Stonasla* (below) are now placed in the subfamily Agallinae and thus presumably represent a colonisation separate from that by the ancestor of most of the other leafhoppers of the island. *N. vulturina* is a mainly black hopper up to 7.5 mm long, with rather small eyes. It seems to be fairly abundant and has been found on Dogwood, Black Cabbage and She Cabbage along Cabbage Tree Road, High Peak and Rural Retreat Gut.

**H   *Nyhimbricus wollastoni.* This is a pale yellow hopper with orange marks on the head and thorax and orange longitudinal bands on the forewings; it is 5-6 mm long. *N. wollastoni* has been found at Casons, Diana's Peak and Vine-tree Gut.

**H   *Sanctahelenia decellei.* Members of this genus have the head narrower than the thorax just behind it. *S. decellei* is yellowish white – paler than *S. sanctaehelenae*. It occurs on Gumwoods at both Peak Gut and Longwood, but has also been found at High Peak and high on the central ridge, where it has been beaten off Tree Ferns.

**H   *Sanctahelenia insularis.* This is a golden yellow hopper with brown markings on the head. Eight specimens were collected by Wollaston at West Lodge, but it has not been seen since.

**H   *Sanctahelenia sanctaehelenae* (the Belgians used the name *S. synavei*). This species is 4-5 mm long and shiny yellow-orange in colour. It has been found only on the central ridge on Tree Ferns.

?*H   *Stirellus* species. This species, which is in a different tribe (Stenometopiini) but the same subfamily (Deltocephalinae) as the main endemic group on the island, was found by us on Gumwoods at Peak Dale. Its relatives elsewhere are normally found on grass. It is not yet clear whether it is a new endemic species.

**H   *Stonasla consors.* The species of *Stonasla* resemble *Nehela* but are somewhat larger: adults of both *Stonasla* species are nearly 10 mm long. *S. consors* is brownish and was found by Wollaston at Diana's Peak and Halley's Mount, and by the Belgians on Dogwood at High Peak.

**H   *Stonasla undulata.* This species is yellowish green. It was found by Wollaston at Casons and by the Belgians on Dogwood at High Peak.

?**H   Undescribed genus and species in the tribe Macrostelini. This is a brown species collected by us from Scrubwood north of Flagstaff; it is considered to represent yet another new genus of cicadellid, but has not yet been formally described.

Stonasla undulata
9 mm

CIXIIDAE – planthoppers (part)

The members of this family and the Delphacidae and Issidae (below) are included in the group generally called planthoppers. Their antennae arise on the sides of the head beneath the eyes (cf. leafhoppers, Cicadellidae, above). Two endemic species of cixiids have been found on St Helena and are now considered as constituting an endemic genus, the two species having evolved by speciation on the island.[38]

**H   *Helenolius dividens.* Both this species and the next are black and yellowish hoppers about 5-9 mm long, the males being smaller than the females. *H. dividens* has the face

[38] J. van Stalle (1986).

350

(between the eyes) black with some yellow markings (cf. *insulicola*). It has been found only near Flagstaff, where it lives on Scrubwood and perhaps other plants.

**H   *Helenolius insulicola*. This species has the face yellow to greyish, with a slight tinge of brown. It is known only from Joan Hill, on both St Helena Tea Plant and Scrubwood.

COCCOIDEA – scale insects

The scale insects (superfamily Coccoidea) are a varied group, and six different families (Coccidae, Dactylopiidae, Diaspididae, Margarodidae, Ortheziidae and Pseudococcidae) are represented on the islands. These are all tiny animals, many of which hardly look like insects at all. Females are wingless and usually legless, and are attached to a plant, often forming a small waxy plate; males typically have one pair of wings but lack mouthparts and do not feed. Scale insects are important agricultural pests, for instance on citrus and other fruit. Separating them is a specialized task and we do not treat them in detail. St Helena has about 30 species, of which one is endemic and a second may prove to be so; the others are probably all introduced and many cause damage to local crops. Ascension has at least six species, none of which are indigenous. We mention only a few species of particular interest.

H   *Dactylopius coccus* (family Dactylopiidae). The Mexican cochineal insect, which feeds on tungies (*Opuntia* species), was introduced twice in the 19th century but apparently did not become established.

HA   *Icerya purchasi*, The Cottony Cushion Scale (family Margarodidae, giant coccids) has caused damage on both islands; on St Helena the plants attacked include citrus, acacias and Gobblegheer, but the pest is kept under control by the ladybird beetle *Rodolia cardinalis*.

HA   *Orthezia insignis*, Jacaranda Bug (family Ortheziidae, ensign coccids). This insect posed a major threat to the survival of the Gumwood on St Helena, but was brought under control when the ladybird *Hyperaspis pantherina* was introduced in 1993.[39] It seems to have been introduced to Ascension in the 1980s and is now causing substantial and widespread damage to the invasive shrub *Lantana camara*.

?*H   *Paracoccus ?sporoboli* (family Pseudococcidae, mealy bugs). This insect is recorded on the basis of a single damaged specimen on Dogwood at High Peak. It is somewhat different from *P. sporoboli* and may prove to be endemic. (Other species in this family have been reported as causing damage to potatoes and other crops on St Helena.)

*H   *Ripersiella mediatlantica* (family Pseudococcidae, mealy bugs). This minute species (known only from females) is 1.8 mm long by 0.7 mm wide; it lacks eyes and has stumpy antennae with six segments and three pairs of short legs each with a well developed claw on the last segment. It has been found only on the central ridge (for instance on dead cabbage trees) and is presumably part of the original fauna. The genus *Ripersiella* has worldwide distribution.

DELPHACIDAE – planthoppers (part)

Delphacids can be distinguished from the other planthoppers by the presence of a large movable spur near the outer end of the longest segment (tibia) of the hind leg; but this

[39] S.V. Fowler (1993).

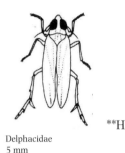

Delphacidae
5 mm

is not easily seen with the naked eye. On St Helena there are six widespread species (in the genera *Matutinus*, *Sogatella* and *Toya*) and also two species in an endemic genus, *Ilburnia*. The latter are evidently derived from a single ancient colonising stock, with distant relatives in the Pacific and in West Africa. Some of the others may be relatively recent natural colonists, but introduction by humans is also possible. We mention only the most interesting species. Ascension has only one species of delphacid.

**H   *Ilburnia dianae*. Both species of *Ilburnia* are flightless, with wings appearing to have been cut off short part way down the abdomen. *I. dianae* is reddish brown and the face is uniform in colour. It occurs above about 500 m, usually on ferns.

**H   *Ilburnia ignobilis*. This species is yellowish brown, with the front of the face (between the eyes) dark reddish brown with a pale line down the centre. It has been collected only on the high central ridge, often in association with Tree Ferns.

HA   *Toya thomasseti*. This African species and its congeners are well known for aerial dispersal; *T. thomasseti* may be indigenous on both islands.

ISSIDAE – planthoppers (part)

H   *Issus coleoptratus*. This is the only member of its family on St Helena and it is clearly introduced.

PSYLLIDAE – jumping plantlice

Psyllids are similar to aphids but have strong jumping legs and longer antennae. Single introduced species have been found on each of the islands.

H   *Trioza erytreae*, Citrus Psylla. This species, which is apparently the only psyllid on St Helena, is a serious pest on citrus fruit trees, causing severe galling and deformation of the foliage.

A   *Heteropsylla reducta*. This psyllid is now well distributed on the Mexican Thorn *Prosopis juliflora* on Ascension, but numbers are generally low, perhaps because of competition with the mirid heteropteran *Rhinocloa* species. *H. reducta* is native to the Caribbean on *P. juliflora* and seems likely to have reached Ascension along with the plant.

Psyllidae
3 mm

PSOCOPTERA – psocids

Psocids (sometimes called booklice or barklice) are tiny, soft bodied insects, generally with long, fine antennae. Some have no wings, but if wings are present there are usually four, and when the animals are at rest these are held roof-wise over the body. They could be confused with small Homoptera such as aphids, but lack the sucking beak (rostrum) that is characteristic of these. Wingless forms look rather like Collembola, but can be distinguished by the lack of a jumping organ (furcula) underneath the abdomen.

The Belgians listed 12 species of Psocoptera in eight families for St Helena; four of the species are endemic; we found two more species, one of which is endemic. On Ascension the Psocoptera prove to be one of the most interesting groups of animals. Although there were no previous records from the island, our work there in 1990 showed that they are widely distributed and diverse in caves and lava flows: these animals, which live on scraps of organic matter, are evidently well adapted to life on a barren seabird island. Eight species are now known from Ascension, in five families; one is a generic endemic. We list only the most interesting species on both islands.

*H   *Blaste (Euclismia) basilewskyi* (family Psocidae). This psocid has many brown patches on the wings. It is taxonomically very distinct and is considered to represent an ancient colonisation of St Helena. It is also the commonest of the endemic species and occurs on the Gumwoods at Peak Gut and in several other places in the central and high parts of the island.

*II   *Caecilius benoiti* (Caeciliidae). This is not common and was found by the Belgians only at Teutonic Hall.

A   *Cerobasis* cf *maya* (Trogiidae). We found this species on barren lava. It is very similar – or even identical – to a species known from a single specimen collected on the Yucatan Peninsula in Mexico; this is very hard to explain, but we consider the species as native to Ascension.

A   *Ectopsocus strauchi* (Ectopsocidae). This winged species is likely to be indigenous.

*H   *Peripsocus leleupi* (Peripsocidae). Found only at Teutonic Hall and Longwood.

*H   *Peripsocus decellei* (Peripsocidae). Found by the Belgians in Ruperts Valley.

A   *Psocathropos lachlani* (= *P. microps*) (Psyllipsocidae). We found this species both in cave thresholds and on lava flows.

HA   *Psyllipsocus ramburii* (Psyllipsocidae). We found this species in a cave on Ascension and in several small underground cavities on St Helena; its populations consist entirely of females, which are capable of reproducing without the intervention of a male. Both this and the previous species are essentially cosmopolitan and are often found in human dwellings. However they are also recorded from natural caves, and it is conceivable that they reached the islands naturally.

A   *Sphaeropsocopsis* cf *microps* (Sphaeropsocidae). A single, damaged specimen obtained in a pipe trap near North East Bay resembles *S. microps*, a species with reduced eyes that is known only from litter habitats in Chile. However, reduction in eyes occurs in almost all cave-dwelling animals and we think that the ancestors of the Ascension and of the St Helena member of this genus (see below) probably reached the islands from southern Africa, where the genus *Sphaeropsocopsis* is still represented.

*H   *Sphaeropsocopsis myrtleae* (Sphaeropsocidae). A single female that we found in the cave beside the cliff path near Ruperts Battery belongs to a new species, and is remarkable in being the first known species of psocid entirely lacking in eyes.[40] This seems to be one of the few known survivors of the original subterranean fauna of St Helena, which has been largely replaced by introduced species.

**A   *Troglotroctes ashmoleorum* (Liposcelididae). This psocid, found in several caves and one surface lava site, is one of the most interesting invertebrates on Ascension, and is considered to represent a new species and genus. It has relatively long legs, is pale in colour and has reduced eyes; these are all characteristics of animals adapted to cave life. Although the species is now wingless we assume that its ancestors reached Ascension by air, and subsequently became adapted to sedentary life in caves.

Troglotroctes ashmoleorum
2 mm

[40] C. Lienhard & N.P. Ashmole (1999).

PHTHIRAPTERA (including Mallophaga) – lice

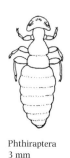

Phthiraptera
3 mm

These are small, usually flattened, wingless insects that feed on the feathers, skin and hair of mammals and birds. The Belgians list 11 species collected from birds on St Helena but two of these were from birds that are not established on the island. Only one species has been recorded from Ascension, but this is probably for lack of searching. All species can be considered indigenous, as they doubtless arrived with seabirds.

COLEOPTERA – beetles

Beetles form the largest order of insects, with more than a quarter of a million species described worldwide. They vary in size from less than 1 mm up to an occasional 125 mm, which means that the St Helena Giant Ground Beetle is only a middling giant. Nearly all beetles have four wings, the front ones (the elytra) being thick and leathery or brittle and meeting in the middle of the back; they often cover the entire abdomen. When the beetle is not flying, the hindwings are folded up under the front ones. In some species the hindwings are reduced and flying ability is lost; this occurs commonly among beetles that live in wet places in decaying wood, and in some other kinds of beetles on remote islands. On St Helena almost all the endemic species have their wings much reduced or absent, this being particularly notable in the numerous species of ground beetles (Carabidae) living in the remnants of the cabbage tree woodland on the central ridge, and in the darkling beetles (Tenebrionidae) found mainly on Prosperous Bay Plain.

The beetle fauna of St Helena was comprehensively studied by Wollaston in 1875-76 and by the Belgians in 1965-67.[41] Although a few additional species will doubtless be discovered, many more will prove to have become extinct since the time of Wollaston; others, though found on the island after accidental introduction, never became established. A total of some 257 species of beetles have been found on the island, including two recently introduced ladybirds and one species which we found; some 36 families are represented. Of the 257 species, we consider 148 as endemic and about 136 of these were treated by the Belgians as 'ancient endemics'. There is an extraordinary total of 32 endemic genera, implying that the endemic species which they include have no close relatives outside the island: members of these groups have been evolving in isolation for millions of years. Apart from the endemic species, the island populations of an additional four species have been considered as endemic subspecies. A few other beetle species may be indigenous but have not differentiated from their relatives on the adjacent continents or islands. The remainder, comprising about 100 species, have almost certainly been introduced by humans.

The beetle fauna of Ascension is very poor in comparison; only 38 species are recorded and none of these is endemic. Three species are considered to be indigenous, with a further six doubtful; the remaining 29 were probably introduced. We mention all of the families represented on the islands and all of the endemic genera; endemic species are all listed except in the family Curculionidae.

[41] Summarized by P. Basilewsky (1985).

Anobiidae
4 mm

ANOBIIDAE – anobiids

Cylindrical or oval and somewhat hairy beetles. Most species eat dry vegetable material and some are destructive to timber. St Helena has two endemic species (one of them in an endemic genus) and three introduced species. One of the latter – *Stegobium paniceum* – was found by Arthur Loveridge to be eating the archives in the Castle in Jamestown; this species has reached Ascension, where there are also two other introduced species.

*H   *Xyletomerus insulanus*. Found by the Belgians in several places in the north of the island, especially Prosperous Bay Plain; it apparently lives on Samphire. *X. insulanus* has close relatives in southern Africa.

**H   *Helenoxylon confertum*. The endemic genus *Helenoxylon* was established for a beetle first recorded by Wollaston from Flagstaff and the Barn; the Belgians found it at West Point (Man and Horse). *H. confertum* is about 4 mm long and is brownish black with large and prominent eyes. It appears to live only on Scrubwood and we must hope that the recent recovery in some populations of this shrub have come in time to save the beetle from extinction. *Helenoxylon* has distant relatives in Africa and evidently represents an ancient colonisation.

Anthicodes fragilis
4 mm   MRAC

ANTHICIDAE – antlike flower beetles

Tiny beetles with the head separated from the thorax by a narrow 'neck'. St Helena has an endemic genus (two species) with distant relatives in Africa and Madagascar. On Ascension there is one species, probably indigenous.

**H   *Anthicodes fragilis*. This small (c.4 mm long) and rare beetle has been found only in dry parts of the island – Flagstaff, Horse Point and Holdfast Tom, Prosperous Bay Plain and Sane Valley. It is delicate and slender, uniform dark reddish-brown and covered with fine grey hairs giving it a silky appearance. It has normally been found under stones. Both this and the next species are unusual in the family in having lost the power of flight.

Anthicodes maculatus
4 mm   MRAC

**H   *Anthicodes maculatus*. This species was discovered by Wollaston, apparently among Gumwoods near Peak Dale, and later seen commonly on the ridge between West Lodge and the summit of High Peak. It was not found by the Belgians, who suggested that it was extinct, but there seems to be a chance of finding it in late winter near High Peak, or on the ground among dead branches of the Gumwoods at Peak Dale. *A. maculatus* is about 4 mm long and is more solidly built than the previous species; it is dark reddish brown-black with brownish hairs and has four pale patches on the elytra.

A   *Omonadus floralis* (ex *Anthicus floralis*). A cosmopolitan species which has reached a number of remote oceanic islands, probably by aerial dispersal.

ANTHRIBIDAE – fungus weevils

The fungus weevils are included in the large superfamily Curculionoidea or snout beetles, which also includes the ordinary weevils (family Curculionidae). The whole group is characterised by the head being more or less prolonged into a beak or snout. The fungus weevils, however, have only a short, broad snout, and the antennae are more or less like a string of beads, without an 'elbow'. Worldwide, the family is not

355

Acarodes gutta
1.5 mm   MRAC

very diverse, but they have undergone an extraordinary adaptive radiation on St Helena, with 27 endemic species in three endemic genera, living mainly on dead wood; many of the species are associated with particular species (or groups of species) of endemic plants. In addition, one cosmopolitan species – *Araecerus fasciculatus* – occurs on St Helena and is doubtless introduced; this species is also recorded from Ascension, but no other anthribids have been recorded from that island: this provides one of the most striking contrasts between the faunas of the two islands, presumably reflecting the geological youth of Ascension and the lack of woodland habitats.

**H   *Acarodes gutta.* This species, which is the sole member of its genus, is a stumpy almost hemispherical beetle with a very short head, and is reddish brown, hairless and shiny. It is abundant on the summits of the central ridge and on High Peak; the adults (c.1.5 mm long) are found on the damp undersides of dead leaves of cabbage trees.

**H   *Homoeodera.* This genus, with 14 species, is closely related to the next (*Notioxenus*) but lacks the distinct border across the rear margin of the thorax which characterises that genus (see below).[42] *Homoeodera* species are all tiny black beetles, 1.2-5 mm long, but the species are diverse in shape.[43] The good descriptions and drawings provided by the Belgians should permit identification of most species, although some magnification is needed. Seven species of *Homoeodera* are essentially restricted to the central ridge. *H. edithia* is found under the bark of dead trees and is often associated with a black toadstool. *H. elateroides* is a rare species found on the Tree Fern and Black Scale Fern. *H. globulosa* is relatively common, and can be found on Tree Ferns and dead leaves and wood of cabbage trees. *H. major* is rare, but has been found on Dogwood and on dead wood of cabbage trees and gorse. *H. nodulipennis* – which resembles a small, black seed and has extraordinary nodules at the tips of the elytra – is known only from two specimens found by Wollaston on the crest of the ridge above West Lodge; it may have been adapted to the False Gumwood and is likely to be extinct. *H. paivae* is also extremely rare, and has been found only in dead wood of a cabbage tree. *H. pygmaea* was found by the Belgians to be fairly common among the cabbage trees on the central ridge.

Homoeodera scolytoides
3 mm   MRAC

Three species of *Homoeodera* are found in dry area in the north of the island. *H. scolytoides* is known only from five specimens from Prosperous Bay Plain. *H. longefasciata* is also found on Prosperous Bay Plain and adjacent areas, where it lives mainly on Samphire. In Ruperts Valley, however, a different species – *H. coriacea* – is abundant on Samphire. The Belgians considered that Samphire was introduced and that it was not the original food-plant of these beetles, but we are not convinced: besides them, several other endemic insects seem to be adapted to life on Samphire and we have little doubt that it is indigenous to the island.

The remaining four species are now relatively widespread on the island and occur on a wide variety of decaying wood. *H. compositarum* and *H. pumilio* occur at both high and middle levels, while *H. alutaceicollis* and *H. rotundipennis* are more clearly species of middle levels. We suspect that all four were originally species of the gumwood forests, but have successfully made the transition to dead wood of other species. Wollaston hesitantly separated from *H. alutaceicollis* another species which he named

---

[42] The thorax in beetles is often entirely covered on its upper surface by a single plate, the pronotum; we shall refer to this simply as the thorax. In some beetles a small and roughly triangular second thoracic plate, the scutellum, is visible between the bases of the elytra.

[43] Both Wollaston and Basilewsky considered that *Homoeodera* should perhaps be split into two or more genera.

H. asteris, on the basis of two specimens collected from Scrubwood between Sugarloaf and Flagstaff. The Belgians merged *H. asteris* with *H. alutaceicollis*, but we think they should be looked at again, since it is very likely that there was a distinct species associated with the previously extensive Scrubwood community.

Notioxenus janischi
7 mm   MRAC

**H *Notioxenus.* This genus, with 12 species, is distinguished from *Homoeodera* by the presence of a distinct transverse line or keel across the rear margin of the thorax, immediately in front of the base of the elytra. These are minute to medium-sized beetles (2-8.5 mm long), and can be found by shaking trees or searching litter of twigs on the ground. Intriguingly, three species (*N. dalei*, *N. grayi* and *N. janischi*) have well-developed wings but the others have lost them completely. As with *Homoeodera* the Belgians' drawings and descriptions should allow identification. Most of these beetles seem to be closely associated with the cabbage tree woodland, where they are found on trees, dead wood and on the endemic Tree Fern and Black Scale Fern; a few species seem to be part of the gumwood fauna.

N. ferrugineus is the only species which has adapted well to the changed vegetation of the island; it is widespread in the middle and upper zones. It is typical of grassy areas and can be found on introduced as well as endemic plants. Five other species were still reasonably common on endemic vegetation on the central ridge at the time of the Belgian expeditions. *N. alutaceus* is a small, abundant species found mainly on dead and decaying wood of cabbage trees, but also on Whitewood and Dogwood. *N. bewicki* is a large species occurring mainly on Black Scale Fern. *N. grayi* is scarce, occurring on foliage of She Cabbage, He Cabbage and Whitewood. *N. rufopictus* is scarce, on Tree Ferns and Black Scale Fern, but also in dead wood of cabbage trees. *N. subfasciatus* is a large species found mainly on the Tree Fern.

Three more species characteristic of the cabbage tree woodland are rare or possibly extinct. *N. aeneus* was found occasionally by Wollaston on dead stumps of cabbage trees, but the Belgians failed to find it and suggested that it was already extinct. *N. congener*, which is closely related to *N. rufopictus*, is perhaps on the verge of extinction. *N. rotundatus* is known from only three specimens (one found by the Belgians) and is clearly in danger of extinction.

The three species associated with the gumwood woodlands are obviously endangered. *N. janischi* is a large species, found only on Gumwoods but still present near Peak Dale at the time of the Belgian expeditions. *N. dalei* is similar but smaller; Wollaston recorded it as fairly common on Gumwoods, but the Belgians found only a single specimen. *N. dimidiatus* is a tiny beetle, which was abundant at Plantation and elsewhere at the time of Wollaston's visit, but was very scarce by the time of the Belgian expeditions.

BOSTRICHIDAE – branch and twig borers

Elongate, cylindrical beetles, most of which are wood-boring and live in both live and dead trees. Two species are present on St Helena, both clearly introduced.

BRUCHIDAE – Seed beetles

Short (c. 3 mm), stout, dull-coloured beetles whose larvae feed on seeds. Three species have been recorded from St Helena, clearly introduced with foodstuffs or plants; one of them – the Bean Weevil *Acanthoscelides obtectus* – seems to be established and is a significant pest of beans. On Ascension two species of bruchids – *Algarobius prosopis* and *Neltumius arizonensis* – have recently been introduced in an attempt to control the invasive Mexican Thorn.

CANTHARIDAE – soldier beetles

H   Elongate soft-bodied beetles which are usually found on flowers; their larvae are predaceous on other insects. On St Helena the Belgians found a single individual of an Indian Ocean species, presumably accidentally introduced.

CARABIDAE – ground beetles

Dark-coloured beetles, often shiny and with striated elytra; they are somewhat flattened, long-legged and run rapidly in the open. There are 20 species on St Helena, with 4 endemic genera and 17 endemic species; all are listed below. No carabids have been found on Ascension.

Aplothorax burchelli larva
25 mm   MRAC

**H   *Aplothorax burchelli*, St Helena Giant Ground Beetle Figure 12. This remarkable species is in a different subfamily (Carabinae) from the other endemic carabids; it may now be extinct. *Aplothorax* represented one of the 'ancient endemics' of St Helena, a lineage that evidently colonised the island many millions of years ago but then became extinct (or transformed) in the continental area from which it came. *Aplothorax* was first described in 1843 by the botanist W.J. Burchell. It is a large (29-38 mm) ground-living beetle with distinctive constrictions between head and thorax and thorax and abdomen; it has long legs and long antennae. Melliss, in 1875, wrote: *"It is confined to the north-eastern corner of the Island, at an altitude above the sea of 2000 ft. It is now extremely scarce, being met with occasionally only, after considerable hunting, under stones on Deadwood or Flagstaff, and sometimes in the ploughed fields at Longwood."* Wollaston in 1875 failed to find this species, and Loveridge never found it in 20 visits to Horse Point Plain between 1957 and 1973. The specimen in the Jamestown Museum was collected on Horse Point. The Belgians, however, evidently collected many individuals and may have severely depleted the population.

Apteromimus platyderoides
4.5 mm   MRAC

**H   *Apteromimus* (2 sp.), *Endosomatium* (1 sp.) and *Pseudophilochthus* (9 sp.). These three endemic genera are treated together, since they are closely related (they are all members of the tribe Bembidiini) and form a group of 12 species representing one of the most interesting cases of island endemism in the whole fauna of St Helena. They have no close relatives outside the island and evidently represent a very ancient colonizing stock. These are tiny beetles (2-6 mm long), blackish or dark brown, solidly built and not very long-legged; they are all completely flightless and most have tiny eyes. The species are all confined to the central ridge, where they live (or lived) in the endemic vegetation. They are generally found in dead trunks of Tree Ferns or cabbage trees, or in decayed plant debris. Some of them use the galleries made by the larvae of wood-boring insects on which they prey; this is an exceptional adaptation for ground beetles, since although members of the group are typically predaceous, they normally hunt in the open. The Belgians considered that as a result of the continued degradation of their natural habitat, the extinction of all three genera was near at hand. It is to be hoped that recent efforts to halt the spread of flax may allow some of them to survive.

Apteromimus platyderoides and *A. wollastoni* are distinguished from the genus *Pseudophilochthus* mainly by the shape of the thorax, which remains broad as it joins

Pseudophilochthus nubigena
6 mm   MRAC

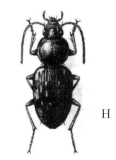

Pseudophilochthus grayanus
5 mm   MRAC

*Pseudophilochthus
gemmulipennis*
2.5 mm   MRAC

the abdomen (though less so in *A. wollastoni*). *A. platyderoides* is 4.4-4.9 mm long and has been found only in dead Tree Ferns. *A. wollastoni* is larger (6 mm) and is known from only two individuals found in the dead trunk of a Whitewood, in galleries made by larvae of an endemic weevil. *Endosomatium megalops*, the sole member of its genus, has a conspicuously massive head and large eyes, and a narrow 'waist' in front of the abdomen; the species is known only from three specimens found by Wollaston.

Pseudophilochthus nubigena* is probably the least rare of the species in its genus and is also the largest (c.6 mm long). *P. grayanus* is somewhat smaller (5 mm) and with a different pattern on the elytra; the Belgians suggested that it was restricted to a small area southeast of Diana's Peak. The three other species found by the Belgians are all less than 2.5 mm long. *P. rufosuffusus* and *P. evanescens* are similar in size and shape but the former species has distinct longitudinal striations on the elytra, which *P. evanescens* lacks. *P. gemmulipennis* also lacks the striations and is similar in size, but has a broader, rounded abdomen. *P. dicksoniae* and *P. trechoides* were not found by the Belgians; they also failed to find *P. fossor* (known only from a single individual) or *P. sublimbatus*, which used to occur at the western end of the ridge above West Lodge but which is probably now extinct.

H *Campalita chlorostictum*. This species is blackish with a bronze tinge and with heavily sculptured elytra (cf. *Laemostenus*); with a length of 16-29 mm it is the largest ground beetle likely to be encountered. It is common on the island, especially at medium and low altitudes. The species is widespread in Africa, but the St Helena specimens are distinct and are considered to represent a separate subspecies, *C. chlorostictum helenae*. The species has well developed wings and may possibly have colonised the island naturally.

*H *Eotachys caheni*. A tiny (less than 3 mm) but fully winged species which has been found only in Lemon Tree Gut and Fishers Valley; though endemic, it has close relatives in Africa.

*H *Harpalus prosperus* and *H. sanctaehelenae*. These two endemic species were discovered by the Belgians. Both are fully winged, but they differ substantially from each other and it is not certain that they originated on the island from a common stock. They belong to a widespread genus, but no close relatives have been identified in Africa. The Belgians suggest that they might possibly be introduced by humans, but we think it more likely that their ancestors reached the island naturally. *H. prosperus* is known only from three male specimens, two of them found under stones on Prosperous Bay Plain and the other – surprisingly – in a dead trunk of Tree Fern near Diana's Peak. *H. sanctaehelenae* is known from a dozen specimens including both sexes, from Flagstaff, Horse Point Plain and Man and Horse.

H *Laemostenus complanatus*. This is a fully winged species about 13-16 mm long; it is shiny black, less heavily sculptured and smaller than *Campalita*. It may originate from North Africa but is now widely distributed; it is evidently introduced to St Helena, where it can be found in many places.

*H *Lymnastis sanctaehelenae*. This minute beetle (2.25 mm maximum) differs from its close relatives in Africa in the strong reduction of the wings, making it flightless. It is widely distributed on St Helena, mainly in damp places under well-bedded rocks.

H *Notaphus mixtus*. This beetle is widespread in Africa but is represented on the island by a distinct subspecies, *N. mixtus mellissi* (originally described as a separate endemic species). It is a streamside beetle, found by the Belgians only in plant debris in Fishers Valley, but previously more widely distributed.

359

CERAMBYCIDAE – long-horned beetles

Cerambycids are typically fairly large, elongate beetles with very long antennae. They are especially diverse in the tropics and the Belgians expressed surprise that they have failed to colonise St Helena naturally; two species have been recorded from the island, evidently after casual introductions; neither seems to be established.

CHRYSOMELIDAE – leaf beetles

The leaf beetles are closely related to the Cerambycidae, but are generally smaller and more oval in shape, and with shorter antennae. The adults feed on flowers and foliage, while some of the larvae are leaf miners, or bore into stems and feed on roots; many members of the family are serious pests. This is another enormous and largely tropical family, but it seems to have achieved only one colonisation of St Helena: there are three endemic species, evidently evolved on the island from a single stock. It has been suggested that they merit the establishment of an endemic genus, but this cannot easily be done without a proper revision of the whole genus *Longitarsus*, which includes nearly 400 species worldwide. The three endemic species are all small (c.3 mm), more or less brassy green beetles with extremely long legs. The sexes are very distinct, the females appearing to have somewhat crumpled elytra. One chrysomelid has been introduced to Ascension.

Longitarsus helenae
3 mm   MRAC

*H   *Longitarsus helenae*. This and the next species are most easily distinguished by reference to the Belgians' drawings, but care is needed since these show only females. Wollaston found *L. helenae* to be widespread in the cabbage tree woodland and commented that: *"it is almost impossible to find a single cabbage-tree from which it may not be beaten in actual profusion."* The Belgians found it near Diana's Peak and at High Peak, but commented that it was dependent on Lobelia and that captures on other plants should be considered accidental. Since Lobelia is now scarce, the species may be in serious danger.

*H   *Longitarsus janulus*. Both Wollaston and the Belgians found this species only on She Cabbage trees just west of Halley's Mount. The She Cabbage is now close to extinction and the beetle may already be lost.

*H   *Longitarsus mellissi*. This species is distinguished from the other two by the presence of two strong transverse grooves on each side of the thorax. *L. mellissi* has been found only near Diana's Peak and at High Peak, where it apparently develops exclusively in the axils of the stipules of both species of Jellico.

A   *Uroplata girardi*. This beetle was introduced in 1970-71 in an attempt to provide biological control of the invasive shrub *Lantana camara* (a tingid heteropteran was introduced for the same purpose). The beetle was still present in 1997.

CLERIDAE – checkered beetles

These are long, hairy and brightly coloured beetles, about 5 mm long. A single species – *Necrobia rufipes* – is present on both islands and has evidently been introduced with cargoes of animal products.

COCCINELLIDAE – ladybird beetles

Small, oval, often almost hemispherical beetles, usually brightly coloured but surprisingly tricky to identify. The vast majority are predatory on aphids or other homopterans. These beetles are well known as aerial migrants, but they are also easily transported with plants. Eight species are known from St Helena but most are evidently introduced and only one is tentatively considered as endemic. Ascension has four species. Only the more interesting species are listed.

HA   *Cheilomenes lunata.* This is a black ladybird with 10 yellow or red spots, which was described in 1775 on the basis of a specimen which was supposed to be from St Helena but which actually came from Africa. It was introduced to Ascension in 1910 to control woolly aphis of apples.

A   *Exochomus troberti.* This African species has recently been confirmed as occurring on Ascension, putting in doubt earlier records of the very similar *E. flavipes* from both islands. *E. troberti* could conceivably be a natural colonist.

Hyperaspis pantherina
2.5 mm

H   *Hyperaspis pantherina.* This species is 2.3-2.7 mm long, black with yellow on the head and the sides of the thorax, and 10 yellow spots. It was introduced to St Helena in 1993 in an apparently successful attempt to control the ensign scale insect *Orthezia insignis* which was threatening the surviving population of Gumwoods at Peak Dale.

HA   *Rodolia cardinalis.* This species, probably originating in Australia, has been introduced to many parts of the world for biological control of the cottony cushion scale *Icerya purchasi. Rodolia* was brought to St Helena in 1896 and 1898, and *Icerya* remains uncommon.

*H   *Scymnus helenae.* This ladybird has been found in many parts of the island. It may turn out also to occur outside the island (ie not to be endemic). Another species of *Scymnus* – *S. africanus* – is also present on St Helena.

COLYDIIDAE – cylindrical bark beetles

These are tiny (<2 mm long), eyeless, hard-bodied, shiny beetles, many of them predatory. Two species have been recorded from St Helena, both clearly introduced; only one has established itself.

CORYLOPHIDAE – minute fungus beetles

Tiny (c.1 mm) round or oval beetles with shortened elytra which leave the end of the abdomen exposed. They live in decaying vegetable matter. Two species have been introduced to St Helena, evidently with plants, and there is one on Ascension.

COSSYPHODIDAE – cossyphodids

These tiny beetles (2-3 mm) have flattened bodies, are reddish brown with short legs and are virtually eyeless; they are always associated with ants. The single species present on St Helena was probably introduced with plants (perhaps from the Canaries) along with ants of the genus *Pheidole*.

CRYPTOPHAGIDAE – silken fungus beetles

These beetles are covered in silky hairs. They feed on fungi and decaying vegetable matter. There is one endemic species on St Helena and one (possibly two) European species in the same genus were found in the 19th century.

*H   *Cryptophagus gracilipes*. A reddish brown, oval beetle less than 2 mm long, with a pitted surface covered with long, soft, whitish hairs. *C. gracilipes* is common at middle and high levels on the island; the Belgians found many at Horse Point Plain, and Wollaston commented that it swarmed underneath garden refuse. It has close relatives in South Africa and elsewhere.

CUCUJIDAE – flat bark beetles

Flat, reddish to yellowish beetles about 2 mm long. A few species infest cargoes of seeds and fruits, and have become cosmopolitan. Two of these have been recorded from St Helena, but it is doubtful if they are established.

CURCULIONIDAE – weevils

The weevils comprise an enormous family of plant-feeding beetles, many of which are serious pests around the world. Along with their relatives the Anthribidae they are sometimes called snout beetles: the head is more or less prolonged into a snout or rostrum. In the curculionids the snout is generally long, with the antennae arising about half way along, and with the mouthparts at the tip. The antennae usually have a long basal segment or 'scape' (which can fit into a groove on the side of the snout) and then a conspicuous 'elbow' before the middle section of several roughly similar segments, and finally a terminal 'club' composed of several more segments. The elbowed antennae (which point forwards as the beetle walks) and long snout usually serve to distinguish curculionids from anthribids. When disturbed, curculionids draw in their antennae and legs and fall to the ground, where they may be hard to distinguish from bits of bark or dirt.

On Ascension there are only four species of weevils (two of them also on St Helena); none are endemic although one is possibly indigenous. St Helena, however, has a rich and complex weevil fauna, with a total of 91 species recorded. Two of these are probably not established on the island. Thirteen species are of little interest, being clearly introduced, although the Eucalyptus Snout Beetle *Gonipterus scutellatus* was a significant forestry pest until controlled by an introduced egg parasite, and the Banana Weevil *Cosmopolites sordidus* causes some damage. A fourteenth species – *Rhyparanotus impar* – has not yet been found outside St Helena but is probably not really endemic; the other members of its genus are from Central and South America, and on St Helena *R. impar* feeds on the wood of introduced plants.

The remaining 77 species, however, are all endemic and represent the most remarkable adaptive radiation that has occurred during the evolution of the fauna of St Helena. Probably only a handful of separate colonising stocks reached the island, but they evidently did so many millions of years ago, and have diversified in conjunction with the endemic plants on which they feed. Intriguingly, all but one of the endemic species have only five segments in the middle section of the antennae, a characteristic that is rare in weevils outside the island. It does occur, however, in at least one African group, suggesting that weevils with this characteristic were more widespread when the island colonisations occurred.

The endemic species are grouped in 17 endemic genera, plus one genus that is also represented in South Africa. They are usually considered as belonging in two subfamilies, but it is not certain that these are valid groups. Better understanding of the relationships among the weevils of St Helena must await studies based on analysis of their genetic material (DNA). For the meantime, we treat them at the level of tribes – small groups of apparently related genera; we do not, however, mention all the species. These are mainly small beetles (mostly less than 5 mm long) and secure identification requires careful study of the descriptions and drawings in the Belgians' account, or comparison with museum specimens.

All of the endemic weevils are termed 'xylophagous', meaning that they are eaters of wood (normally dead and often in various stages of decay); many of the species are closely linked to particular endemic plants, as indicated below. A number of these weevils, however, are also capable of feeding on the wood of introduced trees. Several of the weevils are still abundant, especially in the fragments of original vegetation on the central ridge, but 13 of the previously described species were not found by the Belgians and about ten of these may well be extinct. (Of the other three, two were originally found on the Barn and have not been looked for recently, while the third was abundant at middle levels in the last century and seems likely to have survived somewhere.) Among the species that were not found by the Belgians two – *Pseudomesoxenus scrobiculatus* and *Isotornus aterrimus* – are known only from the Boxwood, which is itself on the verge of extinction. Two others – *Cryptommata cucculata* and *Peltophorus commidendri* – were the sole known members of their respective genera, giving rise to a fear that the endemic genera *Cryptommata* and *Peltophorus* are themselves both extinct.

Cryptommata cucculata
4.2 mm   MRAC

Acanthinomerini

**H   *Acanthinomerus.* 13 species, on cabbage trees, gumwood species, Dogwood and Samphire; two species were not found by the Belgians.

**H   *Chalcotrogus.* 3 species, on cabbage trees; one species was not found by the Belgians.

**H   *Eucoptoderus.* 2 species, on cabbage trees and perhaps False Gumwood.

**H   *Lamprochrus.* 2 species, one restricted to Dogwood and one with two distinct forms, respectively on Black Cabbage and on Gumwood / False Gumwood.

Acanthinomerus chevrolatii
5.2 mm   MRAC

**H   *Xestophasis.* 2 species, one on Gumwood (not found by the Belgians) one probably on Samphire.

Cotasterini

**H   *Hexacoptus.* The single species in this genus is the only endemic species with 6 rather than 5 segments in the middle section of the antennae; it lives on cabbage trees and ferns.

**H   *Peltophorus.* 1 species, on Gumwood, not found by the Belgians.

**H   *Pentarthrodes.* This genus is possibly related to weevils in other Atlantic islands and in northern Africa. There is 1 species, found mainly in dead trunks of the Tree Fern, where it is preyed on by the carabid beetle *Apteromimus platyderoides*.

Pentarthrodes dicksoniae
3.2 mm   MRAC

**H   *Pentatemnodes.* This genus is probably related to one with representatives living on sandy coasts of other Atlantic Islands and in northern Africa. The single species has reduced eyes and may feed on roots, possibly of Samphire.

363

**H *Pseudomesoxenus*. Four almost eyeless species, respectively on cabbage trees, Gumwood/False Gumwood, Boxwood and Tree Fern. The last of these (*P. minutissimus*) has a specific ground beetle predator, *Pseudophilochthus evanescens*.

Cryptommatini

**H *Cryptommata*. 1 species, which used to live on False Gumwood.

Microxylobiini

Microxylobius westwoodi
2.5 mm   MRAC

**H *Isotornus*. Four species, found respectively on Gumwood, Boxwood, Babies' Toes and Samphire, and Scrubwood and Samphire.

**H *Microxylobius*. 15 species, some of them very common. They live mainly on cabbage trees, but two also on Jellico, one also on Rosemary and one also on Tree Fern; one species only on Gumwood, one on Scrubwood and one on Samphire; another lives deep in organic litter and has reduced eyes.

Nesiotini

Tychiorhinus melanodendri
3 mm   MRAC

**H *Nesiotes*. This genus is now known to have fairly close relatives in South Africa. 13 species, largely on cabbage trees, but three species also on Dogwood, two only on Gumwood and one on Tree Fern and Lobelia; four species were not found by the Belgians.

**H *Tychiorhinus*. Six species, only on cabbage trees; one species was not found by the Belgians.

Rhyncholini

Pachymastax crassus
7.5 mm   MRAC

**H *Pachymastax*. One species, on cabbage trees and False Gumwood. This is the largest of the endemic weevils, some individuals reaching a length of 8.4 mm.

*H *Pseudostenoscelis*. All six species of this genus on St Helena are endemic, although other species in the same genus are found in South Africa. Intriguingly, these are the only endemic weevils on St Helena with wings, suggesting that their arrival on the island is more recent than in the other groups. The endemic species are found on cabbage trees, species of gumwoods and Samphire.

Tapiromimi

**H *Tapiromimus*. One species, on cabbage trees.

DERMESTIDAE – dermestid beetles

Dermestes maculatus
8 mm

Dermestids are small to medium-sized beetles (c.4-10 mm), oval or elongate-oval and usually hairy or covered in scales. Both adults and larvae (which are also hairy) feed on a great variety of plant and animal material, and many are destructive pests. Dermestids are often spread around the world in cargoes of organic material on ships. However, they are also abundant in seabird colonies even on very remote islands and may sometimes be transported by seabirds; they are also sometimes dispersed in the air. Four species have been found on St Helena and four on Ascension; we suspect that at least one species of *Dermestes* reached both islands before humans.

ELATERIDAE – click beetles

A large family of somewhat elongate beetles which have the curious ability to jerk themselves into the air by a sudden bending and straightening of the body, often accompanied by an audible click. No elaterids have reached Ascension, but there has evidently been one colonisation of St Helena. This has given rise on the island to two distinct forms, generally considered as separate endemic species. However, the situation is complicated by some evidence that the range of one of the species has altered since the time of Wollaston and perhaps even that there have been evolutionary changes; the destruction of the Gumwood forests has clearly had a major effect on these beetles.

Anchastus atlanticus
9 mm   MRAC

*H   *Anchastus atlanticus*. A brownish black beetle, paler below. The plate covering the thorax is prolonged backwards at the sides in two sharp points extending past the front of the abdomen. *A. atlanticus* is 8-10.5 mm long, on average smaller than the next species. It has been found on the western part of the central ridge, around High Peak, and also at Flagstaff Hill.

*H   *Anchastus compositarum*. A larger species (9.5-13 mm), with the thoracic plate shorter and broader than in the previous species. *A. compositarum* has been found only in the north of the island, at Horse Point Plain and Prosperous Bay Plain.

ENDOMYCHIDAE – handsome fungus beetles

Small oval beetles that feed on fungi; they are shiny but pitted and are usually brightly coloured. One species has been introduced to St Helena: it is tiny (c.1.5 mm), reddish or yellowish and feeds on moulds.

HISTERIDAE – hister beetles

Small, shiny black beetles with the elytra cut off square at their tips, exposing the hind end of the abdomen. When disturbed, histerids draw in their legs and antennae and it becomes hard to see that they are beetles at all. Histerids are predatory on small insects living in dung or other decaying material, and are readily transported around the world. Four species have been found on St Helena, but one of these may not be established. One of the same species is found on Ascension.

HYDROPHILIDAE – water scavenger beetles

Small beetles (about 5 mm long) with varied lifestyles. There is a single species on St Helena.

H   *Dactylosternum abdominale*. This is a predatory species which lives in rotting vegetation. In some parts of the world it is known to attack the Banana Weevil and may exert some control over its populations. *D. abdominale* is widespread in warm parts of the world and is doubtless introduced.

LATHRIDIIDAE – minute brown scavenger beetles

Lathridiids are small (about 2 mm long) brown beetles which like mouldy debris. Three species have been recorded from St Helena, all of them almost cosmopolitan and clearly introduced; one of the species may now have disappeared from the island.

MORDELLIDAE – tumbling flower beetles
These beetles have somewhat wedge-shaped and hump-backed bodies, with a pointed abdomen. The larvae live in decaying wood or plant pith and the adults are found in flowers. There is one endemic species on St Helena, with relatives in Africa.

*H *Glipostenoda mellissiana.* A dark brown, armadillo-shaped beetle about 5-8 mm long; the end of the abdomen forms a powerful spine, and the beetle can hop clumsily across the ground. It has been found on several members of the genus *Commidendrum* and was probably adapted to life in the original forests of gumwoods and Scrubwood.

MYCETOPHAGIDAE – hairy fungus beetles
Broadly oval, flattened, rather hairy beetles which feed on fungi and are often found under bark. They are associated with decaying plant material and have been widely distributed by people. A single species has been recorded from both islands.

HA *Typhaea stercorea.* A red brown to black beetle, 2-3 mm long and conspicuously flattened. It was common on St Helena in the last century but has not been found recently. On Ascension we found it in underground habitats in two barren places; it is conceivably indigenous.

NITIDULIDAE – sap beetles

A varied group of tiny beetles, which feed mainly on decaying fruits, flowers and fungi; they are often transported in cargoes. We have found one species on Ascension; four others have been recorded from St Helena, but one of these was not found by the Belgians and may have been misidentified. All are doubtless introduced.

PTILIIDAE – feather-winged beetles

This family includes some of the smallest beetles known. The hindwings (when present) have a fringe of hairs. There are two species on St Helena, both known from nowhere else, but the first may turn out to be introduced.

?*H *Acrotrichis sanctaehelenae.* A flattened, brownish black beetle about 1 mm long. It can be separated from the next species by the fact that the edges of the main plate covering the thorax extend backwards past the front of the abdomen. This species was not found by Wollaston, but the Belgians found it in several places at middle and high levels. Its relatives are mainly in South America, raising the suspicion that it has been introduced from there relatively recently.

*H *Ptinella matthewsiana.* This minute beetle (<1 mm) is flattened, shiny and yellowish. It occurs mainly on the central ridge, under bark and in rotting wood of cabbage trees and introduced species. Beetles of this genus occur in distinct winged and wingless forms, the latter (which is also eyeless) normally being much commoner. A close

366

relative of *P. matthewsiana* occurs on Tristan da Cunha and it is likely that these beetles are able to travel long distances by air.

PTINIDAE – spider beetles

Long legged, very small beetles in which the head is almost concealed under the body; they are globular and shiny, with long legs. Ptinids often occur as pests in stored grain and have travelled around the world with humans. Three species are present on St Helena and one on Ascension.

RHIZOPHAGIDAE – rhizophagids

Small (2-3 mm), slender, dark-coloured beetles. Most species live under bark or in rotten wood and in spite of the family name which implies root-eating they are actually predatory. Two species are present on St Helena, evidently introduced from Europe; they are often found together under decaying plant refuse.

SCARABAEIDAE – scarab beetles

Scarabs are strikingly heavily built, with broad, oval or somewhat elongate bodies; the front legs may be adapted for digging. The last few segments of the antennae are expanded, forming a sort of club which provides a good means of separation from the generally similar tenebrionids. Many scarabs feed on dung or rotting plant material, but some attack living plants.

St Helena has an endemic genus (*Mellissius*) evidently derived from an ancestral form which arrived long ago and evolved into the three modern species. These beetles, well adapted for digging and quite flightless, may have been the dominant root-feeding beetles in the pristine St Helena. Five other scarabs (including one that is not established) have been accidentally introduced to St Helena. Two herbivorous species are mentioned below, but two others exploit dung, though one of these may have arrived only in the 20th century. Charles Darwin, who visited the island in 1836, expressed his astonishment at the presence of dung beetles on St Helena, where no mammal dung would have been available in the past. Two dung beetles have been recorded from Ascension.

H   *Adoretus versutus*, Vine Beetle. This species was a major pest of vines in the 19th century, feeding by night and eating the leaves and shoots down to the bare wood; it also attacks oaks and other trees, and is implicated in much unexplained foliage injury to ornamental shrubs. This species is fully winged (cf. *Mellissius*), brown and about 12 mm long, and occurs especially in low and intermediate parts of the island.

H   *Heteronychus sanctaehelenae*. In spite of its name this beetle is clearly introduced to the island; its larvae, known as 'white grubs' can be found in pastures, where they do some damage. The adults can be distinguished from *Mellissius* species by their shiny black colour; they are about 13 mm long.

**H   *Mellissius adumbratus*. Adults of *Mellissius* species are stumpy, massive beetles, well adapted for digging; they are shiny red-brown and have only rudimentary wings. The larvae are stout and whitish, with red-brown heads. They can cause bare patches on pastures by eating roots, and on St Helena they are known as hogworms, apparently because in the past pigs were sometimes put out on pastures infested with the larvae, which they dug out and ate. Control

Melissius adumbratus
16 mm   MRAC

of the larvae using DDT was considered in the 1950s. *Mellissius adumbratus* is 14-18 mm long and has a conical tubercle on the head which is larger in the male than the female; it is typical of the far north of the island. Intriguingly, not only has *M. adumbratus* evolved differences from the other two species on the island, but there are also two slightly different forms within the species, living respectively in the area of Horse Point and Deadwood (where there was originally deep soil and many trees) and on Prosperous Bay Plain (with little soil and only scattered shrubs). The seasonal pattern of development of the two forms seems also to differ, the adults appearing a few weeks later on Prosperous Bay Plain than on Horse Point. The larvae of this species presumably now eat the roots of Creeper, but were evidently part of the fauna of the gumwood forests in the past.

**H   *Mellissius eudoxus.* This species, which is 16-19 mm long, can be distinguished from *M. adumbratus* by the lack of a tubercle on the head and from *M. oryctoides* by its much larger size. *M. eudoxus* has been recorded in many places in the central part of the island, but the Belgians found it much less abundant than it had been in the 19th century.

Melissius oryctoides
12 mm   MRAC

**H   *Mellissius oryctoides.* This species was discovered by the Belgians on Horse Point Plain and Prosperous Bay Plain; only the male is known. This is the smallest of the three species (12-13 mm) and is distinguished by a small backward-pointing horn on the head and a large dimple just behind this, near the front of the thorax.

SCOLYTIDAE – bark beetles

Small, cylindrical, brownish or black beetles. The larvae of many species feed on the inner bark of trees, forming characteristic patterns; they sometimes kill trees by infecting them with fungi. On St Helena there are two species; both are probably introduced, although one of them is common in dead wood of Gumwoods and was first described from St Helena. On Ascension there is one species which is certainly different, although there is some doubt about its identity.

SILVANIDAE – silvanids

This family is sometimes included within the Cucujidae. It includes a few species that are now cosmopolitan, and two have been introduced to St Helena. One of these, the Saw-toothed Grain Beetle *Oryzaephilus surinamensis*, can be a major pest in stores of many kinds of food; it is about 3 mm long and is recognizable by the strongly serrated margins to the middle section of the body.

STAPHYLINIDAE – rove beetles

Staphylinidae

Staphylinids are slender, elongate beetles with very short elytra, ranging in length from 2 mm to at least 20 mm; they look rather like earwigs but without pincers, and are active flyers and runners. In general, staphylinids can only be identified by dissection of the genitalia, so we do not attempt to describe the species. Three staphylinids have been found on Ascension and 23 on St Helena. Many of the species are found in manure and have been widely dispersed by people; they are presumably introduced. Two of these – *Oxytelus alutaceifrons* and *Microxytelus nitidifrons* – were originally described from St Helena and considered to be endemic, but have now been found elsewhere. Five species are of more interest.

*H   *Atheta basilewskyana*, *A. caheniana* and *A. helenensis* have been found only on St Helena. The Belgians considered that even these apparently endemic species (and *Philonthus dictator*, see below) were likely to have been imported from South Africa. However, staphylinids are abundant in the 'aerial plankton' and these three species of *Atheta* are linked closely with the endemic vegetation on the central ridge, providing circumstantial evidence of the presence of an indigenous staphylinid fauna. We therefore consider these species as being genuine endemics.

HA   *Atheta coriaria*. This cosmopolitan species has been found on both islands; however, unlike the staphylinids which have been spread most effectively by humans it is not primarily associated with manure and it may be a very effective aerial disperser.[44] *A. coriaria* is closely related to the endemic species on St Helena and may be a representative of the stock from which they evolved.

*H   *Philonthus dictator*. This beetle differs from the endemic species of *Atheta* in being more typical of middle levels on the island; if really endemic, it may have been associated with the gumwood forests. *P. dictator* has close relatives on other Atlantic islands.

TENEBRIONIDAE – darkling beetles

Tenebrionids are ground-living beetles, many of which burrow into the soil; they are mostly smooth and black or brownish. Some are heavily built and can be confused with scarabaeids, but the antennae of tenebrionids are made up of 11 rather similar segments, with the outermost ones not expanded into a club. Tenebrionids generally feed on plant material; many species are pests and some are found in cargoes or are likely to be transported with plants. However, these beetles are tough and well adapted to withstand dessication, so it is probable that some colonising stocks have reached the islands on driftwood.

St Helena has 17 species of tenebrionids (including one – *Hemasodes batesi* – found by us but not listed by the Belgians). There were probably two or more colonisations – millions of years ago – by members of the tribe Opatrini; subsequent evolution on the island gave rise to eight endemic species, currently placed in four endemic genera. The island also has one 'apparent endemic' which is probably really introduced. Two more species (*Gonocephalum simplex* and *Zophobas atratus*) are discussed below, while six others are clearly introduced and are not listed. On Ascension tenebrionids are currently the most diverse beetle family, with a total of nine species. Two of these (*Clitobius ovatus* and *Phaleria* species) probably arrived by rafting from Africa, although the other seven are doubtless introduced (five of them also occur on St Helena).

A   *Clitobius ovatus*. A scavenger found by us near Shelly Beach and in the Wideawake fairs. Elsewhere, it is often found on sandy shores and its range includes the Cape Verde islands and Namibia; we assume it is a natural colonist.

H   *Gonocephalum simplex*. A mud-coloured and mud-coated beetle about 8 mm long, which is abundant in most parts of the island except the central ridge. It is an African species, but the St Helena specimens are slightly different and are sometimes considered as forming a separate subspecies, *G. s. hadroides*. *G. simplex* may therefore. be a natural colonist. The species has been reported elsewhere as a pest of coffee.

---

[44] I. Moore & E.F. Legner (1974).

**H   *Hadrodes helenensis*. This beetle is 7 mm long and is entirely red-brown, with short hairs, but is covered by a grey muddy coating. It has been found only twice, by Wollaston near West Lodge and by the Belgians at Thompsons Wood. It is the only member of an endemic genus and is evidently derived from an early colonisation.

**H   *Helenomelas basilewskyi*. The sole member of an endemic genus. It is a chunky and large beetle (14-15 mm), entirely deep black except for reddish antennae; the anterior part of the body is shiny, the elytra matt. It probably has no close relatives on the island or elsewhere, and is evidently an ancient endemic. The Belgians found this species common on Prosperous Bay Plain.

Helenomelas basilewskyi
14 mm   MRAC

A   *Phaleria* species. A member of this genus was recorded on a dead flying fish a century ago. These beetles are typical of sandy shores and very resistant to salt and exposure; they are represented on many other Atlantic Islands, including the Cape Verdes, so natural colonisation of Ascension seems likely.

**H   *Pseudoleichenum benoiti*. This is the only member of a new genus established by the Belgians. It is 5.5-6 mm long, with the front part of the body appearing more rounded – less angular – than in *Tarphiophasis* species. It is entirely black, but the whole of the upper surface is covered by a thick mat of scaly spines of different colours (dusky, yellow and white) which obscures the basic colour. These scales provide minimal justification for establishing the new genus, which is clearly related to *Tarphiophasis*. *P. benoiti* is the most abundant tenebrionid in the collections of the Belgians, being found especially on Prosperous Bay Plain and Sandy Bay beach.

?*H   *Stenosis sanctaehelenae*. A brown-black beetle with short yellow hairs, 6-7 mm long. The species is apparently confined to Ruperts Valley, where it is common. This distribution strongly suggests that it was introduced at the time of the suppression of the slave trade, and this is supported by the similarity of the species to another member of the genus *Stenosis* in West Africa. Probably *S. sanctaehelenae* is not really endemic to the island.

**H   *Tarphiophasis decellei*. The genus *Tarphiophasis* has given rise to a significant adaptive radiation on St Helena, with five species known. They typically have the upper surface covered with more or less flattened and scaly hairs, and sometimes also a layer of mud, so that the basic colour is often obscured. The tibiae (penultimate leg segments) of the front legs are more or less expanded and spiny, presumably as an adaptation for digging. *Tarphiophasis decellei* is 8 mm long and is an oval beetle, generally similar to *T. leleupi*. However, in *T. decellei* the sides of the plate covering the thorax extend forwards hardly at all, whereas in *T. leleupi* and the other members of the genus they extend forwards like hunched shoulders so that there is a strong notch on each side between them and the head. *T. decellei* has variable colouration, from reddish to brownish-black. However, this is always entirely covered with a muddy layer and also with a thick layer of upright hairs, flattened at the tip, which under high magnification look almost like tiny mushrooms. The Belgians found *T. decellei* abundant on parts of Prosperous Bay Plain.

Tarphiophasis decellei
8 mm   MRAC

**H   *Tarphiophasis insulanus*. Much the smallest member of the genus (3.5-4 mm long). It is shiny black; the anterior part of the body and two or three spots on the elytra are outlined in red, but this pattern is normally obscured by a whitish or grey muddy coating. The Belgians found this species abundant in the branches of Samphire on Prosperous Bay Plain.

**H   *Tarphiophasis leleupi*. This species is 5.5-6 mm long – smaller than *T. decellei* and *T. wollastoni* – but is similar in shape to the latter; it can be distinguished by having only four lines of punctuations on each elytron, close to the mid line. This beetle is entirely black, though always covered with a grey muddy coating. The Belgians found it to be very abundant on Prosperous Bay Plain and Sandy Bay beach.

**H   *Tarphiophasis tuberculatus*. This species is 5.5 mm long and with the whole body extremely rough and warty; it is red brown in colour but covered with a coat of mud and also short scaly bristles. This species is known only from two specimens obtained by Wollaston near West Lodge.

**H   *Tarphiophasis wollastoni*. This species is 7 mm long and is generally similar to *T. leleupi*; however, it has nine lines of punctuations on each elytron (so does *T. decellei*, but the shape of the thorax is different). *T. wollastoni* is brownish red or brownish black, and is known only from a few female specimens collected on Prosperous Bay Plain.

H   *Zophobas atratus*. A uniformly black beetle about 20 mm long. It is a South American species, but the St Helena specimens are apparently somewhat different, and have been considered as a separate subspecies, *Z. a. concolor*. On St Helena the species has been found only in James Valley and Ruperts, strongly suggesting that the species is introduced.

TROGIDAE – trogids

This small group is sometimes included in the Scarabaeidae. Trogids are oblong dark beetles, often covered in dirt. They eat the remains of dry animal carcasses. One species is known from St Helena.

H   *Trox rhyparoides* is about 8 mm long and black; it was evidently introduced from South Africa. Some of our baited underground traps attracted large numbers of this beetle.

TROGOSITIDAE (or Ostomatidae)

The single species recorded from St Helena has been widely transported with cargoes of foodstuffs and used to occur in storehouses on the island; it was not found by the Belgians.

NEUROPTERA – lacewings and their allies

Lacewings have four membranous wings but are not strong flyers; at rest, they hold their wings rooflike over the body, unlike dragonflies, which often rest with the wings extended. Most members of the order are predatory. In addition to the work of the Belgians, Wieland Röhricht and Timm Karisch recently collected some lacewings on both islands.[45]

CHRYSOPIDAE – green lacewings

These are mainly greenish insects with golden or copper-coloured eyes and long, filamentous antennae. The eggs are placed on the end of long stalks, like tiny balloons

---

[45] W. Röhricht (1998).

Chrysopa exul larva
8 mm   MRAC

on strings. The larva is hump-backed and looks rather like an armoured, six-legged slug; it has very long jaws and like the adult is a voracious predator on tiny insects, especially aphids (greenfly). Lacewings are often important in the control of pest species. St Helena has four species, one of which is endemic and the other three probably introduced; one of the latter is also found on Ascension.

*H   *Chrysopa exul.* Adults of this species are 11 mm long, with wings about 14 mm and the antennae longer than the wings; the insect is yellowish green, with the abdomen pale and hairy. It can be distinguished from the introduced species of *Chrysopa* by the four widely spaced dark spots on the anterior part of the thorax (over the front legs). This is the dominant lacewing on St Helena, occurring mainly at middle levels; the Belgians found it on Gumwoods both at Peak Gut and at Longwood, and Röhricht collected it at Hoopers Ridge. The closest relatives of *C. exul* are in Africa, and although the Belgians expressed doubt whether such fragile insects could be transported so far by the wind or by sea, the success of lacewings on other oceanic islands shows that they are excellent long distance colonists.

HA   *Chrysopa pudica.* This species, which is widespread in southern Africa, has been found in Ruperts Valley, Deadwood Plain and Fishers Valley on St Helena, and in December 1955 Timm Karisch collected a specimen near Two Boats village on Ascension; the species may be introduced to both islands. However, in 1892 the German biologist Dahl noted that a species of *Chrysopa* was abundant on the endemic Ascension Spurge, where the larvae preyed on aphids. For a century there were no records of either lacewing or aphids on the spurge, but the recent find of *C. pudica* suggests that this was the lacewing found by Dahl. Two other species of green lacewing, *Chrysopa squamosa* and *C. zastrowi*, are found locally on St Helena; both are probably introduced.

HEMEROBIIDAE – brown lacewings

The hemerobiids are similar to the chrysopids but smaller and usually brown; like chrysopids, they have colonized many oceanic islands. A single endemic species was found on St Helena by the Belgians and is still common at the present time..

*H   *Micromus atlanticus.* This species is 5.5 mm long, with wings about 7 mm and antennae shorter than the wings; it is mainly yellowish brown. *M. atlanticus* is common in the high central part of the island, including the Peaks; we do not know what insects it preys on. The closest relatives of *M. atlanticus* occur in Africa.

HYMENOPTERA – parasitic hymenopterans, ants, bees and wasps

Most members of this order have four membranous wings. Ants, bees and wasps are familiar to most people but the group also includes many parasitic insects which lay their eggs in (or on) other insects; the developing larvae then consume and kill the host. The order is divided into two suborders, Symphyta and Apocrita; all the species on St Helena and Ascension belong to the latter group. These Hymenoptera can be distinguished from other insects by having the front part of the body separated from the main part of the abdomen by a narrow 'waist'. Considering the enormous diversity of the Hymenoptera in general, the known St Helena fauna of about 57 species is relatively small. About 13-18 apparently endemic species have been identified and two endemic genera have been established. Many additional species found by the Belgians were not properly studied because no specialists were available; a number of these species are probably endemic and at least two are likely to represent endemic genera. Very few Hymenoptera (apart from probably introduced ants) have been recorded from Ascension; some minute parasitic species may have been overlooked, but we are sure that there is a genuine paucity of Hymenoptera on the island.

APIDAE – honey bees and bumble bees

H (A) *Apis mellifera*, Honey Bee. Bees have been introduced to St Helena several times but have had a somewhat chequered history. The Death's Head Hawk Moth *Acherontia atropos*, which feeds on the stored honey of honey bees, also occurs on the island. We do not have a reliable record of the first introduction of bees, but the early proceedings of the Agricultural and Horticultural Society mention that they disappeared and were re-introduced from the Cape in 1824. We have gathered later accounts from Melliss, the Belgians, C.R. Wallace, Gosse, Loveridge's notes and the St Helena News. It appears that bees were very abundant in 1854 but disappeared about 1864 or 1866 (simultaneously with the Death's Head Hawk Moth). Dates for their re-introduction are given for 1868, 1869 and 1878, so if these are accurate there may have been more than one attempt. They then apparently disappeared again between the two world wars. Four hives are said to have been imported by the Government in 1930, but we have failed to find an explicit record of this. We have a copy of an invoice dated 5th September 1949 for: "*6 Queen bees; young tested fertile, Italian type, my own strain*" to the Crown Agents from Douglas Roberts of the Bee Farm in the Isle of Wight; these were shipped on the *Rowallan Castle*. Bees were then imported again "*in the fifties*" and Wallace reported that they were abundant during his visit in 1957-59. Loveridge reported many bees dying in 1958, but made no suggestion as to the cause. In 1971 he wrote of many deserted hives near Varneys (the year the Death's Head Hawk Moth reappeared). There is a rumour that the French Consul imported queens at some stage. In 1995 we saw occasional colonies of wild bees, and several people were involved in beekeeping. However, it does seem that bees are likely to go extinct from time to time on St Helena and that protecting them from the depredations of the hawkmoth is advisable.

On Ascension there are now no bees or bee-keepers, but there have been at least two introductions. In 1827 – only 12 years after British occupation of the island – bees were brought in and released on Green Mountain to assist in pollination at the gardens. A century later the Resident Magistrate for the years 1934-36 wrote that: "*During the last two years, we have received from St Helena a hive of bees, which is thriving ...*". It seems that they did not thrive indefinitely: probably the hive was not cared for adequately and the bees failed to establish themselves in the wild.

BETHYLIDAE – bethylids

These are medium sized wasps (up to 8 mm long) which parasitize larvae of moths and beetles. Four species are known from St Helena, all of them endemic; three of them belong to the same genus and have probably evolved from a single colonising stock.

On Ascension two species have been found; one is probably endemic (see below) and the second has not yet been studied.

*H   *Holepyris atlanticus.* This species is about 3 mm long and is black, with the legs and antennae brownish. It is known from only a single male and female, found by the Belgians respectively in dead branches of Samphire on Prosperous Bay Plain and of Scrubwood at West Point; in both cases it was in company with endemic wood-boring beetles. The closest relatives of *H. atlanticus* are in Africa.

*H   *Sclerodermus insularis.* This species is known only from the female, which is wingless and has the antennae, legs, and most of the thorax yellow, the rest of the body brownish. It was found by the Belgians among twigs of Samphire on Prosperous Bay Plain, along with endemic beetles.

*H   *Sclerodermus sanctaehelenae.* Like *S. insularis*, this species is known only from wingless females on Samphire on Prosperous Bay Plain. It differs, however, in being entirely black.

*H   *Sclerodermus wollastoni.* This species is just over 2 mm long. The female is yellowish brown and wingless; the male is black and winged. The Belgians found it at Teutonic Hall.

?*A   *Trachepyris* species. This species, which we found in a Sooty Tern colony on the main island, has not yet been formally named and described but is considered to be endemic.

BRACONIDAE – braconids

Braconids are brownish or blackish insects which parasitize a wide variety of insects. The Belgians recorded two species on St Helena (one widespread elsewhere, the other undescribed) and Simmonds mentioned a different species.

CHALCIDOIDEA – chalcids

Chalcididae
2 mm

Several related families of minute parasitic wasps are grouped in the superfamily Chalcidoidea and referred to as 'chalcids'. Their wings have hardly any veins and in some species the wings are absent in one or both sexes. The antennae typically have an 'elbow' outside the innermost segment, making these tiny wasps look rather like ants (Formicidae). The chalcid families found on St Helena are the Chalcididae, Encyrtidae, Eulophidae, Eupelmidae, Mymaridae and Pteromalidae. Members of these families are parasites of a wide variety of insects and spiders; some of them lay their eggs inside the eggs of other insects, and are themselves among the smallest of all insects. Some 22 species of chalcids have been found on St Helena, although not all have been fully identified or described; they include 3-6 endemic species and one or two endemic genera. Only one chalcid has been found on Ascension; it was collected from the introduced Mexican Thorn and may be a parasite of an insect imported with this tree. We list only the more interesting of the chalcids.

H   *Anaphoidea nitens* (ex *Patasson nitens*) (family Mymaridae). This egg parasite was introduced from South Africa in 1958 as a biological control agent to combat the Eucalyptus Snout Beetle *Gonipterus scutellatus*; *A. nitens* came originally from Australia.

H   *Brachymeria sodalis* (family Chalcididae). This species, previously known from the Seychelles, was collected by the Belgians at traps on Horse Point Plain baited with rotting fish; it doubtless parasitizes calliphorid flies and may be indigenous.

374

?*H   *Charitopodinus ? swezeyi* (family Eupelmidae). Specimens collected in several places at middle levels are similar to – but not identical with – *C. swezeyi* collected in Hawai'i and China. The St Helena specimens have striking metallic colours of blue, purple and green, and may represent an endemic species. One female was a parasite of the endemic anobiid beetle *Xyletomerus insulanus*, which lives in branches of Samphire.

*H   *Cirrospilus nireus* (family Eulophidae). This species was found by Charles Darwin high up on St Helena; it has not been found since.

?**H   Eulophid unidentified. One male and one female of this species were found by the Belgians on the central ridge. It is generally blackish brown, with yellowish legs. The unusual feature is that the female has normal wings but the male reduced ones: this is opposite to the type of wing reduction seen in many species of Hymenoptera. This species is probably endemic, and may even represent an endemic genus.

**H   *Mymarilla wollastoni* (family Mymaridae). Two males were found by Wollaston and another two by the Belgians on Cabbage Tree Road; the female is unknown.

?*H   Mymarid unidentified. Four specimens of an unknown and presumably endemic species were found by the Belgians at High Peak and Cabbage Tree Road. Both sexes seem to be entirely wingless.

*H   *Pteromalus ipsea* (family Pteromalidae). This species was found by Charles Darwin high up on St Helena.

Chrysididae
10 mm

CHRYSIDIDAE – cuckoo wasps

Cuckoo wasps are brilliant metallic blue or green, with a coarsely sculptured surface. They exploit or parasitize other kinds of wasps or bees. We found a chrysidid at Two Boats on Ascension but its host has not yet been identified; it is presumably introduced.

CYNIPIDAE – gall wasps

Three kinds of cynipids have been found on St Helena but only one of these has been described: it forms an endemic genus and is clearly an ancient colonist.

**H   *Polbourdouxia miroscutellaris*. This is a minute, glossy, dark brown insect with paler legs; it is less than 2 mm long, with the antennae as long as the rest of the body (those of the male have 15 segments, of the female 13). The most unusual feature is the reduction of the wings: the anterior pair are minute (only a quarter of the length of the body) and covered with long hairs; the posterior ones are even smaller. This species was found by the Belgians on the high central ridge, at High Peak and at Teutonic Hall.

DIAPRIIDAE – diapriids

Diapriids are tiny, black, shining insects. The antennae have 11-15 segments and arise from a shelf-like protuberance in the middle of the face. Three species have been found on St Helena but none have been identified. In one of them both sexes are entirely wingless.

EVANIIDAE – ensign wasps

The ensign wasps are cockroach parasites. They are black and have a very distinctive somewhat spider-like shape, with a stumpy abdomen arising high up on the thorax and carried on a slender stalk like a flag – hence the name. A single species occurs on both islands.

Evania appendigaster
12 mm

HA   *Evania appendigaster.* This species has travelled around the world with its cockroach hosts, presumably *Periplaneta australasiae* and *Leucophaea maderae* on St Helena and *Periplaneta americana* on Ascension. The eggs are laid in the egg-case (ootheca) of the host.

FORMICIDAE – ants

Ants are small or medium-sized social insects with a separate wingless worker caste as well as functional males and females. The narrow 'waist' found in most Hymenoptera takes a special form, being interrupted by a conspicuous node or scale; the antennae are conspicuously elbowed. Nine species of ants have been recorded from St Helena and the same number of Ascension. There is no evidence, however, that ants were present on either island in pre-human times: all species are probably introduced. Although ants are capable of rafting over short distances they have typically failed to achieve natural colonisation of very isolated islands. Of the nine species on St Helena eight are well known 'tramp' species that have become almost cosmopolitan as a result of being transported by man; the ninth has also been distributed in this way, though less extensively. Ants are abundant on both St Helena and Ascension, although they are absent (or present in very low numbers) at the most barren lava sites on Ascension; one species is present on Boatswainbird Island as well as the main island. Since ants – acting collectively – are efficient predators on many other insects, it seems likely that the arrival of ants – and in particular *Pheidole megacephala* – on both islands may have led to the extinction of many invertebrates that lived on them in their pristine state.

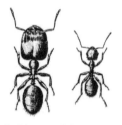

Pheidole megacephala
3 mm

ICHNEUMONIDAE – ichneumons

This is the largest family of insects. Ichneumons are slender parasitic wasps with conspicuous narrow 'waists' and long antennae (normally at least half the length of the body). Their hosts are other kinds of insects. Most have a long ovipositor at the hind end of the abdomen for laying eggs inside their hosts, but few of them can sting. The St Helena ichneumon fauna is very poorly known. One species was found by Darwin: the specimens are in the Dublin museum but have never been described. Six species were mentioned by Melliss but were never formally described. Identification is difficult and we mention only a few apparently endemic species listed by the Belgians. Only one ichneumon has been reported from Ascension and its identity is unclear.

Ichneumonidae
12 mm

*H   *Echthromorpha atrata.* This is a black species, described more than a century ago. It is among the most common hymenopterans on the island and is a parasite of the moth *Opogona sacchari* and other lepidopterans. Endemic species in this genus occur on many isolated islands.

*H   *Netelia insulicola.* This is a common red-bodied ichneumon found at middle levels on the island. We do not know the host.

?*H   *Habronyx* sp. or *Barylypa* sp. (tribe Gravenhorstiini). An ichneumonid belonging to one of these genera was found by the Belgians in several places at middle levels on the island.

?**H   Tribe Gravenhorstiini, ? new genus. Two specimens of this undescribed species were collected by the Belgians on Prosperous Bay Plain. The specialist who examined them considered that they represented a new genus.

MEGASPILIDAE – megaspilids

This is a little known family of tiny insects. Some members of the group are 'hyperparasites', parasitizing the larvae of other parasitic insects inside their hosts. One endemic species has been found on St Helena.

*H   *Dendrocerus wollastoni*. This wasp is 2 mm long, blackish brown, and has hardly any veins in the wings. Only seven females of this species are known; the five obtained by the Belgians were all on Gumwood, at Peak Gut and at Longwood.

SCELIONIDAE – scelionids

Scelionids are tiny, blackish wasps related to the Diapriidae and characterised by the flattened abdomen, with sharp edges; the larvae are generally egg parasites. Four species have been recorded from St Helena; one is apparently endemic but the others are unidentified.

*H   *Macroteleia gracilicornis*. This species, discovered by T.V. Wollaston, occurs on the central ridge but has also been found among dead twigs of Scrubwood on Horse Point Plain.

SPHECIDAE – sphecid wasps

These are predatory, solitary wasps, usually nesting in burrows in the ground. Three species have been found on St Helena, one of which is apparently endemic and another introduced but successful on the island; the third has been found only once, in Jamestown.

H   *Ampulex compressa*, Cockroach Killer. This spectacular wasp is brilliant bluish-green, with body about 22 mm long, reddish legs and long black antennae. It is common at low levels on St Helena in the summer months, and can be seen feeding on the honey-dew secretions of scale insects. When breeding the female stings and paralyses a cockroach and drags and pushes it into a hole, before laying an egg on it and plugging up the hole; the larva gradually consumes the cockroach. Arthur Loveridge was told of one occasion when the hole was in the wall of a house and was plugged with pins that the wasp collected systematically from a box on the dressing-table of Mrs Nicholls, wife of the cabinet-maker in Jamestown; before the wasp was detected, she had reproached her husband for purloining so many of her pins. The Cockroach Killer occurs in the tropics in many parts of the world, but is restricted to coasts and islands. It has probably been carried around the world by ships, along with its cockroach hosts.

*H   *Pison wollastoni*. This wasp was found by the Belgians in several places at middle levels. It is 11 mm long and is black with fine whitish hairs; much of the body has coarse punctuations, but the abdomen is shiny. The females of this group of wasps build mud nests, usually in holes in wood, which they provision with small spiders for their larvae to feed on. As a result of their nesting habits they are sometimes transported by ships to islands, but they seem to reach other remote islands naturally. The St Helena species is apparently unrelated to any African forms and is probably a true endemic.

VESPIDAE (including Eumeninae) – vespid wasps

Many of these wasps build hanging paper or mud nests. There is no record from St Helena but two species are known from Ascension.

A   *Polistes fuscatus fuscatus*. This is a brown wasp that was probably introduced from North America since 1940.

A   *Pachodynerus erynnis*. We collected this species in 1995; it is American and has probably been introduced recently.

LEPIDOPTERA – butterflies and moths

In the world as a whole, there are well over 100,000 species of butterflies and moths (lepidopterans). Members of this group of insects have two pairs of scale-covered wings (the forewings somewhat larger than the hindwings). They usually have a sucking tube or proboscis which is coiled under the head when not in use. Butterflies can be distinguished from moths by their 'clubbed' antennae. They also tend to be brightly coloured and to fly in the daytime, whilst moths are mostly duller in colour and fly at night; however, there are numerous exceptions. All species of lepidopterans go through life stages of egg, caterpillar, pupa (a stage for resting and reorganisation) and adult. The caterpillars are the main growing stage and generally eat green plant material. Some species feed only on particular kinds of plants while others are less discriminating and are termed 'polyphagous'. The latter group include some migratory moths such as the 'armyworms' which can cause catastrophic damage to crops.

The lepidopterans of St Helena have been very little studied in recent years. This is the only major group of invertebrates for which the Belgians never published their results, because they were unable to find anyone to study the specimens. Our information comes mainly from the excellent work of Mrs Vernon (Edith) Wollaston, published in 1879. We have been able to update some of the names, and in the last stages we have obtained much-needed help from Timm Karisch of Dessau, who spent a week collecting moths and butterflies on St Helena in 1995, and from Martin Honey of the Natural History Museum in London. However, a specialist study of the smaller moths ("Microlepidoptera") is badly needed.

St Helena has four species of butterfly and about 100 moths. It seems that just over 50 endemic species are present: in other words, half of the modern fauna is endemic. Three moth families are dominant on St Helena: Tineidae and Noctuidae each have nearly 30 species and Pyralidae have nearly 20 species. The numbers of endemic species within these three groups reflect their contrasting biology: Tineidae have about 29 endemics, Noctuidae about five and Pyralidae about nine. The tineids are sedentary moths, but having colonised the island (at least once) by some remote chance, they have evolved into a whole set of closely related species. The noctuids, in contrast, are superb natural migrants, but they are also readily transported with vegetables; some have been introduced to the islands by humans while others doubtless arrived naturally. The naturally arriving noctuids, however, have shown much less tendency than the tineids to evolve into new species on the island: probably their high mobility tends to prevent speciation (the formation of new species) since the tendency for the island populations to become genetically different from the mainland ones is offset by the occasional arrival of new colonists. The pyralids are somewhat intermediate; several stocks probably reached St Helena naturally, and at least one of these has diversified (the genus *Helenoscoparia*).

On Ascension the Lepidoptera are fairly well known, as a result of a recent study.[46] Thirty five species have been found on the island, but only two are endemic; significantly, both of these are tineids (cf. St Helena). There are 13 noctuids, and of these, we estimate that six are probably indigenous and two introduced; the remaining five are of doubtful origin.

For both islands we mention the endemic and probably indigenous species, together with some others of special importance, *but this is not a complete list of the Lepidoptera of the islands.*

COSMOPTERIGIDAE – cosmopterigid moths
These are small moths which are rather variable in shape and colour; the caterpillars of most species are leaf miners. One genus of this family has undergone a major radiation in the islands of the South Pacific. Two species have been recorded on St Helena (one of them endemic) and one from Ascension.

A   *Cosmopterix attenuatella.* This species, recently collected on Green Mountain, occurs throughout the tropics and is evidently an effective disperser. The larva feeds on sedges and it seems likely that the species is indigenous on Ascension, where the original foodplant would have been *Cyperus appendiculatus.*

*H   *Cosmopterix flavofasciata.* This species has wingspan about 8 mm. The general colour is blackish, but the forewing has a bright yellow transverse band, edged on either side with silvery scales; the hindwings are blackish and very narrow. Mrs Wollaston found this moth common, mainly at middle altitudes; Timm Karisch caught it also in Sandy Bay valley at about 50 m.

DANAIDAE – monarchs or milkweed butterflies

These are large brownish butterflies, usually marked with black and white, and are capable of long distance flights. They have sometimes been included within the Nymphalidae (see below) and they share with this family the characteristic short front legs, which are not used for walking. There is one species on St Helena and a sight record of a vagrant on Ascension.

H(A) *Danaus chrysippus*, African Monarch (Plain Tiger). Plate 24. This is the largest butterfly on St Helena and is very common in the warm parts of the island, especially in low and medium altitude areas with Silk Cotton bushes, where its dramatic grey, black and yellow caterpillars can be found feeding and where the bright green and gold pupae may be seen suspended. The adult is orange brown with black markings. These colours are warning colours and indicate to birds and other

[46] G.S. Robinson & C.M.StG. Kirke (1990).

Danaus chrysippus

hungry predators that the butterfly is distasteful and not worth chasing. The sexes are fairly similar and are easily confused with the female Diadem butterfly (Nymphalidae: see below) which mimic them. The African Monarch can be distinguished by the larger number of dark spots on the hind wings. On the upperside the male has three small black spots and a larger one behind; the female has only the three smaller ones. On the underside the male and female respectively have four and three black spots bordered with white. Close up, one can see that the three small spots in both sexes are at the outer edges of a closed cell formed by the veins on the wings.

The African Monarch – a cousin of the New World Monarch – is a well known migrant and occurs on many isolated islands. It may have reached St Helena several times, but probably could not have established a resident population until relatively recently because its caterpillar feeds only on milkweeds and their relatives (family Asclepiadaceae) and none of these plants were native to the island; Silk Cotton, a member of this family, has been introduced by humans and now there is a thriving population of the butterfly. In the past adults of this species could often be seen on dying leaves of the She Cabbage, from which they apparently obtained pyrollizidine alkaloids for use in the production of pheromones.

GELECHIIDAE – gelechiids

Small to minute moths whose larvae mostly roll or mine leaves, but some also attack tubers. One species is present on both islands; although it might easily have been introduced, natural immigration is also possible.

HA   *Phthorimaea operculella*, Potato Tuber Moth. This is a widely distributed tropical and subtropical species which is well known as a migrant but has also been intercepted in ships' cargoes. Its larvae feed on members of the nightshade family (Solanaceae) which includes potatoes and tomatoes. It is often a pest on crops, mining in the leaves and stalks; on St Helena it does serious damage to tubers of potatoes, although a number of its insect parasites have been introduced.[47]

GEOMETRIDAE – geometrids

The name of this family means 'ground measurer'. The caterpillars are long and slender, with only two pairs of 'prolegs' on the abdomen (as well as three pairs of legs on the thorax); they are known as loopers or inchworms because when moving about on a tree they typically grasp a twig with the prolegs and then move the front of the body forwards to take another hold with the thoracic legs. The adults are varied in shape, but are typically somewhat flimsy; most of them hold the the wings out sideways when at rest. The caterpillars feed on a variety of plants. There are two species on St Helena (one endemic and one widespread) and one on Ascension which has not been fully identified.

*H   *Scopula separata* (ex *Acidalia separata*). This species was originally described along with a supposedly separate species, *Acidalia atlantica*. It is clear, however, that there is only a single variable species, now placed in the genus *Scopula*.[48] The wingspan is c.23 mm and the general colour hoary white, speckled with black. The wings and abdomen are

---

[47] Details are provided by F.J. Simmonds (1973).

[48] M.J. Scoble (1999).

tinged with brown and the wings have a black dot and an undulating oblique white line bordered with blackish brown on the inner side.

GLYPHIPTERIGIDAE – glyphipterigids

These are small day-flying moths with somewhat pointed wings and with a conspicuous ocellus (small simple eye) above each compound eye. The larvae feed mainly as seed borers in sedges and rushes. There is one endemic species on St Helena.

*H   *Glyphipteryx semilunaris*. This moth is about 8 mm in wingspan, with the thorax and forewings rich golden and iridescent bronze with a white half-moon mark. When the moth is at rest these marks on the two wings unite to form a conspicuous white crescent. Mrs Wollaston suspected that the larva was a seedborer. She found this species to be abundant on the central ridge; Timm Karisch also found it in Fishers Valley.

GRACILLARIIDAE – leaf-blotch miners

The gracillariids are tiny moths with narrow, pointed, blade-like wings, which rest with the front of the body raised and the wing tips touching the surface. Their larvae make blotchy 'mines' in leaves (as opposed to serpentine mines in which the path of the larva can be followed); they often also fold the leaves. There is one endemic species on St Helena.

*H   *Phyllonorycter aurifascia* (ex *Lithocolletis aurifascia*).This is a minute moth (wingspan 6 mm), the wings having alternate paler and darker oblique markings. The species seems to have been first collected by Melliss; Mrs Wollaston found it only at Thompsons Wood, where the adults rested in a stone wall and the mines of the larvae were seen in the leaves of the old Gumwoods.

HEPIALIDAE – swifts or ghost moths

These are medium to large moths with very short antennae and all four wings almost the same shape; the base of the forewing carries a spur (jugum) which overlaps the front edge of the hind wing. One endemic species is known from St Helena.

*H   *Eudalaca sanctahelena*. Only the male of this moth is known; it was collected by Major Howland Roberts in about 1880 but was described only in 1951.[49] It has a wingspan of 29 mm and is generally blackish grey above and paler below. The forewings are blackish grey with an oblique transverse band of darker spots, edged with white. The genus is known in the southern half of Africa and the ancestors of the endemic species doubtless colonised St Helena from there.

LYCAENIDAE – blues and their relatives

These are small, brightly coloured butterflies with blue, coppery or brown wings. One species is present on both islands.

HA   *Lampides* (or *Cosmolyce*) *boeticus*, Long-tailed Blue. Plate 24. This is a small blue butterfly. The upperside of the male is violet blue, with two black spots and a small tail at the

---

[49] P.E.L. Viette (1951).

posterior point of the hindwing; the female is browner. The underside is fawn grey with white bars and two tiny peacock spots at the back. The green caterpillar is short and thick, and shaped rather like a woodlouse. The Long-tailed Blue is widespread in warm parts of the Old World and is a well known migrant; it doubtless reached both islands naturally. On St Helena it is now abundant, especially on furze (gorse) in the higher parts of the island, and it also seems established on Ascension. However, the caterpillar feeds exclusively on legumes (the pea family) and there were no indigenous legumes on either island, so the butterfly could not have bred until after the arrival of people and the introduction of furze and other legumes; it is now a minor horticultural pest on St Helena.

LYONETIIDAE – lyonetiids

Small moths with very narrow wings, the hind ones often almost linear. The larvae make serpentine mines in leaves. There is one endemic species on St Helena.

*H   *Cemiostoma auronivea*. This tiny moth has wingspan of 8 mm and is white, with black eye-spots on the forewings and the outer two thirds of these wings gilded. The species seems to have been first collected by Melliss; Mrs Wollaston failed to find it, but speculated that it might be associated with Scrubwood.

MOMPHIDAE – momphids

These moths are closely allied to the cosmopterigids; they are small, with the wings long, narrow and usually pointed at the tips. There is one endemic species on St Helena.

*H   *Stagmatophora trifasciata*. This species has a wingspan of about 8 mm. The forewings are rich velvety brown with three brilliantly metallic bands of silvery and coppery scales; the hindwings are dull blackish brown. The antennae are long and black, with pure white tips. Mrs Wollaston found this moth to have a restricted distribution above Newfoundland west of Diana's Peak; she found it mainly in Blackberry.

NOCTUIDAE – noctuids

This is the largest family of the order Lepidoptera. Noctuids are heavy bodied, dull-coloured night-flying moths with wingspan usually in the range 20-40 mm. They have slender, threadlike antennae and have hearing organs (thin-walled swellings) on either side of the last segment of the thorax (cf. Pyralidae). Some species are well known migrants. The Noctuidae are an important group on both islands. On St Helena there are 30 or so species of which at least four are endemic. The great majority are known as migrant pests which are also polyphagous (feeding on a variety of plants). Such species make good colonists, and a number of them may have reached the island naturally or be the descendants of natural colonists. However, the great volume of shipping in the past and the regular import of fruit and vegetables has provided many opportunities for accidental introduction. There is no up-to-date list, and the situation was not made clearer when E. Berio, a well known Italian lepidopterist, described three supposedly new endemic species (two species of *Discestra* and *Hypena helenae*) without reference to Mrs Wollaston's paper or collections. As well as listing the endemic noctuids, we mention several migrant species that may also be indigenous. Some of these are agricultural pests, but we do not include all the other pest species of noctuids that are probably introduced.

On Ascension 14 species have been recorded, and we suspect that most of them colonised Ascension naturally. However, for any given species it is impossible to exclude the possibility of human introduction, as many of these moths infest crops and could have been transported with foodstuffs.

HA   *Agrotis ipsilon* and *Agrotis segetum*. These cutworms[50] are cosmopolitan species feeding mainly on herbaceous plants. They are pests of many vegetables; on St Helena they cause serious damage to cabbages, tomatoes, carrots and beet and other crops, and have also been noted attacking tree seedlings. On Ascension *A. ipsilon* has been recorded as feeding on Guava, an invasive shrub. Both species are well known as migrants. *A. ipsilon* has been recorded as travelling long distances with locusts in the Middle East, and is possibly indigenous on one or both islands; *A. segetum* is likely to have arrived with imported vegetables.

Agrotis ipsilon

*H   *Cardepia subvelata* (ex *Apamea subvelata* and including '*Discestra basilewskyi*' and '*Discestra bergeri*').[51] This species has a wingspan of c.34 mm and is very dark brown, with black zigzag lines on the forewings. Mrs Wollaston commented that it was associated with the cabbage tree flora in the highest parts of the island.

?*HA   *Chrysodeixis* (ex *Plusia*) *dalei*. This species is known only from St Helena and Ascension. It is not clear whether it is really endemic to the two islands, or whether it has been transported from St Helena to Ascension by humans, or whether the two populations are independently derived from an African relative. It has a wingspan of 38-42 mm, with the forewings rich mottled golden brown with silver markings. Mrs Wollaston found it in various parts of the island and noted that it occurred among Scrubwood on the Barn.

A   *Helicoverpa* (ex *Heliothis*) *armigera*. This is a well known Old World tropical and subtropical migrant pest, eating the leaves of a wide variety of plants. Although the species is recorded as being sometimes transported with vegetables, it might have reached Ascension naturally, as demonstrated by the presence of an endemic species in this genus on St Helena (see below). (*H. armigera* has been reported from St Helena, but this may be a mistake for the next species.)

*H   *Helicoverpa insularis* or *helenae*.[52] This moth has wingspan about 36 mm, with reddish or yellowish brown forewings, ashy grey hindwings and abdomen, and a complex pattern of brown and white markings. Melliss found the caterpillars feeding on geraniums and other garden plants; it would be interesting to look for them on Old

---

[50] We apply this term to caterpillars of noctuids in the genus *Agrotis*, which have inconspicuous coloration and normally attack the basal parts of plants, underground, or close to soil level; they are known in St Helena as 'grubs'. Caterpillars of another noctuid, probably *Spodoptera littoralis*, are relatively brightly coloured and are normally leaf-eaters, but shelter in the soil and sometimes behave as cutworms.

[51] On the advice of Martin Honey of the Natural History Museum in London we place '*Apamea subvelata*' in the genus *Cardepia*, and do not maintain the two species of *Discestra* described by Berio. However, it is possible that one or both of them is an endemic species distinct from *C. subvelata*, since Mrs Wollaston commented that one of her specimens was distinct, and Timm Karisch has collected two forms in different parts of the island.

[52] After discussion with Martin Honey we tentatively consider *Helicoverpa helenae*, described by D.F. Hardwick (1965), as being the same as the species listed in Melliss as *Anchoscelis insularis* Walker and by Wollaston as *Heliothis insularis*. The type specimen of *insularis* is lost, but we think it improbable that such a conspicuous species would have been overlooked until the 20th century. R. Rowe (1995) records *Helicoverpa assulta* subspecies *afra* from the island, but we do not know the basis of this.

Father Live Forever. In spite of confusion over the name, it seems that there is an endemic species of *Helicoverpa* on St Helena, providing an important demonstration of the ability of members of this group to colonise isolated islands.

*H   *Hypena helenae*. This basically grey moth has strongly patterned forewings. It was collected by Arthur Loveridge and then by the Belgians, and was described by Berio as a new species, but is very similar to *H. laceratalis*.[53] In a 1993 report, Simon Fowler mentioned that: *"Hypena laceratalis Walker (=H. strigata Fabricius) was noted causing some damage to gumwoods in addition to its normally beneficial role in causing extensive damage to the weed Lantana camara."* This record presumably relates to *H. helenae*. Timm Karisch found this species on Hoopers Ridge and in several places at middle levels.

HA   *Hypena obacerralis*. This moth has the forewing relatively uniform except for a strong line running diagonally from the centre of the hind edge to the front edge near the tip. The species is widespread; it has been found at middle levels in the drier parts of St Helena, and also occurs on Ascension.[54]

*H   *Leucania ptyonophora*. This species, though described only in 1905,[55] is common and widespread on the island, especially on pastures at middle altitudes. It is rather uniform brown, with the hindwings paler.

A   *Mythimna loreyi*. This is a grass-feeding species from the Afrotropical and Oriental regions, mainly in the subtropics and including a number of Atlantic islands. It is known as a migrant and may be indigenous.

A   *Spodoptera exigua*. This army worm is the most cosmopolitan species in the genus and is well known in Africa as a voracious pest and long distance migrant, with flights of over 2,400 km recorded. It is probably indigenous on Ascension.

HA   *Spodoptera littoralis*. This army worm eats a wide variety of plants (including potatoes and tomatoes) and is sometimes very destructive on both islands, eating foliage and also boring into fruits; it may well be indigenous. The caterpillar is up to 50 mm long, smooth and stout, with a relatively small head. It is pale or dark brown, and each segment has a wedge-shaped velvety black mark on each side, bordered with a yellow line. (A third species of army worm, *Spodoptera litura*, has been recorded on St Helena, but it is likely that *S. littoralis* was really the species concerned.) Two species of hymenopteran parasites were imported in 1975 in an attempt to control *S. littoralis*, but it is not clear whether they have become established.

HA   *Thysanoplusia (or Plusia) orichalcea*. This is another widespread migrant species which eats a wide variety of plants. It is likely to have reached both islands naturally. On St Helena it is particularly troublesome on cabbage.

HA   *Trichoplusia ni*. This is a cosmopolitan migrant species which is sometimes a pest of crucifers. It probably reached the islands naturally.

H   *Trichoplusia vittata* (ex *Habrostola commidendri*). Mrs Wollaston found this species only on Gumwoods and considered that it was endemic, although she recognized that it

---

[53] M. Lödl (1994).

[54] This species was recorded as *H. masurialis* by G.S. Robinson & C.M.StG. Kirke (1990): see M. Lödl (1994).

[55] G.F. Hampson (1905).

had close relatives elsewhere; the St Helena population is now considered to belong to the widespread *T. vittata*, and seems likely to have reached St Helena naturally.

NYMPHALIDAE – brush-footed butterflies

The nymphalids are medium to large butterflies, usually with bright colours and strong patterns; the forelegs are much shorter than the second and third pair and are densely hairy. Many species are long distance migrants. Two nymphalids are present on St Helena and both occur also on Ascension, at least from time to time.

H(A)   *Vanessa* (ex *Cynthia*) *cardui*, Painted Lady. Plate 24. This species is almost cosmopolitan and is another well known migrant; in 1939 a swarm was recorded in mid-Atlantic 1,600 km west of St Helena. It is smaller than the Diadem and with a scattering of white spots on its otherwise rosy buff mottled forewings. On St Helena this is the commonest of the three large butterflies. In April 1995 Philip watched a territorial individual on the summit of Cuckold's Peak in late afternoon. It was based on a few square metres of the grassy path, leaving to pursue vigorously any other Painted Lady that came past, but quickly returning and settling on the path; we had seen individuals there on previous occasions, so the Peaks may be an important area for territories. Painted Lady caterpillars feed on nettles, mallows and thistles; there are no definite records of them feeding on native plants and although migratory groups evidently arrive on St Helena from time to time, the species may not have maintained a permanent population until people had introduced a wider variety of plants. On Ascension there are several records but we now consider it as only a vagrant.

HA   *Hypolimnas misippus*, Diadem Butterfly. Plate 24. The male Diadem is a beautiful and easily recognised butterfly; it is iridescent velvety black with two white spots on each forewing and a much larger spot occupying most of the hindwing. The female, however, is so different that it is hard to believe that she belongs to the same species as the male. She is orange brown with black and white markings, and is a marvellous mimic of the African Monarch (Danaidae). They are extremely difficult to distinguish in the field, unless one can see the hindwings clearly: the female Diadem has only one blackish spot on the upperside of the hindwing, with a faint shadow of a second; on the underside she has two dark spots (the African Monarch has more). Close up, one can see that the veins on the hindwing all run to the edge of the wing, without joining to form a closed cell. Mimicry in colour has often evolved as a way of deterring potential predators. The mimic (which may be palatable) evolves colouration similar to a distasteful species (the model), thus gaining some protection from predators which have learnt to associate a particular colour with a bad taste. The Diadem is an African and Asian migrant species, and has been recorded more than once in mid Atlantic between the Equator and the Cape Verde islands.

Hypolimnas misippus male

H: The Diadem is found at both low and intermediate altitudes. It is not so common as the Monarch and numbers seem to vary from year to year. Melliss said that only a few existed on the low warm land about Jamestown, while Loveridge recorded it only in 1963 and 1974, always within about two miles of Jamestown. In 1995 we saw males and females on several occasions in March and April at Deadwood and Bottomwoods. We have watched males patrolling and repeatedly coming back to the same patch of clear ground.

A: The Diadem has been recorded only occasionally on Ascension. In 1963 John Packer found a number of the butterflies around an isolated pocket of Blue Weed and

Hypolimnas misippus female

385

Camels-foot Creeper near Spoon Crater, and we saw a male near the Devil's Riding School on 12th May 1995. The creeper is indigenous on Ascension, as is Purslane, on which the larvae of this species are known to feed; we suspect that the Diadem is a natural colonist of the island.

OECOPHORIDAE – oecophorids

Oecophorids are somewhat flattened moths. They feed mainly on flower heads and leaves, which they first drape with silk, but some make use of plant or animal debris, including clothes and stored food. Three species have been found on St Helena; one is associated with buildings and was evidently introduced from Europe but the other two are endemic.

*H   *Schiffermuelleria pictipennis* (ex *Oecophora pictipennis*). This species has a wingspan of about 10 mm and is generally brown, with the forewings iridescent bronze with two transverse gold bands; the hindwings are glossy grey and pointed. It was found by Wollaston only on the Peaks.

*H   *Schiffermuelleria splendidula* (ex *Oecophora splendidula*) Slightly smaller ·than *S. pictipennis* and with the forewings brown with two yellowish patches near the front border and a brilliant 'window' of large, iridescent reddish coppery scales near the outer edge. It was found by Wollaston only near the Peaks.

PLUTELLIDAE – diamondback moths

These are small moths with the forewings often brightly patterned; when the wings are folded there may be a line of diamond-shaped spots down the back; the antennae are held forwards at rest. The larvae feed in a light web on leaves, or mine leaves or stems. Two species may now be present on St Helena.

H   *Plutella xylostella* (ex *P. maculipennis*), Diamondback Moth. This pest species was collected on St Helena in the 19th century but was not seen by the entomologist C.R. Wallace in the 1950s. In the 1990s it caused serious damage to brassicas in cultivated areas on the island, but seems not to be widespread. *P. xylostella* is resistant to pesticides, so attempts to control the population are being made using biological control by the microbe *Bacillus thuringiensis* and two kinds of parasitic moths.

?H   *Ypsolopha dentella.* This is possibly the species mentioned by Mrs Wollaston as *Plutella xylostella* feeding on honeysuckle, and by Melliss as *P. cruciferarum*; however, the presence of *Y. dentella* on the island requires confirmation.

Plutella xylostella

PTEROPHORIDAE – plume moths

These are small, slender moths with long bodies and long legs. The forewings and hindwings are usually divided into two or three feathery plumes; at rest, these are folded close together and held out at right angles to the body. There are four species on St Helena (two endemic) and two on Ascension.

*H   *Agdistis sanctae-helenae.* Members of the genus *Agdistis* do not have the wings divided. This species has a wingspan of almost 20 mm and is pale grey brown, with the edges of the wings slightly paler. Mrs Wollaston found one specimen at Plantation and two among Gumwoods at Peak Dale. Timm Karisch obtained single specimens in Bevin's Gut and Rose Hill.

A   *Megalorhipida defectalis.* This species is widespread in the tropics. The larvae are known to feed on *Commicarpus* and since *Commicarpus helenae* may be indigenous on Ascension the moth might also be indigenous.

*H   *Platyptilia subnotatus* (ex *Platyptilus subnotatus*). This species has a wingspan of 13 mm; it is grey and the wings have two rows of three black dots near the tips. With its long legs, it looks at first sight like a large mosquito. Melliss found *P. subnotatus* to be rare, and caught only a single specimen, at the Hermitage. We assume that it is endemic.

HA   *Trichoptilus wahlbergi* (ex *Crombrugghia wahlbergi* and *Oxyptilus rutilalis*). This is a yellow moth which visits flowers and is somewhat sluggish. It is an Old World tropical species in a genus that is represented on many remote islands. It is recorded as feeding on *Ipomoea* and so may have colonised the islands naturally and utilized the indigenous *Ipomoea pes-caprae*. However, it could also have been introduced along with *Oxalis* on which it also feeds

PYRALIDAE (including Crambinae) – snout and grass moths

This a very large family of small and rather delicate moths; the slender abdomen helps to distinguish them from the stouter noctuids. The forewings are often brightly patterned. The abdomen carries tympanal (hearing) organs and there are scales on the proboscis. The larvae can often be recognised by their vigorous wriggling when disturbed. Many of the species are migratory pests. There are nearly 20 species on St Helena (at least eight endemic) and seven on Ascension Island; not all these are listed. In a recent worldwide study of the genus *Scoparia* and its relatives,[56] a new endemic genus *Helenoscoparia* was established for the five endemic species on St Helena previously included in *Scoparia*; evolutionary developments in this group have been discussed in Chapter 5. These moths evidently evolved from a single colonising group which reached the island long ago, and are mainly associated with the endemic cabbage trees and gumwoods.

HA   *Cactoblastis cactorum.* This species was introduced to St Helena from Trinidad in 1971 in the hope of controlling prickly pear (*Opuntia*).[57] Releases were in Sandy Bay and Half Tree Hollow; establishment occurred, and we found the orange and black larvae in tungy pads in Ruperts valley in 1995, but we do not know how much control the species exerts on the prickly pear. *C. cactorum* was introduced to Ascension in 1974, and was still present in 1995, when we found it near Spoon Crater.

H   *Diaphania indica* (ex *Phakellura indica* and *Margaronia indica*). An introduced species (sometimes placed in a separate family, Pyraustidae) which has been found on eggplant; on St Helena it is apparently not a pest of cucurbits.

**H   *Helenoscoparia helenensis* (ex *Scoparia helenensis*). Members of this group feed mainly on moss and lichen, in which they make silken galleries. They often have conspicuous

---

[56] M. Nuss (1999).

[57] F.J. Simmonds (1973).

raised, letter-like markings in the middle of the forewings (but so do some noctuids). *H. helenensis* has wingspan about 18 mm and the antennae are thickened in the middle. Its general colour is pale brownish, with a dark blotch at the base of the forewing. Mrs Wollaston found it less common than *H. lucidalis* and particularly associated with cabbage tree woodland on the Peaks; it now seems to be very rare.

**H   *Helenoscoparia lucidalis*. This is a conspicuous speckled black and white moth with wingspan about 21 mm. It occurs mainly on the central ridge somewhat below the summits; Mrs Wollaston found it to be especially associated with species of gumwoods.

**H   *Helenoscoparia nigritalis*. A dark-coloured moth with wingspan 10-17 mm.[58] This moth is mainly blackish, but the forewings have an ash-coloured band near the base which is made up of silvery metallic scales and is irregularly bordered with deep black. Mrs Wollaston commented that this was the most abundant moth in St Helena, especially at middle levels. It rests on the trunks of trees and flies off in clouds when disturbed, and also flies into open windows at night in great numbers.

**H   *Helenoscoparia scintillulalis*. In this species, which has wingspan about 17 mm, the forewings are rich dark brown, partially blackened but spangled with bluish white scales; the hindwings are bronzy brown, yellowish towards the base. This species is typical of the cabbage tree region and may feed on the lichen *Leptogium tremelloides* which grows on these trees.

**H   *Helenoscoparia transversalis*. This species has wingspan of 15-19 mm. The forewings are rich brownish black, usually with a yellowish transverse band, and the head and thorax are conspicuously yellowish white. *H. transversalis* is abundant on the Peaks, especially at the highest levels, swarming when disturbed out of the moss and other vegetation hanging on the rocks.

HA   *Hellula undalis*. An old world tropical migrant, which is a pest of crucifers. On St Helena it is common in grassy and weedy places, and the larvae have been found on cabbages and stocks. It could have reached the islands naturally by air, or be introduced.

HA   *Herpetogramma licarsisalis* (ex *H. phaeopteralis*). This is a widespread tropical species that occurs on many isolated islands. Its relatives are known to eat ferns, and we consider it as probably indigenous to Ascension; on St Helena, however, it has only recently been reported as a pest of pasture, so it seems more likely to be introduced.[59]

A   *Hypargyria metalliferella*. This is an Old World tropical species; it could be indigenous or introduced.

H   *Marasmia trapezalis* (ex *Botys creonalis*). Melliss described this as a small whitish moth with waved markings on the wings. Mrs Wollaston found it to be abundant at middle and high levels, especially on the Peaks, where she found it by beating ferns and other vegetation hanging on the rocks. She considered the species to be probably indigenous, but did not establish its food plant. If the moth found by Mrs Wollaston really is *M. trapezalis* it is likely to be introduced, as the species is a common pest of agricultural crops.

---

[58] Mrs Wollaston's '*Scoparia similis*' is now considered to be a small form of *nigritalis*.

[59] S.V. Fowler (1993).

H   *Uresiphita gilvata* (ex *Meyna polygonalis, M. rusticalis*).[60] This species has brilliant orange underwings and is one of the more conspicuous moths of the island. It lives mainly on grassy slopes at middle and high levels. The caterpillar grows to about 30 mm and is black, white and bright yellow, with long white erect hairs. The species also occurs in Europe and elsewhere, and is presumably introduced.

*H   *Nephopteryx privata*. This is a long, thin, dark-coloured moth with wingspan about 18 mm. Mrs Wollaston found it at Plantation and on an old Gumwood near Peak Dale; she thought that it might be a member of the native Gumwood fauna.

*H   *Pionea delineatalis* (ex *Udea, Scopula*). This pale brown moth is about 19 mm in wingspan. It is abundant at middle levels and reaches the highest part of the central ridge. It occurs in grassy places, but Mrs Wollaston found it to be most abundant in Vinetree Gut below Halley's Mount, where it was flying over She Cabbages.

?*H   *Pyralis helenensis*. This species has wingspan c.23 mm. The forewings are pale grey brown with two brownish transverse lines. The hindwings are pale grey, speckled with tiny black scales and with two undulating darker lines. Mrs Wollaston found only one specimen and this was in the kitchen garden at Plantation, so the status of the species is uncertain.

Spoladea recurvalis

HA   *Spoladea recurvalis* (ex *Hymenia fascialis*), Beet Weed Moth. This is a widespread tropical migrant pest; it feeds on many plants including Purslane. On St Helena it is abundant at low and middle levels and can often be seen near Diddly Dight. It is also common on Ascension, where we consider it as probably indigenous.

*H   *Zovax whiteheadii* (ex *Prionapteryx whiteheadii*). This species has a wingspan about 10 mm; the forewings are dull whitish with numerous ill-defined brownish longitudinal streaks. Mrs Wollaston found it only at West Lodge.

SPHINGIDAE – hawkmoths
These are mostly large fast-flying moths, with stout, hairy bodies and long front wings. Three species have been found on St Helena and the first of these was once found on Ascension.

H(A)   *Acherontia atropos*, Nantipo Moth,[61] Death's-head Hawkmoth. Plate 24. This is an enormous moth, with wingspan up to 13.5 cm (nearly five and a half inches). The forewings are mottled brown with one tiny white spot, the hindwings yellow with two dark bars. The thorax is brown with a yellow 'death's head' pattern and the abdomen is banded yellow and dark brown. The caterpillars are up to 12.5 cm (five inches) long and are variable in colour, but usually bright yellow or greenish with seven purplish sidestripes edged with yellow. They feed on a wide variety of plants, including potatoes, Wild Brinjal and Moonflower. The Death's Head is a strong flyer and well-known migrant, and probably reaches the islands naturally from time to time. However, such a heavy flying insect has enormous energy requirements and the Death's Head is closely associated with bees, the adults entering nests (and domestic hives) to feed on the honey. The species probably cannot maintain a population on the islands unless bees are also present. Bees were evidently brought to St Helena at least by the early 19th

[60] O. Karsholt & J. Razowski (1996).

[61] This local name was noted by C.R. Wallace (1960) as being a corruption of Fernando Po Moth, the local name given by Melliss.

century, and have been re-introduced several times; they are currently well-established. Melliss commented that the Death's Head: *"is said to have first appeared on the Island in the year 1835, and was afterwards very plentiful until 1854, when it disappeared almost simultaneously with the Honey Bee, to which it was a troublesome enemy."* In a footnote Melliss continued: *"The Honey Bee was re-introduced a few years ago, and it is a remarkable fact, that this moth has just (1874) reappeared in the Island, after an absence of twenty years."* There are a few records from early decades of the 20th century, but Arthur Loveridge, who arrived in 1957, did not see the Death's Head until 1972, although he found it fairly common subsequently, as it is today. On Ascension the Death's Head is only a vagrant: a specimen collected on Green Mountain in 1973 is now in the Georgetown Museum.

H   *Hippotion celerio*, Silver-striped Hawkmoth. This fast-flying moth is much smaller than the Deaths-head and its hindwings are mainly pink. It is a very widespread, migratory species, found throughout much of southern Europe, Africa and Asia. The caterpillars are greenish or a dirty yellowish flesh-colour and grow to about 6 cm long. On St Helena they were noted by Melliss as being very destructive to vines. The species has been abundant on the island in some periods.

H   *Sphinx convolvuli*, Convolvulus Hawkmoth. A single chrysalis of this species was found by Mrs Wollaston more than a century ago.

TINEIDAE – clothes moths and their relatives

Tineids are mainly small, silvery buff moths with wings fringed with hairs; the head is scaly or bristly and the antennae scaly; the proboscis is short or absent. Members of the genus *Opogona* are often patterned with black and yellow. Few tineids feed on green plants; the larvae are mostly scavengers, feeding on dead animal or plant material and often living in portable cases that they construct for themselves.

On St Helena the tineids represent one of the most striking examples of adaptive radiation, with a total of at least 28 endemic species in the genera *Opogona* and 'Tinea'. It seems that the island was colonised long ago by two types of tineids, both of which then multiplied by repeated splitting of the stocks to form new species, thus evolving the rich community discovered by Mrs Wollaston. The ecological relationships among the tineid species will probably never be understood, since their habitats have been largely destroyed and some of the species may now be extinct; nonetheless, studies of the food habits of the survivors would be of great interest.

Neither of the large St Helena tineid groups is represented on Ascension, but there are five tineid species, including two that are undescribed but probably endemic and one or two others that may be indigenous. Although their diversity is much lower than on the older island, they are already demonstrating their potential for future diversification. The implication of the data for the tineids of St Helena and Ascension (and elsewhere) is that these moths are among the most effective insect colonisers of remote islands. They may be particularly good at establishing themselves after arrival, because of their ability to reproduce on dead organic material; many other Lepidoptera, in contrast, require particular kinds of live plants. For reasons that are not understood, tineids also speciate readily even on small islands.

A   *Erechthias minuscula* (or *Decadarchis minuscula*). This species feeds on a wide range of dead plant material and is a pest of stored foodstuffs, particularly tubers. It probably originated in the Pacific and is now widespread in the tropics; it is presumably introduced.

?*A   *Erechthias* species. This is an undescribed but distinct species collected on Green Mountain in 1958 by Eric Duffey. It is a representative of another group of tineids capable of living on detritus which has produced evolutionary radiations on islands in the Pacific and Indian Oceans.

*A   *Eudarcia* sp. After some prickly pear bushes were sprayed with herbicide, specimens of this undescribed and apparently endemic species were found and sent to the Natural History Museum in London. All the specimens were female, so the species may reproduce parthenogenetically (without the intervention of males). Other members of the genus feed on lichens.

*H   *Opogona* species. Plate 24. This is the most diverse group of tineids on St Helena. The genus *Opogona* is in the subfamily Hieroxestinae, a group of tineids with a wedge-shaped, smooth-scaled head which is held in such a way that the moth appears to be preparing to 'head-butt' an opponent; they also fold the wings flat (or only very shallowly roofed) above the body, rather than steeply roofed as in most other tineids. In general, species of *Opogona* graze on fungi, blue-green algae and lichens rather than on green plants. The *Opogona* species on the island form the 'St Helena group', comprising 22 species, 20 of which have been found nowhere else.

   The other two species (*O. omoscopa* and *O. sacchari*) are very puzzling, since they belong taxonomically to the group but are somewhat distinct and have also been found elsewhere. They are very closely related to each other and are relatively large (c.20 and 30 mm wingspan). *O. omoscopa* is now cosmopolitan in the southern hemisphere and also occurs elsewhere; it has been described as new to science under four different names, in Australia, Amsterdam Island, Hawai'i and South Africa.[62] *O. sacchari* is rather less widespread, but was described independently from Mauritius, Rodriguez and St Helena. The larvae of both species sometimes eat living as well as dead material such as rotting wood and decaying plant material; usually live plant tissue is eaten only when close to decaying material. However, *O. sacchari* is now considered a serious pest of sugar cane in the Mascarene Island and West Indies and has recently been attacking a variety of ornamental plants in Florida; on St Helena it causes some damage to bananas. Gaden Robinson of the Natural History Museum in London, a specialist on the group, thinks that they may be endemic species that have 'escaped' from St Helena, travelling on ships to the Indian Ocean and elsewhere. Mrs Wollaston's comments on *O. sacchari* (her *Euplocamus sanctae helenae*) are to the effect that it is one of the commonest members of the group, occuring: *"in intermediate and lofty altitudes; in fact it is abundant throughout those regions which are more or less clothed with the arborescent Compositae."*

   Mrs Wollaston's comments on the 20 strictly endemic species of *Opogona* indicate that many of them are associated with the endemic trees of the island. She had no ecological information about *O. congenera* or *brunneomarmorata*; *O. suboeneella* and *niveopicta* were found around the kitchen garden at Plantation, and *O. binotatella* was a pest of potato crops there and elsewhere. Species that she linked with gumwoods were *O. anticella, apicalis, compositarum, divisa, fasciculata, helenae* and *vilis*; less

---

[62] A taxonomic revision has recently been published by G.R. Robinson & K.R. Tuck (1997). However, some confusion remains about the status of *Opogona omoscopa* on St Helena. Robinson & Tuck (p.385) refer to the presence of this species on the island and they include it in their 'St Helena group'. However, it was not recorded by Mrs Wollaston and Dr Gaden Robinson informs us that although he has a strong recollection of having seen *O. omoscopa* collected on St Helena, he cannot now locate a specimen.

definitely also *flavotincta, helenaeoides, irrorata* and *scalaris*. *O. atlantica* she thought was linked to Scrubwood. *O. actaeon* and *O. recurva* (her *Elachista recurva*) were found only on the Peaks, but no association was made with particular trees or plants. Particularly interesting was her suggestion that *O. ursella* was associated with the cabbage trees (unspecified): *"in the wood of which (particularly, though by no means always, when in a rotten or decomposed condition) I have repeatedly found the larva."* It seems possible that *O. ursella* is the species attacking the few surviving She Cabbage trees in the late 1990s. This or another species of *Opogona* may also be implicated in an account in the St Helena Records for 1822 which states: *"There are a number of Oak Trees in Plantation House Grounds, some of them between twenty and thirty years old, in a dying state from the white worm which generates under the bark."*

A   *Phereoeca allutella.* This is a widespread tropical species. It has been collected on Green Mountain and we found larvae, probably of this species, in hard flat cases in several barren lava sites. *Phereoeca* larvae are the 'wall bagworms' common in many parts of the tropics, which feed on the dry remains of dead insects. We consider the species as indigenous on Ascension.

*H   'Tinea' species. While comparing a moth that we collected on She Cabbages in 1995 with others in the Natural History Museum, Gaden Robinson concluded that eight kinds of small tineids collected by Mrs Wollaston form a closely related endemic group separate from *Opogona*. Their relatives outside the island are unknown, so we leave them provisionally in '*Tinea*'. The species concerned are '*Tinea*' *aureomarmorata, bicolor, fasciolata, flavofimbriata, minutissima, piperata, pulverulenta* and *pulveripennis*.

A   *Tinea subalbidella.* This species is widely distributed in warm parts of the Old World including West Africa. It has a diet that includes feathers and dead insects and there is a flourishing population on Boatswainbird Islet. The species can be a pest of stored products and could have been introduced, but natural immigration also seems possible.

TORTRICIDAE (sometimes separated to give also Olethreutidae/Eucosmidae) – tortricids

The tortricids are small, brown or grey moths with almost rectangular front wings; they rest with the wings held roof-wise over the body. Most species roll up or tie leaves with silk and feed inside the shelter so formed; they often defoliate trees. They are generally not long distance dispersers, but one group has undergone a major radiation in the Pacific. Three species are known from St Helena and two of these also from Ascension; one of the latter may be indigenous.

HA   *Crocidosema plebejana* (ex *Steganoptycha obscura*). This species has a wingspan of about 15 mm, with the forewings mottled brown. On St Helena Mrs Wollaston found it only at Cleugh's Plain, and Timm Karisch found it only on Hoopers Ridge. *C. plebejana* now occurs throughout the tropics. It feeds on Malvaceae and other plants. It might have reached the islands naturally, but is also quite likely to have been introduced with plants.

HA   *Cryptophlebia leucotreta* (ex *Olethreutes leucotreta*), False Codling Moth. This Afrotropical species is a pest of citrus, and other crops; on St Helena it has been recorded on peaches, tunnelling through the flesh. Elsewhere, it has been recorded in ships' cargoes, and it has doubtless been accidentally introduced to both islands.

Siphonaptera

SIPHONAPTERA – fleas

Fleas are small wingless insects that feed as adults on bird and mammal blood. They have a flattened body, long legs and an elegant mechanical arrangement for jumping. Six species have been found on St Helena and one on Ascension.

PULICIDAE (including Dermatophilinae) – pulicids

This is a small family, but includes species important in the transmission of disease, including bubonic plague. Five species have been found on St Helena, all of them presumably introduced; they include the human flea, *Pulex irritans* (which was very abundant in Jamestown as recently as 1967) as well as species infesting dogs, cats, rodents and poultry. On Ascension we are only aware of a single record (see below); it seems likely, however, that other species of flea are present on introduced mammals.

A   *Xenopsylla* close to *gratiosa*. This species was recorded from Ascension by Duffey, without details. It has been recorded from petrels elsewhere and is likely to be an indigenous parasite of one or more of the seabirds.

CERATOPHYLLIDAE – ceratophyllids

This is a large family, represented on St Helena by a cosmopolitan species which is found on the House Mouse.

DIPTERA – flies

The Diptera constitute one of the largest orders of insects. The single pair of wings distinguishes flies from other groups; the second pair are reduced to small knobs called haltere. Similar insects such as sawflies, stoneflies, caddisflies and the smaller Hymenoptera all have four wings. Flies are not well known migrants like swarming locusts and conspicuous butterflies, but many of them are capable of dispersing long distances in the air and have had success in colonising isolated islands worldwide. The Diptera recorded from St Helena and Ascension include a number of widespread genera that may well have reached the islands by air, while a few may have arrived by rafting. Nonetheless, the number of endemic species is relatively low. Whereas the Hawaiian archipelago has more than 1100 endemic species of flies (almost as many as they have of beetles), St Helena has only 16 endemic species in a total fly fauna of some 116 species in 29 families. On Ascension only 28 species of flies are known; none of these are endemic but several may be indigenous.

AGROMYZIDAE – leafminer flies

Agromyzids are very small flies whose larvae mine the leaves and stems of plants. A single species has been found on St Helena; it is widespread elsewhere and is capable of feeding on the leaves of may different kinds of plants. One species – a pest of brassicas – has recently been found on Ascension.

ANISOPODIDAE – wood gnats

This is a small family of flies whose larvae develop in fermenting organic materials such as manure heaps. The only species recorded from St Helena is a common European one with patterned wings.

ASTEIIDAE – asteiids

This is a family of very small flies about which very little is known. A single endemic species is known from St Helena, in a recently described genus which also has species in Africa.

*H   *Anarista vittata*. This tiny fly has reduced veins in the wings and is dull bluish-grey with five brown stripes on the thorax and some yellow on the base of the abdomen and the legs. It has been found in Fishers Valley and Ruperts.

CALLIPHORIDAE (including Sarcophaginae) – blow flies

Most species of blow fly are slightly larger than a house fly and are metallic green or blue. They are scavengers, living on carrion, dung and similar materials, and the larvae do a good service in cleaning up dead animals. There seem to be seven species on St Helena, all of them probably introduced. On Ascension four species are present, but one of them cannot yet be identified because a male has not been found.

CANACEIDAE – beach flies

This is a poorly known family of small flies that live on the seashore. Groups of species have evolved in both Hawai'i and the Galápagos, indicating that these flies disperse effectively, probably by rafting. A representative of the family was recorded on Ascension a century ago but has never been identified; none have been found on St Helena.

CHAMAEMYIIDAE – aphid flies

These small, pale grey flies are predators and parasites of homopteran bugs. A single (unidentified) species has been found on St Helena.

CHLOROPIDAE – chloropids

The chloropids are small and rather bare flies, some of them patterned with yellow and black. They are usually found in grassy places and the larvae typically feed in grass stems. The Belgians found five species on St Helena and we found two of the same ones on Ascension; we suspect that both of the latter reached the islands naturally.

HA   *Cadrema pallida*. This is a mainly coastal species distinguished by its predominantly yellow colour and a long spur at the end of the second main segment (tibia) of the hind leg. The larvae feed on a wide variety of decaying animal matter, including barnacles on driftwood, and the species probably reached the islands in this way. The Belgians found it in Ruperts Valley on St Helena, while we found it in a cave on Ascension.

HA   *Siphunculina striolata*. This species is mainly black. It has been found on islands in the tropics around the world. The Belgians found it on Prosperous Bay Plain and at Great Stone Top. On Ascension we found it on the Ascension Spurge on South Gannet Hill.

394

H   *Elachiptera* species. Three species of this genus have been found on St Helena; one seems to have been introduced from South America while the other two are African. One of the latter has been found near Cape Town and in Namibia, but was first described from St Helena, where it is widespread at middle levels; the second has been found only at High Peak (a single female).

CHYROMYIDAE – chyromyids

This is a small family of little-known flies. Two species have been found on St Helena.

H   *Aphaniosoma approximatum*. This fly was found by Loveridge at Sandy Bay; it has been recorded from north Africa and the Canary Islands. Members of the genus are associated with plants in arid regions, including the seashore, so *A. approximatum* could be indigenous; it may be worthwhile to search for it on Babies' Toes.

H   *Gymnochiromyia flavella*. This species has been found only in Ruperts Valley. Some members of the genus are associated with birds' nests so it is possible that *G. flavella* is indigenous on St Helena.

CULICIDAE – mosquitoes

These are small delicate flies, with relatively long legs. The larval stages are aquatic and adult females have a long blood-sucking proboscis. Two widespread species have been recorded from St Helena, but the Belgians found only one, which is also present on Ascension.

(H)   *Aedes aegypti*. In 1875 Melliss stated that this "Yellow Fever Mosquito" had been found on the island. It seems not to have been recorded since.

HA   *Culex quinquefasciatus (= Culex pipiens quinquefasciatus)*. This is the only common mosquito on St Helena and can be a considerable nuisance; it breeds in water tanks in many places in the uplands. On Ascension mosquitoes are troublesome in Georgetown and at Two Boats, and the specimens that we collected belong to this species. It bites man, and is known to spread certain diseases in Africa.

DOLICHOPODIDAE – long-legged flies

Dolichopodids are small, bristly flies, with a short fleshy proboscis and usually with metallic green or blue-green colouration. They are predatory both as larvae and as adults and are usually found in damp places; some occur on the sea shore. Many species have more or less cosmopolitan distribution. This is much the most diverse family of flies on St Helena, with 21 species, and although none are endemic it seems possible that some reached the island naturally. The only curious occurrence is of a species previously known only from Formosa (Taiwan) and Hawai'i. No dolichopodids have yet been found on Ascension.

DROSOPHILIDAE – vinegar flies

These small flies are usually yellowish and many have red eyes; their larvae feed on fruit and decaying vegetation. They have reached many oceanic islands, and on Hawai'i they have diversified dramatically, with nearly 900 species. On St Helena, in contrast, there seem to be only three endemic species, plus seven that are probably introduced; only the endemic species are listed here. Three widespread species have been found on Ascension; one of these (*Drosophila buzzatii*) was originally a New World species associated with prickly pear (*Opuntia*) and was doubtless introduced with its hostplant; it has not been found on St Helena.

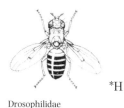

Drosophilidae

*H   *Scaptomyza horaeoptera*. Members of the genus *Scaptomyza* are generally associated with grassland; they are good colonisers and nine species are present on Tristan da Cunha; there are at least three endemic species on St Helena. *S. horaeoptera* is very distinct from the other two (see below) and has been placed in a new sub-genus, *Lauxanomyza*. It is recognizable by its glossy black, narrow abdomen and the wings patterned with strong dark brown markings; it is about 2.5 mm long. *S. horaeoptera* has been found high on the central ridge and also in a few places at middle levels.

*H   *Scaptomyza mimitantalia*. Males and females of this species are respectively 2.1 and 2.5 mm long. The wings are greyish and the posterior part of the abdomen is yellow in the centre. *S. mimitantalia* is known only from three specimens collected by the Belgians at High Peak and Cabbage Tree Road.

*H   *Scaptomyza santahelenica*. Males of this species are only 1.4 mm long, females 2.1 mm. The wings are pale and relatively long and narrow and the abdomen is reddish brown, darker towards the hind end. The males show considerable variation in the spines on the genitalia and the Belgians speculated that the variants might actually represent separate but very similar species. *S. santahelenica* was first collected by Arthur Loveridge at Bishops Bridge; later it was found in Rural Retreat Gut (on She Cabbage trees) and in several other places at high and middle levels.

EPHYDRIDAE – shore flies

These are very small dark-coloured flies. They are found in wet places, either marine or freshwater, and the larvae are aquatic. Ephydrids probably disperse readily by sea and we suspect that most of the species on both islands are indigenous. On St Helena there are two endemic species and four others; two of the latter are also known from Ascension, which also has a third species (not yet definitely identified).

HA   *Atissa pygmaea*. On St Helena this species was found by the Belgians in freshwater habitats at Sandy Bay and Fishers Valley. On Ascension we found it at the South Gannet Flow pools. This is a widespread species which may be indigenous on both islands.

HA   *Hecamede brasiliensis*. This species was found by the Belgians on the beach at Sandy Bay and on Ascension by us at the South Gannet Flow pools. It is a coastal species occurring in the tropics on both sides of the Atlantic and seems to be a specialist on carrion; we consider it as native to both islands.

H   *Parydra tuberculifera*. This species was found by the Belgians at Blarney Bridge in Sandy Bay. It also occurs in Africa.

A   *Placopsidella ?cynocephala*. A single female that we found on spurge at Hummock Point probably belongs to this species; it occurs on several other Atlantic islands and is probably indigenous.

H   *Scatella septemfenestrata*. This fly is recognizable by the wing pattern of seven pale patches on a darkened wing membrane. It is abundant in wet places in Fishers Valley and Sandy Bay.

*H   *Scatella* species. Two endemic species in this widespread genus were found by the Belgians, but they were not formally described.

GASTEROPHILIDAE – horse bot flies

The larvae of these flies are internal parasites of horses, donkeys and mules. A single species has been recorded from St Helena.

HIPPOBOSCIDAE – louse flies

Hippoboscidae
12 mm

These are flat leathery flies – many of them wingless – which are external parasites of birds and mammals. Two introduced species have been recorded from St Helena, but only one, the Sheep Ked *Melophagus ovinus*, has been noted recently. One species that lives on seabirds has been found on Ascension and is doubtless native; it has not yet been recorded from St Helena.

A   *Olfersia aenescens.* This is a widespread species recorded from many kinds of seabirds; it is common on Boatswainbird Island.

LONCHAEIDAE – spear-winged flies

These are small flies with bright metallic coloration. The larvae feed in fruit and vegetables. Two introduced species have been found on St Helena.

H   *Lamprolonchaea aurea.* This fly is about 3 mm long and is brilliant golden-green or blue.

H   *Lonchaea avida.* This species is larger than *L. aurea* and has sombre coloration. It is common on fruit such as tomatoes and bananas.

MILICHIIDAE – milichiids

This is a small family of small black or silvery flies whose larvae live in decaying plant or animal material. Two species have been found on St Helena and three from Ascension; one of the latter may be native.

A   *Leptometopa latipes.* We found this species on Boatswainbird Island. It is widespread in Africa, including the Cape Verde Islands, and has been reared from bird nests; we suspect that it reached Ascension with seabirds, although it could have arrived recently with ships collecting guano.

MUSCIDAE (including Anthomyiinae & Scatophaginae) – house flies and stable flies

In its pristine state the only muscid on St Helena may have been the endemic species of *Limnophora*. Now the island has 14 species (excluding one that was apparently misidentified); the additional species have been introduced by humans, mainly from Europe. On Ascension there are two muscids; one of which may possibly be native. We mention only a few of the species.

H   *Hylemya cilicrura.* The larvae of this species, which is similar in appearance to a House Fly, feed on germinating peas, beans and other vegetables.

*H *Limnophora helenae*. This small black fly (3.5-6 mm long) is placed in a very widely distributed genus, but is a very unusual member of it and cannot be clearly related to any African, European or South American species: it is evidently an ancient colonist of St Helena, derived from a primitive African stock. *L. helenae* has been found mainly in the east of the island, from Prosperous Bay Plain to Great Stone Top, Sheep Knoll and Peak Gut (on Gumwood), but also on the Peaks and at inland sites at middle levels.

HA *Musca domestica*. The House Fly is common on both islands.

H *Stomoxys calcitrans*. The Biting Stable Fly, which is a little larger than the House Fly, is common on the island. It is a worldwide veterinary pest that torments cattle and donkeys, seriously reducing milk yields.

A *Synthesiomyia nudiseta*. This is a common filth fly that occurs throughout the tropics. It prefers carrion for larval food, but we found it on barren lava areas, suggesting that it is not totally dependent on refuse produced by humans; it may have reached the island naturally.

MYCETOPHILIDAE – fungus gnats

These are slender, mosquito-like insects. Some specimens were found on St Helena by the Belgians but no specialist was available to study them.

PHORIDAE – humpbacked flies

These are small humped-back flies with the veins on the inner part of the leading edge of the wings very strongly developed; the innermost main segment (femur) of the hind legs is characteristically enlarged and flattened. Three widely distributed species have been found on St Helena and two different ones on Ascension; one of the latter may have reached the island naturally.

A *Megaselia curtineura*. This species is abundant on Ascension and shows an unusual amount of variation among individuals.[63] Elsewhere, it is now widely distributed in warm areas but may have originated in tropical Africa. Members of the genus are often found at high altitudes in the air and we suspect that *M. curtineura* colonised Ascension naturally.

PSYCHODIDAE – owl midges

These are tiny weakly-flying insects with the wings broad (often pointed) and covered densely with hair and scales. Three species have been found on St Helena; all are widespread elsewhere and have probably been introduced to the island.

SCATOPSIDAE – minute black scavenger flies

The only species recorded from St Helena is a cosmopolitan one which is doubtless introduced.

---

[63] R.H.L. Disney (1991).

SCENOPINIDAE (or Omphralidae) – window flies

This is a small group of flies typical of dry habitats. The single species that occurs on St Helena has become widespread by association with humans; it was probably introduced from Europe.

SCIARIDAE – dark-winged fungus gnats

Some specimens were collected on St Helena by the Belgians but have not yet been identified. We collected one female on Ascension, but in this difficult group females cannot be identified.

SIMULIIDAE – blackflies

Simuliidae
3 mm

These are small, dark-coloured biting flies with a humpbacked appearance, short legs, and broad wings with strong veins on the leading edge. The larvae live in streams, and members of the family have established themselves on many oceanic islands where freshwater habitats are available. The discovery of the St Helena blackflies was one of the outstanding achievements of Arthur Loveridge during his retirement on the island. Three species (all endemic) are now known to be present, and although they are very distinct (and are placed in two different subgenera) we suspect that they may have evolved on St Helena from a single colonising stock originating in Africa. They are all adapted to clinging on to feathers and their ancestors were probably carried to the island by birds; they doubtless sucked the blood of the extinct native landbirds and perhaps also of the seabirds. We have seen no evidence as to whether they now feed on humans or on introduced mammals or birds.

*H   *Simulium atlanticum*. This ancient endemic species is so distinctive that it has been placed in a new subgenus, *Dexomyia*. It is exceptionally large for a simuliid: the wing length is 4.5 mm and the mature larva is about 10 mm long. The larvae may be predators, which is not normal in this family. Adults have been found in Sandy Bay, Fishers Valley and many high parts of the island, but larvae only in the stream leading into Sandy Bay. *S. atlanticum* is active at night and has been caught at lights.

*H   *Simulium loveridgei*. This is a very small species, with wings only about 2 mm in length. It is the commonest of the simuliids and one of the most abundant insects on the island. It breeds in most of the streams from high on the island down to the sea, and the adults can be found throughout the year. The adults are known on the island as 'mint flies' because they are often found near the common streamside mint.

*H   *Simulium politum*. This is a glossy insect with body and legs entirely black or brownish-black; it is intermediate in size between the other two endemic species. *S. politum* is in the same subgenus (*Eusimulium*) as *S. loveridgei* and is related to species in southern Africa. It was found by the Belgians at high and middle levels.

SPHAEROCERIDAE – small dung flies

These are small black or brown flies. The larvae feed on decaying organic matter, including excrement. There are 11 species of Sphaeroceridae on St Helena, making this the third most diverse fly family on the island. One species is endemic and the sole member of an endemic genus; the others are all widespread elsewhere and likely to be introduced.

**H   *Aubertinia sanctaehelenae*. This ancient colonist of St Helena is so distinctive that a new genus has been established for it. Its most striking feature is the entire absence of wings and also of the halteres (or 'balancers') which are characteristic of the order Diptera and are vestiges of the second pair of wings. The fly is just over 2 mm long and is yellow and brown, with a shining black abdomen. The first four specimens were collected by T.V. Wollaston in the 19th century. The Belgians collected 42 specimens, one on Cabbage Tree Road but all the others at High Peak. This important species is evidently dependent on the remnants of the humid native woodland, and represents a conservation priority for the island.

SYRPHIDAE – hover flies

These brightly coloured flies, some of them with black and yellow bands on the abdomen, are often mistaken for bees or wasps. However, they do not sting and their flight is quite distinct, alternating between hovering and darting at great speed to a new position. Adults frequently visit flowers, but the larvae of some species are predatory, for instance on aphids. Five species are known on St Helena; four are widespread elsewhere but the fifth is an ancient endemic, so distinct that it is treated as an endemic genus. Four species have been recorded from Ascension, although the identity of one is not clear.

A   *Eristalomya* (or *Eristalis*) *aeneus*. This coastal species was recorded on Ascension a century ago and may be indigenous.

HA   *Eristalomya* (or *Eristalis*) *tenax*. This species, commonly known as the 'drone-fly', is a dark brown, chunky, hairy fly about 14 mm long. The larva has a long telescopic breathing tube and is known as the rat-tailed maggot. *E. tenax* is widespread on St Helena and has also been recorded from Ascension. It is a cosmopolitan and migratory species.

HA   *Eumerus obliquus*. This is an African species with an endemic subspecies (*E. obliquus lugens*) on St Helena, implying natural colonisation; the species may also be indigenous on Ascension.

H?A   *Ischiodon aegyptius*. This species has been found in several middle-level places on St Helena, where it can be distinguished from *Loveridgeana* by the black markings on the legs. It was probably this or a closely related species which was recorded on Ascension a century ago (under the name *Xanthogramma*) as being associated with aphids on the endemic spurge plants.

**H   *Loveridgeana beattiei*. This species, named in honour of Arthur Loveridge and constituting an endemic genus, has a yellowish white face, yellow legs, and yellow abdomen with a strong black mark in the mid line near the base. This hoverfly has been recorded from many vegetated parts of the island and is of special ecological and evolutionary significance, since it was probably important in pollinating some of the endemic plants.

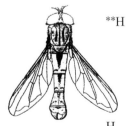

Loveridgeana beattiei
10 mm   MRAC

H   *Syritta stigmata*. This may be the most abundant hoverfly on St Helena, occurring at middle to high levels. It can be distinguished from *Loveridgeana* by the hind legs having the innermost main segment (femur) dark reddish brown to black.

TACHINIDAE – tachinids

These are bristly, medium to large flies. Their larvae are internal parasites of other insects, which they eventually kill; as a result, some tachinids are useful in keeping pest species in check. Two species are recorded from St Helena; one is an African species but the other is so distinctive that it is considered as an endemic genus.

**H   *Atlantomyia nitida*. This species is related to the widespread genus *Ceracia*; its ancestors doubtless came from Africa millions of years ago. Members of the tribe Acemyini (to which these flies belong) are always parasites of Orthoptera, and the Belgians suggested that the host of *A. nitida* may prove to be the endemic grasshopper *Primnia sanctaehelenae* (family Acrididae). *A. nitida* has been found only on Prosperous Bay Plain. It is a strongly built, black, hairy fly 6-9 mm long; the abdomen has a dusty silver band across the hindmost segment but is otherwise polished and shining black (this is the origin of the specific name, *nitida*).

H   *Palexorista quadrizonula*. This species is 6-9 mm long, dull blackish but with dusty yellowish white areas on the abdomen. It was found by the Belgians at Teutonic Hall and in Ruperts Valley. *P. quadrizonula* is widespread in Africa, where it parasitizes the caterpillars of many different kinds of moths. It may be a relatively recent natural colonist of St Helena, although accidental introduction is possible.

TEPHRITIDAE – fruit flies

These are small flies with spotted or banded wings. Their larvae feed on plants and many species are serious pests. Two introduced species are established on St Helena and at least one other has been found on imported fruit.

H   *Ceratitis capitata*, Mediterranean Fruitfly. This fly, which is now widespread in warm parts of the world, was recorded as a pest on the island as long ago as 1904, when attempts were made to exterminate it. The species is still one of the most important agricultural pests on the island. The larvae have been recorded on guava, loquat, orange, fig, apricot, peach, mango, rose-apple, pear, coffee, opuntia and kei-apple.

H   *Dioxyna sororcula*. This is smaller and drabber in colour than the previous species, and seems to be much less common.

TETHINIDAE – tethinids

This is a small group of uncommon flies, most of them typical of the sea shore.

H   *Tethina alboguttata*. A small greyish fly found by the Belgians in Fishers Valley. It was originally described from Spain. Natural immigration seems a possibility for this species.

TIPULIDAE – crane flies

These flies have extremely long legs and look somewhat like overgrown mosquitoes. They are usually found in damp places. On oceanic islands the subfamily Limoniinae tends to be better represented than the larger, heavy-bodied Tipulinae which are less readily transported by the wind. All four species on St Helena are in the Limoniinae, and three of these are endemic, in the genus *Limonia* and subgenus *Dicranomyia*. Among the Diptera only the families Drosophilidae and Simuliidae equal the Tipulidae in the number of endemic species on St Helena.

H   *Erioptera pilipes*. This species, which has a world distribution wider than any other member of the family, has been found in a few places in the north of St Helena, including Bryans Rock; it is possibly indigenous on the island. *E. pilipes* can be distinguished from the *Limonia* species by having 16 segments in the antennae, with the outermost three segments smaller (in *Limonia* species the antennae have 14 segments).

*H   *Limonia basilewskyana*. This and the next species have the wings dusky but unpatterned; they do not seem to have close relatives in Africa. *L. basilewskyana* is known only from three specimens found by the Belgians at Teutonic Hall. It is slightly larger than *L. loveridgeana* (length 8.5-11 mm) and differs in microscopic details.

*H   *Limonia loveridgeana*. This species is 6-7.5 mm long. It was first found at Varneys by Loveridge, but the Belgians found it in several places in the north and centre of the island at medium to high levels.

*H   *Limonia sanctaehelenae*. This species, also discovered by Loveridge, has the wings pale brown, conspicuously patterned with small dark brown dashes near the veins, and scattered small cream-coloured areas. Its closest relatives seem to be in the tropics of the Old World. It has been found only at Varneys, in Fishers Valley and at Teutonic Hall.

402

Chapter 16

Plants

This list includes information on plants of both St Helena and Ascension. On both islands, all plants are assumed to be introduced unless otherwise specified. The list is not comprehensive for either island, but for the flowering plants and ferns it includes all endemic species and any others that are considered as likely to be indigenous on either island. For St Helena and to a lesser extent Ascension, we also include most of the other plants that can be seen growing wild, giving special emphasis to those that are conspicuous or of special ecological interest. We also include a few introduced trees and smaller plants that are widely planted on the island and are likely to attract attention. However, grasses and other plants that are hard to distinguish are treated less thoroughly, and nearly all garden plants and many agricultural weeds are omitted. The mosses are mentioned only briefly.

We have tried to find as many as possible of the plants in the field and to describe them in simple terms; many of the localities mentioned are based on our own records. Apart from this personal knowledge, information for St Helena is derived mainly from the following sources: the unpublished thesis by Q.C.B. Cronk (1984) *The historical and evolutionary development of the plant life of St. Helena*, and his recent book *The endemic flora of St Helena*; R.O. Williams' (1989) unpublished compilation *Plants on St Helena*; the booklet on the endemic flora produced by the St Helena Government (M.D. Holland 1986) and the synopsis of St Helena flora posted on the internet in 1997. Our treatment of the ferns owes much to Ronald Viane and Rebecca Cairns-Wicks

For Ascension the information is more sketchy, since we have spent less time searching for the wild plants. The native plants were few in number and several are now extinct, while introduction of species from all over the world has given rise to an almost entirely artificial flora. Our main debt is to John Packer's (1983) meticulous list of the plants, updated in *Contributions towards a Flora of Ascension Island* by John and Lorna Packer (1998). We have also used historical records, Cronk's (1980, 2000) accounts of the endemic species, and Eric Duffey's (1964) information on the plants present in 1958. We have also received helpful comments from Alan Gray, who went to Ascension in 1998 on a student expedition from Edinburgh University.

The ferns are treated separately from the flowering plants. For the latter, scientific (Latin) family names follow V.H. Heywood (1985) *Flowering plants of the world*. In both lists, families are arranged alphabetically, as are the genera and species within them (using the scientific names). In the index plants are listed by both scientific and St Helenian/English names. Scientific names for St Helena plants are those used by Cronk (1984, 2000), updated in a few cases; for Ascension the names are mainly from Cronk (1980) and Packer & Packer (1998). The few extra scientific names given in parenthesis are obsolete names that have been commonly used in the past.

For plants on St Helena the first of the non-scientific names given is the one we believe to be in general use on the island; most of these names were listed by Cronk (1984) after talking with George Benjamin and other people on the island. In a few cases we have also given alternative names, or have provided names for species that do not have well established local ones. For some of the endemic plants on St Helena, the local names can cause confusion with species from other parts of the world (e.g. Rosemary and Olive); in such cases an expanded local name (e.g. St Helena Olive) is also given. English names for plants present only on Ascension are from Packer & Packer (1998) or from standard books.

CONIFERS AND FLOWERING PLANTS

AGAVACEAE – the agave and dragon tree family

Agave americana Plate 13   American Aloe, Century Plant
The agaves (now usually separated from the true aloes which are placed in the family Liliaceae) have a basal rosette of fleshy, long and pointed leaves. When mature the plant produces a tall pole bearing dramatic clusters of yellow flowers in a spiral arrangement, and sets seed before the plant dies. The American Aloe grows to 8 m and has enormous greyish green leaves that sometimes droop backwards; they have prickles on the edges and at the tip. The fermented sap of this species forms the Mexican drink pulque, and can be distilled to produce the spirit mescal.
    H: This species (in a variegated form) is said to occur only inside High Knoll fort.
    A: A hedge of this species was planted around the lower slopes of Green Mountain and parts of it still survive near Dampier's.

H   *Agave lurida* (ex *A. angustifolia*) Plate 17   Aloe, Fence Aloe
The Fence Aloe was introduced to St Helena in the 18th century and was used extensively for fencing, since the leaves have both a strong, black spine at the tip and also formidable prickles along the edges, making a row of the plants impenetrable to livestock. The leaves are grey green and extremely rigid and the flowering pole is around 3-4 m high. We once watched a rat feeding for half an hour on the flowers on a 3 m pole, apparently eating stamens and sucking nectar. The Fence Aloe is still common in dry places, especially around 400 m.

HA   *Agave sisalana*   Sisal
R.O. Williams mentioned this species as occurring very locally on St Helena, in Jamestown and Mulberry Gut. It was introduced to Ascension in 1847 and occurs locally on the lower slopes of the mountain.

HA   *Furcraea gigantea*   English Aloe, Green Aloe, Mauritius Hemp
This species is recognizable by its lax and yellowish green leaves up to 1.5 metres long, lacking edge-prickles and having only a sharp pointed tip rather than a distinct spine. The flowering pole, which grows around April, may reach 9 m in height, and the flowers are creamy white. The poles also bear bulbils which fall to the ground and take root.
    H: The English Aloe (which actually comes from tropical America) is locally common, for instance near Old Luffkins at about 500 m, and at Cleugh's Plain. Early in the 20th century the latter area was the site of a small commercial venture for the extraction of the fibre 'Mauritius Hemp' from the leaves; previously these were hand-milled and the fibres exported or woven locally to make bags and table mats. The poles have been used for rafters.
    A: The species may have been introduced before 1834; its current status is not clear.

404

H   *Phormium tenax* Plates 3 and 7   Flax, New Zealand Flax
New Zealand Flax grows by producing suckers from an underground horizontal stem
with fleshy, reddish-yellow roots; a full grown plant may have up to 50 suckers. Each
one of these is in the form of a fan with a set of smooth, parallel-sided leaves which
can be nearly three metres in length and about 7 cm wide with a central division. The
strong flowering stalks are up to 5 cm thick and rise only a metre or so above the
leaves. When dead, they form favourite display posts for the Madagascar Fody; they are
produced when the plant is five years old or more. The numerous flowers are red and
yellow, up to 5 cm long and with six stamens and a triangular style.

For many years this plant was the base of a major industry for the exportation of
fibre. When growing was at its peak flax was estimated to cover 1 300 hectares (3,200
acres) in the higher parts of the island; some of this land has now been cleared but
large areas remain. The effects of the flax on the indigenous vegetation have been
discussed in Chapter 7.

AIZOACEAE – the mesembryanthemum family

H   *Aptenia cordifolia*
A sprawling succulent plant with bright pink star-shaped flowers. Occurs on dry rocky
banks and pastures around 300-400 m in the south of the island.

H   *Carpobrotus edulis* Plate 3, bottom   Creeper, Hottentot Fig
A mat-forming, woody, creeping plant closely related to *Mesembryanthemum*. Growth
is by the successive formation of pairs of leaves, formed at right angles to the previous
pair. The leaves are thick and fleshy, triangular in section and varying in colour from
green to red; they taste salty. The flowers are spectacular and daisy-like, about 6 cm
across and usually creamy white but sometimes tinged with pink. The fruit is
goblet-shaped and can be eaten. This highly competitive species was introduced from
South Africa in the 19th century and now occupies large areas in the Crown Wastes,
especially in the north, up to about 400 metres. The plant spreads over arid, dusty
ground, often covering areas where all other plants have been eliminated by grazing
pressure. At times the dead growth has been burnt as fuel.

Babies'Toes

*H *Hydrodea cryptantha* (ex *Mesembryanthemum cryptanthum*) Plate 25   Babies' Toes
The only close relative of this species occurs in South Africa. Babies' Toes is a prostrate
pea green succulent that becomes yellow in drought and finally dries up in
midsummer; young plants spring up after the winter rains. The stems are soft, round,
branched and finger-like and the plant spreads to form a pad up to a third of a metre
across. The flowers, found mainly in late winter, are small and white, and reminiscent
of tiny sea anemones.

Babies' Toes occurs locally in arid areas, often where there are hardly any other plants.
It is commonest in the east, from Turks Cap to Sandy Bay, especially below 100 m and
often close to the sea. However, it is found above 300 m near Bradleys and has been noted
on Prosperous Bay Plain. It was presumably eaten by goats in the past, and its
distribution may now be limited by competition with its relative, the introduced Creeper.

*H *Hypertelis acida* (ex *Pharnaceum acidum*) Plate 25   Salad Plant
The Salad Plant, which was called Longwood Samphire by Burchell, is endemic to St
Helena, with its closest relatives in South Africa. It is a low growing succulent plant up
to a metre across, with characteristic blue green foliage, making the plants identifiable

Salad Plant

on cliffs at a distance. The leaves are fleshy, narrow and about 5 cm long; though typically sharply pointed, some of them are blunt ended or even have a notch at the tip. The leaves have an agreeable acid salty taste, and were formerly used as a salad. The flowers are pure white with yellow centres, and are borne in groups on slender stalks up to 10 cm long, so that they stick up above the level of the foliage.

The Salad Plant is now very local, occurring in small colonies in arid places near the sea and on cliff ledges up to a height of 500 m. Burchell found it *"about Sandy Bay"* and also *"in Longwood towards the sea"*. We doubt if it survives in the latter area, but it still grows between Sandy Bay and the Asses Ears and on Man and Horse Cliffs, and has also been found further inland at Boxwood Hill, Great Stone Top and Bencoolen. It was evidently an abundant plant on the pristine island, but became nearly extinct as a result of herbivore grazing; even now, we suspect that it can only survive in places inaccessible to rabbits.

H   *Mesembryanthemum crystallinum*   Ice Plant
A prostrate, spreading plant with soft, fleshy leaves covered with small, sticky droplets. The leaves are opposite, broad and shaped like a pointed spade, with wavy, more or less red edges; when the plant is stressed by drought, the leaves go entirely red. The flowers are small, white and daisy-like. When the plant dries up in summer it leaves behind the prostrate stems bearing dry five-sided seed capsules. The Ice Plant is locally common in dry places around the coast, and occurs inland in some places, for instance on Prosperous Bay Plain and near the summit of Great Stone Top.

HA   *Tetragonia tetragonioides* Plate 25   New Zealand Spinach
A herbaceous, prostrate plant, usually forming an untidy clump. As in the Ice Plant, the stems and leaves are covered with minute 'epidermal bladder cells' that give the appearance of tiny drops of water. The leaves are alternate, fleshy, soft, stalked, broadest at the base and tapering to a point. The flowers are yellowish and borne in the axils of the leaves, and the fruit are angled and sharp-pointed. New Zealand Spinach is widespread in the tropics and subtropics, and typically occurs close to the sea; it is doubtless indigenous on Ascension and probably also on St Helena, although it has been cultivated on the latter island.

H: Found in dry places, especially in watercourses, where it springs up in the winter rains; it also occurs occasionally as a weed of cultivation.

A: Found near Porpoise Point by John Packer in the 1960s.

AMARANTHACEAE – the love-lies-bleeding family

H   *Alternanthera repens*   Double Gee
A creeping herb with stiff, hairy stems and rounded, opposite leaves. The three-pronged seeds are borne in dense whitish tufts; their fine prickles are dangerous for bare feet and a menace in clothes. Double Gee grows in dry places up to 400 m; it often occurs on roadsides and paths where other plants cannot grow, and can be found in the public gardens in Jamestown; it is also a serious weed, especially at Longwood.

HA   *Amaranthus species*
Several species in this genus occur as weeds on both islands.

AMARYLLIDACEAE – the daffodil family

A   *Hippeastrum reginae*   Ascension Lily
This bulb produces strap-like leaves and a dramatic trumpet-shaped six-parted red
flower. It was well established in the 1950s and is still flourishing in Breakneck Valley.

ANACARDIACEAE – the cashew family

H   *Harpephyllum caffrum*   Sour Date, China Date
This tree can grow to more than 15 m. It has shiny, dark green leaves and bears olive-
sized, red and acid but tasty fruits which are eaten and also used in making a drink.
The China Date was introduced from southern Africa in the 19th century and is now
common at middle altitudes, especially near houses.

H?A   *Schinus molle*   Wild Pepper Tree
This tree, which has New World origins, grows up to 8 m high and has graceful,
pendulous branchlets. The leaves are compound, about 20 cm long, with many
alternate (just), narrow and pointed leaflets. The leaves are highly resinous, with a
characteristic aroma, and a severed leaf will spurt across a water surface as the oil
breaks the surface tension. The flowers are yellowish white in conical, branched
clusters, and give rise to rose-coloured berries the size of peppercorns. The Wild Pepper
Tree grows in dry areas below about 550 m; it is found near the sea at Ladder Hill and
in Jamestown and Ruperts. The Wild Pepper Tree hybridises with the Wild Mango; at
least one of these species is present on Ascension.

H?A   *Schinus terebinthifolia* (ex *S. mellissii*) Plate 25   Wild Mango
A small but stout tree with pale, fissured bark; the compound leaves have seven serrate
leaflets that give off a turpentine-mango smell when crushed. Flowering is mainly in
late summer; the flowers are small and whitish, borne in bunches near the tips of the
branches, and are an important source of nectar for bees. The berries are green at first
but red when ripe. On St Helena this tree has spread during the last hundred years and
is widespread in dry areas, mainly between 300 and 500 m; it forms dense thickets in
gullies and valley bottoms, for instance in Sharks Valley, Sandy Bay Valley and near
the Heart Shape Waterfall, often making access difficult. The species may also be
present on Ascension.

APOCYNACEAE – the periwinkle and oleander family

Apart from the species listed, the pink-flowered Oleander *Nerium oleander* has been
planted in a few places on both islands. Each of the islands also has a low-growing
periwinkle in the genus *Vinca*, although the species may be different in each case.

HA   *Catharanthus roseus* (ex *Vinca rosea*) Plate 25   Venus Rose, Madagascar Periwinkle
A shrub up to 1 m high, with upright stems, glossy, dark green, rounded leaves and
shocking pink to purple salver-shaped flowers with five petals united below into a tube.
As well as the normal pink form there is a genetic variant with white flowers; in this,
the flower stalks are green, while in the pink form the stalks are red.
   H: The pink form is local on hillsides and in guts in dry parts in the south, especially
near Sandy Bay beach. The white form was also recorded by Melliss but has not been
noted recently.

407

A: Introduced early in the 19th century and seems to have spread rapidly. Efforts were made to eradicate it in 1910. Although these were apparently successful, the plant reappeared and is common in dry areas at medium altitude, for instance near Travellers, where the white form is also present.

ARACEAE – the arum family

H   *Colocasia esculenta* Plate 25   Yam, Taro
This is the Yam of St Helena.[1] It is a stemless perennial herb up to one metre high, with long upright leaf stalks attached near the centres of enormous heart-shaped leaves; flowering is rare and propagation is by means of suckers. The species was introduced for food in the 17th century from tropical Asia and its edible tuber, the coco yam, formed the staple starch for the island in the early years of the colony. There were several types, distinguished by the islanders as red yam, white yam, black yam, etc, of which the white variety was the one mainly cultivated. The roots (which are technically corms) contain crystals of calcium oxalate which have to be destroyed by baking or boiling, even before being fed to pigs; on St Helena it was normal to steam the roots for twelve hours. The use of yams seems to have declined gradually, at first probably as a consequence of increased cultivation of potatoes, but then in parallel with rising imports of rice in the early part of the 19th century; yams are now little used, but various types grow wild in wet guts over a wide range of altitudes.

HA   *Monstera deliciosa*   Fruit Salad Vine, Mexican Breadfruit
A non-woody climber with thick stems and aerial roots, which can form a dense clump several metres across. The leaves are dark green, glossy and huge, with indentations and holes. The enormous arum-like flower is white and about 30 cm long; the green fruit has many segments and is edible though it can irritate the mouth; it is said to taste like a mixture of pineapple and banana.
   H: Widely scattered, mainly high up.
   A: A few plants near the tunnel through the mountain and elsewhere about this level.

H   *Zantedeschia aethiopica*   Arum, White Arum Lily, Calla Lily
The Arum has large, long-stalked, arrow-shaped leaves, dull green above, shiny below. The flower, borne on a stalk up to 30 cm long, is pure white, the spathe enclosing a yellow flowering finger or spadix. The Arum was introduced to the island in the 18th century and the roots and stems were used for feeding pigs. It is common along streams above 600 m; and can also be found in dryer places close to ruined buildings, for instance the telegraph station at Man and Horse. The striking white flowers in October and November are followed by yellow fruits in January and February, forming a conspicuous feature of the landscape; for this reason the Arum was adopted as an emblematic flower of St Helena.

ARAUCARIACEAE – the monkey-puzzle family

HA   *Araucaria excelsa* (ex *A. heterophylla*)   Norfolk Island Pine
A straight-growing tree which is native to Australia and Norfolk Island. It can reach a height of 70 m, with horizontal branches in regular whorls and small (<10 mm), linear, pointed leaves. The mature cones are almost spherical and about 10 cm across, and the seeds have well developed wings.

---

[1] The true yams in the family Dioscoreaceae have never been important on St Helena; although the Coast or Winged Yam *Dioscorea alata* and a related species were cultivated to a small extent, they apparently did not thrive.

H: This tree is frequently planted and grows well, but does not regenerate spontaneously on St Helena. Two large specimens on Cuckold's Point and Mount Actaeon are landmarks on the island.

A: Introduced in 1860, apparently because of its suitability for ships' masts; there is a fine plantation in Breakneck Valley (with natural regeneration) and individuals elsewhere.

ASCLEPIADACEAE – the milkweed family

HA   *Asclepias curassavica.*   Milkweed, Redhead
A herb growing to about 1 m, with long, narrow, boat-shaped and pointed dark green leaves and flowers with five orange red down-curved petals and bright yellow erect stamens; the seeds have a cluster of hairs and are borne in vertically oriented pods.

H: Recorded by Roxburgh, and by Melliss as rather rare in gardens; it has not been noted in recent times.

A: This plant was recorded in the late 19th century; it is apparently spreading in the Two Boats area.

H   *Asclepias rotundifolia* Plate 24   Silk Cotton, Poppy
A low-growing shrub with reddish or greenish, hairy stems and milky sap. The leaves are opposite, boat-shaped and shiny. There are bunches of white flowers which give rise to inflated green seed pods full of silky, white hairs; the seeds are dark brown. Silk Cotton is common but local in dry areas. It is the major food plant on the island of the African Monarch Butterfly, whose black and white caterpillars can often be seen on the plants.

BEGONIACEAE – the begonia family

A   *Begonia hirtella*
This is a small species with pinkish-green stems and small white flowers. It is now common in the farm area, mainly on cinder cliffs, and can be found alongside the endemic grass *Sporobolus caespitosus* and the fern *Asplenium erectum*.

BIGNONIACEAE – the jacaranda family

HA   *Tecoma stans* Plate 13   Pops, Yellowboy (A)
A loose growing erect shrub reaching about 4 m in height. The opposite leaves are long stalked and composed of one to three pairs of leaflets and a terminal one; the leaflets are lance-shaped, elongate and with strongly toothed edges. The flowers are bright yellow, trumpet-shaped and about 3 cm across; the unopened flowers can be 'popped' by squeezing, hence the St Helena name. The winged seeds are borne in long, slender, papery brown pods that are conspicuous from a distance. This shrub is related to the violet-flowered Jacaranda, perhaps the most striking flowering tree of the tropics, which is widely planted on St Helena but does not grow wild.

H: Pops was introduced in about 1860 and seems to be still spreading in dry areas at fairly low elevations; it is conspicuous mainly in James Valley.

A: Yellowboy is a dominant part of the vegetation in many places at intermediate levels, including Cricket Valley and Dampier's. The plants seem variable and a second species of *Tecoma* (and hybrids) may also be present.

BORAGINACEAE – the borage and heliotrope family

*†H   *Heliotropium pannifolium*   Shrubby Heliotrope
This endemic species was recorded only once and is presumably extinct; Burchell found it growing in Sandy Bay at the top of Broad Gut in 1808. It was a shrub with broad leaves and clusters of white flowers.

A   *Heliotropium* species.
A grey-leaved, white flowered species has been found since 1995 in several arid places. On South Gannet Hill it grows with the Ascension Spurge, and it may present a threat to that species.

CACTACEAE – the cactus family

H   *Opuntia cochinillifera* (or a close relative) Plate 25   English Tungy, White Tungy
In spite of the vernacular name, both this and the next species of prickly pear are native to Central America. They were apparently introduced to St Helena in 1780-90 in relation to an attempt to harvest cochineal, which is obtained from a homopteran bug that feeds on *Opuntia*. The taxonomy is confused and up to six species may be present, but plants on St Helena seem to fall into two main types. The English Tungy has oval pads, about twice as long as broad. The spines are small and whitish, and there are about 30 groups of them on each side of the pad. The flowers are apricot to orange-scarlet. The oval fruits are about the size of a chicken's egg and are green, ripening to yellowish (purple in some plants); they are edible and make a good ingredient of a salad. This species is common in dry areas, perhaps especially in the north west, and sometimes grows mixed with the Red Tungy. (One other member of this family, the Night-flowering Cactus *Hylocereus triangularis*, occurs locally in the north of the island.)

HA   *Opuntia vulgaris* (or a close relative)   Red Tungy
On this species the pads are only slightly longer than broad. The spines are large and yellowish brown, and there are only about 12-15 groups of them on each side of the pad. The flowers are variable in colour but usually pinkish. The fruits are goblet shaped and only about 3 cm long; they are green, becoming purple when ripe, and are edible.
    H: The Red Tungy is common in dry areas, covering whole hillsides in parts of the northwest.
    A: Introduced in the mid 19th century and now widespread in drier parts of the island at middle levels. The moth *Cactoblastis cactorum* was introduced in 1974 to Cricket Valley in an attempt to control it; the effect seems to have been to make space available for Yellowboy. (At least one other species of *Opuntia* is also present on Ascension.)

CAMPANULACEAE – the bellflower family

**H   *Trimeris scaevolifolia* (= *Lobelia scaevolifolia*) Plate 25   Lobelia
The Lobelia is the sole member of an endemic genus, with its closest relatives possibly in the Andes or Pacific. The early settlers called this plant Milkwood because cut leaves or branches exude a milky sap, but it is now generally known as Lobelia. It is a fleshy-stemmed shrub growing 1-2 metres high; it can form dense stands, for instance under Black Cabbages, but does not thrive in deep shade. The stems are green and polished, with prominent pale brown leaf scars. The bright green leaves are alternate,

410

Lobelia

long-stalked and up to 15 cm long; they are leathery, toothed and with slightly crinkled edges. The white flowers are about 12 mm across, borne singly or in twos and threes, on fairly long, slender stalks; they are five-petalled (two above and three below). Flowering is in winter and spring. The tiny seeds are in two-compartments in a green capsule with five stiff sepals that form a star at its apex. Lobelia occurs locally on the central ridge above 700 m between Mt Actaeon and the Depot, with a good clump at High Peak. It used to be much more abundant, but was probably always local, growing in places where light penetrated the canopy. Young seedlings often grow epiphytically on the stems of cabbage trees and Tree Ferns.

*H   *Wahlenbergia angustifolia* Plate 26   Small Bellflower

Small Bellflower

This and the next three species seem to have their closest relatives in South Africa or South America. The Small Bellflower is a creeping mat-forming perennial found on steep slopes or cliffs. The stems are long and thin but stiff, with knobby leaf scars. The leaves are borne in a whorl, mainly near the tip of the stem; they are 2-4 cm long but only 5 mm wide, and with widely spaced small prickles on the edges; the undersides of the leaves bear small spines. The flowers can be found at all times of year, but especially in July and August; they are borne singly or in groups of two or three, and have long stalks that hold them up or out from the cliff, where they continually sway in the wind. The flowers are five-petalled, white, bell shaped and 12-18 mm across; the seeds are minute. The Small Bellflower is widespread on the island but now has a patchy distribution, occurring in crevices on cliffs and other exposed places (including road verges) between 550 and 800 m.

*†H   *Wahlenbergia burchellii*   Burchell's Bellflower
This species grew in thickets on the central ridge, and was last recorded in 1877. It was apparently similar to the Large Bellflower, but more upright – growing to at least 1 m – and with a dozen or so flowers on a stem rising above the leaves.

*H   *Wahlenbergia linifolia* Plate 26   Large Bellflower

Large Bellflower

A perennial plant up to half a metre high, with spreading wiry brown stems and rosettes of alternate leaves towards the end of the branches. The leaves are unstalked, 3-5 cm long, parallel-sided and with minute, widely-spaced teeth along the edges. The inflorescence is an upright terminal stem about 12 cm high, branched and carrying a small number of beautiful bell-shaped flowers; these are five-petalled, white (sometimes with a tinge of pink) and about 2 cm across. The Large Bellflower typically grows on the trunks of Tree Ferns and cabbage trees, but sometimes occurs on cliffs. It was abundant on the central ridge even in the last century, but has now become very rare, probably because of habitat destruction and competition from flax and other invasive plants. It was still to be found on the south face of Mount Actaeon a few decades ago, but is now thought to occur only at High Peak. This species sometimes forms hybrids with the Small Bellflower.

A   *Wahlenbergia procumbens*
A low-growing plant with bell-shaped pale blue flowers; five petals united into a corolla tube. It occurs on Coronation Peak and growing with *Sporobolus caespitosus* and *Asplenium erectum* on Elliot's Path.

*†H   *Wahlenbergia roxburghii*   Roxburgh's Bellflower
This species was last recorded in 1872. It was a slender shrub with sparse erect branches, which grew to at least half a metre, in thickets on the south of the central

411

ridge.The leaves were broad, hairy and greyish and the flowers large and white. It used to be called Dwarf Cabbage Tree by the islanders.

CANNACEAE – the canna family

HA   *Canna indica*   Lily Shots

A perennial herb with broad, lance-shaped leaves and spectacular red and yellow flowers. The seeds are hard, round and black, and Melliss comments: *"The seeds are often used as a substitute for shot, by boys whose means will afford the purchase of a gun only."*

H: Grows in wet guts and waste places in the uplands. (Some ornamental species of *Canna* are cultivated in gardens.)

A: Very scarce on the mountain.

CARYOPHYLLACEAE – the carnation family

HA   *Polycarpon tetraphyllum*   Four-leaved Allseed

A semi-prostrate, fleshy, hairless annual, with oval leaves either opposite or in groups of four. Flowers minute, white and with five petals which are shorter than the hooded sepals.

H: A fairly frequent weed. (At least two other weedy members of this family are present on St Helena.)

A: Local, found mainly at lower altitudes after rain.

CASUARINACEAE – the casuarina family

A   *Casuarina equisetifolia*   Beefwood, Casuarina, She-oak (Packer)

A graceful evergreen tree with arching filamentous branchlets; the leaves are reduced to whorls of toothed sheaths around the joints of the stems, the effect being strongly reminiscent of horse-tails. The tiny pinkish flowers are succeeded by conspicuous, round, brown, knobbly seed capsules resembling pine cones. The tree is tolerant to salt and wind. Introduced in the mid 19th century, it now grows in Georgetown and especially around Two Boats; in about 1982 an avenue was planted along the road to North East Bay. This tree is now spreading on to the lower slopes of Green Mountain and Sisters; we think that in the case of Sisters an attempt to prevent the spread would be worthwhile, because of the outstanding interest and beauty of the naturally bare volcanic landscape and also the likelihood of competition with the Ascension Spurge. Other species of *Casuarina* may be present on St Helena.

CELASTRACEAE – the spindle tree family

H   *Elaeodendron capense*   White Olive

This South African species is a small tree, often with multiple trunks and with pale bark. The leaves are dark green and strikingly leathery, usually with prickles reminiscent of holly. The fruit are the size and shape of an olive, green ripening to waxy white. The White Olive is very commmon in the uplands around 500-600 m; it regenerates from seed, forming thickets in waste places and is not eaten by stock. The pink or white wood is good for making boats.

CHENOPODIACEAE – the sugarbeet family

This family is difficult taxonomically and the status of some species on the islands has not yet been fully established.

H   *Atriplex nummularia*   Saltbush, Orache
An upright bush with small, fleshy, greyish leaves which are salty to the taste. This species has been grown extensively on the Crown Wastes to provide forage.

H   *Atriplex semibaccata* Plate 26   Saltbush, Orache
This species is now common in the Crown Wastes (often mixed with Samphire), but it was not recorded by Burchell and is unlikely to be indigenous. It is a prostrate, trailing plant, typically less than 30 cm across, with very slender stems and small (1 cm) coarsely toothed grey-green leaves; both stems and leaves are more or less tinged with purple. The red fruits are tiny (5 mm), kite-shaped and succulent, and are eagerly eaten by Pigeons. (One or more additional species of *Atriplex* can be found growing in the Crown Wastes and as weeds elsewhere, but are not easily distinguished.)

HA   *Chenopodium ambrosioides*   Goosefoot
A pungent weed growing to about 45 cm high, with hairy stems, leaves about 5 cm long, narrow and irregularly toothed; inflorescence upright, long and pointed, with minute greenish flower clusters..
   H: Occurs locally on waste ground and as a weed in cultivated areas.
   A: Local at middle to high levels.

*H   *Chenopodium helenense*   St Helena Goosefoot
We treat this species as endemic, but it is closely related to *C. murale* (see below) and may be merely a variant formed on the island by random genetic events after introduction of a few plants or seeds. It was discovered by Burchell near Longwood and was thought to be extinct, until found again by Quentin Cronk in 1986 in Bilberry Field Gut.

HA   *Chenopodium murale*   Sowbane
This straggly plant grows to about 30 cm, with widely spreading, angled stems. The diamond-shaped leaves occur in untidy bunches, have long stalks and are sparsely and irregularly toothed. The tiny reddish flowers grow in tight clusters among the leaf bases near the tips of the stems.
   H: Grows as a weed, and locally in the Crown Wastes, for instance at Great Stone Top.
   A: Has been found on the lower slopes of the mountain.

H   *Suaeda fruticosa* (ex *Salsola helenae*) Plate 3   Samphire
The Samphire of St Helena is probably best considered as a southern form of *Suaeda fruticosa*, which also occurs on the coasts of Africa and on the Cape Verde Islands. The Belgian entomologists considered it as introduced., but we are convinced that it is indigenous, especially since it is the principal food plant for at least two ancient endemic insects, the bug *Hirtopsallus suedae* in the family Miridae (a generic endemic whose scientific name reflects its food preference) and the beetle *Homoeodera coriacea* (family Anthribidae). Samphire is a spreading shrub up to one metre high, with stiff, arching branches. The twigs, which often leave the stems in pairs, bear leaves along their whole length. The leaves are about 1.5 cm long, cylindrical and fleshy, greyish green but sometimes bright grey blue when dying. Samphire is salt tolerant and is very common in the Crown Wastes, especially in the north, often near sea level but also on dry hills up to 300 m. Its use as a source of soda was mentioned in Chapter 5.

413

COMMELINACEAE – the spiderwort family

HA   *Commelina diffusa*   Tallowvine, Water Grass
A creeping, grass-like, slightly succulent herb related to *Tradescantia*, with slender, ribbed, jointed stems and pointed leaves with parallel veins. The flowers are small and pale blue, with bright yellow anthers.
    H: Tallowvine is common in damp, grassy places around 500-700 m, especially beside streams, and is sometimes cut for feeding livestock. (A white-flowered species is also present.)
    A: Shady places on the mountain, especially around the farm.

COMPOSITAE (or ASTERACEAE) – the daisy family

A large proportion of the endemic trees of St Helena belong to this family, as do a number of the most successful introduced plants. It is worth noting that members of this family have flower heads derived from large numbers of minute flowers; the apparent 'petals' in flowers such as daisies have an origin quite separate from petals in other plants and are known as 'ray florets'.

HA   *Ageratum conyzoides* Plate 24   Blue Weed, Goatweed (A)
An upright, hairy weed growing up to at least half a metre high, with a disagreeable, pungent, somewhat goaty smell. The stem is purple and angled, and the leaves fairly long stalked, cordate/elliptic and coarsely toothed. The scented blue-purple flowers are borne in a loose terminal cluster.
    H: This plant is a weed of cultivated ground, but is also very common on roadsides, in gut bottoms and in dry scrub, and even along paths on the peaks.
    A: Widely distributed and common at middle levels on the mountain.

H   *Chrysanthemoides monilifera* Plate 26   Wild Coffee
A dense shrub originally from South Africa. It grows to around three metres, and has dark green, slightly fleshy leaves with a few coarse teeth and reddish edges; the untidy yellow daisy flowers have only about seven ray florets. The fruits are pea-sized, green ripening to dark purple; the fleshy outer layer of the unripe berry tastes of coffee when chewed. As the bush grows the inside leaves die and go black-brown, giving it an unattractive appearance. Wild Coffee is one of the commonest shrubs of barren ground and seems to be still spreading; it is evidently dispersed by Mynas, which deposit seeds throughout the dry parts of the island. The leaves are bitter-tasting and are not eaten even by donkeys and goats.

H   *Cineraria saxifraga*
A low-growing, straggling plant with woody stems and fan-shaped, lobed leaves about 1.5 cm across. The flower heads are small, yellow and cup-shaped. This plant grows wild only locally in the southwest, in dry pastures and rocky places, especially around High Hill.

**H   *Commidendrum robustum* Plates 7 and 26   Gumwood
The Gumwood and the following three species probably had a common ancestor on St Helena with the Black Cabbage *Melanodendron integrifolium*; the closest relatives of the two genera (which are in the tribe Astereae) may be in Australia or South America. The Gumwood is now considered to include a subspecies, *Commidendrum robustum* subspecies *gummiferum*, which was previously treated as a distinct species (*C. burchellii*);[2]

---

[2] Q.C.B. Cronk (1995b, 2000).

Gumwood

it grew at higher levels than the typical form and was characteristic of the moist gumwood woodlands between 500 and 650 m on the central ridge, where it occurred with Redwood and Rosemary. Subspecies *gummiferum* is probably now extinct, but some of the Gumwoods at Peak Dale may be hybrids between it and the normal form.

A young Gumwood is a compact bush, but it later forms an open umbrella-shaped tree sometimes as much as eight metres high, shaped by the prevailing wind and with crooked, often lichen-covered trunk. The leaves are in whorls, and are variable in size but usually 7-10 cm long, tapering to the base, with toothed edges; they are dull blue green to dark green and fairly fleshy, rather sticky and hairy, with the undersides silvery felted; the leaf-scars are conspicuous and almost diamond-shaped. The flowers are borne singly or in small groups at the ends of the branches; they are long-stalked and drooping, 2-3 cm across, with white ray florets and pale yellow centres. Flowering is usually in winter and spring. Burchell noted that the Gumwood: *"Has a resinous, spongy wood, making a delightful fire"*, and Melliss commented that not only did it supply the chief fuel to the inhabitants, but they also obtained a drink from the stem, by tapping it and catching the liquid that flowed from the wound; we imagine that this was then fermented.

The Gumwood was probably once the most abundant tree on St Helena, dominating much of the woodland between about 300 and 600 m. In 1678, 240 pieces of Gumwood timber, ten feet long and five inches broad, were cut at the head of Sane Valley for use in covering over the Crane Battery after two soldiers were killed by falling rocks. Melliss recorded that persons still living could recollect losing their way in the Gumwood forests at Longwood. In 1868 he estimated the numbers of surviving individuals in various parts of the island, reaching a total of 1300-1400, half of which were in the Longwood/Deadwood area. The Gumwood used to regenerate freely from seed when enclosed to prevent goats and pigs from eating the young growth. In 1977 it was adopted as St Helena's National Tree.

The main surviving grove of Gumwoods is at Peak Dale, where there is a wood with over 500 trees, but some 20 wild trees survive in Deep Valley and there are small numbers in other places; Burchell recorded a grove at Man and Horse. Four old trees can still be seen at Longwood, within the area originally occupied by the 'Great Wood' (see Chapter 7), but these may have been planted early in the 20th century. In the early 1990s the trees at Peak Dale were badly affected by the Jacaranda Bug, *Orthezia insignis*, a scale insect from South and Central America which also feeds on *Lantana*. However, the infestation seems to have been brought under control by introduction of a predatory ladybird, *Hyperaspis pantherina*.

Replanting of Gumwoods on Horse Point Plain was started in 1988 by Norman Williams and continued in the 1990s by George Benjamin and his team from the Endemic Section of the Agriculture & Forestry Department; this is now the site of the Millennium Grove Forest Project and hundreds of trees have now been established there. Re-establishment is also now in progress at a number of other sites, as well as clearance of invasive species from around surviving wild trees.

**H   *Commidendrum rotundifolium* Plate 26   Bastard Gumwood
The Bastard Gumwood forms a small, open tree similar in form to the Gumwood, but perhaps generally smaller. The leaves are 5-7.5 cm long and are spoon-shaped, with the stalk accounting for at least half the length (compare Gumwood and False Gumwood); they are coarsely toothed and are yellow green and shiny when young, but become dull green when mature. The flowering heads form in branched clusters

415

Bastard Gumwood

near the ends of the branches, and are either drooping or roughly horizontal (compare False Gumwood); they are whitish yellow, ageing to brown, and are typically produced between March and June.

The Bastard Gumwood was orginally an important component of the gumwood woodlands, especially on the drier sites between about 400 and 520 m, but it declined rapidly after settlement. In the first decade of the 19th century Burchell noted that the largest and most ancient trees were in Sharks Valley. One tree survived at Longwood until late in the nineteenth century, but when this was blown down the species was thought to be extinct until a single tree was found in 1982 by Stedson Stroud, on an inaccessible cliff between Dry Gut and Horse Pasture. It died in 1986, and although some trees were propagated from it and are now mature, they rarely set seed; however, a few more individuals have been propagated as cuttings. The best hope for the species is that more than fifty seedlings have recently been raised from stored seed obtained some years ago, at a time when Bastard Gumwoods and False Gumwoods were growing close together at Pounceys. These are probably mainly hybrids between the two species, but genetic research on them is under way and in the long run it may be possible to re-establish a wild population similar to the original Bastard Gumwood.

Scrubwood

**H   *Commidendrum rugosum* (ex *Aster glutinosus*) Plates 6 and 26   Scrubwood
The Scrubwood is a low, spreading, long-lived bush, often dome-shaped and up to 1.5 m high when on level ground; the stems are dark and show strong leaf scars. The leaves are in whorls at the tips of the branches; they are unstalked but narrow gradually to the base; they have toothed edges, are somewhat succulent and covered with sticky hairs. The flowers are borne singly and have erect stalks about 7.5 cm long; they are showy and daisy-like, about 2.5 cm across, and are initially white but changing to pink and then pale crimson before they die; they are produced almost the whole year round. There is great variation in form even in plants growing close together, some having small rounded leaves and others larger and more pointed ones.

The Scrubwood was one of the dominant shrubs of the arid parts of St Helena before the arrival of humans, but as a result of grazing by goats starting in the 16th century, it became almost entirely confined to cliffs, especially along those coasts where onshore winds give rise to condensation near the cliff tops; it is also fairly tolerant of salt. Burchell commented that the largest and most ancient trees were near Little Stone Top. When the feral goats were progressively reduced in numbers during the middle decades of the 20th century, the Scrubwood responded quickly to the relaxation of grazing pressure: it has spread naturally from some of its refuges on the cliffs on to more gently sloping ground nearby. This spread is doubtless aided by the updrafts over the cliff tops which can carry seeds inland. The species could probably be used effectively in erosion control.

False Gumwood

**H   *Commidendrum spurium* Plate 26   False Gumwood
The False Gumwood is typically smaller than the Gumwood, but in the past may sometimes have grown to 5-6 m. The pale green leaves are in whorls near the ends of the branches, and are diamond shaped, tapering gradually to the base (compare Bastard Gumwood); they are up to 10 cm long and with the edges coarsely toothed; they are rather limp, not fleshy, and are slightly shiny, with hairs on the veins. The flowers are white and daisy like, with a yellow green centre, and are borne in terminal, branched clusters that stick up rather than drooping as in the Gumwood. Flowering occurs in December to March or April.

416

The False Gumwood was originally a major component of the moist cabbage tree woodland just below the peaks, a vegetation type that is lost today, but which also included Redwood, Rosemary and Gumwood. In the late 1990s only ten trees survived in the wild, eight on cliffs at Mount Vesey, one in pasture at Oaklands and one on a sheer cliff at Coles Rock. However, propagation of this species has been successful; seedlings from below the Coles Rock tree were grown at Scotland, large numbers of seedlings were raised from seed collected at Mount Vesey, and re-establishment of trees in the wild is well under way.

HA   *Conyza bonariensis* (ex *Erigeron bonariensis*)
A somewhat woody daisy-like weed sometimes reaching more than one metre in height, with a basal rosette of narrow, strongly serrated leaves and an erect inflorescence bearing linear greyish green leaves. The flowers are white and fluffy, lacking conspicuous ray florets, and are borne in a loose, branched head.
   H: This is a common weed of roadsides, but also occurs in remote areas.
   A: Local at medium altitudes.

H   *Cotula coronopifolia* Plate 27   Pagoda Plant
A low-growing plant of very variable size which grows in dry rocky places around 200-400 m, appearing mainly after rain in late winter. It has conspicuous, small, button-like, bright yellow daisy flowers without ray-florets, borne on long thin stalks; the leaves are small, slightly succulent and lobed. The species is from South Africa, although it has been suggested as conceivably indigenous. The name refers to the resemblance of the flower to the small gold coin bearing a representation of a pagoda, value four shillings, which was minted by the East India Company in Madras in the 18th century and which was used on St Helena. (A related species, *Cotula australis*, has less conspicuous flowers and occurs as a weed around 400-600 m.)

H   *Eupatorium pallidum* Plate 24   Whiteweed, White Flower
A shrub growing up to 4 m high, with opposite leaves which are long-stalked, lanceolate, soft, downy and coarsely toothed. The flowers are small and white, in clusters at the tips of the shoots. A common invasive shrub in guts at mid altitudes. The flowers are attractive to butterflies, especially the Painted Lady.

H   *Gnaphalium luteo-album*   Jersey Cudweed
This is a small (up to 30 cm) upright silver-green herb with narrow leaves and clusters of small yellowish-brown flowers; the young plant has only a rosette of leaves at ground level. Widespread along roadsides and in dry places. (One other species of *Gnaphalium* has been recorded on St Helena in the past and two species are present on Ascension.)

H   *Helichrysum bracteatum*   Everlasting
This showy plant is a native of Australia. It is an annual herbaceous weed of extremely variable size, reaching over one metre in places but often less than 20 cm. The leaves are muddy green; those on the flowering stem are long and very slender, with elongate points; those at the base are broader and with serrated edges. The flowers are yellow daisies, with chaff-like ray florets, and retain their colour when dried. The Everlasting is very common in dry areas at middle altitudes.

H   *Hypochaeris radicata*   Dandelion, Common Cat's-ear
This is a troublesome herbaceous weed, common in gardens and dry pasture around 500-700 m. It has a basal rosette of undulate-toothed rather narrow leaves up to

417

30 cm long, and erect, branched flower stalks up to 60 cm high; the yellow flowers open flat and are 2.5-4 cm across.

**H   *Lachanodes arborea* (ex *Senecio redivivus, S. prenanthiflorus*) Plate 27   She Cabbage

The She Cabbage is considered as forming a genus endemic to St Helena. Its ancestors must have reached the island many millions of years ago, as fossilized pollen grains belonging to the genus have been found in a deposit about nine million years old (see Chapter 4). It is a member of the tribe Senecioneae and its closest surviving relatives seem to be in the Mascarene Islands, Australasia and South America.

She Cabbage

The She Cabbage grows to about 8 m high, typically with a slender, straight stem. The leaves are pale green; those on young trees are large (up to 60 by 20 cm) and reminscent of a cabbage, but on older branching trees they are much smaller. The leaf-stalks are relatively short and are bright purple-red, as are the veins and shoots. The tiny flowers have long, slender stalks and form terminal sprays which are branched and drooping.

The She Cabbage was previously common on the central ridge, from about 600 m upwards. It became nearly extinct, but in 1977 a group of mature trees was discovered in a boundary hedge of Thorn trees near Osbornes just north of the Sandy Bay ridge; there is also a small wild population at Coles Rock. During the 1990s most of the roughly 90 trees at Osbornes died, probably as a result of ageing combined with attacks by larvae of a moth in the family Tineidae (see Chapter 16), and by 1999 there were only a handful of mature trees left. However, groups have now been established in several new sites from seedlings and cuttings, and the Coles Rock population has been reinforced. In the She Cabbage, in contrast to the situation in some of St Helena's other trees, much of the original genetic variability that is characteristic of the species has been preserved, at least for the moment.

Both this species and the He Cabbage are adapted to become established in light-gaps and grow fast into the canopy; the She Cabbage can exceed seven metres after ten years. These ecological traits tend to go with short lifespan, and both species will remain vulnerable to extinction so long as their overall populations remain low. However, the present situation is encouraging and a credit to the work of conservationists on the island.

**H   *Melanodendron integrifolium* Plates 7 and 27   Black Cabbage

The Black Cabbage is the only species in its genus, but it is thought to have diverged evolutionarily from the genus *Commidendrum* after arrival of a common ancestor on the island; their closest relatives may be in South America.

This is a spreading tree up to 4 m high, with furrowed moist bark that is often blackened with lichens and mosses. The leaves are borne in rosettes at the tips of the branches, and are up to 15 cm long. They are thick and fleshy, stiff and boat-shaped, with the edges smooth and rolled down, and are very glossy; leaves of seedlings are toothed, providing a link with the genus *Commidendrum*. The flowers are white or brownish white and are borne on stalks up to 12 cm long in loose clusters; each flower head is about 12 mm across, and is like a small white daisy. Flowering is in spring. The seeds often germinate on the trunks of the Tree Ferns.

The Black Cabbage is longer-lived than the other cabbage trees, and would have originally been codominant (with the Tree Fern, Olive and Dogwood) in the climax forest on the summit of the central ridge from Green Hill in the east to the Depot in the west. Its range is now much contracted, but in March 1996 more than 780 Black

418

Cabbages were still growing on the Peaks; they are mainly above 700 m near Diana's Peak and Mount Actaeon, with a few at High Peak and a couple at the Depot. The population appears secure provided that the trees are not attacked by alien pests or crowded out by invasive trees and shrubs.

*H   *Osteospermum sanctae-helenae* (ex *Tripteris burchellii*) Plate 27   Boneseed
A low growing plant with thin rough stems straggling to about 45 cm high. The grey green leaves are unstalked and strap-shaped, and both leaves and stems are covered with hairs and small, glistening sticky drops. The daisy-like flowers, borne singly on long stalks arising in the axils of the leaves, are about 12 mm across and have yellow ray florets. The sticky, hard, angular seeds (hence 'Boneseed') are about 2 mm long and are grouped in the form of a star on the ripened flower head.

Boneseed is not an easy plant to find, occurring locally between 30 and 250 m altitude in the driest, hottest parts of the island, sometimes in company with Babies' Toes or Scrubwood. It has been found on Bencoolen and Boxwood Hill and near Turks Cap and Prosperous Bay, but especially in the dry valleys near Sandy Bay; we saw it near the base of the Asses Ears. Burchell also recorded it from the Heart Shape Waterfall, and Norman Kerr found it between Flagstaff and Sugar Loaf. Boneseed is an annual or short-lived perennial, germinating with the onset of the winter rains, flowering and producing seed quickly, then dying back completely during the hot dry summer season.

**H   *Petrobium arboreum* Plate 27   Whitewood
This is the sole member of an endemic genus with no close relatives. Whitewood is now seen as a small, bushy-crowned upright tree less than 4 m high, but Roxburgh described it as growing to be a large tree with straight, upright trunk; the bark is dark and rather smooth but with small cracks. The young twigs are rough with much short brown hair and occur alternately; the leaves, however, occur in opposite pairs. The leaves are dark green, but when young they have characteristic patches of bright orange brown; their stalks are purple and about 7 cm long, oval and somewhat arched; they are finely toothed, oval and not sharply pointed (compare Dogwood). The Whitewood – like the Dogwood – has separate sexes. The conical-cylindrical flowers are about 13 mm long and are borne at the ends of the branches in loose groups of about ten; flowering occurs from March to June. The seeds are four-sided. Whitewood was a major component of the cabbage tree woodland of the central ridge and also occurred in the Tree Fern thicket; it is in the fragments of the latter habitat that it survives, with a population of rather more than 80 individuals; a few large trees survive on the lower slopes but most take the form of bushes on the highest peaks. Little natural regeneration occurs but seeds and cuttings are now being collected and replanting is planned.

Whitewood

**H   *Pladaroxylon leucadendron* Plate 27   He Cabbage
The He Cabbage is the only member of an endemic genus with distant relatives in South America, Australia and the Mascarene Islands. Although it is in the same tribe (Senecioneae) as the She Cabbage its ancestors undoubtedly reached the island separately. The He Cabbage forms a small tree up to 4 m high. The saplings are unbranched until they reach 1.5-2 m in height, growing quickly up into the canopy after becoming established in a light-gap; when mature, they form a spreading crown, but are short-lived. The saplings have green stems with prominent leaf-scars, but the adult trees have light brown, fissured bark. The leaves are in whorls at the tips of the

He Cabbage

branches, and on young plants may be over 30 cm long; on older trees they tend to be smaller. The leaves are oval, slightly toothed and downy below, and with very prominent veins. On young trees the leaf stalks (but not the shoots) are slightly purple. The flower-cluster is borne at the tip of a branch and is large and somewhat reminiscent of a cauliflower. The flowers are white and about 6 mm across. Blooming is in winter.

The He Cabbage was once abundant but local on the central ridge a little below the summits; Melliss commented that it grew distinctly lower down than the other cabbage trees. There are now nine surviving groups within the National Park, with one to 35 individuals, and a few trees at High Peak. The He Cabbage does not compete well with invasive shrubs such as Bilberry and Quinine, and if it is to survive, clear spaces will probably always have to be maintained for it.

H   *Senecio mikanioides* (or *Delairea odorata*)   Devil's Guts
This rambling plant has fan-shaped, somewhat fleshy, ivy-like leaves with up to 12 points. The striking yellow flower clusters are borne either in leaf axils or terminally; individual flowers are small and without petals, and have a strong scent of honey. The underground stems are blue-mauve, giving rise to the common name. The species is widespread in wooded areas.

H   *Tagetes minuta*   Billy Goat Weed
An upright weed growing to 1 m high. Leaves pinnate, the leaflets up to about 4 cm long, narrow and linear, with strongly toothed edges. Flowers borne terminally in groups, tubular, yellowish green, with a pair of tiny whitish ray florets at the tip. The plant has a strong smell similar to the related marigolds. It occurs mainly near the road at Ladder Hill and elsewhere in James Valley, and was probably introduced from South Africa at the time of the Boer War.

CONVOLVULACEAE – the convolvulus family

Apart from the species listed, a species of bindweed (genus *Calystegia*) with white flowers has been seen on the central ridge of St Helena. At least two introduced species of *Ipomoea* also occur on St Helena, including a vigorous blue-flowered convolvulus and the Sweet Potato *I. batatas*, which is an important crop plant.

H   *Dichondra repens*   Monkey's Ears
This is a prostrate, creeping herb with round leaves which cannot easily be distinguished – except when flowering or fruiting – from *Centella asiatica* (Umbelliferae), which has the same local name. Burchell recorded *D. repens* from Little Stone Top and it has also been found on the Barn and in other dry places. It has been suggested as conceivably indigenous.

?(H)A *Ipomoea pes-caprae*   Camel's-foot Creeper
This convolvulus is probably indigenous on both islands, but perhaps now absent from St Helena. *I. pes-caprae* is a prostrate, vigorous, spreading plant with stems up to 6 m long. The leaves are smooth, untoothed, oval and blunt-ended or indented at the tip (hence the name), and characteristically boat-shaped; they have long, purple stalks. The flowers are borne singly or in pairs in the axils of the leaves, on long, pale green stalks; they are mauve, with five petals joined to form a funnel. This is a classic tropical strand plant whose seeds are dispersed by the sea; it is said that the seeds can survive six months and more in the water.

H: Burchell found *I. pes-caprae* at Sandy Bay, and in spite of the absence of other records we suspect that this creeper formed an important part of the vegetation on the 'apron' of the island during periods of low sea level (see section on Geology in Chapter 3).

A: *I. pes-caprae* was recorded from Ascension in 1698, 1754 and 1877 but missed by several 19th century botanists; it evidently grew locally on the coast and in dusty places like Waterloo Plain where the airstrip was subsequently constructed (see Figure 24). It is now rampant in some places around settlements and beside roads at intermediate levels and up to the old NASA site, but is probably still also present in a few places on the coast..

CRASSULACEAE – the stonecrop family

HA   *Bryophyllum pinnata (= Kalanchoe pinnata).*   Lucky Leaf, Chandelier Plant
This is a succulent originating from Madagascar which is now widespread in the tropics. It has fleshy serrated-edge leaves and hanging rose pink flower clusters. Fallen leaves sometimes establish themselves as new plants, hence the local name.
    H: Found in some dry areas at mid altitudes. (Two other members of this family are established in the High Knoll/Half Tree Hollow area.)
    A: First recorded in 1956, by Packer, but already well established and spreading on the mountain and other high fairly dry areas. (A second species is present at Two Boats and in gardens elsewhere.)

CRUCIFERAE (= BRASSICACEAE) – the cabbage family

HA   *Coronopus didymus (= Senebiera didyma = Senebiera heleniana)*   Lesser Swine-cress
This is a more or less prostrate annual or biennial weed, with stems up to 40 cm long; the leaves are pinnate and pungent when crushed, and the flowers are tiny and white.
    H: A common weed of gardens. Some specimens are distinctly woody and this gave rise to the suggestion that the plants on St Helena represented a separate species.
    A: Local on Green Mountain.

H   *Rorippa nasturtium-aquaticum (= Nasturtium officinale)*   Water Cress
Water Cress is a creeping, hairless, perennial herb which grows in and beside running water. The leaves are dark green and pinnate and the white flowers of typical crucifer type are followed by pods with two rows of seeds. Water Cress grows at French's Gut, Sandy Bay beach and a few other places; it was introduced from Europe in the 18th century and sold in bags to visiting sailors, for whom it was an important food. (Several other small crucifers occur as weeds on the island.)

CUPRESSACEAE – the cypress family

H   *Cupressus macrocarpa*   Macrocarpa, Monterey Cypress
This cypress is pyramidal in early life but later forms a broad crown; it grows rapidly and can reach 25 m. The branchlets are densely clothed with tiny, overlapping, scale-like leaves. The cones are ovoid and 2.5-4 cm long, with about 10 scales, each with a sharp projection. The Macrocarpa is widely planted and individuals grow wild in a few places: we have found one near the bottom of Dry Gut.

HA   *Juniperus bermudiana* Plate 14   Cedar, Bermuda Cedar
A spreading tree with dark green foliage, growing to about 10 metres. Twigs four-angled, scaly, brown (green near the tips); fruit peppercorn-sized, purple-black when ripe with a pale blue bloom. The wood is reddish, scented and resistant to termites.

H: This tree was introduced in the mid 19th century from Bermuda. It thrives at middle and high levels on the island, being spread by the Mynas, which eat the seeds. It can colonise arid and barren areas and may eventually become dominant in parts of the Crown Wastes.

A: Introduced in the first half of the nineteenth century and now widespread and spreading at middle levels, especially on the northern slopes of Green Mountain and on Weather Post.

CYPERACEAE – the sedge family

The sedges are upright, grass-like, usually perennial plants with rootstocks or tubers. They can be distinguished from grasses by their solid and usually triangular stems, without joints at the leaf junctions (grass stems are jointed, hollow and rounded or compressed). As in the grasses, the flowers are small and enclosed in chaffy overlapping scales, and are termed spikelets; often these are bunched into tight heads. The seeds – which are important in identification – are buoyant and a few species seem to have reached the islands naturally.

*H   *Bulbostylis lichtensteiniana* Plate 27   St Helena Tuft-sedge
This endemic sedge has relatives in Africa. It looks like a rush (*Juncus* species), forming tufts of very slender wiry stems up to about 30 cm high. The flowering heads are small, brown, and borne at the extreme tips of the stems. The species is common in dry places between 300 and 600 m, including remote eroded areas such as Sandy Bay Barn and near the Asses Ears.

*?†H   *Bulbostylis neglecta*   Dwarf St Helena Tuft-sedge
This species was clearly distinct from the preceding one, but has not been seen for a long time and may be extinct. Burchell collected it from beside Side Path opposite High Knoll.

*H   *Carex dianae* (including *C. praealta*, sometimes considered to be separate) Plate 27
                                                                        Diana's Peak Grass
This endemic sedge, which grows in clumps up to almost a metre high, has broad, strap-like leaves with prominent longitudinal ridges. It was a component of the Tree Fern thicket that formed the original vegetation on the summit ridge of the island, and can still be seen in the surviving fragments of this habitat.

HA   *Cyperus* species
In this genus the flowering heads are spreading and somewhat umbrella-like. Several species are widespread in both islands, but apart from *C. appendiculatus* from Ascension (see below) all may be introduced. *C. rotundus* (Nut Grass) which is very common on St Helena around 300-500 m, can be a troublesome weed; it has chains of deep underground tubers the size of peas, and springs up after rains, growing at a phenomenal rate in warm conditions.

A   *Cyperus appendiculatus*
This sedge is evidently indigenous on Ascension. The species was first described from the island but was later found on Tristan da Cunha and Fernando de Noronha. It

occurs locally both at fairly high levels on the mountain and in dry watercourses in the lowlands, where it has a more compact growth form.

HA   *Cyperus brevifolius* (ex *Kyllinga brevifolia*)
This is a single-headed sedge about 25 cm high, with three subtending leaves, which can be confused with *Cyperus rotundus*. When crushed it has a characteristic odour reminiscent of castor-oil.

HA   *Cyperus distans*
This is a large species that has been suggested as conceivably indigenous on both islands.

HA   *Cyperus polystachyos* (= *Pycreus polystachyos*)
A widespread tropical sedge growing to about 30 cm high and with basal grass-like leaves 15-20 cm long.
    H: Found in Fishers Valley and other wet places, but also among rocks on Sandy Bay Barn. It has been suggested as being possibly indigenous.
    A: Local on Green Mountain.

H   *Scirpus antarcticus.*
Members of this genus are known as club-rushes, referring to the compact, stalkless flowering head reminiscent of a spiked club. *S. antarcticus* is widespread in the southern hemisphere and may be indigenous. It is a low-growing plant with thread-like stems, and is occasional in dry pastures, for instance Deadwood.

H   *Scirpus chlorostachys.*
This sedge may be indigenous; it also occurs in southern Africa. It is a tufted, delicate sedge with thread-like stems without leaf blades, only 7.5 cm high. It is very common on paths on the central ridge and in damp places elsewhere. Burchell commented that it was mixed with mud for plastering instead of hair.

H   *Scirpus nodosus* (= *Fimbristylis textilis*)   Thatching Rush
This large plant is a relative of the sedges rather than the members of the rush family (Juncaceae) which it resembles. It is widespread in the temperate part of southern hemisphere and is apparently indigenous on St Helena. It has no leaves, and the smooth, glossy, deep green, columnar stems can grow to a height of nearly two metres, in dense tufts. Thatching Rush has been used for making baskets throughout the period of settlement on St Helena, and in the 17th and 18th centuries it was extremely important for thatching; it was said that a good substantial covering could remain weatherproof for 10-15 years. Thatching Rush now grows mainly in semi-barren areas at middle altitudes, such as Man and Horse and Horse Pasture; it has also been found in pockets of soil on the cliffs of High Hill.

H   *Scirpus prolifer*
This is another possibly indigenous species, also found in South Africa and Australia. It is similar to *S. chlorostachys*, but the stems grow somewhat longer; the spikelets are in stalkless clusters with a small number of bracts. This species can reproduce by growing new plantlets on the tips of the drooping stems. Melliss commented that it: *"...in great abundance covers all the streams and moist parts of the Island."* It is still common on wet cliffs, in guts and in other damp places.

EBENACEAE – the ebony family

H   *Diospyros dicrophylla* (= *Royena pallens*) Plate 28   Poison Peach
A small tree up to 5 m high. It has alternate, dark green, elliptic leaves about 6 cm long, with the edges rolled back. The creamy white flowers are 8-9 mm across and are visited by bees. The fruit is tomato-shaped and about 2.5 cm across, with a velvety green skin divided into five sections by pale longitudinal lines; it is borne on a five-pointed star-shaped base and remains hard even when ripe. The wood was formerly used for boat building. Poison Peach is a common coloniser of dry land at middle altitudes.

EUPHORBIACEAE – the spurge family

*†H   *Acalypha rubrinervis* (= *Acalypha rubra*)   Stringwood
This extinct endemic species used to occur sparsely on the central ridge above 600 m; it was last seen in 1865 in a garden. It is thought to have been most closely related to plants of the same genus on islands in the Indian Ocean. The Stringwood was a small shrub with oval stalked leaves; the twigs, stalks and veins were all smooth and red. The name relates to the red, pendent and tassel-like male spikes.

H   *Cluytia pulchella* (sometimes spelled *Clutia*) Plate 28   Wild Pepper
An upright shrub from South Africa, growing to 2 m high, with many slender stems and the leaves mainly near the tips. The leaves are alternate, lance-shaped, and sometimes show an orange tinge. The flowers are small and white, and the seeds form in a six-sided capsule. Wild Pepper is very common in dry places at middle altitudes, often under pines; it spreads by means of root suckers and can be invasive. In 1883 samples of sticks of Wild Pepper (together with Privet *Canthium lividum* and Furze) were submitted to a major London firm concerned with the manufacture of walking sticks, who were cautiously optimistic about the possibility of marketing such sticks; we do not know if any attempt was made to establish an export business.

*H   *Euphorbia heleniana* Plate 28   French Grass
This species is considered endemic to St Helena, although it has relatives throughout the tropics. It is a small, prostrate plant with slender, straight, purplish-red stems. The leaves are opposite, about 5 mm across and almost round; they are green and unmarked. The flowers spring from the leaf axils and are minute and white with dark marks. The fruits are green and with three sections. This species occurs only in dry, barren places; Burchell noted it in Banks Valley and at Potato Bay and in the valleys in Sandy Bay; we have found it in Broad Gut and on Prosperous Bay Plain.

*A   *Euphorbia origanoides* Plate 28   Ascension Spurge
The Ascension Spurge is one of the few species endemic to Ascension Island; it has close relatives in Africa. The plant is easily recognized and attractive, though also poisonous. When actively growing, it forms dome-shaped, bushy plants, up to one metre across and about half a metre high. The stems are crimson and the leaves are about 10 mm long, oval and with finely saw-toothed edges; they are stalkless and form in pairs at regular intervals on the stem. The flowers are small and yellowish, and are borne in terminal and often paired clusters. This plant has the typical milky juice of the spurges. Be careful, as the juice is said to cause blindness if it gets in the eyes. This important species is now very scarce, but the trend is hard to determine since the populations are subject to drastic fluctuations (probably related to rainfall) and small groups are easy to

miss. Colonies are still present in a number of places, up to 300 m above sea level. The healthiest colonies we saw in 1995 were on South Gannet Hill and south of Hummock Point, but the second of these has declined since then. In the past, the colonies near Cross Hill have suffered from the introduced cottony cushion scale *Icerya purchasi*.

HA   *Euphorbia* species
In addition to the species mentioned above, several species of prostrate, weedy euphorbias have been introduced to both islands. Q.C.B. Cronk (2000) gives characters for distinguishing those on St Helena from the endemic species there.

HA   *Ricinus communis* Plate 28   Castor Oil, Physic Nut
This perennial introduced plant can become a small tree but on the islands is normally less than 3 m high; it dies back to the roots in drought. It has dark green, shiny, long-stalked, fan-shaped leaves up to 50 cm long and with as many as 11 lobes; the sap is watery, in contrast to the euphorbias, which have latex. The flowers are inconspicuous but the fruits are round and spiny, first green, then rich brown and woody; they eventually explode to release three shiny and mottled black or grey bean-like seeds from which castor oil is obtained.
     H: Grows mainly in the east of the island at elevations up to about 500 m where it is local in scrubby places, especially in valley bottoms including near sea level in Broad Gut.
     A: Widespread in the desert lowlands, but flourishing only after rain.

FAGACEAE – the oak family

H   *Quercus robur*   Oak
The Oak has lobed leaves and forms characteristic fruits (acorns) in the form of a nut enclosed in a cup at the base. In young trees the bark is grey, smooth and shiny but it becomes rough and furrowed with age. It was introduced in 1749 and apparently flourished, becoming widespread in the uplands, but most trees are now stunted and do not produce good timber. (Some other species of oak and also the Sweet Chestnut *Castanea sativa* have been planted in the past.)

FLACOURTIACEAE – the Kei Apple family

HA   *Doryalis caffra*   Kei Apple
The Kei Apple originates from South Africa; it is a thorny shrub up to 5 m high, with clusters of alternate, blunt, oval, dark green leaves about 4 cm long. Strong thorns several centimetres long stick out at right angles to the twigs, so that a thicket is quite impenetrable. The flowers are small and inconspicuous and the fruits resemble a small yellow apple; they are very acid but can be made into jam or pickle with other fruits.
     H: Kei Apple occurs locally at low to mid altitudes, for instance near sea level at Sandy Bay, on Mundens Hill and at Scotland.
     A: Not listed by the Packers, but we noted a specimen near Two Boats in 1995.

FRANKENIACEAE – the sea heath family

*H   *Frankenia portulacifolia*   Tea Plant, St Helena Tea
This endemic species has relatives throughout the subtropics of the southern hemisphere. It is a wiry brittle bush up to 1.5 m high, with twigs and leaves opposite.

425

St Helena Tea

The leaves are minute (2 mm long) with the edges rolled downwards so far that they almost meet at the back, but leaving a conspicuous cleft. The leaves turn brown as they die, and the vernacular name apparently arose because the dead ones that collect below the plants look rather like black tea. The wood is hard and mahogany coloured. The small, starry, white flowers have five petals and yellow centres. The minute seeds are formed in an egg-shaped capsule and it seems likely that the ancestors of the Tea Plant reached St Helena by means of floating capsules. It is suspected that introduced House Mice now eat many of the seeds.

The Tea Plant is now restricted to a few sites on cliffs in the east and south of the island, from sea level to 300 m, including the Barn, Turks Cap Ridge, between Prosperous Bay and Gill Point, and scattered along the south coast; in 1995 it was estimated that there were more than 1000 plants on Man and Horse Cliffs. It was previously more widespread, occurring, for instance, on High Knoll. Members of this family are well known for their tolerance to salty conditions and the Tea Plant was probably an important component of the Scrubwood scrub community on the steep, loose slopes above the sea in the far south of the island: we saw many large, spreading, dead bushes – and some live ones – below Castle Rock Plain. We found larvae of a wood-boring weevil in the stems of living plants, but they were not identifiable.

GERANIACEAE – the geranium family

In addition to the endemic *Pelargonium*, the Scarlet Geranium *P. inquinans* sometimes grows wild in dry places, and cultivars of various scented Pelargoniums which were tried for oil production in the 19th century may also persist.

*H   *Pelargonium cotyledonis* Plate 28   Old Father Live Forever

The closest relatives of this species occur in southern Africa. Old Father is a low-growing succulent shrub with swollen, shiny, tortuous, grey brown rootstock on the surface of the ground, sometimes losing its leaves and appearing lifeless in the dry season: hence the local name. The stalked, geranium-like leaves which appear after rain are rich green, thick and downy. The bark is thick and fleshy, peeling off in small fragments. The flowers are borne in a small group on the end of a long thin stem, and are five-parted, about 2 cm across, pure white and scentless. Flowering is mainly after the summer rains around May and June, and sometimes starts while the plant is still leafless. The fruits are pointed and the small seeds are dispersed by the wind. Old Father is found on cliffs on Turks Cap Ridge and in various places between Sandy Bay Barn and Man and Horse, including the cliffs of the Gates of Chaos; it used to occur also at High Knoll and Coles Rock.

Old Father Live Forever

GRAMINEAE (= POACEAE) – the grass family

Grasses have hollow, jointed, rounded or compressed stems, sheathed by the bases of the leaves; the flowers are typically borne in spikes or more elongated inflorescences. Quentin Cronk has pointed out that the colonisation of St Helena by plants started at a time when grasses were still relatively rare in Africa, so one would not expect ancient colonisations to have produced highly distinctive endemic grasses on the island. In fact, only one of some 56 species of grasses recorded from St Helena is considered endemic; nearly all the rest are undoubtedly introduced, but a few may have colonised naturally from Africa, but not have had time to become distinct. Ascension Island became available for colonisation by plants more than 10 million years later than St Helena, at a time when there was a rich grass flora in southern Africa; it has representatives of several groups of modern African grasses among the plants considered to be native; two of these are endemic.

We list below the few grasses that are perhaps indigenous on one or other of the islands, together with some of the more important introduced species. One of the earliest requests of the St Helena settlers to the Directors of the East India Company in England was for hayseed, and many European and other grasses have been introduced to both islands.

(H)   *Agrostis bergiana*
This grass, which is also known from South Africa, may have been indigenous on St Helena: it was collected by Burchell in Sharks Valley but has not been seen since.

H   *Agrostis capillaris* (ex *A. tenuis*)   Hay Grass, Common Bent Grass
This is a slender grass that can produce a delicate, spreading, brown panicle up to more than half a metre high, but is more often seen as a low-growing pasture grass. It was probably introduced in the late 17th century and used to be abundant between 400 and 800 m, but has now declined.

H   *Anthoxanthum odoratum*   Hay Grass, Sweet Vernal Grass
This perennial tufted grass grows to half a metre high; it has flat leaves and the flowers form a compact spike. The species is a common hayfield grass in Europe and was probably brought to St Helena in the earliest decades of the colony. It is one of the most abundant grasses in pastures from 400 m to the summits of the ridges; in the past meadows of it were cut for hay from November to January.

A   *Aristida adscensionis* Plate 28
On Ascension this vigorous species is typically 7-25 cm high and bears its flowers in the form of a fairly compact panicle. It is indigenous and was described from the island in 1698, but was later found to be widespread in the Mediterranean and the tropics. Members of the genus are evidently good colonists and have undergone an adaptive radiation in the Galápagos; the seeds probably travel caught up in the plumage of birds. This grass is still common – though local – in the dry regions at low altitudes; above 600 m it is now scarce and local, but it was widespread on the mountain before the spread of Greasy Grass *Melinis minutiflora*.

HA   *Bambusa* species   Bamboos
The bamboos are large perennial grasses with strong, woody, conspicuously jointed stems.
   H: Several species grow at intermediate levels, including the impressive Giant Bamboo in the forest near Plantation House, and Bamboo Hedge in Sandy Bay. A species growing to about 6 metres is used for rishing rods, and pieces of the stem of a larger one are cut open and baited with poison for rats.
   A: A dense bamboo forest around the Dewpond on the Peak of Green Mountain was established near the end of the 19th century.

HA   *Cynodon dactylon*   Wire Grass, Bermuda Grass
A creeping, salt-tolerant tropical grass that produces stolons and is almost ineradicable if it invades a garden bed. The leaves are short and the live and dead ones lie in rows like oblique teeth in a double-sided comb. The flowers are borne in a fan of finger-like spikes clustered at the top of the stem. In some parts of the world, this grass is poisonous.

H: Melliss referred to this species as perhaps the most abundant grass in the island; it is still common but local in dry areas, including places close to the sea at Sandy Bay; it may be indigenous.

A: Common but local in dryer areas. Packer suggests that it was introduced via Australia in 1875.

HA   *Digitaria ciliaris*   Tropical Finger Grass

This species is variable in size and has flowers in a series of narrow finger-like spikes near the tip of the stem. It is widespread elsewhere in the tropics, and may be indigenous on both islands.

H: Common in dry places around 200 m, as well as in the uplands. (Several other *Digitaria* species have recently been introduced.)

A: This seems to be the species recorded by Duffey as *Digitaria* cf. *adscendens* H.B.K., and may be the grass collected – as *Panicum sanguineum* – by J.G. Forster in 1775. It is quite common in the lower parts of the humid zone, above about 250 metres.

H   *Ehrharta* (ex *Erharta*) species

At least three species of *Ehrharta* are present on St Helena, including the very common Summer Grass, *Ehrharta erecta*, which occurs in rocky and often dry places over a wide range of altitude.

A   *Enneapogon cenchroides* (= *E. mollis*).

This grass springs up on Ascension after exceptional rains and temporarily covers large parts of the lowland desert with hay. The botanist who first recorded an episode of this kind suggested that the seeds had been brought to the island in about 1915, caught up in the plumage of Wideawakes.[3] We find the idea of recent natural arrival of the species unconvincing in terms of probability (Ascension was there for a million years before people); recent introduction is plausible, but we suspect that the species is indigenous and was unrecorded previously because it becomes apparent only at long intervals..

H   *Eragrostis cilianensis*.

This is an elegant, tiny grass with miniature 'bottlebrush' inflorescences, which grows in tight tufts. It is typical of dry areas below 350 m and is one of the few plants capable of surviving in hostile environments such as Prosperous Bay Plain and the scoria near Gill Point, the dry hills in Sandy Bay and on Ladder Hill. It is widespread in warm dry areas of the old world and is probably indigenous on St Helena.

*H   *Eragrostis saxatilis* Plate 29   Hair Grass

This endemic species has its closest relatives in southern Africa. It is larger than *E. cilianensis* and grows in dense tufts; in the past the hair-like leaves were chopped up and used as a strengthener for lime mortar. It is now confined largely to phonolytic intrusions such as Lot and the adjoining ridge (where it was found by Burchell), High Hill and on cliffs in the south and west, especially Man and Horse, where it grows with Scrubwood, Tea Plant and Salad Plant.[4] (Other species of *Eragrostis* also occur on Ascension and St Helena.)

---

[3] O. Stapf (1917).

[4] Q.C.B. Cronk (2000) mentions that an undescribed species of *Eragrostis*, similar in growth form to *E. saxatilis*, is prsent on these cliffs and on Sandy Bay Barn. The photograph of the inaccessible clumps in Plate 29 shows one or other of these species.

A   *Melinis minutiflora* Plate 29   Greasy Grass
A hairy, sticky grass with a characteristic musty scent; the flowering heads are tall, elegant, purple spears. This grass has been very common on the lower slopes of the mountain since at least 1886, and its spread may have led to the disappearance of some indigenous species.

H   *Panicum coloratum*
This small grass bears its flowers in loose panicles. The species is widespread in tropical and subtropical Africa, and may be indigenous on St Helena; it occurs around 400-600 m in dry rocky places, including barren slopes below Distant Cottage.

HA   *Panicum* species
Several other species of *Panicum* are present on both islands, including Guinea Grass *P. maximum*, a tussocky species which is an important perennial forage crop on St Helena.

HA   *Paspalum scrobiculatum*   Cow Grass
This is a coarse and unpalatable species introduced in the 18th century. It is common but unwelcome in pastures and invades land cleared of flax; in the past it was used for thatching ricks, stuffing mattresses and in forming stoppers for bottles of milk. (Other species of *Paspalum* are present on both islands; *P. conjugatum* is common on Green Mountain on Ascension.)

H   *Pennisetum clandestinum*   Kikuyu Grass
This grass is one of the latest arrivals on St Helena, having been introduced only in 1934; now it is the most abundant grass on the island, having largely replaced *Anthoxanthum odoratum* and *Agrostis ciliaris* to become the main constituent of pastures between 400 m and the summits; it makes less good hay and silage than the species it replaced, since its creeping stems are woody.

H   *Pennisetum macrourum* (ex *Gymnothrix caudata*)   Thatching Grass
This tussocky grass can grow to almost two metres high, and its sharp serrated edges make it unpalatable to cattle and very unpleasant to walk through. In the past it was used for thatching cottage roofs and hay ricks; it is widespread both in dry pastures and in damp gut bottoms,

HA   *Plagiochloa oblitera*
This is a small creeping grass adapted to dry conditions in barren places. It was originally described from St Helena but also occurs in South Africa as well as on Ascension, and is now considered to be probably introduced.
     H: Occurs locally in dry places, including High Knoll fort.
     A: Scarce on Green Mountain.

H?A   *Polypogon monspeliensis*   Annual Beard-grass
This grass grows up to nearly a metre high, in tufts in wet places. The leaves are flat and the flowers are borne in a dense silky spike. The species is widespread in warm parts of the Old World and it may be indigenous on St Helena. (Other species of *Polypogon* occur on both islands and it is also possible that *P. monspeliensis* is present on Ascension.)

HA   *Setaria verticillata*   Love Grass, Rough Bristle-grass
A low-growing grass with leaves up to 1.6 cm wide; the flowers are borne in long clinging spikes, which adhere to clothes.
     H: Found in shady places fairly high up.
     A: Widespread but local in the desert lowlands and the foothills of the mountain.

HA   *Sporobolus africanus*   Cape Grass, African Dropseed
This is an aggressive species growing to one metre high, with a long (up to 35 cm) and very narrow upright inflorescence.
  H: Very common at middle to high levels.
  A: Probably a fairly recent introduction, but now dominant on the north and west sides of Green Mountain above about 600 m.

*A   *Sporobolus caespitosus*
This tiny perennial endemic grass, less than 10 cm high, grows in thick tufts in which the outer leaves are often all dead. The flowering spike is hidden among the leaves. *S. caespitosus* grows on bare rock slopes and steep cinder banks exposed to strong winds and mist, above about 600 m. It is now rare and confined to the northern and eastern sides of Green Mountain; a population of just over 300 individuals was recorded in 1998. The species used also to occur on the exposed western face of Weather Post. It was probably ousted from the less steep slopes under competion with a number of alien plants, but survives on the nearly vertical ones where there is less competition.

*?†A   *Sporobolus durus*
This endemic grass, which may now be extinct, grew in tussocks up to 30 cm high, which is much larger than *S. caespitosus*. The last recorded specimens were found in 1886 at 460 m on the west side of Weather Post (Eric Duffey's record from 1958 was incorrect), and members of an Edinburgh University Expedition found no sign of it in 1998. The introduced grasses *Melinis minutiflora* and *Sporobolus africanus* are now dominant in this area and may have entirely displaced *S. durus*.

HA   *Stenotaphrum secundatum*   Mat Grass
A creeping leafy introduced grass that forms a soft, green, velvety-looking turf.
  H: Very common in lawns and pastures from 300 m to the summits of the ridges.
  A: Recorded from near Rock Cottage on Green Mountain.

HALORAGACEAE – the gunnera family

†H   *Gunnera* species
Gunneras have enormous, long-stalked leaves and bulb-like rhizomes. They have not been on St Helena during historic times, but Quentin Cronk informs us that the group was represented on the island in the distant past (see Chapter 4).

IRIDACEAE – the iris family

H?A   *Romulea rosea* (ex *Trichonema ochroleucum*)   Wild Pansy
A small bulbous herb, usually small but reaching 30 cm high in certain places. The leaves are narrow with the edges curled under, and the stalk is triangular. The flowers (appearing around September) are six-petalled, pink and star-shaped.
  H: Wild Pansy is common in dry, grassy places such as Longwood and Rosemary Plain.
  A: An unidentified species of *Romulea* has been found in pastures on Green Mountain.

H   *Watsonia iridifolia*   Sour Bulb
A bulbous plant similar to Gladiolus. Leaves are sword-shaped, the flowers about 3.5 cm across, six-petalled and orange-red, with three dark anthers. Blooming is

430

around October, and the plants die back after flowering. This South African species is common along the central ridge at high elevations. (Other species of this and related genera are cultivated and a few have escaped and grow wild locally.)

JUNCACEAE – the rush family

Several members of the genus *Juncus* have been introduced to St Helena; these have rigid tubular stems and lack leaf blades. The flowers are small and inconspicuous and occur in tufts at the top or on the side of the stem; unlike those of grasses and sedges, they have six petalloid structures (tepals) that open in a conventional way, with the fruit forming in the centre. Apart from the ones listed below, an additional species – *Juncus lomatophyllus* – has been found in the past; it was probably introduced from South Africa.

H   *Juncus bufonius*   Star Grass
A small rush about 20 cm high, somewhat branched and with flowering heads at the forks and at the tips of the branches. It has sometimes been treated as probably indigenous, but Cronk considers it to have been introduced from Europe in the 18th century.

H   *Juncus capillaceus*   Bull Grass
A very slender but tough rush growing in dense clumps. The stems are up to 20 cm high and the flowers are individually stalked but borne in small groups some way below the tips of the stems. This rush is common in pastures above about 400 m, for instance near Fairyland; it originated in South America

H   *Juncus effusus*   Soft Rush
This rush, which is common in wet pastures in Europe, forms clumps up to 1.5 m high; the stems are sheathed at the base; untidy tassel-like spikelets arise from the side of the stalk.

LABIATAE (= LAMIACEAE) – the sage family

Apart from the species listed, several labiates occur as weeds or have escaped from cultivation on St Helena.

A   *Hyptis suaveolens*
This is an upright herb with a mint-like scent up to 30 cm high, with small blue flowers. It was found by Mrs Kay Hutchfield after heavy May rains, in gullies on Donkey Plain, at Grazing Valley and near Two Boats; we think it is probably a recent introduction.

H   *Leonotis nepetifolia* Plates 3, top left and 29   Nargy Plant, Lion's Ear
The local name is after Nargy Williams who is said to have introduced this species in the 20th century, although there is confusing information suggesting that it may have been present much earlier. It is an upright weed growing to 1.2 m high, with broad, soft, hairy leaves. The flowers are orange red and tubular, and are borne in winter in sharp-spined balls about 5 cm across, set at regular intervals on the stems; these are golden brown, stiff and square in section, and persist throughout the dry season. The Nargy Plant is spreading in the valleys of the northwest coast of the island. In the mid 1970s Williams found it confined to the Jamestown valley and Half Tree Hollow, but it is now dominant in much of Breakneck Valley, making it difficult to walk away from the paths. This may be yet another example of a casual introduction of an alien species liable to cause inconvenience and eventually to require costly remedial action.

431

HA   *Leonurus sibiricus*

A stiff, erect, hairy herb with a square stem growing to almost one metre, with a spike of purple flowers in whorls from which pairs of strap-like leaves protrude; the lower leaves are lobed. The dead flower spikes can be used in flower arrangements.

    H: Occurs as a weed of cultivated ground.

    A: Can be found locally at middle levels on Green Mountain.

H   *Mentha aquatica*   Wild Mint, Water Mint

This was probably the species introduced by the Portuguese in the 16th century. It grows to about 30 cm, with leaves 5 cm long; the flowers are lilac pink. Melliss recorded that people dried it for use as a substitute for tea, and also scattered the plant around their cottages to destroy fleas. Wild Mint used to be abundant but is now relatively uncommon, occurring in brackish streams, as at Manati Bay, but also sometimes in dry pastures. (Another species of mint is grown in gardens.)

HA   *Stachys arvensis*   Field Woundwort

A square-stemmed, hairy, erect annual weed up to 25 cm high. The leaves are opposite and oval with serrated margins and rather like a garden mint; the flowers are pale lilac and borne in the axils of the leaves.

    H: A troublesome weed of higher land.

    A: Scarce on Green Mountain.

H   Unidentified labiate   Balm of Gilead

This obscure species, tentatively identified as *Phlomis* species by Melliss, has square stems, pink flowers and leaves that smell of menthol when crushed; in the past, they were used to prepare a tea. It occurs very locally at about 600 m.

LEGUMINOSAE (= FABACEAE) – the pea family

In addition to the trees and shrubs listed, St Helena has a number of introduced, weedy, leguminous herbs in the genera *Desmodium*, *Medicago*, *Melilotus* and *Vicia*.

A   *Acacia farnesiana*

The identity of this small (1.5 m) tree has recently been confirmed by the Royal Botanic Gardens at Kew; it is rather similar to the Mexican Thorn (*Prosopis*). The stiff, spreading branchlets are brown with many slightly raised oval spots; they follow a distinctly zig-zag course and pairs of strong thorns often spring from the point at which the stem changes direction. The flowers are in numerous, small, bright orange yellow balls. This tree is abundant locally near Two Boats and in other places in the foothills of Green Mountain. (This species was reported from St Helena by Roxburgh but does not seem to have been noted recently.)

HA   *Acacia longifolia*   Port Jackson Willow, Sydney Golden Wattle

A small tree (up to 8 m) in which the dark green 'leaves' (actually phyllodes, which are winged leaf stalks) are up to about 15 cm long, and are narrow, with parallel veins and blunt, slightly asymmetrical tips; they are confusingly like the leaves of some eucalypts, but those have normal, branching veins. In spring the tree produces a blaze of pale yellow flowers in spikes. The seeds are borne in thin brown pods about 15 cm long, and are black, oval and 5 mm long.

    H: Port Jackson Willow has been planted extensively but also seeds itself, and is probably now the commonest acacia on the island, especially at middle altitudes. Older

432

Babies' Toes *Hydrodea crypytantha* ***H**

Salad Plant *Hypertelis acida* ***H**

Lobelia *Trimeris scaevolifolia* ****H**

New Zealand Flax *Phormium tenax*, Yam *Colocasia esculenta*, Furze *Ulex europaeus*, Blue Weed *Ageratum conyzoides* and other invasive plants choking a gut **H**

Wild Mango *Schinus terebinthifolius* **H**

New Zealand Spinach *Tetragonia tetragonioides* **HA**

Prickly Pear (English Tungy) *Opuntia cf cochinillifera* **H**

Wild Currant *Lantana camara* with Venus Rose *Catharanthus roseus* **HA**

PLATE 25

PLANTS OF THE ISLANDS

Small Bellflower
Wahlenbergia angustifolia ***H**

Large Bellflower
Wahlenbergia linifolia ***H**

Gumwood
Commidendrum robustum ****H**

Saltbush *Atriplex semibaccata* **H**

Wild Coffee
Chrysanthemoides monilifera
H

Bastard Gumwood *Commidendrum rotundifolium* ****H**

False Gumwood *Commidendrum spurium* ****H**

Scrubwood *Commidendrum rugosum* ****H**

PLATE 26

PLANTS OF THE ISLANDS

Black Cabbage
Melanodendron integrifolium **H

She Cabbage
Lachanodes arborea **H

He Cabbage
Pladaroxylon leucadendron **H

Whitewood *Petrobium arboreum* **H

Boneseed *Osteospermum sanctae-helenae* *H

Pagoda Plant
Cotula coronopifolia **H**

St Helena Tuft-sedge
Bulbostylis lichtensteiniana *H

Diana's Peak grass
Carex dianae *H

PLATE 27

PLANTS OF THE ISLANDS

Left, top to bottom
Tea Plant (St Helena Tea) *Frankenia portulacifolia* ***H**
Old Father Live Forever *Pelargonium cotyledonis* ***H**
French Grass *Euphorbia heleniana* ***H**

Top right Ascension Spurge *Euphorbia origanoides* ***A**

Centre, top to bottom
Wild Pepper *Cluytia pulchella* **H**
Grass *Aristida adscenionionis* **A**

Right, top to bottom
Poison Peach *Diospyros dicrophylla* **H**
Castor Oil *Ricinus communis* **HA**

PLATE 28
PLANTS OF THE ISLANDS

Left, top to bottom
Greasy Grass *Melinis minutiflora* **A**
'Hair Grass' *Eragrostris* species ***H**
growing with Salad Plant *Hypertelis
acida* ***H**
Hogweed *Commicarpus helenae* **HA**

Centre, top to bottom
Sida cordifolia **HA** with Nargy Plant
Leonotis nepetifolia (top) **H**
Black Olive *Olea africana* **H**

Right, top to bottom
Guava *Psidium guajava* **HA**
Buddleia *Buddleja madagascarensis* **HA**
Seed-work Acacia
Leucaena leucocephala **HA**

PLATE 29
PLANTS OF THE ISLANDS

Left, top to bottom
Yellow Thistle
Argemone mexicana **HA**

Rosemary (Island Rosemary)
Phylica polifolia ***H**

St Helena Plantain *Plantago robusta* ***H**

Centre, top to bottom
Passion Flower *Passiflora suberosa* **A**

Sweet Spoor *Pittosporum undulatum* **H**

Purslane *Portulaca oleracea* **HA**

Top right Spoor *Pittosporum viridiflorum* **H**

Below
Olive (St Helena Olive) *Nesiota elliptica* ****H**

PLATE 30

PLANTS OF THE ISLANDS

Redwood (St Helena Redwood) *Trochetiopis erythroxylon* **H

Dogwood (St Helena Dogwood) *Nesohedyotis arborea* **H

Diddly Dight *Solanum nigrum* group **HA**

Wild Brinjal *Solanum sodomaeum* group **HA**

Boxwood *Mellissia begonifolia* **H PHOTO: Vanessa Thomas

Ebony (St Helena Ebony) *Trochetiopis ebenus* **H

Bilberry *Solanum mauritianum* **H**

PLATE 31

PLANTS OF THE ISLANDS

Top left Jellico *Sium bracteatum* ***H**

Top right Dwarf Jellico
Sium burchellii ***H**

Centre left Black Scale Fern
Diplazium filamenstosum ***H**

Bottom left Tree Fern
Dicksonia arborescens ***H**

Bottom centre
Elaphoglossum dimorphum (top
centre) ***H**, *Elaphoglossum
bifurcatum* (centre, dissected) ***H**,
Elaphoglossum conforme (bottom
centre) **H** and *Elaphoglossum
nervosum* (bottom right) ***H**

Right, top to bottom
Tribulus cistoides **H**

Fern *Asplenium erectum* **HA**

Fern *Nephrolepis* species **A** with
Psilotum nudum **A**

PLATE 32

PLANTS OF THE ISLANDS

trees are very susceptible to attack by the Damp-wood Termite, which hollow out the trunks; but these are naturally short-lived trees so their lifespan may not be much affected.

A: Introduced in about 1861 and planted extensively, but now only locally present on the mountain.

H   *Acacia melanoxylon*   Blackwood, Australian Blackwood, Blackwood Acacia
This tree is fast growing and reaches at least 20 m in height. As in the last species the 'leaves' are really phyllodes, with parallel veins; in *A. melanoxylon* they are broader, oval but pointed, and dark green. The flowers are creamy-yellow and are small round heads in racemes, produced in late winter; the pods are long and brown. The Blackwood was introduced in the mid 19th century and has been extensively planted, but it also regenerates naturally by seeds or root suckers and is now very common at middle altitudes.

HA   *Acacia species*   Acacias, Mimosas, Wattles
On St Helena numerous other species of *Acacia* have been planted and a few are now common in the wild. There are probably a few other species on Ascension.

H   *Albizia lopantha* (= *A. distachya*)   Black Boy, Plume Albizia
This is a small tree (up to 5 m), lacking thorns and with feathery pinnate leaves when young. It can be distinguished from acacias by the numerous stamens which protrude from the flower like a tassel but are united at the base (those of acacias are free); the flowers are yellow and the jet-black seeds are used in ornamental beadwork; the wood is used as fuel. This species is fairly common at around 500 m and provides good fodder.

HA   *Cassia occidentalis*   Stinking Weed
An unpleasant-smelling shrub up to half a metre high, with pinnate leaves. The yellow flowers are in groups of 2-4 on short stalks and the petals – unusually for this family – are almost equal in size; when ripe, the seeds rattle in the conspicuous pods. The species is widespread in warm parts of the world.

H: Now rare, but was evidently much more common in the last century, in dry, rocky places, for instance near Lot. The seeds have been used to make a bitter coffee. (Other species of *Cassia* are also present.)

A: Very common in the dryer areas.

(H) *Entada scandens*   Sea Bean
The brown seeds of this plant, 5-7 cm across, are sometimes washed up on the windward shores, having apparently floated round from the Indian Ocean. Melliss recorded that they sometimes germinated and the plants achieved a considerable size, but the species is not established on the island.

H   *Erythrina caffra* Plate 7   Thorn, Thorn Tree
Although introduced from South Africa only in the 19th century, it quickly became a common and conspicuous tree on land between about 500 and 700 m. It often occurs on boundaries because pieces of stem stuck in the ground usually take root and form permanent markers. Thorn trees can attain great size (about 20 m) but the large (up to half a metre long) trifoliate leaves are much used for fodder, so the trees are usually lopped or pollarded for this purpose and thus become grotesque in shape. The trunks are more or less spiny and up to 1.5 metres in diameter; old trees are often hollow. The flowers are scarlet, about 7.5 cm across and borne in spectacular crowded terminal

433

groups; the flowering season is prolonged, but with a peak in July and August. The seeds are bright red and are used for bead work, often in combination with those of *Leucaena leucocephala*.

HA   *Leucaena leucocephala* (= *L. glauca* = *Piptadenia peregrina*) Plate 29
Seed-work Acacia, Wild Tamarind
A rapidly growing shrub with smooth greyish bark, which reaches 4 m in height. The feathery leaves bear numerous small leaflets that close up at night; the leaflets are shorter than in *Prosopis* and have pointed tips (rounded in *Prosopis*). The flowers are white, in small round heads. The thin, narrow pods, which are initially green but later brown and conspicuous, have strong ribs indicating the position of the small, shiny, dark-brown seeds; these are collected and strung together, often with those of Thorn, to make necklaces and other jewellery.

    H: Seed-work Acacia grows frequently in dry areas in the north, from about 200-500 m.

    A: One of the commonest shrubs of the dry lava areas.

A   *Prosopis juliflora* Plate 15   Mexican Thorn (locally Thorn), Mesquite
A small tree, reaching a height of five metres and diameter of ten metres, in which the branches grow almost horizontally, drooping towards the tips so that the lower ones touch the ground. The twigs follow a slightly zig-zag course, with vicious 2 cm thorns at each angle and leaves at some of them. The tap-root can penetrate 30 m into the ground to reach water. The leaves are much-divided and fern-like, the leaflets parallel-sided and with rounded tips (compare *Leucaena leucocephala* in which the leaflets are shorter and slightly pointed). The inconspicuous flowers are catkin-like and lemon yellow, in hanging clusters. The long pods are initially green with the line of seeds conspicuous, but later turn yellow and swell up with a sweet pulp around the seeds. The pods are eaten by donkeys and sheep, and intact viable seeds can be found in the dung. The Thorn is clearly being spread around the island in this way; its effect on the island ecosystem has already been discussed.

H   *Psoralea pinnata*   Gobblegheer
This species has sometimes been considered indigenous, but was probably introduced from South Africa in the 18th century. It is a tall (up to 4 m) shrub with straight branches and fine, needle-like leaves giving the impression of a conifer. Because of this, and the fact that the blue and white flowers appear around Christmas time, it is often used in decorations. Gobblegheer occurs locally in fairly damp places in the southwest, for instance at Man and Horse and High Hill, but it is also cultivated.

HA   *Ulex europaeus* Plate 25   Furze
This is a much branched, rigid shrub covered with spines which are modified leaves. The bright yellow flowers are grouped mainly at the branch tips; blooming is prolonged, but on St Helena occurs mainly in winter.

    H: Furze was introduced from Europe in the 18th century for fodder, fuel and stock fencing. It thrives at medium to high levels (500-750 m.), is capable of competing with New Zealand Flax and is a serious invader of pastures. Furze is the main food plant of the Long-tailed Blue Butterfly on St Helena.

    A: Introduced from Britain around 1850 as browse for horses and cattle; now local on the mountain.

LEMNACEAE – the duckweed family

HA   *Lemna minor*   Common Duckweed
This floating aquatic plant is reduced to a pad-like frond less than 10 mm long, with no more than one root and half a dozen veins. This species occurs in Europe and is presumably introduced.
H: Now only occasional in guts and standing water, or growing on the faces of waterfalls; it seems to have been more abundant in the time of Melliss.
A: Occurs in standing water bodies in the higher parts.

LILIACEAE – the lily family

HA   *Aloe* species.
Aloes resemble agaves (Agavaceae) in having a rosette of fleshy, long and pointed leaves near ground level and an upright flowering stem. However, aloes can bloom annually and have flowers that hang down when mature; agaves, in contrast, bloom once at the end of their lives and have upward-facing flower clusters. Several species of aloes have been cultivated on both islands and a few can be found growing wild.

H   *Aloe grandidentata*   Wild Sicreviver, Sempervivum
This aloe, which comes from South Africa, grows to half a metre high. It has dull green backwardly-curved leaves, blotched with white and with prickly edges; the tubular flowers are rose-coloured. The local name refers to the fact that the yellow, gummy, foul-smelling sap has been used against fevers. This species is drought resistant and occurs on waste ground and in dry places at middle levels.

H   *Aloe vera* (= *A. barbadensis*)   Sicreviver, Aloe Vera
Sicreviver grows to half a metre and has pale green or pinkish, gently-tapering leaves with prickly edges; the flowering stem may be branched and the tubular flowers are yellow. The gelatinous sap is used in cosmetics and has an immediate soothing effect on burns; it then forms a clear protective seal that promotes healing. This species grows locally on waste ground at middle levels.

LOGANIACEAE – the buddleia family

H   *Buddleja brasiliensis*[5]   Buddleia
A small shrub, only a metre or so high, with strongly angled stems. The leaves are up to 15 cm long, opposite, with their bases wrapping around the stem; they are lanceolate, toothed, green above and silvery-felted below, as are the stems. The flowers are orange yellow, densely clustered into a narrow terminal spike. This species occurs locally at middle and high altitudes, for instance under pines near High Hill.

HA   *Buddleja davidii*
This species has pale green leaves and mauve to purple small flowers, massed cylindrically.
H: Common in gardens.
A: Introduced in 1858 and spread quickly on the mountain; it was partially cleared around 1900, but is still common in places.

---

[5] The correct spelling of the scientific genus name is now considered to be *Buddleja*.

A   *Buddleja globosa.*
This species has flowers in orange balls 2 cm across. It was found by Packer on the path to the Dew-pond.

HA   *Buddleja madagascariensis* Plate 29   Buddleia
This Buddleia is a vigorous straggling shrub with silvery leaves and hanging loose groups of small orange flowers in a terminal spike, produced especially in winter. The scurf of the stems and leaves can cause irritation, coughing and apparently even death; nonetheless, the plant is much used by rats.

   H: A straggling shrub which was noted as invasive by Melliss; it is found on the central ridge above 550 m.

   A: Occurs on the weather side of the mountain, with the fern *Marattia*.

MALVACEAE – the mallow family

H?A   *Gossypium indicum*   Cotton
A shrub growing to about 3 m. The leaves are long-stalked and palmate. The flowers are large and pale yellow, fading to brown, with their bases enclosed by two large bracts. These bracts persist in the fruit, which is hard and brown, with three compartments; this opens to expose the white fibres that form the cotton of commerce, in which the hard, nut like seeds are embedded. Cotton was introduced to St Helena in 1678 and again in the early 18th century; it is now local in dry areas below about 400m. (*Gossypium barbadense* has been recorded from Ascension, but we have not confirmed its identity.)

H   *Hibiscus diversifolius*   Rock Rose
Species of *Hibiscus* are generally recognizable by the large and brightly coloured five-petalled flowers with a central projecting column which carries both the stamens and the stigma. *H. diversifolius* is a rigid, many-stemmed small shrub with heart-shaped leaves, stiff hairs and conical prickles. The flowers are primrose yellow with a dark red centre. The seed capsules are egg-shaped and covered with hairs and black dots. This species has been growing wild for a long time and is now found on roadsides, in valley bottoms and in waste ground at all altitudes. (Other species of *Hibiscus* are present on both islands, but mainly in gardens.)

H?A *Hibiscus trionum*   Bladder Ketmia
This plant has oval to lobed leaves and creamy white flowers with purple-black centres. It occurs in southern Europe and other warm regions, and was apparently introduced to St Helena in the 18th century. It has been noted as a weed and was seen as recently as 1955. From Ascension Cunninghame in 1698 described in Latin a plant which was subsequently referred to this species, but it has not been found since. (Several other small mallows with pink or yellow flowers have been noted on St Helena and there is probably at least one on Ascension.)

HA   *Sida cordifolia* Plate 29
An upright herb growing to more than half a metre, with the twigs green and the leaves (which are up to 2.5 cm long) pointed, toothed, hairy and with prominent veins. The mallow-type flowers are white or very pale yellow with yellow centres. When the plant dies back in the dry season the pale brown, wiry stems remain, carrying delicate whitish seeding heads. *S. cordifolia* is widespread in the tropics. (Other species of *Sida* are probably present on both islands.)

H: Quite common in dry places near the sea in the northwest of the island.

A: Scattered but widespread, including Cricket Valley and the open northern slopes of Green Mountain.

MELASTOMATACEAE – the melastoma family

A   *Clidemia hirta*   Koster's Curse.
An invasive small shrub from tropical America. The leaves are stiff with five conspicuous veins and the berries are small and black. Frequent on the upper parts of Green Mountain, for instance along Elliot's Path.

MELIACEAE – the mahogany family

HA   *Melia azedarach*   Pride of India, Bead Tree
This tree grows to about 9 m, and is often branched at the base. The leaves are double-compound, long and stalked, reminiscent of European Ash; the leaflets are shiny and with elongate points. Around Christmas the tree produces an array of small, five-parted, fragrant, lilac-coloured flowers, in loose clusters at the end of the branches; these are followed by poisonous fruits, shaped like small olives, which are yellow when ripe; the hard seeds were sometimes used in rosaries. The leaves, steeped in hot water, are said to ease bruises and strains. Melliss commented that in Jamestown the termites hollowed out the trunks, leaving them as shells of bark which eventually snapped off without warning.
   H: Widespread and occurs over a wide range of altitude.
   A: Scarce, occurring mainly near the farm and at Palmers.

MORACEAE – the fig and mulberry family

HA   *Ficus carica*   Edible Fig
The Edible Fig grows well on St Helena, but the fruit are usually spoilt by fruit-fly or taken by Mynas. It was present on Ascension in the past but has not been recorded recently. (Some other species of fig are present in small numbers on both islands.)

H   *Ficus terebrata*
This species withstands salt and drought, and has been planted as a shade tree in Jamestown; it is also present on the hillsides above, and in the past its wood was much used as fuel. (The Peepul *F. religiosa* has also been planted in Jamestown.)

HA   *Morus* species   Mulberry
Mulberries were introduced to St Helena in the early decades of the 19th century, but are now scarce; probably two species were involved. On Ascension one unidentified species has been recorded.

MUSACEAE – the banana family

HA   *Musa* species   Banana
The Banana 'tree' is technically a herb because the trunk is not woody but is made up of tightly-packed bases of the leaves, which are up to two metres long. The flowering stem pushes its way up through these and emerges at the top. The female flowers are borne on

437

a series of 'hands' on which the developing bananas form the fingers; the male flowers are in an enormous, pendulous, purple bud.

H: Widespread in sheltered valleys. R.O. Williams commented that the Banana was by far the most important fruit crop in the 1970s; he found eight distinct types on the island, with fruits including flavoursome small bananas and the larger, bland plantains.

A: Bananas grow in ravines, mainly on the north side of Green Mountain.

MYRTACEAE – the eucalyptus family

Eucalypts, which are diverse in Australasia, can generally be recognized by their untoothed, leathery, oval or pointed leaves and often smooth grey bark; separation of the species is difficult and not all those that have been introduced to Ascension and St Helena have been definitely identified.

A   *Eucalyptus camaldulensis*   River Red Gum
The only eucalypt established on Ascension is said to be *E. camaldulensis*, a species which in Australia only regenerates after its habitat has been temporarily flooded. It was introduced from Kew in 1847, and is now common on the mountain and in some other areas at medium levels.

H   *Eucalyptus grandis*   Rose Gum
This is the most widely planted species on St Helena and can become a large tree, up to about 35 m high. The bark peels in long strips, leaving a light-coloured, smooth trunk; there is often a 'stocking' of rough bark at the base. The leaves are alternate, unequal at the base and up to 12 cm long. Flowers are in groups of 5-7 and creamy white, without petals. This is an important timber tree, with fairly hard, red wood. This species and some other eucalypts suffer damage from the Eucalyptus Snout-beetle *Gonipterus scutellatus*, but the effect has been diminished by biological control of the beetle.

H   *Eucalyptus lehmannii*   Dry Land Tree
A low-growing, spreading tree used with acacias in erosion control on the Crown Wastes. The bark is smooth, the leaves up to 10 cm long, with a sharp tip. The flower is globose, 10 cm in diameter and with a mass of stiff, yellowish anthers and styles; before opening the flowers resemble protruding nipples; when mature the fruits become woody and reminiscent of a mace or spiked club.

HA   *Psidium guajava* Plates 14 and 29   Guava
Some varieties of Guava form a small tree (up to 10 m), but on both islands the species more often occurs as a low-growing stiff shrub. It has satiny, peeling bark and the leathery leaves are opposite, oval and boat-shaped. The white flowers are five-petalled and about 3 cm across, and the spherical edible but acid fruits are green ripening to yellow, with many hard seeds in a pink pulp.

H: Guava grows to a substantial size in the Jamestown valley; it is local elsewhere in dry scrub, for instance in Sandy Bay below Lot, and in this habitat it may be expected to spread, as on Ascension. (One other member of this family, the Rose Apple *Syzigium* (ex *Eugenia*) *jambos* can be found in a few places near houses around 600 m.)

A: Common and widespread at middle levels, forming the main component of the vegetation in some areas on the windward side; it has probably been spread by the donkeys. The Packers comment that futile attempts were made to destroy it around 1900.

NYCTAGINACEAE – the bougainvillea family

HA   *Commicarpus helenae* (ex *Boerhaavia verticillata*) Plate 29   Hogweed
This species, first described from St Helena, is probably indigenous on both islands. It
is capable of growing in the dry coastal zones, and the fruits are glandular and sticky;
those of a related species have been found sticking to the plumage of birds such as
Wideawakes, so we suspect that the plant was brought to the islands by seabirds. It is
a rambler that tends to become yellowish in summer and dies back in February-March
to shoot again in the spring. It has slender, repeatedly bifurcating green stems and
sparse, opposite, dark-green leaves which are soft, broad, dished and crinkled. The
flowers can be either purplish or white.
     H: Occurs on low, barren land near the sea; in the past it has been recorded among the
rocks in the Jamestown area (where Burchell found both purple and white-flowered forms)
and low down in Sandy Bay; we found the white-flowered form near Lot's Wife's Ponds.
     A: This species is not listed by the Packers but was growing near Collyer Point in
1995, with purple flowers.

HA   *Mirabilis jalapa*   Four o'clock, Marvel of Peru
A bushy perennial herb, up to one metre high, with tuberous roots that have been used
as a purgative. Leaves are opposite, heart-shaped and pointed. The fragrant flowers,
which open at about four o'clock, are tubular and funnel-shaped, with five lobes; they
are yellow, white rosy purple or red, with projecting stamens and stigma; the seeds are
black and ribbed.
     H: Almost wild at lower altitudes, mainly in the Jamestown valley.
     A: Common on the upper ramps.

OLEACEAE – the olive family

H   *Olea africana* Plate 29   Black Olive
This species, probably introduced in the 19th century, has hybridized with *O. europaea*
and there are now many intermediate types. The Black Olive grows to about 7 m, with
narrow, pointed leaves varying enormously in length, and in colour from bright green
to grey green, sometimes turning yellowish in drought. Flowers are small and
yellowish white, fruit spherical, green, becoming black when ripe. The Black Olive is a
very common shrub of dry rocky areas at middle altitudes (300-650 m). (Another
African species, *Olea capensis*, has been recorded on the island in the past.)

HA   *Olea europaea*   European Olive
A small tree to 6 m high, with narrow, grey-green leaves and small yellowish-white
flowers. The green fruit eventually turn black.
     H: Originally planted at the Briars, more recently at Bamboo Hedge. This species has
not spread far from habitations but has hybridised with *O. africana*. The surviving
European Olives apparently now rarely produce fruit.
     A: Occurs on the northeast of the mountain and in Breakneck Valley.

ONAGRACEAE – the fuchsia and evening primrose family

H   *Fuchsia boliviana* (ex *F. corymbiflora*)   Giant Fuchsia
A large shrub originating in South America; it grows to at least 2 metres and is
noticeable for its crimson, pendent, tubular flowers up to 10 cm long, and its dark

purple fruit. The leaves are broad, lance shaped and about 15 cm long, with purple veins. This plant is common in shady places in the uplands around 500-700 m.

H   *Fuchsia coccinea*   Fuchsia
A low-growing, scrambling shrub with slender stems. The leaves are opposite, about 5 cm long and with red veins. Flowers are red and are produced mainly in winter. This species was well established in Sandy Bay by the early 19th century and has now gone wild among the Tree Ferns above 700 m on the central ridge. (Another member of this family which is occasionally found as a weed is an evening primrose *Oenothera* species.)

OXALIDACEAE – the wood sorrel family

Members of this family are mostly low-growing herbs; some are grown in rock gardens and others are troublesome weeds. The leaves are alternate, the flowers five-parted and the seeds are dispersed explosively; many species fold their leaves downwards at night.

HA   *Oxalis* species
Several species are present on one or both of the islands, but are presumably introduced; they include *O. corymbosa* (Ladies Thimble) with pink flowers, and *O. corniculata* (Sorrel or Clover) and the aggressive poisonous weed *O. pes-caprae* (Sour Bells or Bermuda Buttercup) with yellow flowers.

PALMAE (or ARECACEAE) – the palm family

Palms were once important in the flora of St Helena. Pollen of two species of palms was found in the fossil pollen beds on the island (see Chapter 4) but both probably became extinct long ago. Now, there are only a few introduced species. Apart from those listed, a few other species of palms have been planted on the islands.

A   *Cocos nucifera*   Coconut Palm
Coconut Palms were planted in various part of Ascension in the last century and there are still about 50 trees widely scattered over the island.

HA   *Phoenix dactylifera*   Date Palm
The Date Palm grows to 25 metres, with a crown of long leaves shaped like ruffled feathers. The sexes are separate, the females bearing large bunches of dates just below the crown.
      H: This palm was introduced by the Portuguese in the 16th century and some trees still survive in James Valley. It is also found near Sandy Bay beach and a few other places.
      A: Introduced before 1850; it is now scarce and local, but can be seen in Cricket Valley, as well as near Georgetown Hospital and Two Boats Club.

PANDANACEAE – the screwpine family

A   *Pandanus* species (? *odorata*) Plate 14   Screwpine
The screwpines are branching palm-like trees with long, narrow leaves and aerial roots that form buttresses around the base of the stem, which shows annual scars of old leaf bases. The cone-like fruits are in sections, reminiscent of pineapples. The Screwpine is scattered on Green Mountain.

440

PAPAVERACEAE – the poppy family

HA   *Argemone mexicana* Plate 30   Yellow Thistle, Prickly Poppy
A thistle-like annual herb with rigid stems and prickly, coarsely lobed, grey-green leaves with conspicuous white veins. The flowers are poppy-like, pale yellow or orange and 5-6 cm across; the seed capsules are prickly. A broken stem will leak yellow latex.
   H: In 1814 Roxburgh commented that this was the most common weed on the island; it is now local in arid places from near sea level (for instance in Broad Gut) to 200 m.
   A: First recorded in 1828 and has evidently been widespread in the dryer parts of the island ever since.

HA   *Fumaria muralis*   Chickweed, Common Ramping-fumitory
A slender annual with pinnate leaves and clusters of about a dozen tubular, lipped flowers which are pink with dark purple tips.
   H: A common weed of gardens at fairly high levels.
   A: Found once by Packer near the mountain farm.

PASSIFLORACEAE – the passion flower family
Several species of passion flowers occur around houses on St Helena and two species have been found on Ascension, one of which is now widespread in the wild.

A   *Passiflora suberosa* Plate 30   Passion Flower
A straggling creeper of open ground, with thin and stiff stems, tendrils and glossy green leaves, either pointed-oval or palmate. The elaborate white flowers are star-shaped, and the fruit pea-sized and green, turning blue black when ripe. The Passion Flower is common on ash slopes, cinder cliffs and lava in the misty areas east of the mountain.

PINACEAE – the pine family

HA   *Pinus pinaster*   Pine, Cluster Pine, Maritime Pine
This tree can grow up to 30 m tall and is pyramidal with spreading and somewhat pendulous branches and reddish-brown fissured bark. The leaves are in clusters of two, stiff and sharply pointed and 10-20 cm long. The cones are borne in clusters and are symmetrically conical; when mature they are glossy light brown and 9-18 cm long; each scale has a prominent prickle.
   H: 'The pineaster' or 'Fir' was introduced from Europe in the late 18th century and planted on a large scale; it thrives on the island between 500 and 750 m and is an important timber tree, with especially fine woods in the area of High Hill; no other pines regenerate naturally on St Helena.
   A: This pine was present on the island in the mid 19th century and may possibly still survive.

PITTOSPORACEAE – the pittosporum family

HA   *Pittosporum undulatum* Plate 30   Sweet Spoor
There is some confusion about the species of *Pittosporum* on the islands, and we are still not sure of the situation on Ascension. *P. undulatum* is a small tree (up to 8 m) which is generally similar to the following species, but with the leaves yellowish green, lanceolate and sharply pointed, usually with conspicuously wavy edges (hence the scientific name).

441

The small, five-petalled flowers are creamy white and fragrant, especially at night; they give rise to conspicuous cherry-sized orange fruit, which split to show scarlet seeds.

H: Much less common than Spoor; we have seen it at Long Range.

A: Present locally, for instance near the Residency and in Breakneck Valley.

H   *Pittosporum viridiflorum* Plate 30   Spoor

A small tree (up to 12 m) with leaves clustered near the tips of the branches. The leaves are leathery, dark green and somewhat convex above; they are up to 10 cm long, oblong, often blunt-ended and with almost straight edges. Flowering is around April and is noticeable because of the strong scent of the tiny yellow flowers, which quickly fade to brown. The fruit are pea-sized green-gold capsules; the seeds are sticky and are evidently dispersed by Mynas. Spoor is common and probably actively spreading in dry places. The leaves are good fodder, and the trees are often kept low by lopping. (A third species of *Pittosporum*, probably *P. tobira*, can be found in gardens; it has large, white, scented flowers.

PLANTAGINACEAE – the plantain family

HA   *Plantago major*   Ground Plantain, Greater Plantain

This is a stemless plant forming a rosette at ground level, with long-stalked, ribbed leaves and cylindrical flowering spikes.

H: Found mainly in damp places around 300-700 m; we noted it below the Heart Shape Waterfall, where the St Helena Plantain was present on the cliff.

A: Has been found on Green Mountain, especially near the farm. (The Ribwort Plantain *P. lanceolata* also occurs on Ascension).

St Helena Plantain

*H   *Plantago robusta* Plate 30   St Helena Plantain

This endemic species has relatives on Pacific islands, South America and southern Africa. The plant varies greatly in size. Large specimens have a thick tap root and a 'trunk' up to 1 m long, crowned with a cluster of very narrow, fleshy leaves up to 40 cm long, and strongly marked with the scars of the fallen ones; small specimens appear as ground-hugging rosettes. The flowering stalk is long and somewhat straggly, reminiscent of a rat's tail, and has tiny green flowers along its length. The seeds of plantains are minute, flat and sticky, so the ancestors of the St Helena endemic species were probably brought to the island on the plumage of birds. The plants now grow especially on cliffs kept moist by dripping water (as at the Heart Shape Waterfall) or by condensation from air rising up high sea cliffs, as at the Barn, Flagstaff and the Stonetops, on Peak Gut Waterfall and on the cliffs near the south west coast. In the past it seems to have been widespread on hilltops at medium levels.

PODOCARPACEAE – the podocarp family

HA   *Podocarpus elongata* Plate 7   Cape Yew

A tall tree capable of growing to 30 m, with brown flaky bark. The leaves are alternate and form a continuous whorl along the green, square twigs. They are up to 7 cm long and 5 mm wide, coming to a slender point, and are dark, glossy green. The fruits are borne in small clusters and are stalked, round and about 2 cm across; they are green, becoming yellow when mature, and contain a single, large seed.

H: This species, introduced early in the 19th century from South Africa, thrives at upper levels on the island. It regenerates by seeding in shady places such as Plantation forest, where there are magnificent mature trees. Cape Yew is an important – though

442

slow growing – forestry species, producing excellent scented furniture timber; it is also good for boat building.

A: Introduced in the first half of the 19th century; some large specimens are present on Green Mountain.

POLYGONACEAE – the knotweed and dock family

In addition to the plant described below, St Helena has two species of *Rumex*, the Curled Dock *R. crispus* and Sheep's Sorrel *R. acetosella*, which occur in cultivations and damp places; another member of the family, *Emex australis*, is found as a weed of low altitudes.

H   *Polygonum glabrum*
This species is widespread in tropical regions and may be indigenous on St Helena, but is now very rare on the island. A vigorous straggling plant with dark green leaves springing from rings on the fleshy stems. The leaves are stalkless, up to 25 cm long, lance shaped and pointed. The small, pink flowers are borne in dense terminal spikes about 4 cm long. *Polygonum glabrum* survives in the wild at Cat Hole, the only site noted by Burchell in the first decade of the 19th century, and can be seen from above when walking along Barnes Road.

PORTULACACEAE – the purslane family

HA   *Portulaca oleracea* Plate 30   Purslane
We consider Purslane to be probably indigenous to both islands. It is a prostrate, spreading plant with straight, swollen and shiny stems that branch forming a regular pattern. The leaves are pale green, slightly fleshy and almost circular, and the flowers are small and yellow, with five petals. The seeds are small and are capable of surviving immersion in the sea; they doubtless floated to the islands, separately or wedged in crevices of driftwood. The species is salt tolerant and is widespread in the tropics on coasts and islands, being one of the first plants to invade coral islets.

H: Purslane was recorded by Burchell early in the 19th century; it is now common in dry rocky areas from about 100 to 400 m, springing up after winter rains. In the past it was gathered and used as spinach, although it is said to be occasionally poisonous.

A: First recorded in 1754; it is now widespread but scarce in dry regions, sometimes close to sea level as at Mars Bay; in the past it was evidently more abundant on the foothills of the mountain. Purslane was eaten by feral goats, and was also used as a salad by members of the garrison in the decades after settlement.

PRIMULACEAE – the primrose family

HA   *Anagallis arvensis*   Pimpernel
This is a low-growing, hairless weed with square, slender, branching stems. The leaves are opposite, stalkless and soft, and the long-stalked, five-parted solitary flowers are borne in the axils of the leaves.

H: Occurs at a wide range of levels. The flowers are generally vivid blue, which has doubtless given rise to the local name Forget-me-not, which is elsewhere applied to blue flowers in the genus *Myosotis* (family Boraginaceae) which apparently do not grow wild on St Helena.

A: The red-flowered form (Scarlet Pimpernel) occurs locally in moist places on Green Mountain.

443

PROTEACEAE – the protea family

HA   *Grevillea robusta*   Silk Oak, Golden Pine, Silver Oak
A tree which grows to 50 m in its native Australia, with alternate and leathery and deeply divided leaves, dark green or coppery green above, silvery below; a young seedling can make a fern-like pot plant. The flowers are golden yellow and borne in a conspicuous one-sided terminal cluster, each flower having a long projecting stigma. Fruit are round with long 'tails' and the seeds are winged.

H: Introduced in the 1930s and thriving over a wide range of altitude; it grows rapidly and is resistant to drought and termites. This tree has the potential to provide valuable timber, coarsely grained but durable.

A: Introduced around 1860 and now local but common around the farm, at Palmers and elsewhere on the mountain.

RANUNCULACEAE – the buttercup family

H   *Ranunculus bulbosus*   Buttercup, Bulbous Buttercup
A hairy plant with much divided, toothed leaves and yellow flowers 1.5-3 cm across. It is local on the central ridge in grassy, damp places. A second species of European buttercup, *Ranunculus trilobus*, occurs in much the same places.

RHAMNACEAE – the buckthorn family

**H   *Nesiota elliptica* (ex *Phylica elliptica*) Plate 30   Olive, St Helena Olive
This species is endemic to St Helena and is currently considered to represent an endemic genus, though this is related to – and presumably derived from – the genus *Phylica*. The latter genus is the one to which the Island Rosemary (see below) belongs, and has highest diversity in southern Africa but is also represented in the Mascarene Islands. The Olive forms a spreading, rounded tree which in the past apparently reached as much as 9 m in height; the wood is dark and hard, and was considered very useful. The leaves are simple, about 6 cm in length and pale green, but the foliage appears greyish green from a distance. The pink flowers 10 mm across are borne in clusters and appear over a prolonged flowering season; the seeds form in a capsule.

The Olive used to be common on the highest parts of the eastern central ridge, especially on the north side, but is now extinct in the wild. It became very rare in the 19th century and was later thought to be extinct, but a single tree was discovered by George Benjamin in 1977 on Cuckold's Point. That tree died in October 1994, but a cutting taken from it had formed a tree four metres tall by 1995, cared for in a special fenced enclosure at Scotland. However, by 1997 it was dead, apparently as a result of fungal infection, and in spring 2000 the only surviving stock of the species consisted of two young trees, one grown from a seed collected from the last wild tree, and one from a seed produced by a cutting that later died. Self-pollination is normally impossible in the Olive; in the wild this ensures outcrossing and maintains genetic variability, but reduces seed set when the population is very small. However, the Environmental Conservation Section recently managed to achieve self-pollination of one of the survivors, obtaining 16 seeds; in March 2000 these were sent to the Royal Botanic Gardens at Kew, in the hope that seedlings can be raised by conventional and micro-propagation techniques, and that any infections can be treated. There is thus still a slim chance that it may eventually be possible to return some trees to the wild, although inbreeding is bound to be a persistent problem.

St Helena Olive

Rosemary

*H   *Phylica polifolia* Plate 30   Rosemary, Island Rosemary, St Helena Rosemary
The Rosemary is endemic to St Helena, with its closest relatives on the Mascarenes and islands in the Southern Ocean. It is now seen only as a straggling or upright shrub up to about 1.5 m high and somewhat resembling the European Rosemary (though quite unrelated to it). In the past, however, it formed a medium-sized timber tree with a short, thick and crooked trunk, and was described by Roxburgh as being of great beauty and fragrance. The leaves are narrow and about 2.5 cm long; they are dark green above but with white felted backs, so that the foliage appears grey-green from a distance. The flowers are small and greenish white, and are produced in October; the green capsules are pea-sized, round and splitting into three, with black seeds. The Rosemary was previously found in dry places in the west of the island, including Rosemary Plain, but was in serious decline by the mid 19th century. It is now restricted largely to a few sites on hard intrusive rocks including High Hill and Lot; in these situations it typically roots in pockets of soil and sprawls over the cliffs. Seeds and plants have recently been collected in the hope of re-establishing the species in other sites on the island.

ROSACEAE – the rose family

HA   *Eriobotrya japonica*   Loquat, Nispero
The Loquat is a small (5 m) tree with large, boat-shaped leaves with strong ribs making a feather pattern; they are dark glossy green above and hairy below. The flowers are white and in clusters, and the fruit are yellow, like small downy plums; they are rather acid for eating raw but are good stewed or for making jelly.
   H: The Loquat was widely planted near houses at middle altitudes; it often seeds itself and is hardy, so it often survives on abandoned properties. The fruit were highly esteemed in the 19th century.
   A: Still grows in some ravines on the north slopes of Green Mountain.

HA   *Rubus pinnatus*   Blackberry
A scrambling, perennial shrub with long, thorny, arching stems. Leaves pinnate, leaflets glossy and toothed. Flowers white, fruit green, turning red and finally blackish.
   H: The Blackberry was introduced from the Cape in about 1775, and quickly became a menace, spreading over the best pasture lands. In the first years of the 19th century considerable efforts were put into control measures, and the Blackberry is now common mainly above 650 m on the central ridge, where it forms impenetrable thickets. Melliss commented that it was: *"assisting in the destruction of the indigenous flora"*.
   A: This species or a closely related one was widespread on the mountain in the middle of the 19th century, and is still common on the weather side.

HA   *Rubus rosifolius*   Raspberry
A bright green shrub with prickly stems and pinnate leaves; the leaflets are toothed. The flowers are rose-type, 3-4 cm across and with five white petals. The fruits are green, turning scarlet, and sit on a five-pointed star formed by the sepals.
   H: This plant, native to tropical Asia, is now local at middle altitudes. The fruit are edible but insipid; in the time of Melliss they were collected and sold for jam making, but the custom may now have died out.
   A: Recorded from Green Mountain in 1958 and widespread in 1998.

445

RUBIACEAE – the bedstraw and coffee family

In addition to the species listed, both islands now have substantial plantations of Coffee *Coffea arabica*, which has scented, white flowers and green berries ripening to red.

A   *Borreria verticillata*
An upright woody plant growing to 50 cm high, with narrow whorled leaves 2-3 cm long. The flowers are borne at the tips of the stems and are white and clover-like. This species is now widespread at fairly high levels, especially on Cronk's and Elliot's Paths, and appears to be spreading.

H   *Canthium lividum* (ex *Canthium huillense*)   Privet
A woody shrub or small tree which is unrelated to the species known as privet in Britain. The Privet of St Helena can be confused with Ink (Solanaceae); the leaves are opposite, elliptical and small (usually less than 3 cm long). The flowers are small and yellow, and are borne in small groups at the bases of the leaves. This shrub can be made into a strong hedge, and also makes good walking sticks. Privet occurs locally at around 500 m.

H   *Cinchona succirubra*   Quinine, Peruvian Bark
A slender tree reaching about 6 m in height. The leaves are opposite, up to about 8 cm long, with long stalks; they are lance-shaped, pointed and glossy, with reddish petioles and veins, and sometimes have swollen glands at the bases of the veins. As they die, the leaves go brilliant red. The purple flowers are borne in dense groups on long stalks in the axils of the leaves, and are tubular, with five petals opening to form a star at the tip.

In the 1860s an attempt was made to establish Quinine – which originates from the Andes – as an island crop. Seed was sent from Kew, the south face of Diana's Peak was cleared and four species of *Cinchona* were planted out in 1868/69. Only *C. succirubra* survives in any numbers, although a few individuals of a second species (*C. officinalis* or a close relative) may still be present. However, the clearance was a tremendous setback for the endemic trees and shrubs; the Quinine bushes were largely succeeded by exotic invasive species such as Blackberry and Buddleia, as well as by the endemic Black Scale Fern.

**H   *Nesohedyotis arborea* Plates 7 and 31   Dogwood, St Helena Dogwood
The Dogwood is the sole member of a genus endemic to St Helena, with its closest relatives possibly in India and Malaysia. It is a small tree up to 7 m high, which when flourishing produces straight upright shoots, often from the base. The leaves are opposite, almost unstalked, hairless, lance-shaped and up to 10 cm long; they are shiny dark green above, whitish green below. They have long, pointed 'drip tips' that curl downwards and even back towards the stem; these tips are an adaptation associated with mist interception, and the Dogwood may be the most effective at this of all the endemic trees. The flowers are only 2-4 mm across and are greenish white, with four tiny white petals; they are borne in dense, rounded clusters at the tips of the branches, and are produced in summer. The fruits are dark brown to black, with tiny seeds in globular capsules.

Dogwoods are still present on both sides of the central ridge above about 700 m, with about 130 individuals known, mainly in very steep places within Diana's Peak National Park; a few are present east of Coles Rock, at High Peak and the Depot. The species was previously well distributed on the ridge, and is still the second most abundant native tree on the Peaks (after the Black Cabbage). Individuals are

Dogwood

long-lived, and may survive even after falling over, by putting down adventitious roots and growing new vertical shoots. The Dogwood has recently been shown to have effectively separate sexes, and seedlings (which sometimes grow on stems of the Tree Fern) are normally found only near trees that function predominantly as females.

*†A   *Oldenlandia adscensionis* (ex *Sherardia fruticosa*)
This important endemic species is apparently now extinct. It was a shrub with woody, hairless stems and thick, leathery, linear leaves, often in whorls of three; the growth form, as recorded in herbarium specimens, is highly variable. Flowers white, 5-petalled and with long corolla tube. *Oldenlandia* was evidently widespread on the slopes of the mountain on the pristine Ascension Island, but declined under the assault of the goats and finally disappeared as a result of competition with vigorous alien plants; the most serious competitor may have been the small leguminous tree *Leucaena leucocephala*.

The last records of *Oldenlandia* were near the end of the 19th century. In August 1874 a naturalist with a German expedition found some plants in a dry watercourse south of Sisters Peak at about 200 m, and in 1888 or 1889 H.J. Gordon, a naval surgeon on the island with an interest in botany, sent a collection to Kew Gardens which included a specimen of the plant, perhaps from the same locality. Since that time, no-one has been able to find this species, the most distinctive of Ascension Island's endemic plants and the only one to achieve the size of a shrubby tree. The closest surviving relatives of *Oldenlandia adscensionis* are in Africa and are mainly herbaceous, suggesting that its ancestors reached the island from the east long ago.

RUTACEAE – the citrus family

HA   *Citrus* species
Several kinds of citrus fruit trees were introduced to both islands. On St Helena they thrived at first, but were later afflicted by a range of pests and diseases; very few trees are now present.

SALICACEAE – the willow and poplar family

A species of willow, perhaps *Salix babylonica* from China, was commonly planted on St Helena in the past, for instance around Napoleon's tomb, at Willowbank and in Grape Vine Gut, being used as food for cattle. However, we are not sure that any trees survive; when 'willow' is referred to on the island it now often relates to Port Jackson Willow *Acacia longifolia* (Leguminosae).

H   *Populus alba*   Poplar, White Poplar
Although this tree can grow to more than 20 m, on St Helena it is typically found in the form of thickets, with stems about 3 m high and propagating by suckers. The bark on young growth is whitish and the leaves are silvery green, with dense felting underneath; the catkins are inconspicuous. The Poplar occurs locally at middle altitudes, between about 400 and 550 m.

SCROPHULARIACEAE – the figwort and foxglove family

Apart from the species listed, a number of cultivated and weedy members of this family, including several speedwells (*Veronica*) are present on both islands.

H *Maurandia erubescens* (ex *Lophospermum scandens*)   Mexican Creeper
A scrambling weed that climbs by twining leaf-stalks. It has rose pink tubular flowers about 7 cm long. The branches are long, slender and hairy, and the leaves are heart shaped, hairy and unevenly toothed. This species occurs mainly on banks and rocky places around the central ridge, for instance at the start of Cabbage Tree Road.

H *Verbascum virgatum*   Twiggy Mullein
A herbaceous biennial with alternate leaves; it has a rosette of oval, notched leaves at ground level, but then produces a flowering stem up to 1 m high, with an array of yellow flowers 3-4 cm across and with five roughly equal lobes. It occurs in open places between 500 and 600 m and is most often seen along roadsides.

SOLANACEAE – the potato family

Apart from the species listed, the Potato *Solanum tuberosum* is widely grown and forms the most important crop on St Helena, even though it is attacked by a wide variety of pests. A few others member of the family have also been cultivated or grown as ornamentals on St Helena but have not gone wild.

H *Cestrum laevigatum*   Ink, Ink Bush
A shrub or small tree which can reach at least 3 m, with rather spindly growth. The alternate, boat-shaped, pointed leaves are bright green and around 6 cm in length; when they fall, they leave prominent scars on the twigs. The greenish yellow flowers have a long tube with five (or four) finger-like petals; they are scented, at least at night, and form in small clusters on the stems. The small, oblong fruits are borne in cups like tiny acorns; they are initially green, then blue-black, with purple juice used by children as ink. The foliage is poisonous to cattle but not to sheep. Ink is very common both in dry scrub and in damp gut bottoms, between about 400 and 650 m altitude.

HA *Datura stramonium*   Thorny Apple
A large-leaved, spreading, branched annual herb up to 60 cm high, with purple or green stems. The long-stalked leaves have a shape reminiscent of oak leaves and are dark green, soft and foul-smelling when broken. The flowers are five-lobed, long and funnel-shaped, white often tinged with lilac or purple. The fruit is like a small walnut, but covered with fine spines of varying length; green, turning pale brown and splitting along four seams to release many small black seeds. The plant is avoided by livestock and both leaves and seeds contain alkaloid poisons.
   H: Fairly common in waste places and in cultivated ground, from about 100 m to 500 m; it can be a serious weed.
   A: Local and scarce.

HA *Datura suaveolens*   Moonflower, Ladies Petticoats
A small, poisonous tree up to 4 m in height, typical of moist and sheltered places. The leaves are up to 30 cm long. The abundant and spectacular scented flowers are pendulous, white, five-pointed trumpets up to 30 cm long.
   H: The Moonflower occurs locally in guts on the central ridge, especially near roads.
   A: Present locally in ravines on Green Mountain.

HA *Lycopersicon esculentum*   Scrunchy Apple, Wild Tomato
Wild Tomato plants form large straggling masses, often in totally barren places. The yellow flowers are followed by tiny orange fruits with particularly strong flavour,

rather as if every tomato had a set 'dose' of essence of tomato, irrespective of its size.

H: Can be found on rocky hillsides, for instance in Sarah's Valley and beside the path to Lot's Wife's Ponds.

A: Grows on dry ashy slopes, for instance near White Hill. Cricket Valley was apparently overgrown with it in 1878.

**H   *Mellissia begoniifolia* Plate 31   Boxwood
This shrub is the sole member of its genus; it is probably related to *Withania*, which occurs in Africa and southern Europe, including the Canary islands. The Boxwood is a tough, much-branched shrub growing to 2.5 m, with crooked stems and a smooth, brownish trunk up to about 8 cm thick. The leaves are clustered and are small, curved, soft, grey green and hairy. The pendent bell-shaped flowers are about 3 cm across, with five fused white petals concealed among the five fused green sepals. The flowers appear around October and are strongly scented, while the plant as a whole has a smell reminiscent of sweaty feet. The Boxwood was formerly abundant in the dry southeastern parts of the island, especially at Boxwood Hill, Long Range Point and the Stone Tops. It survived longest at the latter two sites, but was thought to have become extinct around the end of the 19th century. Late in 1998, however, Stedson Stroud of the St Helena Nature Conservation Group found a single live bush and several dead ones among boulders near Lot's Wife. Although the last bush has now died, seeds collected from it have germinated, offering some hope for the survival of the species.

HA   *Nicandra physaloides*   Apple of Peru, Shoo-fly Plant
A herbaceous annual that grows to one metre and has alternate leaves and bell-shaped, drooping, five-lobed flowers, blue or occasionally white. The fruit is a juiceless berry reminiscent of the Cape Gooseberry. Its presence is reputed to rid a greenhouse of pests.

H: Occurs locally in dry places around 200-300 m, springing up after rains.

A: Local on Green Mountain.

HA   *Nicotiana glauca*   Wild Tobacco
A tall but spindly shrub up to 3 m high, with sparse, characteristically blue-green, long-stalked, oval and pointed leaves with a bloom on them. The five-parted flowers are long yellow tubes, borne in groups at the tips of the slender drooping branches. The copious nectar can easily be shaken out of the flowers.

H: A common shrub in some of the driest parts of the Crown Wastes, from near sea level in guts (for instance near Sandy Bay beach) to about 400 m.

A: Probably brought in recently as an ornamental and now spreading rapidly in dry, dusty areas, especially around Travellers Hill camp, Two Boats and near North East Bay.

HA   *Nicotiana tabacum*   Tobacco
Tobacco is an upright sticky herb growing to two metres and distinguished from the previous species by the yellowish green leaves and pink or white flowers.

H: Apparently already growing on the island in 1697; it is now very local around 150-400 m, for instance near Horse Pasture.

A: Widespread but very local, for instance near Cricket Valley, Dampier's Drip and Spoon Crater.

HA   *Physalis peruviana*   Cape Gooseberry
A spreading, long-lived shrub growing to one metre, with soft, downy, heart-shaped leaves up to 12 cm long. The flowers are borne singly in the leaf axils and are about

449

1.5 cm across. The five petals are pale yellow with a brownish purple mark at the base; they are joined together by their edges, so that the yellow or reddish berry is enclosed in a membranous pointed bag reminiscent of a Chinese lantern. The berries are edible and are stewed or made into jam; they are also appreciated by poultry and pheasants.

H: Common by paths and in waste places, and sometimes invades land cleared of flax. Since the plant is not eaten by goats it flourished in the 19th century when the vegetation was at its nadir, the berries forming a significant resource for the islanders.

A: This plant had reached the island by 1825 and the fruit were gathered by members of the garrison; it is still common in shady places on Green Mountain.

HA *Solanum mauritianum* Plate 31   Bilberry[6]
A large (5 m) invasive shrub, easily recognized from a distance by the silver-green appearance of the foliage, caused by the fine whitish felt that covers the twigs and the underside of the leaves. The leaves are up to 30 cm long, alternate, lance-shaped and with narrow points. The five-petalled flowers are borne in long stalked clusters and are violet with conspicuous yellow anthers. They are quickly followed by poisonous, round fruits, green ripening to yellow or red and reminiscent of the fruits of potato plants. This Central American plant is one of the more unfortunate of the introductions to St Helena from Kew Gardens in the 19th century. Since its arrival around 1870 the plant has become abundant both in dry areas and damp guts from about 600 to 700 m, and adversely affects the indigenous vegetation on the central ridge. This species is also invasive in Madagascar but not in the Azores, where it grows in exposed places. Cronk has recently reported the presence of this species at Damper's Drip on Ascension.

HA *Solanum nigrum* group Plate 31   Diddly Dight, Black Nightshade
An annual shrub up to one metre high, with green, angled stems and dark green, small, lanceolate leaves. The local name is probably a corruption of 'deadly nightshade'. The flowers are borne in groups and are five-petalled, small and white. The berries, resembling tiny tomatoes, are green (at which stage they are poisonous) and finally black; they used to be collected, cooked and eaten on both St Helena and Ascension.

H: Diddly Dight is common in waste ground, but also occurs locally in dry places well away from cultivation, as at the base of Lot. Several closely related species are thought to have been brought to the island and the resulting population is highly variable.

A: Recorded as early as 1829, and now scattered in dry places, including Bears Back and inland from South East Crater.

HA *Solanum sodomaeum* group Plate 31   Wild Brinjal, Sodom Apple
This spreading low shrub (up to one metre high) has indented, crumpled, prickly leaves and purple, 5-petalled, star-like flowers. The fruits are tomato-like, mottled green changing to yellow when ripe, and up to 5 cm across.

H: Wild Brinjal occurs only locally at middle levels, in scrubby places; we have found it at Rock Mount and also at Botley's, where Burchell mentioned that the largest and finest bushes were found.

A: Widespread but scarce.

---

[6] The name Bilberry is now in use locally for *Solanum mauritianum*, although it was historically applied to *Physalis peruviana*; *S. mauritianum* has sometimes been called Elderberry, but by the time of Simmonds (1973) it was already known as False Bilberry.

450

STERCULIACEAE – the cocoa family

Ebony

**H

Trochetiopsis ebenus (ex *T. melanoxylon*) Plates 8 and 31   Ebony, St Helena Ebony
This and the next two species form an endemic genus related to the genera *Dombeya* and *Trochetia* of Madagascar and the Mascarene Islands.[7] Pollen similar to that of modern *Trochetiopsis* has been found in an ancient organic deposit near Turks Cap (see Chapter 4). The Ebony has been listed under the scientific name *Trochetiopsis melanoxylon* in most recent accounts, but had to be renamed in 1995 after the discovery that the specimens to which the name was given are actually of the Dwarf Ebony.[8]

The Ebony is a small tree or low-growing shrub, with trunk diameter of up to 30 cm at the base and a maximum height of 4 metres. The leaves are about 7.5 cm long and are lance-shaped, dark green above, and felted below with golden brown hairs, which are particularly noticeable on the veins and which are also present on the young shoots; the leaves turn red as they die. The flowers are usually borne singly and are about 7 cm across, with five petals about twice as long as the sepals; they are white with a deep purple centre, and gradually change to rose pink before they die; they stick out sideways from the plant (in contrast to the Redwood) and have no noticeable fragrance. Blooming is prolonged, but mainly in winter. The brown seed capsule is about 1.5 cm long, with five compartments; it opens to form a white-centred star; the seeds are angular and about 4 mm long.

Rebecca Cairns-Wicks investigated the pollination system of the Ebony and Redwood, observing bushes planted in a conservation programme.[9] She measured nectar production and recorded insect visitors to the flowers. Her data show that these Ebonies – which were growing in a hot dry site – produced most of their nectar between 5 pm and 9 am (again in contrast to the Redwood), suggesting that the species is adapted to nocturnal pollinators. However, honey bees (which are introduced) are probably the main pollinators at present. Hoverflies including the endemic *Loveridgeana beattiei* visit the flowers, and moths including the endemic pyralid *Pionea delineatalis* are active around the bushes, but it is not clear that they transfer pollen.

The Ebony was formerly common in dry places at middle altitudes (200-500 m), especially in the south and west of the island. However, it lacks defences against grazing and was quickly eliminated from much of its range after the introduction of goats and other herbivores. After the Ebony thickets near the coast in Sandy Bay had been killed by goats, the wood was gathered as fuel for the limekilns. The wood is hard, heavy (sinking in water) and black brown, and is very durable (though brittle); sound pieces of it are still occasionally washed up by the sea, or found in remote parts of the island, although the trees probably died more than a century ago. Until at least the 1970s ebony wood from this source was used in locally made furniture and inlay work (the latter craft introduced by Boer prisoners of war).

The Ebony was thought to be extinct for over a hundred years until George Benjamin and Quentin Cronk found two bushes in 1980 on a cliff north of the Asses Ears. Charles Benjamin was lowered on a rope to collect cuttings, and the ebony has since been successfully propagated and replanted in parts of its original range.

---

[7] W. Marais (1981).

[8] Q.C.B. Cronk (1995a).

[9] R. Rowe (1995).

In cultivation hybrids are formed between Ebony and Redwood, giving rise to a vigorous and beautiful shrub, the Rebony. This is technically known as *Trochetiopsis ×benjaminii*[10] after George Benjamin and is now much planted in island gardens and elsewhere. It is intermediate between the parent species in many ways, and can be distinguished from them by having both silvery and brown hairs on the undersides of the leaves; the wood is pink. Intriguingly, the first generation hybrids have a growth rate double that of either of their parents, indicating that the handful of survivors of the parental species are suffering severe genetic problems as a result of inbreeding during the last few hundred years.

**H

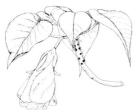

Redwood

Trochetiopsis erythroxylon Plate 31   Redwood, St Helena Redwood

The Redwood differs from its relative the Ebony in being a more upright, medium-sized tree (up to at least 6 m in the past) growing straight on suitable soil. The bark is dark brown, even and fairly smooth, and the wood reddish-brown, close-grained, hard and durable. The leaves of the Redwood are about 7.5 cm long and 5.5 cm wide, paler green than those of Ebony, and on the underside they are green with white-felted veins; they turn yellow and reddish as they die. The flowers are generally borne in pairs, are about 7.5 cm long by 4.5 cm across and are pendulous, never opening widely; they are initially white but quickly turn rose pink and finally brownish red. They have a delicious, sweet and delicate fragrance and produce abundant nectar, mainly by day. The flowers are produced over a long period in summer (with a peak in November) and are visited by many different moths and flies, but especially by the introduced honeybee; it is not clear what would have been the main original pollinator. The fruit is a capsule similar to that of the Ebony and contains 3-5 seeds.

In former times the Redwood was common in the damp woodland just under the central ridge between 500 and 700 m above sea level, occupying the best land for plant growth on the island, along with the She Cabbage. It was still common in 1659 when the East India Company colonised the island, and since the wood is hard and durable, it was used by the settlers for building houses. The tree was also of great importance because its bark (like that of the Ebony) was suitable for tanning the hides of the cattle. As a result of these uses, and because it never regenerated easily, the Redwood quickly became very scarce. In about 1722 it was evidently with difficulty that Byfield (who was later Governor) obtained a couple of young plants no more than an inch high, and raised them to produce seed. The species seems to have been extensively planted after this, since in 1757 the St Helena Records note that the *Queen Sophia* was loaded *"with Bale Goods, Pepper, Salt Petre, and Redwood, Bound for Copenhagen"*. Thereafter, the Redwood was found mainly in island gardens, but a few trees were known to grow in the wild, near Diana's Peak and High Peak.

The last known wild Redwood grew near the base of the waterfall at Peak Gut; it died around 1960. Norman Williams (a retired Forestry Officer) used to collect seed from this tree, and resulting seedlings were planted at Scotland and other sites on the island. Later generations have been grown and planted at High Peak, Scotland, Stitches and Hardings, and a good specimen grows at Mount Pleasant. However, these trees have been produced by self-pollination and are very inbred. Attempts are now being made to arrange cross-pollination among the survivors so as to maximise the genetic variability of the stock.

---

[10] Q.C.B. Cronk (2000), although listed as *benjamini* by Cronk (1995a).

**†H   *Trochetiopsis melanoxylon*   Dwarf Ebony
The Dwarf Ebony is known from only five herbarium specimens, collected between about 1690 and 1772. It probably became extinct at about the end of the 18th century, but seems to have grown on the cliffs around Jamestown and in other arid places in the north of the island below 400 m elevation.

Dwarf Ebony was probably always a small shrub. Specimens can be distinguished from those of Ebony by the leaves, which are less than 4 cm long and with white hairs on the upper as well as the lower surface. The flowers are only about 10 mm across and the petals hardly longer than the sepals; they grew more or less upright on the plant. The seed capsule is about 11 mm long and the seeds are smooth and about 2.5 mm long.

A   *Waltheria indica* Plate 16
A low-growing shrub with straight, brown, rough stems covered with felted hairs. The leaves are oval, crinkled, densely hairy and reminiscent of Alder *Alnus glutinosa*. The flowers are pale yellow, minute, surrounded by hairy bracts and borne in tight clusters. *Waltheria* is a dominant plant in many parts of the desert lowlands, on cinders and in runs, for instance at Mars Bay and South Gannet Hill. It appears to be still spreading.

TROPAEOLACEAE – nasturtium family
HA   *Tropaeolum majus*   Nasturtium
An annual rambling plant from South America, with fleshy stems and round leaves; the brilliant orange flowers are trumpet-shaped and spurred.

H: The Nasturtium grows luxuriantly at all altitudes and is sometimes considered a weed. However, both flowers and young leaves can be used in salads and the seeds can be pickled.

A: Not widespread, but has been seen near the mountain garden.

UMBELLIFERAE (or APIACEAE) – the carrot family
The members of this family can be recognized by the shape of the inflorescence, which is shaped like an inverted umbrella, with all the stalks arising from the top of the main stem.

H   *Apium graveolens* Plate 7   Wild Celery
This plant is a reversion from celery cultivated by the early settlers, which escaped before 1771. The stems are ridged, the leaves deeply lobed and the white flowers are borne in small umbels. Wild Celery occurs locally in guts at lower levels, including the Heart Shape Waterfall and Broad Gut. (Fennel *Foeniculum vulgare* and Parsley *Petroselinum crispum* have also gone wild in a few places.)

HA   *Centella asiatica*   Monkey's Ears
This species is widespread in the tropics and subtropics and has been considered as possibly indigenous on St Helena, but Cronk suggested that it was introduced in the 19th century. It is a prostrate, creeping plant with kidney-shaped leaves; the foliage is hard to distinguish from *Dichondra repens* (Convolvulaceae), which has the same local name.

H: Found in pastures, roadsides and crevices in walls at middle altitudes.

A: On the mountain, including Breakneck Ravine.

453

Jellico

*H   *Sium bracteatum* (ex *Sium helenianum*) Plate 32   Jellico, Angelica

This and the next species have their closest relatives in Africa. Jellico is an impressive herb which can grow to at least 3 m tall, with fleshy, ribbed, green stems that are cylindrical and hollow. The leaves are shiny and pinnate, the leaflets oval and with their bases almost surrounding the stem; they have a fringe of sharp points like delicate teeth of a saw. The flowers are borne at the top of the plant in a spreading umbel with numerous groups of hundreds of tiny white flowers which turn pink with age. Flowering is usually in December but can vary with weather conditions. The fruits are small and green, later turning brown. In the past Jellico was local but abundant, growing among the cabbage trees and ferns on the eastern part of the central ridge. It suffers from competition from invasive weeds, but several patches are still present on the southern face of the ridge, from the upper part of Deep Valley as far as High Peak. In the past the green stems of Jellico were frequently offered for sale in the market and street stalls of Jamestown, being eaten raw.

Dwarf Jellico

*H   *Sium burchellii* Plate 32   Dwarf Jellico, Dwarf Angelica

Dwarf Jellico is usually considered as a separate endemic species, but it seems sometimes to hybridize with the ordinary Jellico and it may prove to be an 'ecotype' (a genetically distinct form) of that species, adapted to exposure on the windward side of the central ridge. Dwarf Jellico has a maximum height of well under one metre and has hollow fleshy stems. The leaves are glossy green, compound and ladder-like, up to 40 cm long; the leaflets wrap around the leaf stalk and have coarse teeth – almost prickles – round the edges. The inflorescence is less than 50 cm tall, leafy near the base and with umbels of white flowers; the fruits are small and green, later turning brown. Flowering is in December. Dwarf Jellico now occurs only in a few exposed places on the windward side of the rocky parts of the central ridge, at High Peak and the Depot. Burchell and Melliss recorded Dwarf Jellico from near Diana's Peak, and seedlings have recently been planted there in an attempt to re-establish this eastern population.

URTICACEAE – the stinging nettle family

H   *Urtica* species   nettles

The Stinging Nettle *Urtica dioica* was recorded as common at middle levels in the last century and perhaps earlier, but the only nettle seen in recent decades has been in the Longwood area. This is probably the Small Nettle *U. urens*, an annual species growing to only about 60 cm, with coarsely toothed leaves about 30 cm across.

VERBENACEAE – the teak and verbena family

Apart from the species mentioned, a few other members of this family can occasionally be found growing wild on St Helena.

A   *Clerodendrum fragrans*

A shrub growing to c.1.5 m with large, broad, dark green leaves. The flowers are whitish purple with five petals and are borne in clusters like tiny bunches of roses. It is found at middle levels on Green Mountain, especially near the mountain road.

HA   *Lantana camara* Plates 24 and 25   Wild Currant, Black Sage, Lantana

This stiff, wide-spreading shrub, which originated in Brazil, can grow to at least two metres and has angular, rough and sometimes prickly stems; it is also poisonous,

454

causing photosensitization and gastro-enteritis in stock. The leaves are up to 7 cm long and are dark green, broadly oval and coarsely toothed. The flowers are small and borne in dense, flat-topped clusters within which there is almost always a contrast in colours since the flowers open yellow or pink and change to orange or scarlet. The berries are deep purple when ripe, and are eaten by Mynas which thus also spread the seeds.

H: *Lantana* was introduced to St Helena in the 19th century and quickly spread to cover whole hillsides at low and medium altitudes. Although it slows erosion it is useless to livestock, and in the 1970s an attempt at biological control was initiated. The tingid heteropteran bug *Teleonemia scrupulosa* was introduced, along with two other insects which failed to establish. The bug was fairly successful and in many areas the *Lantana* is now dead or moribund. Since this effort followed the removal of goats, it seems to have resulted in colonisation of many of the areas where *Lantana* was previously abundant, by other shrubs including – in some places – the endemic Scrubwood.

A: *Lantana* may be a recent introduction but is probably spreading; it occurs from near sea level at North East Bay to Elliotts Path and the cowsheds on Green Mountain.

H   *Lippia nodiflorum*
An aquatic, trailing plant with strongly ribbed stems. The leaves spring in groups from nodes on the stem and are small (2 cm) and coarsely toothed. The inflorescences originate at the same points and have a long stalk and a dense flowering head. We have not seen previous records of this plant on the island, but have found it growing in the stream at Sandy Bay Beach, just above the arch in the fortifications.

H   *Verbena bonariensis*   Argentinian Vervain
A stiff, rough, erect herb up to one metre high. The stems are square and the leaves strongly veined, pointed and stem-clasping. The vivid blue-purple flowers are borne in conspicuous terminal heads. This plant can grow in pastures but also in waterlogged situations.

A   *Vitex trifolia*   Lovechaste
An aromatic shrub up to five metres high, with light grey-green foliage and aromatic purple flowers in loose clusters at the end of the branches. This plant was used to form hedges around the southeast and southwest sides of the island in the late 19th century; it is still common on the mountain.

ZINGIBERACEAE – the ginger family

HA   *Alpinia speciosa* (ex *A. nutans*)   Ginger, Large Ginger Plant, Shell Ginger
This is a luxuriant many-stemmed plant up to 3 m high, with strap-like pointed leaves up to 70 cm long; the flowers are white with pink tips and are somewhat reminiscent of sea-shells; they are borne in nodding sprays.

H: Common on the central ridge in guts and on roadsides; a smaller pink-flowered species may also be present.

A: Common around Elliot's Path and covers large areas just below the peak of Green Mountain.

H   *Hedychium chrysoleucum* (or a related species)   Ginger, Primrose Flowered Ginger Lily
In this species the flowering stems are about 2 m high; the flowers are yellow and sweetly scented, about 6 cm across and in the form of a giant bottle-brush. It occurs on the central ridge in guts and on roadsides. (John Packer found a species of *Hedychium*, probably *gardneranum*, around Elliot's Path on the north side of the mountain in 1997).

455

ZYGOPHYLLACEAE – the lignum vitae family

H   *Tribulus cistoides* Plate 32

This is a prostrate, spreading herb with straight stems and opposite, compound leaves. The flowers are showy, yellow and five-petalled; the seeds are large and spiny. This salt-tolerant plant is typical of shell-sand beaches and occurs in the driest parts of the island. Burchell collected it near the lime-kiln at Sandy Bay, Melliss found it near King and Queen Rocks and we found it near Lot's Wife's Ponds. This species is cosmopolitan in the tropics and is adapted for dispersal attached to the plumage of birds. We consider it as probably indigenous on St Helena, and suspect that it is a much more important element in the flora during glacial periods when sea level is lowered and sand accumulates on the exposed shelf.

PTERIDOPHYTA – ferns, club-mosses and relatives

The clubmosses (lycopods) are creeping or stiffly tufted plants with minute, simple, scale-like leaves that clothe both the rhizome and the roughly cylindrical branching stems. They are of particular interest since they were the dominant land plants in Carboniferous times, some 300 million years ago. The ferns, however, are much more successful today; they have flattened leaves which may be strap-like but are often pinnate (divided like a feather) with pinnae (singular pinna) or leaflets on either side of midrib (rachis) which may bear scales or hairs. In 2-pinnate leaves the pinnae are themselves divided (giving pinnules); 3-pinnate and 4-pinnate leaves also occur. Leaves can be either sessile or have a stalk (stipe) which often bears scales at its junction with the stem (often called a rhizome).

Ferns reproduce by means of minute spores. These develop in spore cases (sporangia) which are usually borne in clusters called sori on the underside of the leaves; they may be naked or covered by a membrane (indusium). Spores are very light and drift easily in the air. When a spore lands in a suitable place, it grows into a tiny often heart-shaped plant – called a prothallus or gametophyte – on the surface of the soil or on another kind of plant. The prothallus never grows into a large plant. Instead, it produces egg- or sperm-containing structures (archegonia or antheridia) or both. Upon maturity and in the presence of water the sperm swim to the eggs to fertilize them, and this means that most ferns can only reproduce in moist places. The fertilized egg then grows into the spore-producing fern plant (sporophyte) that we normally notice.

Ferns are efficient colonists of islands because of their tiny spores, and it is almost certain that they formed the major part of the first plant communities to become established on St Helena and Ascension. On Ascension they retained their dominance in the high part of the island until humans brought in large numbers of exotic trees and other flowering plants. On St Helena trees arrived naturally and produced a canopy over much of the island, under which the ferns persisted; at the highest level the Tree Fern itself formed a major part of the canopy.

On St Helena there are now at least 30 species of ferns growing wild, of which 13 are endemic and another 12 probably reached the island naturally (Table 4C); the remainder seem to have been brought in by people. On Ascension the situation is less clear; there are five endemic species and about eight others which are probably indigenous (Table 11B). For both islands we omit some of the introduced species, not all of which are securely identified.

ASPLENIACEAE – the spleenwort family

These are mostly small, evergreen ferns that grow in tufts, bearing their sori along the veins on the underside of the leaf.

H   *Asplenium aethiopicum (= A. furcatum)*
This elegant indigenous fern is a very variable species with a wide range in the tropics. It is typically 10-30 cm long and has characteristic 'tiered' pinnae, each one broad at the base and narrowing towards the tip in two or three steps. It has a local distribution mainly between 400 and 600 m in relatively dry places, including High Knoll.

H   *Asplenium compressum*   Plastic Fern, Hen and Chicks Fern
This is a large, bright yellow green fern with pinnate fronds up to 1.5 m long and a thick midrib. The pinnae are undivided and up to 20 cm long; each one seems to interlock with the next and the fern gives the impression of being made of plastic. The pinnae have almost straight margins, becoming slightly wavy near the slender, pointed tips. Sori up to 1.5 cm long are conspicuous on the under surface of the pinnae. On the upper surface near the edges there are often tiny new individuals (known as gemmae) attached as if with a brown button; these can take root and form new plants. This species is locally common in damp shady places on the central ridge above about 600 m, often growing with *A. platybasis* and the Black Scale Fern.

Asplenium compressum

HA   *Asplenium erectum* Plate 32
This species, which is indigenous on both islands, is a member of the *A. erectum-lunulatum* group of Africa and occurs in the tropics there. It is much smaller than *A. compressum* and has narrow fronds about 25 cm long, sometimes branching at the tip; the midrib is narrow and dark. The pinnae are short (only about twice as long as broad), strongly toothed and each one expanded in a fan at the base on the side towards the tip of the frond; the sori are conspicuous on the lower surface. As in the last species, new juvenile plants can grow on the fronds, either at the end of the midrib or at the tips of the pinnae.

H: This fern is common in shady places above 550 m, often forming carpets, especially on the north and west slopes of the central ridge; it has also been recorded from the Barn, where it resembles the Ascension form.

A: The form of this fern occurring on Ascension has sometimes been considered as an endemic species, *A. ascensionis*, but is probably best considered as an endemic variety, *Asplenium erectum* variety *ascensionis*. It is a small, glossy, dark green fern which grows in tufts that often fan out against a rock wall. It is now local on Green Mountain in damp, sheltered places, for instance in the side ravines of Breakneck; it sometimes grows on almost vertical artificially cut cinder slopes and has also been found in crevices in trachyte lava, for instance on White Hill. In the past, when it suffered less competition from introduced species, it used to grow larger, proliferating at the tips of the fronds; it was also much more common, forming part of the *"carpet of ferns"* described by Hooker as forming the main vegetation high on the mountain in the mid 19th century.

*H   *Asplenium haughtoni*   Barn Fern
This tiny fern, previously treated as an endemic variety of *Ceterach* (or *Asplenium*) *cordatum* from Africa, is now considered an endemic species and was recently listed by Cronk as

457

Ceterach haughtonii; we treat it as *A. haughtoni* on the advice of Dr Ronald Viane. The fronds are lightish green and up to 10-15 cm long, 2-pinnate and with a black midrib and about ten pairs of rounded pinnae. The sori are along the veins and when mature are thick, covering much of the under surface of the pinnae. This fern grows in tufts in moist rock crevices where it is sheltered from the scorching sun, dying away in hot weather but sprouting again after the winter rains. It is rather rare, occurring at about 200-500 m on cliffs and rocks in dry barren areas, including the Barn, High Knoll, Bunkers Hill and near Gregory's Battery; Burchell recorded it from Friar's Ridge and Ruperts.

Asplenium platybasis

*H   *Asplenium platybasis*
This fern grows in tufts at the apex of a creeping rhizome, under the shade of the Tree Ferns. It has firm leathery fronds growing to 60 cm, with a thin black central rib and dark green pinnae with toothed edges; the numerous sori are along the veins. This species is less common than *A. compressum* but can be found above 600 m on the east and central parts of the main ridge, including Diana's Peak and High Peak; it often grows in the shade of the Black Scale Fern.

BLECHNACEAE – the hard fern family

?A   *Blechnum australe*
This fern has not been found recently and confirmation is needed that it is really present on Ascension.

DENNSTAEDTIACEAE – the bracken family

A   *Histiopteris incisa* (ex *Pteris incisa*)
This indigenous fern occurs on mountains in the tropics around the world, and also in South Africa and some other parts of the south-temperate zone. It grows up to a metre high, and patches of the dead fronds on a hillside could easily be mistaken for bracken, but the fronds are not branched.. It is frequent on the southeast weather slopes of Green Mountain at medium to high levels; on the pristine island it was probably the dominant plant in this area.

H(?A) *Hypolepis rugosula*   Sticky Fern
This fern, which is indigenous on St Helena, has sometimes been considered as an endemic species, *H. helensis*, or as an endemic variety, but is now considered to belong to a species that is widespread in warm regions. It is a large fern with fronds up to 1.5 m, but usually about 60 cm. The slender stem has a characteristic reddish brown colour and there is a definite groove along the whole length of the upper side. It is hairy and the whole plant secretes a sticky substance which distinguishes it from all the other ferns on the islands. The pinnae are almost opposite on the midrib and there are two widely separated rows of 2-5 sori.

H: *H. rugosula* grows lower down than many of the other ferns and is fairly common around 500-650 m on the central ridge; it is often found among Black Scale Fern and Brown Scale Fern.

A: A specimen was collected on Ascension in 1889, but confirmation of its presence there today is needed.

458

DICKSONIACEAE – *Dicksonia* the tree fern family (sometimes included in Cyatheaccae)

Dicksonia arborescens

*H   *Dicksonia arborescens* Plates 7, 8, 32   Tree Fern
An extraordinary plant that may occasionally reach 6 m in height but is more often 4-5 m. The substantial trunk is often branched near the base and reaches at least 30 cm in diameter; it is covered with hair-like adventitious roots and if it falls it can sprout along its length to form new growth. The live fronds are borne in a tuft at the top, almost like a palm tree, and are up to 3 m long, with the pinnae arising from the outer half or more of this length; the lower end of the stalk is densely hairy and brown, and at a young stage the frond is reminiscent of a monkey's tail. The leathery dark green pinnules are alternate and almost equally spaced; they are about twice as long as broad, with smooth margins rolled downwards and prominent veins.

   This species is dominant in the Tree Fern thicket above 700 m near Diana's Peak and at High Peak. It used also to be a major component of the cabbage tree woodland at a slightly lower level, for instance at Halley's Mount and at Casons (where it still survives). The Tree Fern has relatives in several southern continents and islands, and its ancestors were already present on St Helena about nine million years ago.

DRYOPTERIDACEAE – the buckler fern family

*H   *Diplazium filamentosum* (ex *D. nigropaleaceum*) Plate 32   Black Scale Fern
The genus *Diplazium* is sometimes placed in the Aspleniaceae or Athyriaceae. The Black Scale Fern is a large species with broad, dark green fronds up to 1.5 by 1 metre; the stipe is greenish and deeply channelled, thickly covered with black hairs. The sori are about 5 mm long and extend obliquely along the side veins of the pinnule lobes. The Black Scale Fern grows fast, often forming dense thickets and tending to spread quickly into disturbed areas, for instance where Tree Fern has been cleared. It was an important component of the original vegetation on the central ridge, and is still common above 550 m, for instance on the steep south face of the Sandy Bay ridge above Wranghams; it also occurs in Grapevine Gut and at Napoleon's Tomb. A related species occurs in wet glades at high altitudes in the West Indies.

*?†A   *Dryopteris ascensionis* (ex *Nephrodium (Lastrea) ascensionis*)
Dryopteris species are medium to tall ferns which grow in tufts; the spore cases are roundish, on the veins beneath the leaves. The two endemic species on St Helena, together with the one from Ascension, form a distinctive group.

   D. ascensionis may now be extinct. It is characterized by its densely chaffy rhizome and stipe, with scales up to 25 mm long, unlike any other fern on Ascension. The fronds are 15-20 cm long and almost equally wide at the base; they are lurid green and somewhat fleshy. This species formed part of Hooker's *"carpet of ferns"* in the 19th century, between about 400 and 550 m, but has evidently been outcompeted by introduced species. It was last reported by Eric Timm in 1975 beside Ruperts Path, on a moss-covered cinder slope. It was not found by the Edinburgh University party in 1998, but may perhaps survive in moist ravines on the weather side of Green Mountain.

*H   *Dryopteris cognata*   Kidney Fern
The fronds of this species grow in tufts and are usually about 60 cm long, but can grow to one metre; they are darkish green with distinctive large, brown scales on the stipe and along the midrib. The sori often extend to the tips of the pinnules. This fern

is uncommon on the central ridge, growing in shady places on Diana's Peak near Wells Gut, and at Purgatory and High Peak.

*H   *Dryopteris napoleonis*   Lesser Kidney Fern
This fern, which is much smaller than *D. cognata*, also grows in tufts. The stipe is densely covered near the base with small, dark brown scales. The lightish green fronds usually grow to only 25 cm, with conspicuous dark veins. The sori are usually close to the midrib. This species is commoner than the last, occurring among rocks and on banks in shaded and moist places, mainly above 600 m on the central ridge, but also on the Barn.

GRAMMITIDACEAE

H   *Grammitis ebenina*
This interesting indigenous species has sometimes been considered endemic; it has now been recorded from Africa, but it is possible that the St Helena population is distinct. *G. ebenina* is a tiny fern with simple delicate fronds less than 5 cm long, green with a thin black border, which grow in clusters of 10-20 on the trunks of Tree Ferns and cabbage trees (especially the Black Cabbage), and occasionally on rock faces. It is now rare, occurring locally above about 700 m on the central ridge between the Depot and Mt Actaeon.

*A   *Xiphopteris ascensionensis*[11]
This is now considered an endemic species, though it has sometimes been treated as a form of *X. trichomanoides*, a widespread tropical species. It is a fern of the mist zone of the highest part of the mountain. It requires constant moisture and grows very locally in rock crevices and on trees, always amongst moss. It is often associated with the endemic mosses *Campylopus smaragdinus* and *Calymperes ascensionis*, which with other mosses have colonised many kinds of introduced trees (including the bamboos on the peak); the fern has benefitted from this extension of its habitat.

HYMENOPHYLLACEAE – the filmy fern family

*H   *Hymenophyllum capillaceum*   Filmy Fern
A delicate, creeping and somewhat moss-like plant with a threadlike, creeping, dark brown rhizome and slender, thin, translucent, greenish brown leaves up to 15 mm in length, with intricate branching veins. It is common above 700 m on the central ridge, forming a mat – often mixed with moss – on the branches of cabbage trees and Tree Ferns.

LOMARIOPSIDACEAE

Members of this family have simple tongue-like fronds and grow as epiphytes on other plants.

*H   *Elaphoglossum bifurcatum* (ex *Microstaphyla furcata*) Plate 32   Mossy Fern
A small and delicate tufted fern with fronds reaching only about 8 cm long. The pinnae are almost linear and sometimes branched, giving a twiglike effect. In treating this species as *E. bifurcatum* we are following advice from Dr Ronald Viane. It is closely related

---

[11] Spelt thus in Q.C.B. Cronk (2000) but as *X. ascensionense* in Cronk (1995a).

to *E. nervosum*, and has even been considered as a form of that species, which it resembles in almost all characters (details of scales, rhizome, glands, spores);[12] placing it in a different genus thus seems unreasonable. However, it differs dramatically in the 'dissection' of the frond. *E. bifurcatum* occurs above 600 m on the central ridge and on Flagstaff Hill; it is local but where present it is often abundant, clothing damp rocks and banks (including those on roadsides), as well as growing as an epiphyte on trunks.

H   *Elaphoglossum conforme* Plate 32   Common Tongue-fern
This indigenous species is found all over the tropics. The small simple fronds are up to 30 cm long and have undulating but smooth margins; they are almost identical to those of *Pleopeltis macrocarpa* (see Polypodiaceae), but do not grow in rows. Another distinction is that the spore cases are spread all over the underside of the leaf (in *Pleopeltis* they are in round patches arranged in rows). *E. conforme* usually occurs above 750 m on the Peaks, growing as an epiphyte on the trunks of Tree Ferns, cabbage trees and introduced shrubs, and on moist banks.

*H   *Elaphoglossum dimorphum* Plate 32   Toothed Tongue-fern
A delicate fern with darkish green, strap-like but strongly toothed and crinkly fronds up to about 10 cm long, of which the bottom third is a bare stem. Parallel veins are present, but much less conspicuous than in *E. nervosum*. The spore cases may entirely cover the lower surface. This species used to be common on the central ridge, but it is now found only locally above about 750 m, growing in tufts on soil among grass on banks and among rocks, and on mossy trunks.

*H   *Elaphoglossum nervosum* Plate 32   Veined Tongue-fern
A fern with a stiff scaly stem and strap-like leaf up to about 15 cm long and 3.5 cm wide, rather like a miniature banana leaf. The most characteristic feature is that the underside of the frond has a series of conspicuous parallel dark veins running across it about 1.5 mm apart, reminiscent of the barbs on a feather. The top of the frond is dark green with the edges untoothed but somewhat irregular; the veins also show here, and some of them are branched. This fern is uncommon and restricted to high levels at the wetter eastern end of the central ridge, where it usually grows as an epiphyte on Tree Ferns and cabbage trees.

LYCOPODIACEAE – the clubmosses

H(A)   *Lycopodium axillare*
This indigenous clubmoss, which has sometimes been considered endemic, is closely related to the widespread *L. saururus*. It is less branched than *L. cernuum* (below) and grows to 20 cm, resembling a sprig of Norfolk Island Pine.
   H: This species used to occur at a few sites – including Halley's Mount and the Depot – above 650 m on the central ridge, sometimes among grass. The only individual now known grows among moss on a branch of Cape Yew on the Peaks.
   A: Recorded by Hooker in the mid 19th century, but not found subsequently.

HA   *Lycopodium cernuum*   Buckshorn
This species, which is evidently indigenous on both islands, also occurs elsewhere in the tropics and further south. It grows to a height of about 60 cm and is a repeatedly

[12] J. Mickel (1980).

461

branching, somewhat grey-green plant, the branches recalling the antlers of a deer. Each 'twig' is clothed with a series of thin, curved, finger-like projections ending in a sharp point.

H: Buckshorn has a patchy distribution, mainly above 600 m, but is often abundant where it occurs, as on some moist banks and roadsides. In the past it was used to help catch houseflies, since the flies are attracted to the plant and settle on it, when they can easily be caught.

A: Found mainly on the weather side of the mountain, around Elliot's and in pasture west of Breakneck valley.

MARATTIACEAE

*A   *Marattia purpurascens*
This impressive fern is endemic to Ascension, although it has sometimes been considered a subspecies of *Marattia fraxinea*, a widespread African species. It has broad, brittle fronds up to a metre in length which may divide into three branches (pinnae), each with half a dozen or more pairs of pinnules which are not divided further (though they are slightly toothed). The sori are in ovals along the edges of the pinnules. This fern still has healthy populations on the island. It occurs in two forms: in deep shade among the bamboos on the peak it has thin stems and broad pinnules, while on exposed slopes on the east side of the mountain it is stouter and with narrower pinnules. Cronk found the finest plants among invasive *Buddleja* and *Rubus* plants beside Elliot's path.

NEPHROLEPIDACEAE

HA   *Nephrolepis exaltata*   Pheasant Tail Fern
A very variable tufted fern introduced from Africa, with long, stiff, narrow fronds that taper gradually towards the tip. The simple pinnae are placed alternately on the stem and are short and broad, tapering gradually towards the apex.

H: Common near houses at 500-600 m on the central ridge. (*Nephrolepis cordifolia*, another widely cultivated species, is also present in gardens. The SEDS report [Government of St Helena 1993] also included '*Nephrolepis rudii*' in the list of ferns for the island, but we know nothing more about it.)

A: Collected by Packer near gardens on the mountain.

A   *Nephrolepis hirsutula*
A specimen collected by John Packer from a cleft in the centre of the Devil's Riding School was identified as "*N. hirsutula* (G. Forst) C. Presl var." by Kew Gardens, who commented that they held additional specimens from Ascension, and that all differed from those from other parts of the Old World, in bearing very few of the narrow brown filamentous scales normally seen. It therefore seems likely that the species is indigenous, and it may even represent an endemic variety. The Packers comment that this is perhaps the commonest fern of Ascension's drier areas. Their illustration shows the pinnules as narrow at the base, almost parallel-sided and up to four times as long as broad, but tapering towards the tip; the sori are in a line along each edge of the pinnule. The fern on Ascension in Plate 32 may be this species.

OPHIOGLOSSACEAE – the adder's-tongue family

Species of *Ophioglossum* have broad undivided leaves quite unlike a typical fern. The spores are borne at the tip of a separate pencil-like spike.

H   *Ophioglossum polyphyllum*
The *Ophioglossum* occurring on St Helena has sometimes been considered as *O. vulgatum*, or *O. opacum* from Tristan and South Georgia, but we follow Cronk in treating it as belonging to the widespread *O. polyphyllum*; it is considered indigenous on St Helena. It has a single upright leaf that grows to 5-10 cm high. It is an annual, appearing in the winter months. It grows locally in dry hot places at mid altitude, on hillsides around James and Ruperts Valleys and is particularly common at Mundens Battery. Smaller scattered populations can also be seen on the hillsides of the south west of the Island, near the Asses Ears and Lot's Wife.

A   *Ophioglossum* species
O. vulgatum was recorded as common on Green Mountain in the 19th century, but Duffey reported it only from the lower, drier parts of the island; there are no recent records. The name has been subject to some confusion in the past, so the identity of the species on Ascension needs confirmation. The species concerned may be indigenous.

POLYPODIACEAE – the polypody family

H   *Phlebodium aureum*
This fern grows from a rhizome with conspicuous golden scales, and has fronds about 50 cm long and up to 40 cm wide, with spear-shaped simple pinnae including a conspicuous fingerlike one at the tip of the frond. The undersides of the pinnae are blue-grey, and the sori are spaced in a single irregular line on each side of the central vein. *P. aureum* is widespread but generally uncommon on the island, mainly in cool shaded places up to 600 m, from the hillsides of Jamestown (Sampsons Battery) to Oakbank (where it is abundant along the roadside) and Mount Pleasant, but occasionally in drier places such as High Knoll and Ladder Hill. This is an introduced species originating in South America.

H   *Pleopeltis macrocarpa*
This tiny fern is indigenous to St Helena but occurs all over the tropics and subtropics. The fronds are simple, leaf-like and 10-15 cm long; they are almost identical to those of *Elaphoglossum conforme*, but in *Pleopeltis* they arise singly at intervals from a rhizome that may be seen (or felt) running along the ground or other surface. The sori occur in a double row along the underside of the frond (cf. *Elaphoglossum*). On the island it grows on the trunks of trees and Tree Ferns and on rocks and walls above about 500 m, along the central ridge from Long Ground to High Peak and also on the Barn and locally elsewhere; many can be seen on the trunk of the old Norfolk Island Pine on Cuckold's Point.

PSILOTACEAE – the stagmoss family

A   *Psilotum nudum* Plate 32
This curious and very distinctive plant is a member of a small and enigmatic group which have often been considered separate from both the ferns and clubmosses, but

463

are now usually considered as a family of ferns that have lost many of the normal fern features. *P. nudum* has no roots, but forms a rhizome, from which springs a forking cluster of wiry green stems, often with orange brown tips; the stems have sparse, tiny, scale-like leaves, some of which bear spore cases which are first yellow and then brown. It occurs mainly in moist rocky places on the eastern and southern slopes of Green Mountain. *P. nudum* is widespread in warm countries and occurs on many oceanic islands; it is presumably indigenous on Ascension, but curiously, it seems to be absent from St Helena.

PTERIDACEAE – the maidenhair fern family

H?A   *Adiantum raddianum*   Maidenhair Fern
The identity of Maidenhairs on both islands has been subject to confusion, but Ronald Viane is convinced that the species on St Helena is *A. raddianum*. This is a delicate fern with repeatedly branched fronds and lobed leaflets; the stems are wiry, shiny and reddish brown.

   H: The Maidenhair was probably introduced in the 19th century from Africa. It is now found locally in shady, damp places, including the Heart Shape Waterfall.

   A: A species of Maidenhair is widespread on the island; it has been recorded as *A. capillus-veneris* but confirmation is needed. It is probably introduced.

*?†A   *Anogramma ascensionis*
Anogramma is sometimes placed in a separate family, Hemionitidaceae. This endemic species is very distinct from other members of its genus; it may now be extinct. It grows in tufts and is small and slender, with delicate, fan-shaped or lobe-shaped pinnae and sori in a double row on the undersides. It is an annual species, depending on moist conditions but with drought-resistant spores. This fern originally grew on wet rocks and banks on the weather side of Green Mountain, from middle to high levels. It was last seen in 1958, and searches in 1976 and 1998 both failed to locate it; however, both these years were dry.

H   *Cheilanthes multifida*
This is a delicate species that withers away in summer. It has relatively small (usually less than 10 cm) fronds, 2-3 pinnate with discrete sori along the edges. It is fairly common around 500-600 m in rocky places and crevices in drier parts of the island, including High Hill, Horse Pasture, Breakneck Valley and High Knoll. It is probably indigenous, and also occurs in South Africa.

*A   *Pteris adscensionis*
This fern is generally considered as an endemic species, but is similar to *Pteris dentata* subspecies *flabellata*, which occurs on St Helena (see below). It has bright green fronds with sori in continuous lines along both edges of the pinnules. It sometimes grows in large tufts up to nearly a metre in height, and has been found from near the base to the top of Green Mountain. *P. adscensionis* was probably an important element in the original vegetation of the island, and can evidently survive in drier conditions than many ferns, but has been outcompeted by more luxuriant vegetation in the moister areas of the peak. The most recent records are from a gulley on the northwest side of Cricket Valley (where about 100 plants grow in crevices on the rock walls) and on the southeast spur of Green Mountain.

464

H   *Pteris dentata* subspecies *flabellata*

This indigenous fern is also widely distributed in Africa. It is a large species, with pale green fronds reaching 1.5 m in length and a good deal longer than broad. The sori do not extend to the tips of the lobes of the pinnae, which have shallow teeth. It is widely distributed above about 450 m, including Peak Dale and Mount Pleasant, but is not common; it can grow in rocky and dry places provided that they are shady.

*H   *Pteris paleacea*   Lays Back Fern

A medium-sized fern usually reaching about 60 cm but sometimes as much as one metre. The stipe is erect and with long brown scales, and the fronds are robust and dark green. The lower pinnae are branched at the base and the others are stiff and overlapping, so that the frond spreads out like a fan. The pinnules are somewhat leathery, the upper surface having a central valley and the edges rolled downwards. The sori are along the whole length of the edges of the lobes of the pinnae. This fern was an important component of the Tree Fern thicket on the central ridge but now occurs only locally on the eastern part of it, growing especially in the shade of Tree Ferns.

THELYPTERIDACEAE – the marsh fern family

These are large ferns in which the fronds arise from a creeping rhizome.

H   *Christella chaseana*

The species of *Christella* have sometimes been included in the genus *Thelypteris*. They can generally only be identified with the aid of a microscope, by microcharacters of scales, glands etc, and it is not certain that the species present on the islands are correctly identified. This species, which has been recorded from the central ridge, is possibly indigenous on St Helena. The fronds are about 60 cm long and the pinnae are finely divided.

HA   *Christella dentata*

An introduced fern which is common in the tropics.

   H: *C. dentata* has been said to occur frequently on the central ridge, but confirmation of the species is needed.

   A: One of the commonest ferns on Green Mountain.

H   *Christella parasitica*

An introduced fern provisionally identified as this species is very common on roadside banks and has been found below 450 m in Sandy Bay. The fronds are up to a metre long and have strongly toothed pinnae which are alternate and rather widely spaced. The pinnules have one, two or three sori.

*H   *Pseudophegopteris dianae*   Brown Scale Fern

This endemic species has relatives around the tropics but is quite distinct. It is a large handsome fern that grows in tufts. The fronds are up to 1.5 m high and darkish green and the stems are thickly coated with brown hair-like scales. The long pinnae are borne almost opposite each other and have 10-20 deeply incised pinnules. The sori are numerous and away from the midrib. This fern is common above about 600 m in the Tree Fern thicket and amongst the Black Scale Ferns on the east and central parts of the ridge; it has been found in dense woods but also sometimes invades cleared flax land. Melliss commented that the young undeveloped fronds yield a remarkable perfume, much like that of a ripe peach.

BRYOPHYTES – liverworts, hornworts and mosses

The bryophytes of St Helena are of considerable interest.[13] A total of 54 species have been recorded, comprising 20 species of liverworts (Hepaticae), two species of hornworts (Anthocerotae) and 32 species of mosses (Musci). Seventeen species are endemic to St Helena, with another two occurring also on Ascension but not elsewhere.

Ascension bryophytes are of no less interest, with a total of 43 species (12 liverworts, two hornworts and 29 mosses), of which 15 are endemic. Most species are recorded from the moister areas on the sides of Green Mountain.

It is likely that future studies will increase the number of bryophytes from both islands, as many recent collections have yet to be identified. However, the number of endemics may well be reduced, as some of them have not been re-examined since they were first collected over a hundred years ago, when the bryophytes of Africa and other relevant areas were much less well known. The non-endemic bryophytes of St Helena and Ascension – apart from a number of cosmopolitan ones – include species with African, American and subantarctic-southern hemisphere affinities.

---

[13] M.J. Wigginton & R. Grolle (1996); F. Müller (1999); B.J. O'Shea (1999).

Bibliography

Abele, L G & Felgenhauer, B E (1985) Observations on the ecology and feeding behavior of the anchialine shrimp *Procaris ascensionis*. *Journal of Crustacean Biology* 5: 15-24.

Agriculture & Forestry Department, St Helena (1995) *A Sustainable Ecology of St Helena Seminar.*

Aitken, A D (1975, 1984) *Insect Travellers*, Vols. I and II. Ministry of Agriculture, Fisheries and Food, HMSO, London.

Allan, R G (1962) The Madeiran Storm Petrel *Oceanodroma castro*. *Ibis* 103b: 274-295.

Ashmole, N P (1962) The Black Noddy *Anous tenuirostris* on Ascension Island. Part 1. General biology. *Ibis* 103b: 235-273.

Ashmole, N P (1963a) The biology of the Wideawake or Sooty Tern *Sterna fuscata* on Ascension Island. *Ibis* 103b: 297-364.

Ashmole, N P (1963b) Sub-fossil bird remains on Ascension Island. *Ibis* 103b: 382-389.

Ashmole, N P (1963c) The extinct avifauna of St Helena Island. *Ibis* 103b: 390-408.

Ashmole, N P (1963d) The regulation of numbers of tropical oceanic birds. *Ibis* 103b: 458-473.

Ashmole, N P (1965) Adaptive variation in the breeding regime of a tropical sea bird. *Proceedings of the National Academy of Sciences* 53: 311-318.

Ashmole, N P & Ashmole, M J (1988) Insect dispersal on Tenerife, Canary Islands: high altitude fallout and seaward drift. *Arctic & Alpine Research* 20: 1-12.

Ashmole, N P & Ashmole, M J (1997) The land fauna of Ascension Island: new data from caves and lava flows, and a reconstruction of the prehistoric ecosystem. *Journal of Biogeography* 24: 549-589.

Ashmole, N P & Ashmole, M J (2000) Fallout of dispersing arthropods supporting invertebrate communities in barren volcanic habitats. Case study: Canary Islands. *In* Wilkens, J H, Humphreys, W & Culver, D, (eds). *Ecosystems of the World, Vol. 30, Subterranean Ecosystems.* Elsevier Science, Oxford.

Ashmole, N P, Ashmole, M J & Bourne, W R P (1999) Bulwer's Petrel *Bulweria bulwerii* on St Helena. *Bulletin of the British Ornithologists' Club* 1999: 91-94.

Ashmole, N P, Ashmole, M J & Simmons, K E L (1994) Seabird conservation and feral cats on Ascension Island, South Atlantic. Pp. 94-121 in *Seabirds on Islands: Threats, Case Studies and Action Plans.* Birdlife Conservation Series No. 1.

Ashmole, N P, Oromí, P, Ashmole, M J & Martín, J L (1992) Primary faunal succession in volcanic terrain: lava and cave studies on the Canary Islands. *Biological Journal of the Linnean Society of London* 46: 207-234.

Ashmole, N P, Oromí, P, Ashmole, M J & Martín, J L (1996) The invertebrate fauna of early successional volcanic habitats in the Azores. *Boletim do Museu Municipal do Funchal* 48 (264): 5-39.

Atkins, F B, Baker, P E, Bell, J D & Smith, D G W (1964) Oxford Expedition to Ascension Island. *Nature* 204: 722-724.

Atkinson, I A E (1985) The spread of commensal species of *Rattus* to oceanic islands and their effects on island avifaunas. In P.J. Moors (ed) *Conservation of Island birds.* International Council for Bird Preservation, ICBP Tech. Publ. No. 3: 35-84.

Baker, A J & Moeed, A (1987) Rapid genetic differentiation and founder effect in colonizing populations of common mynas (*Acridotheres tristis*). *Evolution* 41, 525-538.

Baker, I (1968) *The Geology of Saint Helena Island, South Atlantic.* Ph.D. thesis, University of London.

Baker, I, Gale, N H & Simons, J (1967) Geochronology of the Saint Helena volcanoes. *Nature* 215: 1451-1456.

Barnes, J (1817) *A tour through the Island of St Helena.* J.M. Richardson, London.

Bartlett, L S (c.1936) *Bartlett's Book.* Unpublished manuscript in the Fort Hayes Museum, Georgetown, Ascension Island.

Basilewsky, P (ed) (1970, 1972, 1976, 1977) La faune terrestre de d'ile de Sainte-Hélène. Parts 1, 2, 3, 4. *Annales Musée Royal de l'Afrique Centrale, Séries In8⁰, Sciences zoologiques*:181 (Généralités, Vertébrés, Insectes: Collembola - Dermaptera); 192 (Insectes: Coleoptera); 215 (Insectes: Embioptera - Heteroptera); 220 (Arachnida, Myriapoda, Crustacea, Vermes, Mollusca).

Basilewsky, P (1985). The South Atlantic island of Saint Helena and the origin of its beetle fauna. Pp. 257-275 *in* Ball G E (ed) *Taxonomy, Phylogeny and Zoogeography of Beetles and Ants*. Dr W. Junk, Dordrecht.

Beatson, A (1816) *Tracts relative to the Island of St. Helena; written during a residence of five years*. G. & W. Nicol and J. Booth, London. (Includes an appendix with Dr. William Roxburgh's plant list).

Beeckman, D (1718) A Voyage to and from the Island of Borneo. T. Warner & J. Batley, London.

Beier, M. (1960) Pseudoscorpione von der Insel Ascension. *Annals & Magazine of Natural History* series 13(3): 593-598.

Belgians. *See* Basilewsky, P (ed) (1970, 1972, 1976, 1977).

Bell, B D & Ashmole, P (1995) The feasibility of the eradication of feral cats and rats from Ascension Island. Report prepared on behalf of the Royal Society for the Protection of Birds, for the Foreign and Commonwealth Office.

Berio, E (1972) Descrizione di tre Lepidotteri (*Noctuidae*) nuovi dell'Isola di S.Elena (Atlantico del Sud). *Revue de zoologie et de botanique africaines* 86(3-4): 290-292.

Bester, M N et al. (2000) Final eradication of feral cats from sub-Antarctic Marion Island, southern Indian Ocean. *South African Journal of Wildlife Research* 30: 53-57.

Biernhaum, C K (1996) Biogeography of coastal and anchialine amphipods of Ascension Island, South Atlantic Ocean. *Journal of Natural History* 30: 1597-1615.

Blair, M. (1989) The RAFOS expedition to Ascension Island, 1987. *Journal of the Royal Air Force Ornithological Society* 19: 1-34.

Blofeld, J H (1852) Notes on St. Helena. *Proceedings of the Geological Society* 8: 195-196.

Booth, R G, Cross, A E, Fowler, S V & Shaw, R H (1995) The biology and taxonomy of *Hyperaspis pantherina* (Coleoptera: Coccinellidae) and the classical biological control of its prey, *Orthezia insignis* (Homoptera: Ortheziidae). *Bulletin of Entomological Research* 85: 307-314.

Borror, D J, De Long, D M & Triplehorn, C A (1981) *An Introduction to the Study of Insects*, 5th edn. Saunders College Publishing, Philadelphia.

Bourne, W R P (1956) Notes on a skull of the genus *Bulweria* from St. Helena. *Bulletin of the British Ornithologists' Club* 76: 126-129.

Bourne, W R P & Curtis, W F (1985) South Atlantic seabirds. *Sea Swallow* 34: 18-38.

Bourne, W R P & Loveridge, A (1978) Small shearwaters from Ascension and St Helena, South Atlantic Ocean. *Ibis* 120: 65-66.

Bourne, W R P & Simmons, K E L (1998) A preliminary list of the birds of Ascension Island, South Atlantic Ocean. *Sea Swallow* 47: 42-56.

Bourne, W R P & Simmons, K E L (In press) The distribution and breeding success of seabirds on and around Ascension in the tropical Atlantic Ocean, and its relation to El Niño in the Pacific. *Atlantic Seabirds*.

Bowen, B W, Meylan, A B & Avise, J C (1989) An odyssey of the green sea turtle: Ascension Island revisited. *Proceedings of the National Academy of Sciences of the USA* 86: 573-576.

Brooke, T H (1808) *A History of St. Helena from its Discovery by the Portuguese to the Year 1806*. Black, Parry & Kingsbury, London.

Brown, C W (1990) The significance of the South Equatorial Countercurrent to the ecology of the green turtle breeding population of Ascension Island. *Journal of Herpetology* 24: 81-84.

Brown, L C (1981, 1982) *The land resources and agro-forestal development of St Helena*, Vols. 1 and 2, 1981 (also Project Record 59, 1982, The flora and fauna of St Helena, and Project Record 60, 1981, Hydrology and soil analysis data). Land Resource Study No. 32. Land Resources Development Centre, ODA, Surbiton, Surrey.

Brozena, J M (1986) Temporal and spatial variability of seafloor spreading processes in the northern South Atlantic. *Journal of Geophysical Research* 91: 497-510.

Brozena, J M & White, R S (1990) Ridge jumps and propagations in the South Atlantic Ocean. *Nature* 348: 149-152.

Burchell, W. (Manuscript) St. Helena Journal. Burchell's St. Helena diary, transcribed by Prof. E.B. Poulton. Hope Department, Oxford Univesity Museum.

Cambridge, O P (1869) Notes on some spiders and scorpions from St. Helena, with descriptions of new species. *Proceedings of the Zoological Society of London* 1869: 531-544.

Cambridge, O P (1873) On the spiders of St. Helena. *Proceedings of the Zoological Society of London* 1873: 210-227.

Cameron, R A D, Cook, L M & Hallows, J D (1996)

Land snails on Porto Santo: adaptive and non-adaptive radiation. *Philosophical Transactions of the Royal Society of London* B 351: 309-327.

Carlquist, S (1974) *Island Biology.* Columbia University Press, New York.

Carr, A (1987) New perspectives on the pelagic stage of sea turtle development. *Conservation Biology* 1: 103-121.

Carr, A.& Coleman, P J (1974) Seafloor spreading and the odyssey of the green turtle. *Nature* 249: 128-130.

Chaffey, D J, Cliff R A & Wilson B M (1989) Characterization of the St Helena magma source. Pp. 257-276 in *Magmatism in the Ocean Basins* (ed) A D Saunders & M J Norry. Geological Society Special Publication No. 42.

Chapin, J P (1954) The calendar of wideawake fair. *Auk* 71: 1-15.

Chace, F A, & Manning, R B (1972) Two new caridean shrimps, one representing a new family, from marine pools on Ascension Island (Crustacea: Decapoda: Natantia). *Smithsonian Contributions to Zoology* 131: 1-18.

Christiansen, K A (1998) New species of *Pseudosinella* (Collembola) from Ascension Island. *Journal of Natural History* 32: 149-156.

Cronk, Q C B (1980) Extinction and survival in the endemic vascular flora of Ascension Island. *Biological Conservation* 17: 207-219.

Cronk, Q C B (1983) The decline of the Redwood *Trochetiopsis erythroxylon* on St Helena. *Biological Conservation* 26: 163-174.

Cronk, Q C B (1984) *The historical and evolutionary development of the plant life of St. Helena.* Unpublished thesis, Cambridge University.

Cronk, Q C B (1986a) The decline of the St Helena Ebony *Trochetiopsis melanoxylon. Biological Conservation* 35: 159-172.

Cronk, Q C B (1986b) The decline of the St Helena Gumwood *Commidendrum robustum. Biological Conservation* 35: 173-186.

Cronk, Q C B (1987) The history of endemic flora of St Helena: a relictual series. *New Phytologist* 105: 509-520.

Cronk, Q C B (1988) W.J. Burchell and the botany of St Helena. *Archives of Natural History* 15: 45-60.

Cronk, Q C B (1989) The past and present vegetation of St Helena. *Journal of Biogeography* 16: 47-64.

Cronk, Q C B (1990) The history of the endemic flora of St Helena: late Miocene 'Trochetiopsis-like' pollen from St Helena and the origin of *Trochetiopsis. New Phytologist* 114: 159-165.

Cronk, Q C B (1992) Relict floras of Atlantic islands: patterns assessed. *Biological Journal of the Linnean Society* 46: 91-103.

Cronk, Q C B (1993) Extinction and conservation in the St Helena flora: the palaeobiological and ecological background.). *Boletim do Museu Municipal do Funchal,* Sup. No. 2: 69-76.

Cronk, Q C B (1995a) A new species and hybrid in the St Helena endemic genus *Trochetiopsis. Edinburgh Journal of Botany* 52(2): 205-213.

Cronk, Q C B (1995b) William Roxburgh's St Helena plants. *Bulletin of the Natural History Museum, London (Botany)* 25(1): 95-98.

Cronk, Q C B (2000) *The Endemic Flora of St Helena.* Anthony Nelson Publishers, Oswestry, UK.

Cunningham, J T (1910) On the marine fishes and invertebrates of St. Helena. *Proceedings of the Zoological Society of London* 1910: 86-131.

Cunninghame, J (1699) A catalogue of shells, etc., gathered at the island of Ascension by Mr James Cunninghame. *Philosophical Transactions of the Royal Society* 21 (No.7): 295-300.

Dahl, F (1892) Die Landfauna von Ascension (Anhang zu Kapitel VII). *Ergebnisse der in dem Atlantischen Ocean von Mitte Juli bis Anfang November 1889 ausgefuhrten Plankton-Expedition der Humboldt-Stiftung,* Vol.1 (ed. V. Hensen) pp 204-209. Lipsius & Tischer, Kiel.

Daly, R A (1925) The geology of Ascension Island. *Proceedings of the American Academy of Arts and Sciences* 60 (No.1): 1-80, 21 plates.

Daly, R A (1927) The geology of Saint Helena Island. *Proceedings of the American Academy of Arts and Sciences* 62 (No.2): 31-92, 25 plates.

Dampier, W (ed. John Masefield) (1906) *Voyage to New Holland 1699-1701.* E. Grant Richards, London.

Darwin, C (1844, reprinted 1890) *Geological Observations on Volcanic Islands.* John Murray, London.

Davis R A (1965) Report on Rodent Control on the Island of St. Helena 1965. Government Printing Office, St Helena.

Davis, R A (1966) Ascension Island. Report to the Governor of St. Helena on the problems of rats, feral cats and donkeys. Reprint No. 4288. Rodent Pests Department, Ministry of Agriculture, Fisheries and Food, London.

Disney, R H L (1991) The Ascension Island scuttle fly (Diptera: Phoridae). *Entomologist* 110: 82-93.

Dorward, D F (1962) Comparative biology of the White Booby and the Brown Booby *Sula* spp. at Ascension. *Ibis* 103b: 174-220.

Dorward, D F (1963) The Fairy Tern *Gygis alba* on Ascension Island. *Ibis* 103b: 365-378.

Dorward, D F & Ashmole, N P (1963) Notes on the biology of the Brown Noddy *Anous stolidus* on Ascension Island. *Ibis* 103b: 447-457.

Duffey, E (1964) The terrestrial ecology of Ascension Island. *Journal of Applied Biology* 1: 219-251.

Edwards, A (1990) *Fish and Fisheries of Saint Helena Island.* Government of Saint Helena and the University of Newcastle upon Tyne.

Ellis, A B (1885) *West African Islands.* Chapman and Hall, London.

Encalada, S E et al. (1996) Phylogeography and population structure of the Atlantic and Mediterranean green turtle *Chelonia mydas*: a mitochondrial DNA control region sequence assessment. *Molecular Ecology* 5: 473-483.

Fairbanks, R G (1989) A 17,000-year glacio-eustatic sea level record: influence of glacial melting rates on the Younger Dryas event and deep-ocean circulation. *Nature* 342: 637-642.

Forbes, J (1813) *Oriental Memoirs,* Vol. 2. R. Bentley, London.

Forster, G (1777) *A Voyage Round the World in H.B.M. Sloop, Resolution,* commanded by Capt. James Cook, during the years 1772, 3, 4 & 5. Vol.2. B. White *et al.,* London.

Foster, R C (1934) The Voyage of Thomas Best to the East Indies 1612-1614. Hakluyt Society, London.

Fowler, S V (1993) Report on a Visit to St Helena 6-25 June 1993. International Institute of Biological Control, Silwood Park, Ascot, UK.

Fowler, S V (1998) Report on the invasion, impact and control of 'Mexican Thorn', *Prosopis juliflora,* on Ascension Island. International Institute of Biological Control, Silwood Park, Ascot, UK. Report to the Administrator, Ascension Island.

Gates, G E (1969) On the earthworms of Ascension and Juan Fernandez Islands. *Breviora* 323, 1-4.

Gill, R & Teale, P (1999) *St Helena 500 A Chronological History of the Island.* Lacks publication details.

Godley, B J, Broderick, A C & Hays, G C (In press) Nesting of green turtles *Chelonia mydas* at Ascension Island, South Atlantic. *Biological Conservation.*

Gosse, P (1938, 1990) *St Helena 1502-1938.* Cassell, London, and Anthony Nelson, Oswestry.

Gould, S J (1978). Senseless signs of history. *Natural History* 87: 22-28.

Government of St Helena (1993) *Report on Sustainable Environment and Development Strategy and Action Plan for St Helena,* 3 vols. Royal Botanic Gardens Kew in association with International Institute for Environment and Development.

Grant, B (1883) *A few notes on St. Helena, and Descriptive Guide.* Benjamin Grant, St Helena Guardian Office, Jamestown.

Grove, R H (1995) *Green Imperialism. Colonial Expansion, Tropical Island Edens and the Origins of Environmentalism, 1600-1860.* Cambridge University Press, Cambridge.

Gullan, P J & Cranston, P S (1994) *The insects: an outline of entomology.* Chapman & Hall, London.

Hall, B A (1989) Westward-moving disturbances in the South Atlantic coinciding with heavy rainfall events at Ascension Island. *Meteorological Magazine* 118: 175-181.

Hammer, W H (1988) The 'Lost Year' of the Sea Turtle. *Trends in Ecology and Evolution* 3 (No.5): 116-118.

Hampson, G F (1905) *Catalogue of the Lepidoptera Phalaenae in the British Museum,* vol. 5, 643 pp.

Haq, B U et al. (1987) Chronology of fluctuating sea levels since the Triassic. *Science* 235: 1156-1167.

Hardin, G (1968) The tragedy of the commons. *Science* 162: 1243-1248.

Hardwick, D F (1965) The Corn Earworm complex. *Memoirs of the Entomological Society of Canada,* No. 40, 247 pp. (see p.106).

Harris, C, Bell, J D & Atkins, F B (1982) Isotopic composition of lead and strontium in lavas and coarse-grained blocks from Ascension Island, South Atlantic. *Earth and Planetary Science Letters* 60: 79-85.

Hart-Davis, D (1972) *Ascension. The Story of a South Atlantic Island.* Constable, London.

Haydock, E L (1954) A survey of the birds of St. Helena Island. *Ostrich* 25: 62-75.

Hays, G C, Godley, B J & Broderick, A C (1999) Long-term thermal conditions on the nesting beaches of green turtles on Ascension Island. *Marine Ecology Progress Series* 185: 297-299.

Heatwole, H & Levins, R (1972) Biogeography of the Puerto Rican Bank: flotsam transport of terrestrial animals. *Ecology* 53: 112-117.

Hemsley, W B (1885) Report on the botany of the Bermudas and various other islands of the Atlantic and southern oceans. In C W Thompson & J Murray, *Report on the scientific results of the voyage of H.M.S. Challenger...1873-76, Botany* 1(3): 1-299.

Heywood, V H (1985) *Flowering Plants of the World.* Croom Helm, London.

Holland, M D (ed) (1986) *The Endemic Flora of St Helena: a Struggle for Survival.* The Department of Agriculture and Forestry and the Department of Education of the Government of St. Helena.

Holman, J (1834) *A voyage round the world in H.M.S. sloop* Resolution. 2 vols. London.

Holt, D (1995) The real shape of St Helena. *Wirebird* Autumn 1995.

Holt, D (2000) St Helena: Where have all the beaches gone? *Wirebird* Spring 2000.

Hooker, J D (1867) On insular floras. *The Gardeners' Chronicle and Agricultural Gazette* January 1867: 6-7, 27, 50-51, 75-76.

Howarth, F G & Mull, W P (1992) *Hawaiian Insects and their Kin.* University of Hawaii Press, Honolulu.

Hughes, B J (1999) The status of Sooty Terns *Sterna fuscata* on Ascension Island, South Atlantic. *Adjutant* 28: 4-13.

Humphrey, N (1956) *Review of Agriculture Forestry in the Island of St Helena.* The Crown Agents for Overseas Governments and Administrations, London.

Hutchinson, G E (1950) The biogeochemistry of vertebrate excretion. *Bulletin of the American Museum of Natural History* 96.

Huxley, R C (c.1998) *Ascension Island and turtles: a monograph.* Leaflet.

Jackson, E L (1903) *St. Helena: the Historic Island. From its Discovery to thePresent Date.* Ward, Lock, London.

James, R (1985) *Lava caves of Ascension Island South Atlantic.* Unpublished report in the library of the Ascension Island Heritage Society, Georgetown.

Janisch, H R (1885) Extracts from the St. Helena Records. Privately printed, Jamestown.

Kar, A, Weaver, B, Davidson, J & Colucci, M (1998) Origin of differentiated volcanic and plutonic rocks from Ascension Island, South Atlantic Ocean. *Journal of Petrology* 39: 1009-1024.

Karsholt, O & Razowski, J (1996) *The Lepidoptera of Europe. A distributional Checklist.* Apollo Books, Stenstrup.

Kerr, N R (1970) *The endemic plants of St. Helena.* Leaflet. Solomon & Co. (St. Helena) Ltd., Jamestown.

Kitching, G C (1937, 1995) A handbook and gazetteer of the island of St Helena including a short history of the island under the crown 1834-1902. Miles Apart, Newmarket.

Kwon, D H, Ferrara. F & Taiti, S (1992). Two new species of *Laureola* Barnard, 1960 from India and Vietnam (Crustacea, Oniscidea, Armadillidae). *Revue suisse de Zoologie* 99: 645-653.

La Caille, N L de (1763) *Journal historique du Voyage fait au Cap de Bonne-Espérance.* Paris.

Lack, D (1943) *The Life of the Robin.* H.F. & G. Witherby Ltd, London.

Lamb, H H (1957) Some special features of the climate of St. Helena and the Trade-Wind Zone in the South Atlantic. *Meteorological Magazine* 86 (No. 1017): 73-76.

Lesson, R P (1826) *Voyage autour du Monde pendant les Années 1822, 3, 4 et 5.* Paris.

Lewis, J G E (1996) On a new species of *Tuoba* from Ascension Island. *Fragmenta entomologica*, Roma 28(1): 15-20.

Lienhard, C (1996) Psocoptères nouveaux ou peu connus de queleques îles atlantiques (Canaries, Madère, Açores, Ascension) et de l'Afrique du Nord (Insecta: Psocoptera). *Boletim do Museu Municipal do Funchal* 48: 87-151.

Lienhard, C & Ashmole, N P (1999) *Sphaeropsocopsis myrtleae* sp. n., a blind subterranean psocid from St Helena (Psocoptera: Sphaeropsocidae). *Revue suisse de Zoologie* 106 (4): 905-912.

Lindroth, C H, Andersson, H, Bodvarsson, H & Richter, SH (1973) Surtsey, Iceland. The development of a new fauna, 1963-1970. Terrestrial invertebrates. *Entomologica Scandinavica Suppl.* 5. 280 pp.

Lödl, M (1994) Revision der Gattung Hypena Schrank, 1802 s.l., der äthiopischen und madagassischen Region, Teil 1 (Insecta: Lepidoptera: Noctuidae: Hypeninae). *Annalen des Naturhistorischen Museums in Wien* 96B: 373-590.

Lohmann, K J et al. (1997) Orientation, navigation and natal beach homing in sea turtles. Pp. 107-135 in P L Lutz & J A Musick, *The Biology of Sea Turtles*, CRC Press, Boca Raton.

Lonsdale, P & Batiza, R (1980) Hyaloclastite and lava flows on young seamounts examined with a submersible. *Geological Society of America Bulletin Part I* 91: 545-554.

Loveridge, A (1959) Notes on the present herpetofauna of Ascension Island. *Copeia* 1959 (1): 69-70.

Loveridge, A (1960) An east African Gecko colonising Ascension Island. *Journal of the East African Natural History Society* 23 (No. 7): 296-297.

Loveridge, A (c.1977) Notes on Natural History of St Helena, 1952-1972. Unpublished manuscript in the St Helena Archives Office, Jamestown, St Helena.

Lowe, P R (1923) (Untitled, but concerning a new genus of rail, *Atlantisia*). *Bulletin of the British Ornithologists' Club* 43: 174-176.

Lubbock, R (1980) The shore fishes of Ascension Island. *Journal of Fish Biology* 17: 283-303.

Luschi, P, Hays, G C, Del Seppia, C, Marsh, R. & Papi, F (1998) The navigational feats of green sea turtles migrating from Ascension Island investigated by satellite telemetry. *Proceedings of the Royal Society of London* B 265: 2279-2284.

Luxton, M (1995) A new genus of oribatid mite from Ascension Island (Acari: Oribatida). *Acta zoologica Academiae scientarum hungaricae* 41 (2): 131-136.

Mahnert, V (1993) Pseudoskorpione (Arachnida: Pseudoscorpiones) von Inseln des Mittelmeers und des Atlantiks (Balearen, Kanarische Inseln, Madeira, Ascension), mit vorwiegend suterraner Lebensweise. *Revue Suisse de Zoologie* 100: 971-992.

Manning, R B & Chace, F A Jr (1990) Decapod and stomatopod Crustacea from Ascension Island, South Atlantic Ocean. *Smithsonian Contributions to Zoology* No. 503. 91 pp.

Marais, W (1981) *Trochetiopsis* (Sterculiaceae), a new genus from St. Helena. *Kew Bulletin* 36: 645-646.

Mathieson, I K (1990) The agricultural climate of St Helena (with reference to Ascension). Report published by the Overseas Development Administration and the Department of Agriculture and Forestry, St Helena. 63 pp, 7 appendices.

McCulloch, N (1992) The status and ecology of the St Helena Wirebird. *British Trust for Ornithology, Thetford.* BTO Research Report No. 97.

Melliss, J C (1875) *St. Helena: a Physical, Historical, and Topographical Description of the Island, including its Geology, Fauna, Flora, and Meteorology.* L. Reeve & Co., London.

Merrett, P & Ashmole, N P (1997) Redescription of *Catonetria caeca* Millidge & Ashmole from Ascension Island (Araneae: Linyphiidae). *Bulletin of the British Arachnological Society* 10: 247-248.

Mickel, J (1980) Relationships of the dissected elaphoglossoid ferns. *Brittonia* 32: 109-117.

Montgomerie, B B (1994) *The first "St Helena".* Printsetters, Bristol.

Moore, I, & Legner, E F (1974). Have all the known cosmopolitan Staphylinidae been spread by commerce? *Proc. Ent. Soc. Washington* 76, 39-40.

Morrell, B (1832) *A Narrative for Four Voyages to the South Sea.* Harper, New York.

Morris, D (1884, 1906) *A Report (written in 1884) upon the Present Position and Prospects of the Agricultural Resources of the Island of St. Helena.* Colonial Reports - Miscellaneous, No. 38, London.

Mortimer, J A & Carr, A (1987) Reproduction and migrations of the Ascension Island Green Turtle (*Chelonia mydas*). *Copeia* 1987(1): 103-113.

MRAC: See Basilewsky, P (ed) (1970, 1972, 1976, 1977).

Muir, M D & Baker, I (1968) The Early Pliocene flora of St. Helena. *Palaeogeography, Palaeoclimatology, Palaeoecology* 5: 251-268.

Müller, F (1999) Bryophytes of St Helena. *Tropical Bryology* 16: 131-138.

Murphy, R C (1936) *Oceanic Birds of South America.* American Museum of Natural History, New York.

Nielson, D L & Sibbett, B S (1996) Geology of Ascension Island, South Atlantic Ocean. *Geothermics* 25: 427-448.

Nunn, P D, (ed) (1982) *Final Report of the 1981 University College London St. Helena Expedition.* University College London Press.

Nunn, P D (1984) Evidence for Late Quaternary sea level change around St. Helena Island, South Atlantic. *Catena* 11: 187-195.

Nuss, M (1999) Revision der Gattungen der Scopariinae. Lepidoptera: Pyraloidea, Crambidae. *Nova Supplementum Entomologica* 13: 3-151.

Oliver, J R (1869) *The Geology of St. Helena.* Grant, Jamestown.

Olson, S L (1973) Evolution of the rails of the South Atlantic islands (Aves: Rallidae). *Smithsonian Contributions to Zoology* 152: 1-53.

Olson, S L (1975) Paleornithology of St. Helena Island, South Atlantic Ocean. *Smithsonian Contributions to Paleobiology* 23: 1-49.

Olson, S L (1977) Additional notes on subfossil bird remains from Ascension Island. *Ibis* 119: 37-43.

Olson, S L (1981) Natural history of vertebrates on the Brazilian islands of the mid South Atlantic. *National Geographic Society Research Reports* 13: 481-492.

Osbeck, P (1771) *A Voyage to China and the East Indies* (translated from German by John Reinhold Forster). London.

O'Shea, B J (1999) Checklist of the mosses of sub-Saharan Africa (version 3, 11/99). *Tropical Bryology Research Reports* 1: 1-133.

Owens, D W, Comuzzie, D C & Grassman, M A (1986) Chemoreception in the homing and orientation behavior of amphibians and reptiles, with special reference to sea turtles. Pp. 341-355 in *Chemical signals in vertebrates*, vol. 4, ed. D. Duvall, D. Muller-Schwarze & R.M. Silverstein. Plenum Press, New York.

Packer, J E (1968a) *St Helena Island. A Narrative of Two Visits in 1962 and 1968, with Special Reference to the Geology and Natural History.* Leaflet.

Packer, J E (1968b, 1974, 1983) *The Ascension Handbook. A Concise Guide to Ascension Island, South Atlantic.* Georgetown, Ascension Island.

Packer, J E & Packer, L (1998) *Contributions towards a Flora of Ascension Island.* Revised edition. Ascension Heritage Society, Georgetown.

Pearce-Kelly, P Cronk, Q C B (eds) (1990) *St. Helena Natural Treasury.* Proceedings of a symposium held at The Zoological Society of London, 9th September 1988. The Zoological Society of London.

Penrose, F G (1879) Notes on a collection of birds' skins and eggs made by Mr D. Gill, F.R.A.S., on Ascension Island. *Ibis* (4) 3: 272-282.

Percy, DM & Cronk, Q C B (1997) Conservation in relation to mating system in *Nesohedyotis arborea* (Rubiaceae), a rare endemic tree from St Helena. *Biological Conservation* 80: 135-145.

Perrin, W F (1985) The former dolphin fishery at St Helena. *Report of the International Whaling Commission* 35: 423-428.

Philander, S G H (1986) Unusual conditions in the tropical Atlantic Ocean in 1984. *Nature* 322: 236-238.

Pickup, T (1998) *Ascension Island Management Plan.* The Royal Society for the Protection of Birds, Sandy, UK.

Pinhey E (1964) The St. Helena Dragonfly (Odonata, Libellulidae). *Arnoldia* 1(2): 1-3.

Procter, D & Fleming L V (eds) (1999) Biodiversity: the UK Overseas Territories. Joint Nature Conservation Committee, Peterborough.

Prytherch, R (1996) The Distribution of *Prosopis* sp on Ascension Island. Report to the Adminstrator, Ascension Island.

Ragge, D R (1972) An unusual case of mass migration by flight in *Gryllus bimaculatus* Degeer [Orthoptera Gryllidae]. *Bulletin de l'I.F.A.N.*, 34 sér.A, 869-878.

Ratcliffe, N (1999) Seabirds on Ascension Island. *World Birdwatch* 21(1): 16-18.

Reverdin, G & McPhaden, M J (1986) Near-surface current and temperature variability observed in the equatorial Atlantic from drifting buoys. *Journal of Geophysical Research* 91(C5): 6569-6581.

Richardson, J I & McGillivary, R (1991) Post-hatching loggerhead turtles eat insects in *Sargassum* community. *Marine Turtle Newsletter* 55: 2.

Ritchie, M & Pedgley, D (1989) Desert Locusts cross the Atlantic. *Antenna* 13: 10-12.

Robinson, G S & Kirke, C M StG (1990) Lepidoptera of Ascension Island - a review. *Journal of Natural History* 24: 119-135.

Robinson, G S & Tuck, K R (1997) Phylogeny and composition of the Hieroxestinae (Lepidoptera: Tineidae). *Systematic Entomology* 22: 363-396.

Röhricht, W. (1998) About the Neuroptera of St. Helena and Ascension islands (South Atlantic Ocean). *Acta Zoologica Fennica* 209: 217-219.

Rosenbaum, M S (1992) The geology of Ascension Island. *Geology Today* 8 (No.5): 180-184.

Rowe, R E (1995) The population biology of *Trochetiopsis*: a genus endemic to St Helena. Unpublished D. Phil. thesis, Oxford University.

Rowlands, B W (1992) Fernao Lopes - St Helena's first settler - an English translation of the original account. *Wirebird* 6: 13-16.

Rowlands, B W (1995) St. Helena's offshore outliers, 1989-1992. *Sea Swallow* 44: 44-48.

Rowlands, B W & Trueman, T (2000) First Atlantic record of a Murphy's Petrel *Pterodroma ultima*, at St Helena. *Bulletin of the African Bird Club* 6: 25-28.

Rowlands, B W, Trueman, T, Olson, S L, McCulloch, M N & Brooke, R K (1998) *The Birds of St Helena.* British Ornithologists' Union Checklist No. 16. British Ornithologists' Union, Tring, UK.

Roxburgh, W. *See* Beatson, A (1816).

Sabine, J (1835) Communications on the island of Ascension. *Journal of the Royal Geographical Society of London* 5: 243-262.

Schoener, T W. & Spiller, D A (1987) High population persistence in a system with high turnover. *Nature* 330, 474-477.

Scoble, M J (ed) (1999) *Geometrid Moths of the World. A Catalogue (Lepidoptera, Geometridae)*, 2 vols. CSIRO Publishing, Collingwood, Victoria, Australia, and Apollo Books, Stenstrup, Denmark.

Scullion, J (1990) Review of the fish resources, fisheries and oceanography within the exclusive fishing zone of Ascension Island. Report to the Latin America, Caribbean and Atlantic Department of the Overseas Development Administration, London.

Seale, R F (1834) *The Geognosy of the Island St. Helena, illustrated in a series of Views, Plans and Sections.* Ackermann and Co., London.

SEDS. *See* Government of St Helena (1993).

Simmonds F J (1973) Report on a visit to St. Helena - March 4-23, 1973. Commonwealth Institute of Biological Control.

Simmons, G F (1927) Sinbads of science. *National Geographic Magazine* 52, July, No. 1: 1-75.

Simmons, K E L (1970) Ecological determinants of breeding adaptations and social behaviour in two fish-eating birds. Pp 37-77 in J H Crook (ed) *Social Behaviour in Birds and Mammals.* Academic Press, London.

Simmons K E L (1990) The status of the Red-footed Booby *Sula sula* at Ascension Island. *Bulletin of the British Ornithologists' Club* 110: 213-222.

Simmons, K E L & Prytherch, R J (1998) Ascension Island 1997. *Ibis* 725-727.

Smith, D (1996) A rescue plan for the threatened tree fern thicket of Diana's Peak National Park, St Helena. *Botanic Gardens Conservation News* 2: 46-48.

Smith E A (1892) On the land-shells of St. Helena. *Proceedings of the Zoological Society of London* 1892: 258-270.

Sowerby G B (1844) Extinct land-shells from St. Helena. *In* C. Darwin's *Geological Observations on the Volcanic Islands.*

Stapf, O (1917) *Enneapogon mollis* in Ascension Island. *Bulletin of Miscellaneous Information, Royal Botanic Gardens Kew* No. 6: 216-219.

Stalle, J van (1986) *Helenolius*, a cixiid bug genus endemic to St Helena (Insecta: Homoptera). *Journal of Natural History* 20: 273-278.

Stock, J H (1995) Biogeography and evolutionary scenario of aquatic organisms in Macaronesia. *Boletím Museu Municipal do Funchal* Sup. no. 4: 729-745.

Stock, J H (1996) The genus *Platorchestia* (Crustacea, Amphipoda) on the Mid-Atlantic islands, with description of a new species from Saint Helena. *Miscel-lània Zoològica* 19.1: 149-157.

Stock, J H & Biernbaum, C K (1994) Terrestrial Amphipoda (Talitridae) from Ascension and Saint Helena (South Central Atlantic). *Journal of Natural History* 20: 1347-1380.

Stonehouse, B (1960) *Wideawake Island. The story of the B.O.U. Centenary Expedition to Ascension.* Hutchinson, London.

Stonehouse B (1962a) Ascension Island and the British Ornithologists' Union Centenary Expedition 1957-59. *Ibis* 103b: 1-123.

Stonehouse, B (1962b) The tropic birds (genus *Phaethon*) of Ascension Island. *Ibis* 103b: 124-161.

Stonehouse, B (1963) The laying dates of some St. Helenan sea-birds, 1958-59. *Ibis* 103b: 480-482.

Taiti, S & Ferrara, F (1986) Taxonomic revision of the genus *Littorophiloscia* Hatch, 1947 (Crustacea, Isopoda, Oniscidea) with description of six new species. *Journal of Natural History* 20: 1347-1380.

Taiti, S & Ferrara, F (1991) Two new species of terrestrial Isopoda (Crustacea, Oniscoidea) from Ascension Island. *Journal of Natural History* 25, 901-916.

Tanimoto, T & Zhang, Y-S (1992) Cause of low velocity anomaly along the South Atlantic hotspots. *Geophysical Research Letters* 19(15): 1567-1570.

Teale, P L (1978, 1981) *St Helena 1502-1659 before the English East India Company*, Vols 1 and 2. University of Natal, Durban.

Temple, R C (ed) (1914) *The Travels of Peter Mundy in Europe and Asia, 1608-1667.* Vol. 1. Hakluyt Society, London. (Mundy's 1634 voyage.)

Temple, R C (ed) (1919) *The Travels of Peter Mundy in Europe and Asia, 1608-1667.* Vol. 2. Hakluyt Society, London. (Mundy's 1638 voyage.)

Temple, R C & Anstey, L M (eds) (1936) *The Travels of Peter Mundy in Europe and Asia 1608-1667*, Vol. 5. Hakluyt Society, London. (Mundy's 1656 voyage.)

Thompson, J A K (1947) *Report on Ascension Island*. W.E. Henry, Government Printer, St. Helena.

Thornton, I W B, New, T R , McLaren, D A , Sudarman, H K & Vaughan, P J (1988) Air-borne arthropod fall-out on Anak Krakatau and a possible pre-vegetation pioneer community. *Philosophical Transactions of the Royal Society* B 322, 471-479.

Tiele, P A, (ed) (1885) *The Voyage of John Huyghen van Linschoten to the East Indies*, Vol. 2. Hakluyt Society, London.

Tomlinson, J N (1947) Occurrence of the Red-footed Booby at Ascension Island. *Ibis* 89: 122-123.

Trueman, T (undated) *The Birds of St Helena South Atlantic Ocean*. Unpublished manuscript in library of the Agriculture and Fisheries Department, Scotland, St Helena.

Tryon, R (1970) Development and evolution of fern floras of oceanic islands. *Biotropica* 2: 76-84.

Vagvolgyi, J (1975) Body size, aerial dispersal, and origin of the Pacific land snail fauna. *Systematic Zoology* 24: 465-488.

Viette, P E L (1951) Contribution to the study of Hepialidae (25th Note). On some new or little known species in the British Museum. *Annals and Magazine of Natural History* (12) 4: 1272-1282.

Vonk, R & Stock, J H (1991) *Caecostenetroides ascensionis* n. sp., a blind marine interstitial isopod (Asellota Gnathostenetroidoidea) from Ascension island, South Atlantic. *Tropical Zoology* 4: 89-98.

Wace, N M (1999) The discovery of oceanic islands in the South Atlantic by the Portuguese during the sixteenth century. *Portuguese Studies Review* 8 (1): 126-156 & 187-188.

Walker, C A (1977) The rediscovery of the Blofeld and the Wilkes collections of sub-fossil birds from St. Helena. *Bulletin of the British Ornithologists' Club* 97: 114-116.

Wallace, A R (1880, 1892) *Island Life*. MacMillan & Co., London.

Wallace, C R (1960) Report on an Investigation of Agricultural Pests in St Helena 1957-1959. Colonial Office, London.

Watson, G E (1966) *Seabirds of the Tropical Atlantic Ocean*. Smithsonian Press, Washington, D.C.

Weaver, B (1991) *A guide to the Geology of Saint Helena*, 2nd edition. University of Oklahoma, Norman, Oklahoma.

Weaver, B (1999) *A Guide to the Geology of Ascension Island and Saint Helena*. School of Geology and Geophysics, University of Oklahoma, Norman, Oklahoma 73019, USA.

Webb, M D (1987) The endemic Macrostelini of the island of St-Helena (Homoptera, Cicadellidae). *Revue zoologique africaine* 100: 453-464.

Wetmore, A (1963) An extinct rail from the island of St. Helena. *Ibis* 103b: 379-381.

White F B (1878) Contributions to a knowledge of the hemipterous fauna of St. Helena, and speculations on its origin. *Proceedings of the Zoological Society of London* 1878: 444-477.

Wicker, F D P (1990) White sand. Pp. 4-6 *in* P Pearce-Kelly P & Q C B Cronk (eds) *St. Helena Natural Treasury*. Proceedings of a Symposium held at The Zoological Society of London, 9th September 1988. The Zoological Society of London.

Wigginton, M J & Grolle, R (1996) Catalogue of the Hepaticae and Anthocerotae of sub-Saharan Africa. *Bryophytorum Bibliotheca* 50: 1-267.

Williams, R O (1989). *Plants on St Helena*. Unpublished manuscript. (A few copies can be found on St Helena.)

Wollaston, T V (1861) On certain coleopterous insects from the island of Ascension. *Annals and Magazine of Natural History* 7: 299-306.

Wollaston, T V (1877) *Coleoptera Sanctae-Helenae*. John Van Voorst, London.

Wollaston, T V (1878) *Testacea Atlantica or the Land and Freshwater Shells of the Azores, Madeira, Salvages, Canaries, Cape Verdes, and Saint Helena*. L. Reeve & Co., London.

Wollaston, Mrs T V [Edith] (1879) Notes on the Lepidoptera of St. Helena, with descriptions of new species. *Annals and Magazine of Natural History*, fifth series 3: 219-233; 329-343; 415-441.

Wragg, G M & Weisler, M I (1994) Extinctions and new records of birds from Henderson Island, Pitcairn group, South Pacific Ocean. *Notornis* 41: 61-70.

Index

Note. The index includes scientific names of all genera of animals and plants mentioned in the book, and English names of species if these are in common use. Entries in block capitals refer to higher taxonomic groups, mainly families of plants and orders of animals. For both animal and plant species and groups, the last page number indicated (higher than 252) generally refers to the main entry in the systematic section (Part IV). Only simple subject indexing is provided; further information on the topics covered is available in the Contents list. Numbered figures, and also the un-numbered marginal drawings of animals and plants in Part IV, are indexed by page number in bold type. Colour photographs are indexed by Plate number: Plates 1-8 are of St Helena, 9-16 are of Ascension, 17-24 are animals and 25-32 are plants.

North Point

English Bay

Power Station

BBC Relay Station

Pyramid Point

Comfortless Cove

Daly's Crags

Packers Hole Cav

'Fumaroles'

Per

Bates Point

Long Beach

Clarence Bay

Georgetown

Sisters Peak

Two Boats Village

Deadman's Beach

Cross Hill

One Boat

7°56'

Catherine Point

Collyer Point

Traveller

Lady Hill

DONKEY PLAIN

Trave Hill

U.S. Base

Cat Hill

South West Bay Red Hill

Table Crater

Payne Point

Clarkes Beach Cave

Clarkes Beach

Chapel Grotto Cave

Command Hill

Devil's Riding School

Spoon Crater

Command Hill Cave

Dark Crater

Wideawake Airfield

Bird Cave

Ravine Cave

G

7°58' S

South West Bay

South R

Portland Point

South Gannet Hill

Sandy Run

Mars Bay Nature Reserve

WIDEAWAKE FAIRS

WIDEAWAKE FAIRS

0   1 mile

0   1   2 km

Mars Bay

Shelly Beach

Gannet Bay

South Point